STRUCTURAL GEOLOGY

International Series in the Earth Sciences

ROBERT R. SHROCK, *Consulting Editor*

Kenneth O. Emery, *Woods Hole Oceanographic Institution*
Fritz Koczy, *Institute of Marine Science, University of Miami*
Konrad Krauskopf, *Stanford University*
John Verhoogen, *University of California, Berkeley*
Sverre Petterssen, *University of Chicago*

STRUCTURAL GEOLOGY

L. U. DE SITTER

Professor of Structural and Applied Geology

University of Leiden

Second Edition

McGRAW-HILL BOOK COMPANY

New York   San Francisco

Toronto   London

STRUCTURAL GEOLOGY

Library of Congress Catalog Card Number 63–23533

456789–MAMM–754321
ISBN 07-016573-4

Preface

This book is intended for students who have a certain familiarity with the elements of structural geology and with its terminology and for professional geologists. It tries to cover the whole territory of structural geology from outcrop size to a global point of view, from metamorphic rocks to synsedimentary deformation.

Owing to the vast amount of accurate mapping that has been carried out for economic and scientific purposes, an enormous mass of facts about the forms of tectonic features has been accumulated. This book is primarily concerned with systematizing this detailed knowledge so that we may be able to distinguish genetic relationships. It tries to show that we really have advanced beyond the argument about the sealing wax which you can break with your hands but which will still flow when left alone, beyond the point where folds and faults are synonymous with flow and rupture, where underthrust and overthrust are opposite, where gravity is either ignored or presented as the one and only force, and where images conceal facts.

The theoretical geologist who develops the theories of orogenesis works independent of, rather than with, the practical geologist. There is a very good reason for this gap in communication between the practical and theoretical geologist. The man who is most familiar with the enormous diversity of structural forms is the field geologist, but, submerged as he is in the ocean of facts, he seldom feels the urge to theorize. Fortunately, at present there is distinct improvement in that the theoretical geologist is applying his detailed laboratory and field experience directly in the field, and the results have given us a much better understanding of the development of the earth's crustal deformation.

The aim of this book is to establish a link between theory and practice. Starting with the physical properties of rocks (Part One), it deals in considerable detail with comparative structural geology, proceeding from simple to more complex structures (Part Two). Finally, in Part Three, an attempt is made to define some characteristics of the largest structural units and to discuss theories concerning their origin. The comparative method predominates throughout, for in a young science such as ours, hampered in its development by the vastness and inaccessibility of its subject, theorizing must remain a secondary function, and to a certain extent a luxury, for some time to come.

Since the first edition of this book, great advances have been made in the analysis of natural rock deformation by applying new methods of measuring the intricate internal structure of the rock material. A much better understanding of the successive deformational stages and their relation with stress and temperature has been reached, in particular by studying the transitional stages between the pure stages. Laboratory experiments have been a great assistance in this matter.

In addition, geophysical research has in many respects opened up new roads for investigation. Isotopic rock dating, paleomagnetic measurements, seismic research based on man-made vibrations and earthquakes, and oceanic research have developed immensely in the last decade.

These spectacular developments in the science of structural geology necessitated an almost complete rewriting of many parts of the first edition.

As a field geologist I tend to believe what I see more than what I read. This book must therefore undoubtedly have a personal flavor and be limited in content, and I beg forgiveness of those colleagues whose work has not received the attention it deserves. I hope they will let me know my omissions.

I want to extend my thanks to the numerous colleagues and collaborators who have pointed out errors and have suggested improvements. In particular I want to express my gratitude to Dr. H. J. Zwart and J. Savage, M.Sc., for their unwearying assistance in preparing the revised manuscript.

L. U. de Sitter

Contents

PART THREE   GEOTECTONICS

PART ONE

Theoretical Structural Geology

Chapter 1

Introduction

STRUCTURAL GEOLOGY IN RELATION TO OTHER EARTH SCIENCES

Structural Geology and Stratigraphy. Structural geology was originally concerned only with analyzing the deformation of sedimentary strata. Before this object can be attained, it is essential to know the depositional sequence of the strata involved. When folding is relatively mild, the stratigraphical sequence is clear from the law of superposition. When, however, the layers are thoroughly disturbed by steep folds, or by thrusts, or other great disturbances, one must either know the stratigraphical sequence beforehand or find fossil or sedimentary evidence of the sequence in the structures themselves.

In other words, the tectonics of a particular region cannot be elucidated without a basic knowledge of its stratigraphy; and the stratigraphy cannot be worked out without a general knowledge of the structures. In mapping a region and solving its geological problems, stratigraphical and tectonic investigations must proceed hand in hand.

The influence of movements of the earth's crust may be either simultaneous with or subsequent to the deposition of sedimentary strata or to intrusion of igneous rocks; or, as often happens, there may be both simultaneous and subsequent effects. One of the most difficult problems to solve by structural analysis is the precise relationship between tectonics and stratigraphy.

In the simplest case, that of quiet sedimentation and no subsequent folding or large-scale faulting, we can deduce the epeirogenic motion of the crust by a careful analysis of the thickness and facies variations over a relatively large area. Thus the degree of sinking of a basin floor can be determined by measuring the increase of thickness toward the center of the basin. The Mid-Continental region of the United States is particularly rich in examples because of the intensive search for oil there. Much drilling, combined with gravitational and seismic

3

work, has established the existence of numerous basins with but slight subsequent disturbances. In a section through the Appalachian basin (Fig. 1), we can follow the epeirogenic sinking as if enacted in a film. Of particular interest are intraformational unconformities, demonstrated by the wedging out of certain strata toward the basin edge.

Another interesting example in which much of the structural evidence is derived solely from stratigraphical data is offered by the survey of the Roer Valley rift in the SE of the Netherlands. This deep rift is flanked to the NE and SW by more stable blocks; the latter, however, in the course of their Mesozoic history of regression and transgression, have been uniformly tilted to slope northeastward. Figures 2 and 3 give a synopsis of the combined movement of sinking of the rift valley and tilting of the flanking blocks. The movement occurred in three main phases: a first Jurassic phase of downfaulting and tilting, a second Cretaceous phase of uplift of a formerly downfaulted block, and a third Tertiary phase in the same sense as the first movement. The last phase is probably still active, as is indicated by occasional earthquakes (de Sitter, 1942). In this instance the subsequent tilting of earlier abrasion surfaces is of particular interest (Fig. 3).

In these quiet regions the epeirogenic disturbances of the crust can be followed step by step because no later folding has complicated the original structure. When later folding does occur, the interpretation is no longer so simple.

When, for instance, thrusts and unconformities remain unrecognized, serious errors in correlation are likely to result. Such difficulties arise especially in strongly folded regions with abrupt facies changes, a combination which often occurs since both phenomena arise from the instability of the region. When the facies change is, for example, from a massive offshore reef limestone to a thick soft marl of deeper-water facies, the facies boundary is often extremely abrupt. Subsequent folding will invariably cause disturbances along the facies boundary because the two rock types are so different in their reaction to stress. In such a case it is often almost impossible to evaluate the amount of movement along these predisposed surfaces; attempted interpretations are apt to range widely, from the supposition of large overthrusts to the supposition of but minor faults with little throw.

The same kind of uncertainty can arise when low-angle overthrusts or glided nappes are suspected in a region where the stratigraphy is insufficiently known. A typical example can be found in the "Cantabric nappes" of northern Spain proposed by Mengaud in 1920. At that time nappe structures were much in favor, and on the sole evidence of unfossiliferous black schists of supposedly Albian age cropping out below a Carboniferous limestone, the existence of an enormous "Picos

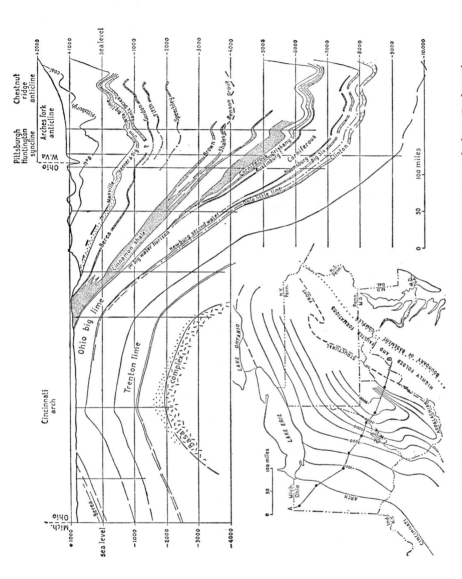

Fig. 1 Appalachian basin, section from Ohio to West Virginia. (*After Appalachian Geological Society, 1951. Published by permission of the American Association of Petroleum Geologists.*)

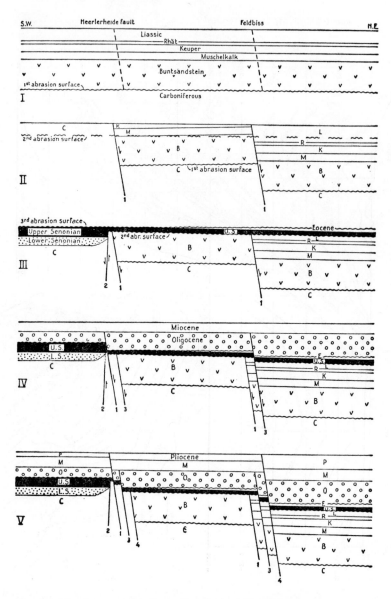

Fig. 2 Schematic cross section across step faults showing development of Roer Valley rift in southeast Netherlands. Each major movement along the two main faults is represented by a new parallel fault, although in nature all the movement occurred more or less along the same fault plane. Vertical scale exaggerated. (*After de Sitter, 1942. Published by permission of Geologisch Bureau, Heerlen.*)

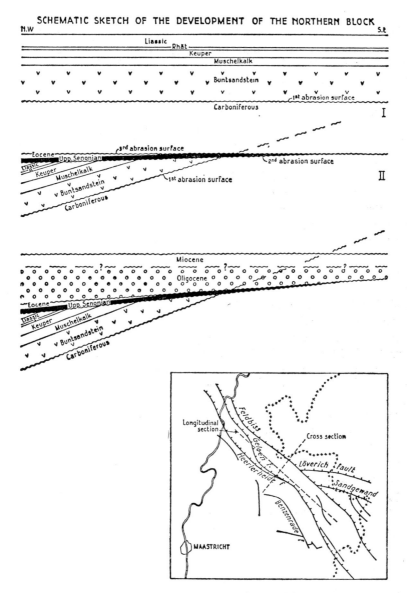

SCHEMATIC SKETCH OF THE DEVELOPMENT OF THE NORTHERN BLOCK

Fig. 3 Schematic longitudinal-section development on tilted fault step along Roer Valley rift. Vertical scale exaggerated. (*After de Sitter, 1942. Published by permission of Geologisch Bureau, Heerlen.*)

de Europa nappe" was suggested. Sampelayo (1928), however, found plant remains with *Calamites* in the black schists, and thus refuted the hypothesis. Finally, Mengaud had to admit in 1932 that all his nappe constructions were in error, mostly because of faulty interpretation of the stratigraphy. In other instances, such as the Marctic overthrust (E. Cloos and Hietanen, 1941), it is impossible to gather enough irrefutable stratigraphical evidence to prove or to disprove the nappe hypothesis, either because of the metamorphic state of the rocks or the complete absence of fossils.

The interdependence of stratigraphical and structural knowledge is well known to every field geologist; and recent progress in sedimentology is now widely used by structural geologists. The older methods of determining the top and bottom of a layer have been augmented by new ones, such as the graded texture of sandstone beds and the cyclic nature of a succession of beds, and in particular, by a better understanding of the characteristics of the bottom of a sand bed. It has been known for a long time that even the cleavage or schistosity of the bedding can help us in defining the bottom and top of a bed, and this is of particular use in low-grade metamorphic rocks. But to supplement this well-known tool, modern sedimentology has given us a much better insight into the filling of a basin, and therefore into its structural history as well. The recognition of the mechanism of turbidity currents and of the determination of the current direction by flow markings, current bedding, etc., certainly teaches us much about the development of a basin.

Finally, it will be shown that variations in lithological succession have a strong influence on the subsequent fold structures. The alternation of incompetent and competent beds, the total thickness of the whole series, the thickness of its components, and their lateral changes of facies determine to a very large degree the shape and locality of folds.

Thus we find that structural geology, in all its aspects, is always dependent on the stratigraphy of the rock sequence.

Structural Geology and Physiography. Structure depends largely on stratigraphy, and physiography depends largely on structure. But the older the structure, the less marked is its physiographical expression. Precambrian orogenic belts seldom coincide with present mountain ranges, and Hercynian structures are often obscured by Tertiary movements. The facial expression of geotectonics is therefore almost exclusively due to Tertiary movements, even in cases such as the Late Paleozoic Appalachians, where a mountain chain which began to rise in the Cretaceous is the basis, again uplifted later, of the present mountain system. There still remains a secondary relation between the original folded belt and the present mountain system. This applies to most Tertiary orogenic belts as well. We have to distinguish, as we shall see later, between a folding, or orogenic, period and a later morphogenic period of uplift, often after a prolonged period of denudation. But in less severely compressed areas, such as basins and their peripheries, no later uplift intervenes between the folding and erosion, and we find the direct physiographic expression of structure. The basin is still a basin surrounded by its uplifted borders.

Thus we can distinguish between a first-order relationship, in which structural features gave rise directly to geomorphological features (Fig. 4), and a second-order relationship, in which denudation and aplanation intervened between the creation of structures and the creation of the geomorphological features connected with them (Fig. 5).

Large geomorphological features of the first order are commonly of negative form; e.g., sinking parts of the crust are reflected as basins, deep-sea furrows, ocean basins, etc. Most orogenic belts are second-order structures, but some are believed to be of the first order. The arcuate island belts of the western Pacific, the Indonesian island arcs and their prolongation in Malaya, and perhaps the Himalayan orogenic belt in part are regarded as first-order structures. Besides these major first-order structures, smaller structures in moderately folded regions are often of the first order. Late Tertiary anticlines and synclines in basins are almost invariably first-order structures all over the world (Fig. 4). The anticlines form rows of hills; the synclines contain the swamps. Even if the relief has been reversed, and we find synclinal ridges and subsequent anticlinal rivers, they still may be of the first order (i.e., no flat-surface stage in between). What has been said of folds is equally true of faults in so far as they are connected with folding. Block-faulted areas, on the other hand, and in particular the great rift valleys of the earth, are all relatively young or rejuvenated structures. They generally possess very pronounced geomorphological features and have often been recognized in the first place by these features and not by geological structure. For many of the great rift valleys, the Lower Rhine Valley rift and the African rifts, for instance, it has been proved that the structure originated

Fig. 4 First-order morphology. Anticlines and synclines appear as rows of hills and valleys.

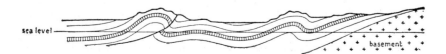

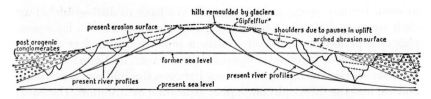

Fig. 5   Second-order morphology. (1) Orogenic phase folding causing strong upheaval of central region of mountain chain and subsidence of marginal troughs filled up in later stages of folding. (2) Morphogenic phase after the peneplenization, rhythmic uplift of aplanation surface in big arch, followed by remodeling by river and glacial erosion.

early in the Mesozoic and was progressively accentuated by subsequent similar movements which continued into recent times. The geomorphological expression is of course mainly due to the latest movement.

The reason for the fact that no large rift valleys of Hercynian or earlier age are known remains obscure.

We need not enter here into a detailed description of the physiography produced by folds or faults. Any textbook on geomorphology treats this matter *in extenso,* but I should like to make a few remarks on the role of physiographical evidence in structural mapping.

When one has come to understand the structure of a region in detail, it becomes clear that almost every feature of its topography is caused by some particular structural item, but one cannot understand the geomorphology unless the structure is known in great detail beforehand. In other words, structural analysis of geomorphological features in the field and on the map is possible only when the structure is known in advance. Without such knowledge the method almost invariably leads to serious errors, except in the case of recent block faulting. Nevertheless, a good eye for topographical features is very useful in tracing the prolongation of observed structural features through unexposed areas.

Structural analysis from aerial photographs, however, can be surprisingly accurate, particularly in regions which have been disturbed only once, e.g., in regions which have experienced only Tertiary or Mesozoic folding. This method has therefore become a most important tool in mapping work. It should even precede the field work, and the photographs should be consulted again during and after the field work. Many features, particularly faults, show better on photographs than in the field; often the photographs reveal structural details which can be found and checked only with great difficulty in the field. But every structural inference from aerial photographs ought nevertheless to be checked in the field, for misinterpretations are common. I know personally of an exceptional case in which three geologists independently analyzed a structure clearly standing in the photograph as an anticline. In the field it proved to be a syncline! Structural analysis of aerial photographs is a valuable tool in the hands of an experienced field geologist, but it can never replace the field work.

In the typical sequence of events which mould a mountain chain, there is first the folding, which forms the primary structure; then denudation, which reduces the axial zone to an old mellow relief and fills the marginal troughs with thick conglomeratic sediments; and then the morphogenic phase—a succession of uplifts with intervals of repose. During this phase consequent streams develop on the flanks of the resuscitated chain. They flow away from its axis, their headwaters cut back toward it, and the uplifted old surface at the axis becomes reshaped by glaciers.

In such a sequence the mountaintops will represent the hilltops of the old mellow relief before the morphogenic phase. There is no reason or need to presume that this level ("Gipfelflur") represents a still older surface of erosion. The old relief is sometimes well preserved in the axial zone, but in many instances it has been destroyed almost completely by the later episodes of erosion. When it is still recognizable, it indicates the total uplift during the morphogenic phase.

The succession of uplifts is discernible in the shoulders on the slopes of the valleys. By careful correlation of these features, the history of the morphogenic phase can be established.

During the rejuvenation of the old mountain chain, its structural peculiarities again affect the geomorphology, but the main consequent river systems retain the courses they have already established.

In this connection it is interesting to observe that in Tertiary mountain chains structural control of the physiography remains pronounced, whereas in Hercynian mountain chains this control is considerably weaker.

Structural Geology and Petrology. Petrology and structural geology are often so completely interwoven that it is impossible to say whether one is studying a petrological problem by structural methods or a structural problem by petrological methods. The little we know of the mechanism of the internal deformation of rocks has clearly demonstrated that the texture and structure of the rock determine to a large degree the kind of deformation which will take place under certain stress conditions. If we also take account of the all-important factor of the temperature rise before, during, and after deformation, we arrive in the midst of the controversial subjects of metamorphism and granitization. Such phenomena are very properly regarded as petrological problems, but they are also extremely important structural problems. The purely structural evidence should be taken into account by the petrologist, and vice versa. We shall see, farther on, that a complete orogenic cycle contains three or four magmatic phases of different character: an initial or geosynclinal ultrabasic phase, a syntectonic leucocratic granite phase, a late tectonic granodioritic phase, and a posttectonic volcanic phase. Moreover, we can distinguish, in addition to orogenic magmatism, a nonorogenic, or kratogenic, magmatic activity of basaltic and alkaline character, very similar to the magmatic activity connected with block faulting of the rift-valley type.

As soon as we advance beyond the limits of purely descriptive structural geology, an intimate knowledge of the petrology of both sedimentary and igneous rocks is a prerequisite.

Structural geology has even created its own method of study, the petrofabric technique. This allows us to determine the directions of the principal stresses which have affected a rock by measuring the orientation of recrystallized and original crystals, on the assumption that a systematic rearrangement of the originally random orientation is produced by the stress field. Structural petrology based on these methods has become a science in itself and will be treated only briefly in this book. The methods of recording and manipulating these crystal orientations have been applied with great success to field measurements of cleavages, lineations, and other minor structural details. Combined with the microscopic work, this methodical study of rock deformation in nature has advanced our understanding enormously.

Structural Geology and Economic Geology. The relationship between structural geology and the geology of economic mineral deposits is a matter of degree of "structural control," of how far the distribution of the economic mineral is related to structural features. It is obvious that the disposition of a coal seam, as of any other sedimentary bed, is wholly determined by the structure of the region and by the original lateral extent of the seam. In oil geology a similar relation exists, although the actual oil content of a reservoir rock is a secondary feature determined largely by the permeability of the reservoir. Both oil and coal geologists must always employ structural geology in their daily work.

Structural control of bedded sedimentary ores is comparable with that of coal. Alluvial and eluvial ores are only superficially related to structure.

The structural control of magmatic ores, whether of hydrothermal, pneumatolytic, or another mode of deposition, is much more complicated. In the first place, the magmatic or metamorphic activities which produce the ore are in their turn almost invariably of orogenic origin. Second, the host rock may have been prepared to receive the ore by orogenic forces, either by the shattering of the rock or by the creation of minimum stress, tension, or fracture zones where the mineralizing agent could penetrate. In the third place, the fault pattern, which in itself is also an expression of the stress field to which the rock has been submitted, may act in various ways as channels for the ore bodies. It is frequently found that, in a particular region, some fault directions are sterile whereas others are mineralized, and this is a strong indication that the mineralization occurred more or less simultaneously with the faulting. Recurrent mineralization may show that the faults were also active during several succeeding phases, and in the same sense. Finally, structural deformation after mineralization may be an important factor for the present distribution of the ore bodies.

Structural Geology and Geophysics.   The science of applied geophysics has been extensively developed as a means of determining hidden structures, and has become an important tool in the hand of the tectonician. The seismic-reflection method, for instance, measures strike and dip at depth. Electrical-resistivity measurements in boreholes enable detailed correlation from one hole to the next, and thus facilitate determination of the structure. Other methods, such as seismic refraction, and gravity measurements of various kinds, give the broad outline and sometimes also the details of raised and subsided regions of the earth crust and so contribute to our knowledge of its deeper layers. It is no overstatement to say that only since geophysical methods have been employed to explore basins for oil have we obtained positive knowledge of their structure.

Applied geophysics is of great value in the elucidation of structures in the upper crust; in the purely scientific study of the earth's interior, geophysical methods assume an even greater importance. Seismic evidence from earthquakes and from a variety of man-made vibrations forms almost the only factual evidence we have concerning the mantle and the core. Together with general conclusions from measurements of the earth's gravity and of its magnetic field, it provides the basis for the current theories about the interior, from which all orogenic forces originate.

This brief review of the relationships between structural geology and other earth sciences has shown, on the one hand, that structural geology leans heavily on information from its brother sciences and, on the other hand, that it serves as a basis for many inquiries into the nature of our globe. Since structural geology has developed its own methods of investigation and its own systematic classification of the data with which it is concerned, it has earned the right to be regarded as a full-grown member of the assembly of earth sciences.

OUTLINE OF A CLASSIFICATION OF STRUCTURAL PHENOMENA

Structural geology is concerned with all aspects of the earth's crustal distortion. It is a descriptive science which needs its own systematic classification of rock deformation, i.e., comparative structural geology. Since it also aims to explain how the crust has been distorted, it needs a theoretical and experimental background. This is found in theoretical and experimental structural geology. Finally, it must explain why the earth's crust has been deformed at all, which necessitates an analysis of the distribution and interrelations of structural features all over the earth's crust. This is the concern of the science of geotectonics.

Comparative structural geology is concerned in the first place with the outward shapes of the disturbances and classifies them into groups as folds and faults, with various different characteristics. By observing the distribution and frequency of the separate groups of the classification within structural units of larger size, within basins and mountain chains, for instance, a distinct correlation appears. This leads to the following broad subdivisions of structural regions:

Block-faulted regions, where faults separate blocks which have moved in relation to one another, without major distortion of the unit blocks. Faults may be either of normal (horst-and-graben structure) or of wrench-fault type. In both cases the movement of the blocks may have created folds (Saxonic type of folding), but the folds are only secondary features (e.g., the Basin and Range province in North America, and Palestine).

Paratectonic regions, where simple interrelated folds occur in relatively large regions, all of them composed of rocks of roughly the same age (folded basins, for instance). They contain curved folds, predominantly of concentric type without thickening of the strata in the hinges, accompanied by faulting which is secondary to the folding. Folding is restricted to sedimentary basins, and the basin structure is not destroyed by the folding. The absence of important magmatic activity within the region is typical. Detailed analysis of the phases of folding reveals more and more of them, distributed irregularly in time and space and without distinct correlation with the phases in other paratectonic regions. Physiographic expression of the structure is usually a first-order morphology (e.g., Paris basin; San Joaquin Valley).

In *orthotectonic regions* mountain chains are distinguished by very intense folding of a characteristic type, usually accompanied by development of cleavage and schistosity. Magmatic phases are an essential part of the orogeny. The original basin is completely destroyed and can be reconstructed only by linking up different sections. The folding is chiefly concentrated in a few very large paroxysms which can be correlated in time with similar phases in other orogenes. The orogenes are always built up in longitudinal belts, each characterized by a particular style of deformation.

The physiography is often of the second order; i.e., a subsequent morphogenic phase of uplift rejuvenates the eroded chain (e.g., the Alpine mountain chain, the Appalachian belt).

This subdivision into three different styles of structural regions is far from being absolute; there are all kinds of transitional regions, as, for instance, the marginal troughs of orogenes, which are characterized by paratectonic features although they undoubtedly belong to an orthotectonic unit. Although a later uplift, separated from the last orogenic paroxysmal phase by a period of erosion, is typical of orthotectonic regions, it is by no means restricted to them. Some paratectonic regions show the same kind of morphogenic phase. On the other hand, first-order physiographic expression of folds and faults is typical of paratectonic regions. The same is true of very young or still moving orthotectonic regions (islands arcs, for instance). Nevertheless, the broad outline of this classification is not arbitrary. On the contrary, it has a fundamental basis, which will be more fully discussed in Part Three of this book.

METHODS IN STRUCTURAL GEOLOGY

The study of the distortion of rocks can take several courses. The most common kind of investigation is the study of structural shapes, which leads to a comparison of observed features, on the one hand, and to a classification into related groups, on the other. This comparative structural geology is mostly concerned with external features and, without the help of other methods of approach, leads to only super·ficial conclusions about the origin and development of the structures .

This has led to other methods of approach, first of all the theoretical, which, as a physical science, tries as far as is possible to isolate in the laboratory the various properties of rocks. This is done by reducing the number of factors which are involved in natural deformation in order to get a clearer picture of each of them successively and separately. Such purely theoretical study has not yet been developed and is still completely in the exploratory experimental stage.

Second, an investigation of much more detailed character has been developed by microscopical study of the preferred orientation of mineral grains in deformed rocks. This technique of structural petrology using petrofabrics as its basis has evolved enormously since 1930, the date of Sander's first treatise on this subject. It still suffers, however, from the same lack of theoretical and experimental background, as does simple comparative tectonics. It has given us a wealth of information, but we are ignorant of the way to use it. The science works with concepts of "flow," "flattening," and "shear" structures, but as the reader will perceive for himself, the exact sense of these words for motions, which need thousands of years to develop in solid material under the influence of elastic stresses, is still obscure.

Quite another kind of approach to the understanding of structural shapes is the imitative experiment, which, in spite of a lack of theoretical background, has blundered into quite surprising results. Nonetheless, its limitations are now clearly visible, and we do not believe it can ever bring us much fundamental knowledge.

Finally, the most fascinating subject of structural geology, the geotectonical synthesis of all structural knowledge, is at the same time in a certain sense its most unsatisfactory branch, because so many totally unknown and untested properties of the deeper crust, the mantle, and the core of the earth are involved. It is the territory of the most unchecked and flamboyant fantasy, built up by piling hypotheses on theories, which are themselves shored by very rare and thin reeds of geophysical facts. Even the factual geological data are woefully inadequate for a geotectonic description of our earth's surface, and too many immense regions are totally unknown, or only superficially known. Nevertheless, it seems useful to marshal those facts which are known, and those which can be directly interpreted from them, into one comprehensive picture. My effort in this direction is contained in Part Three; its usefulness perhaps lies principally in bringing out the flimsiness of all present geotectonic concepts, including my own.

Chapter 2

Physical Properties of Rocks

The deformations which a geologist observes at the surface of the earth's crust can be studied either from the point of view of the shapes that have been created by external stresses or as a problem of internal deformation of rock material. Both points of view pose a physical-mechanical problem, but nevertheless differ in their way of approach. The study of rock deformation needs, first of all, a knowledge of the physical properties of rocks, in relation to deformation. These properties are concerned either with elastic or with plastic deformation or with rupture. We shall see in the course of our investigation that nearly all the deformations in which we are interested lie in a zone between the plastic and elastic fields and that rupture and plastic deformation can hardly be distinguished, from a physical point of view.

Originally, our knowledge about the physical properties of rocks had been inferred principally from experiments performed by civil engineers, and as these people do not construct buildings to last millions of years and use a large safety margin anyway, their findings are usually little concerned with the time factor. Only recently have laboratory experiments been made from a purely geological point of view. It then soon became apparent that, even in relatively short experiments, time plays a predominant role. In other words, the boundary between elastic and viscous deformation has become ill defined. It is therefore important to study these fields carefully before developing any theories about deformation either of the earth's crust as a whole or of a special layer of it.

ELASTIC PROPERTIES OF ROCKS

An elastic deformation is defined as one which disappears again when the load which caused the deformation has been removed. Ideal elasticity would exist if the deformation on loading and its disappearance on unloading were both instantaneous. This is never quite realized in actual materials, however, since there is always some retardation, known as hysteresis, in the unloading process.

With a purely elastic deformation the strain is a linear function of the stress (Hooke's law), or in the case of a bar of the length l and diameter of 1 cm², stretched by the stress σ acting in the direction of the bar,

$$\text{Strain } \epsilon = \frac{\Delta l}{l} = \frac{\sigma}{E}$$

where Δl is the change in length, and E the *elasticity*, or *Young's modulus*, a constant for the material of the bar. Since E is a constant, the deformation curve in a stress/strain diagram is a straight line (Fig. 6).

Instead of using a normal stress σ, we may use a shearing stress τ. In that case the deformation will be of another type (Fig. 7), known as simple shear. The strain γ is given by the angle φ. When the deformation is purely elastic, we have

$$\gamma = \tan \varphi = \frac{dx}{dy} = \frac{\tau}{G}$$

where G is known as the shear modulus, or *rigidity*, which is also a constant for the material.

When a body is subjected to a change of hydrostatic stress, the volume change per unit pressure change is called the *compressibility*:

$$K = \frac{dV/V}{dP}$$

where V is the volume, and P the hydrostatic stress.

These three constants, E, G, and K, define the elastic properties of the material, but they are not independent of one another. The relation between them may be expressed in terms of Poisson's ratio (μ), which is the ratio of the lateral contraction to the longitudinal extension in the case of a bar lengthened elastically by a tensile stress, or the ratio of the lateral expansion to the shortening in the case of a bar shortened elastically by compressive stress.

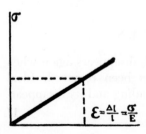

Fig. 6   Elasticity, or Young's modulus E.

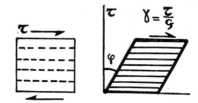

Fig. 7 Rigidity *G*.

It must be remembered that in these considerations tensile and compressive stresses differ only in sign. In Fig. 8 the compressive stresses σ_1, σ_2, and σ_3 are taken as variable.

When $\sigma_3 < \sigma_1 = \sigma_2$, the elastic deformation of the body will be a stretching in the direction of σ_3. When $\sigma_3 = \sigma_2 = \sigma_1$, we should consider the stress condition as a hydrostatic (or confining) pressure, and when $\sigma_3 > \sigma_1 = \sigma_2$, we should have an elastic shortening of the cube.

The deformative stress which results from a stress condition when $\sigma_3 > \sigma_2 > \sigma_1$ (Fig. 8) is

$$\Delta\sigma = \sigma_3 - \frac{\sigma_2 + \sigma_1}{2}$$

or when $\sigma_2 = \sigma_1$,

$$\Delta\sigma = \sigma_3 - \sigma_1$$

the sign being positive when the stress is directed toward the specimen, and negative when in the opposite direction. We can now return to the Poisson constant and the relation between E, G, and K. Experimentally, it has been shown that elastic shortening in one direction is accompanied by an elastic lengthening in both perpendicular directions, or a lengthening of Δl is accompanied by a shortening of $-\mu \, \Delta l$. When we consider the edges a, b, and c of the cube in question (Fig. 8) after elastic deformation under the stress condition of σ_1, σ_2, and σ_3, we can calculate for each of these stresses individually the

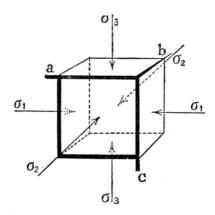

Fig. 8 Unit cube in a stress field.

lengthening and shortening of each of the edges, and we find that the stress σ_1 has added the following values to a, b, and c:

$$-\frac{\sigma_1}{E}a, \quad +\mu\frac{\sigma_1}{E}b, \quad +\mu\frac{\sigma_1}{E}c$$

and the stress σ_2:

$$+\mu\frac{\sigma_2}{E}a, \quad -\frac{\sigma_2}{E}b, \quad +\mu\frac{\sigma_2}{E}c$$

and the stress σ_3:

$$+\mu\frac{\sigma_3}{E}a, \quad +\mu\frac{\sigma_3}{E}b, \quad -\frac{\sigma_3}{E}c$$

The change of the length of edge a is the algebraic sum of the change due to each principal stress, or

$$a_1 = a - \frac{\sigma_1 - \mu(\sigma_2 + \sigma_3)}{E}a$$

and

$$b_1 = b - \frac{\sigma_2 - \mu(\sigma_1 + \sigma_3)}{E}b$$

$$c_1 = c - \frac{\sigma_3 - \mu(\sigma_1 + \sigma_2)}{E}c$$

and when $\sigma_1 = \sigma_2 = \sigma_3$ (= hydrostatic pressure),

$$a_1 = a\left[1 - \frac{\sigma(1 - 2\mu)}{E}\right]$$

and the volume becomes

$$V_1 = a_1b_1c_1 = abc\left[1 - \frac{3(1 - 2\mu)}{E}\sigma\right]$$

when we neglect the higher powers of the small second term.

The compressibility is therefore

$$K = \frac{3(1 - 2\mu)}{E} \quad \text{and} \quad \mu = \frac{1}{2} - \frac{EK}{b}$$

In a similar way one can derive the relation between the rigidity and the Poisson constant, the result being

$$G = \frac{1}{2}\frac{E}{1 + \mu}$$

The four elastic constants—the elasticity modulus E, the compressibility K, the rigidity G, and the Poisson constant—are therefore not independent of one another; there are only two independent constants, which we may choose from the four at our disposal. Perhaps the natural choice is to select the compressibility (resistance to change in volume), on the one hand and the rigidity (resistance to change in shape), on the other. From the relation between E, K, and μ it follows that μ must be positive but smaller than 0.5 (otherwise E or K would become negative, which would mean a shortening or compression by a tensile stress).

Table 1 gives the constants of some different rocks (Ide, 1936).

Table 1

		E		G		
		$P = 1$	$P = 4,000$	$P = 1$	$P = 4,000$	μ
Granite:	Rockport, Mass.	3.54–4.34	8.36	1.71	3.36	.180
	Quincy, Mass.	2.38–6.05	4.49	1.55–2.9	3.45	.045–.124
Diabase:	Vinalhaven, Maine	10.20–10.70	11.40	4.17–4.21	4.46	.258–.275
Gneiss:	Hell Gate, N.Y.	....	—	1.64–1.82	3.38	—
Schist:	Chlorite	7.05	—	3.15	4.13	.18
Sandstone:	Quartzitic, Pennsylvania	6.36	9.6	3.24	4.42	.115
Slate:	Everett, Mass.	4.87	—	2.18	2.72	.115
Limestone:	Solenhofen, Bavaria	5.77–6.27	6.3	2.31	2.47	.25
Dolomite:	Pennsylvania	7.1	—	3.23		

E = Young's modulus in 10^{11} dynes/cm^2
G = rigidity in 10^{11} dynes/cm^2
μ = Poisson's ratio
P = hydrostatic pressure in kg/cm^2
SOURCE: "Handbook of physical constants," *Geol. Soc. Am. Spec. Papers*, No. 36, 1942.

The strict application of the principles concerning the elastic properties of rocks to tectonic problems cannot lead to any results, because natural rock deformation has a permanent character.

Nevertheless, a modified application of the laws of elasticity might perhaps be possible, for our experiments on the strain of rock, both elastic and permanent, have shown that the elastic properties of a specimen which has been plastically deformed are not destroyed. We may therefore assume that, during the tectonic deformation, each unit volume of the rock is partially in a condition of elastic strain, and it may well be that this elastic condition controls the orientation and magnitude of the principal stresses in the rock. In that case each successive minute change of shape is fundamentally an elastic strain which eventually becomes permanent. In fact, experiments have failed to demonstrate detectable differences between deformations leading to permanent set (viscous deformation) and those of simple elasticity.

The elastic properties of rocks are of great importance for seismology, because the propagation of shock waves is a purely elastic phenomenon.

For longitudinal waves we have, for the velocity,

$$V_{long} = \sqrt{\frac{1/K + \frac{4}{3}G}{D}}$$

and for transverse waves,

$$V_{trans} = \sqrt{\frac{G}{D}}$$

where D is the density of the rocks. Because transverse shock waves cannot traverse the core of the earth, it is assumed that at least the material of the core has no rigidity. Deep-focus earthquakes prove that rigidity for a shock wave is still present to a depth of 700 km.

Pure elastic strain of rocks is also demonstrated by the phenomenon of "rock bursts" occurring along the walls of deep underground tunnels, as, for instance, in the quartzite rocks of the South African gold mines which reach depths of 3 km below surface and in tunnels through the high Alpine mountains. The elastic strain is due to, or anyhow maintained by, the heavy overburden, and the sudden release of stress caused by tunneling causes the rock to burst along planes subparallel with the tunnel walls.

RUPTURE, STRENGTH, AND SHEARING

The field of elastic strain of rocks is not unlimited. With a rise of the deformative, or differential, stress, rocks rupture along certain planes and, under high confining pressure, slip planes develop and shearing takes place along them. Permanent deformation sets in after a certain limit of elasticity has been passed. In the next chapter we shall see that many different kinds of permanent deformation exist, but that all of them are subject to the condition of the internal stress of the rock, which we shall consider later.

In a general way a stress field can always be represented by three perpendicular stresses acting on unit cube, P_1, P_2, and P_3, P_3 being the smallest stress, P_2 the medium stress, and P_1 the largest stress, as in Fig. 8. The deformative stress P (or $\Delta\sigma$) can be derived from these values (p. 19). As the failure of the material will always occur in planes perpendicular to the plane containing the largest stress difference $(P_1 - P_3)$, thus being parallel to P_2, we can simplify our theoretical considerations by using a two-dimensional representation containing only P_1 and P_3 or only P.

The slip planes which develop in the rock specimen make a certain angle α with the deformative stress P (Fig. 9). On the oblique plane two forces are active, a normal stress σ and a shearing stress τ. In Fig. 9 we take the distance ab as unit; then $cd = 1/\sin \alpha$, and as a

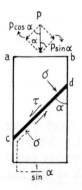

Fig. 9 Normal stress σ and shearing stress τ on oblique shear plane.

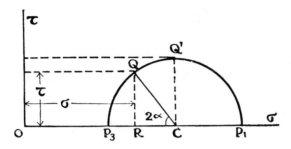

Fig. 10 Mohr circles.

stress is a force per unit area, σ and τ expressed in terms of P and α are

$$\sigma = P \frac{\sin \alpha}{1/\sin \alpha} = P \sin^2 \alpha = \tfrac{1}{2}P(1 - \cos 2\alpha)$$

$$\tau = P \sin \alpha \cos \alpha = \tfrac{1}{2}P \sin 2\alpha$$

The shearing stress τ will have a maximum value when $\sin 2\alpha = 1$, that is, when $\alpha = 45°$, and we actually observe in experimental specimens slip planes which make an angle not far different from 45° with the stress P. Although the shearing force τ has its maximum value on a 45° plane, the resistance of the rock to shearing may not be equal in this plane to that in any other plane; indeed, experiments have shown that it varies with the normal stress σ on the plane. Therefore, although $\tau_{\max}$ is always at 45° to applied stress, the yield stress $I = f(\sigma)$, so that the fracture angle will be a compromise. The relation between τ and σ on different planes can be very clearly demonstrated by introducing the Mohr diagram (Mohr, 1914), representing in a simple way the relation between the principal stresses P_1 and P_3 and their derivates τ and σ (Fig. 10).

When we consider the plane in which P_1 and P_3 are situated and measure their values on the abscissa to the right of the zero value when positive, as in Fig. 10, then the normal stress σ on a plane which makes an angle α with P_1 is equal to OR and the shearing stress τ is equal to RQ.

This follows since, in the figure,

$$OC = \frac{P_1 + P_3}{2} \quad \text{and} \quad CQ = CP_3 = \frac{P_1 - P_3}{2}$$

then

$$OR = OC - CR = \frac{P_1 + P_3}{2} - \frac{P_1 - P_3}{2} \cos 2\alpha = \sigma$$

and

$$RQ = \frac{P_1 - P_3}{2} \sin 2\alpha = \tau$$

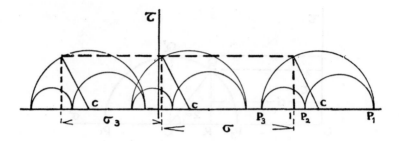

Fig. 11   Shift of Mohr circles.

The Mohr circle thus is a nomograph which solves these equations because they agree with those derived from Fig. 9, where P_3 was taken as equal to zero. Therefore the Mohr-circle construction gives us an easy way to study the relation between σ, τ, and the primary stress field.

When $\alpha = 45°$, Q is situated perpendicularly above C and τ reaches its maximum value. When, in Fig. 10, the values of the principal stresses approach each other, the circles become smaller and smaller, and when $P_1 = P_3$, they have become one point—under hydrostatic conditions there is no shearing stress and the normal stress is equal on every plane. The complete diagram of Fig. 10 may be shifted toward the left by subtracting an equal amount from each principal stress, their differences remaining the same, as in Fig. 11. Hence this amounts to lowering the confining pressure. The normal stresses now differ appreciably (since they depend on $P_1 + P_3$, which has changed), but the shearing stresses remain the same (since they depend on $P_1 - P_3$, which has not changed). However, the *maximum supportable* shearing stress on a given plane (yield, or shearing strength) has changed, along with the normal stresses of which they are a function. As shown in Fig. 12*a*, this function can be represented by

$$\tau_{\text{yield}} = f(\sigma) = c + \sigma \tan \beta = R$$

where R = resistance to shearing (shearing strength), c = a constant, the threshold value of the shearing strength (i.e., the value when $\beta = 0$), and β = so-called "angle of internal friction."

Then

$$R = c + \left(\frac{P_1 + P_3}{2} - \frac{P_1 - P_3}{2} \cos 2\alpha\right) \tan \beta$$

and the difference between the resistance R (shearing strength) and the actual shearing stress $\Delta \tau$ is

$$R - \tau = \Delta\tau = c + \left(\frac{P_1 + P_3}{2} - \frac{P_1 - P_3}{2} \cos 2\alpha\right) \tan \beta - \frac{P_1 - P_3}{2} \sin 2\alpha$$

On those planes where this difference between the strength and the shear stress becomes minimal the material will rupture; therefore, when

$$\frac{d\,\Delta\tau}{d\alpha} = 0$$

then

$$\tan \beta \,(P_1 - P_3) \sin 2\alpha - (P_1 - P_3) \cos 2\alpha = 0$$

or

$$\tan \beta \sin 2\alpha = \cos 2\alpha$$

or

$$\tan 2\alpha = \cot \beta = \tan (90° - \beta)$$

and

$$\alpha = 45° - \frac{\beta}{2} \qquad \text{and} \qquad \beta = 90° - 2\alpha$$

According to these considerations, the angle between the plane of rupture and the deformative stress will be in general less than 45°.

The shearing plane angle α is dependent on the angle of internal friction β, a specific property of the material which in itself may vary with the normal stress (Fig. 12b). The internal friction is large for sandstones and small for clays; moreover, it increases rapidly with growing confining pressure in sandstones and only little in clays. We can introduce the curve of $\tau_{yield} = f(\sigma)$ very easily into Mohr's graphic representation, because both have the shearing stress and the normal stress on the y and x axes. If, in Fig. 11, we chose to draw only the largest possible P_1/P_3 circles (i.e., the circles representing the stresses at which the material starts to break), we should find that the circles decrease in size toward the left. For, although the shearing stresses on arbitrary planes remain theoretically the same (Fig. 11), the maximum supportable shearing stress τ_{max} decreases, since $\tau_{max} = f(\sigma)$, and σ decreases when the circle is shifted to the left. This gives rise to Fig. 13. The τ_{max} curve must be tangent to the largest possible P_1/P_3 circles, because otherwise there would be shearing stresses larger than

Fig. 12 Angle of internal friction β in (a) independent and (b) dependent of the normal stress.

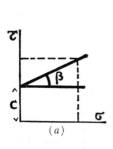

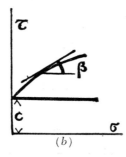

(a)   (b)

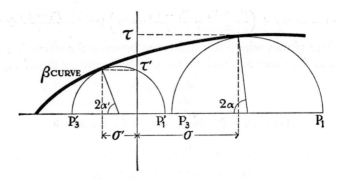

Fig. 13 Enveloping β curve and variation of α and β by shift of Mohr circles.

the maximum the material can support. The point at which the τ_{max} curve touches a P_1/P_3 circle gives the values for τ and σ at the breaking point, as well as the angle of shear failure α and the angle of internal friction β, the latter being the angle between the tangent and the x axis ($\alpha = 90° - \beta/2$). Figure 13 shows that, under decreasing confining pressure (leftward shift of the P_1/P_3 circle), the angle 2α decreases and β correspondingly increases.

Different materials are characterized by different τ_{max} curves (Fig. 14). The steeper the curve, the larger the angle of internal friction for a given stress condition and the more rapidly the shearing stress needed for rupture (τ_{max}, or shearing strength) increases with increasing confining pressure. It follows that shear strength under tension is smaller than shear strength under compression. From empirical evidence it appears that when this difference between tension strength and compression strength for a certain material is large, we call the material brittle, and when the difference is small, we call it ductile. With increasing confining pressure the β curve tends to flatten, the shear-plane angle α increases, and the difference between ductile and brittle material disappears. Whether the compression strength of rocks is still dependent on the changing confining pressure or not is dependent on where this flattening of the curve sets in, and we may expect that it will be different for various kinds of rocks. As we shall see later, competent (hard or brittle) rocks like sandstone and limestone have a different enveloping curve: the sandstone curve remains

Fig. 14 Enveloping curves typical for different rock types.

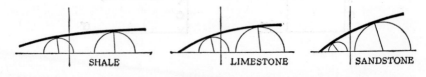

Table 2

Rock	K_c, kg/cm², av	K_s, kg/cm²	K_t, kg/cm²
Granite	1,480	200	40
Sandstone	740	150	20
Limestone	960	200	45
Marble	1,020	. . .	60
Slate	1,480	. . .	205
Basalt	2,500	100	. . .

steep under increasing confining pressure, whereas that of limestone flattens and clay or shale has always a flat enveloping curve (Fig. 14). In the light of these considerations one can see why brittle materials like rocks under high confining pressure behave as ductile materials, such as copper, under atmospheric pressure. Under a differential stress greater than their strength at atmospheric pressure, they no longer rupture (in the sense of disintegration), but flow along an infinite number of small shear planes, just as metals do under atmospheric pressure.

When the stress conditions are such that the smallest principal stress is negative, there is a maximum tension stress in all planes perpendicular to this direction. Instead of rupture along shear planes, the material may be torn asunder along such planes. In that case there is no question of shearing stress, because along that plane the shearing stress is zero; but brittle materials with little internal cohesion may rupture in this way before the stress difference $P_1 - P_3$ has caused a sufficient shearing stress τ along inclined planes. In the light of the foregoing reasoning, it is obvious that, although tensional rupture plays an important role in near-surface structures, it will not occur at great depth. Tensional cracks are always parallel to the largest principal stress direction.

The strength of a material, as tested in the laboratory, is therefore generally given as three different strengths, the compression strength K_c, the shearing strength K_s, and the tensile strength K_t. For rocks under atmospheric pressure, values are as given in Table 2.

The compression strength for some of these more or less brittle rocks is about thirty times larger than their tensile strength.

FLOW OF ROCKS

We have seen that, in elastic deformation, the strain γ is dependent on the rigidity G and the shearing stress:

$$\tau = \gamma G \quad \text{and} \quad \gamma = \frac{\tau}{g}$$

In a viscous fluid, the amount of strain is no longer governed by the rigidity, which is absent but has become a function of time. The strain ratio D is now dependent on the shearing stress and the viscosity η.

$$\tau = D\eta \qquad \text{or} \qquad D = \frac{\tau}{\eta}$$

The viscosity is measured in poises; that is to say, when $\tau = 1$ dyne/cm² and there is a distance of 1 cm between two surfaces of area 1 cm² (which volume is occupied by the viscous fluid), and if the velocity is 1 cm/sec, then the viscosity is 1 poise. The dimension of a viscosity is therefore $[M/L^1/T^1]$.

The fluids which follow this law of $\tau = D\eta$ are called Newtonian fluids, the relation between D and σ being linear (Fig. 15, curve a). The study of non-Newtonian fluids and imperfectly elastic solids has been called the science of "rheology." In non-Newtonian fluids the viscosity curve is not straight, but curved (Fig. 15, curve b), and is determined by $d\tau/dD$. Non-Newtonian fluids have a differential viscosity, which is given at every point by the tangent to the curve. The viscosity is a function of the stress, and decreases with increasing stress. We have assumed that when the flow is viscous, the motion starts at zero, but some viscous materials seem to have a starting point farther to the right (Fig. 15, curve c), which means that the fluid (or solid—the distinction is uncertain here) has a certain threshold value below which no viscous flow exists. The threshold value may be called the strength of the non-Newtonian substance. We might use the presence of a strength as the determining factor between fluids and solids. Many solids do not rupture when loaded above their strength, but start to flow. They have then a stress/strain diagram of the kind of Fig. 16. When the load $\Delta\sigma$ is increased, the first

Fig. 15 Linear (a) and differential (b and c) curves of viscosity, c with threshold value. D = strain ratio.

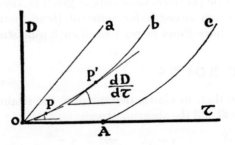

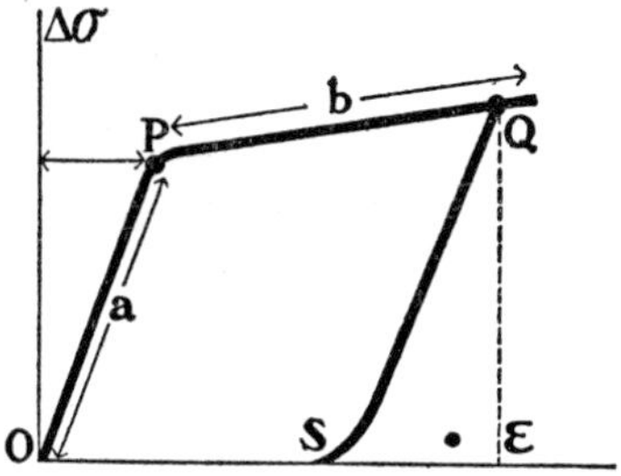

Fig. 16 Elastic-viscous flow of solids in a stress/strain diagram. Curve *a* is for elastic strain, recovered after unloading; *b* is for viscous strain, not recovered.

part of the strain curve is steep, and then flattens out rather suddenly. The steep part of the curve represents the elastic strain, and *P*, the threshold value, the strength; the flat part of the curve, the plastic deformation or flow. In unloading, the elastic strain *a* is recovered, but not the plastic strain *b*. Similar curves to these, which are typical of metals, have been obtained with rocks under high confining pressure, as we shall see later. A remarkable feature of these experiments is that, although the strength has been surpassed and the material has flowed, it has not lost its elastic properties (compare p. 21). It is said that the material has an elastico-viscosity. One might imagine the process as an elastic strain which is internally eased by small successive translations of molecules or other small units within the crystal lattice. By such a process of relaxation the elastic strain would disappear after a certain time and be replaced by a permanent strain. By maintaining the load, the double process of elastic strain and relaxation continues and an elastico-viscous flow is the result. This combination of elastic and plastic deformation which we have considered is not the only possible kind of combination. There is a method (Burgers, 1935) which successfully illustrates several varieties of combination: a spiral spring represents an elastic property, and a piston in a cylinder represents a plastic flow. The tension of the spring equals αK, when K is the stress and α the elasticity of the spring. The piston will be displaced by the force K with a velocity determined by $dx/dt = \varphi K$, where φ represents the viscous property of the piston cylinder system. In Fig. 17, these two properties are coupled in two different ways, in series and in parallel. In Fig. 17*a* the total stretch x is the sum of stretch of each element and the force K acts equally on both elements. In Fig. 17*b*, however, the total stretch is equal to that of both elements. The stretching process can be represented in two diagrams, a strain/time and a force/time diagram. The corresponding diagrams for the in-series and in-parallel connections can be found in Fig. 17. In each diagram the force K is active during the time interval t. The strain of the connection in series starts with an immediate strain of the spring, which equals αK, and then begins

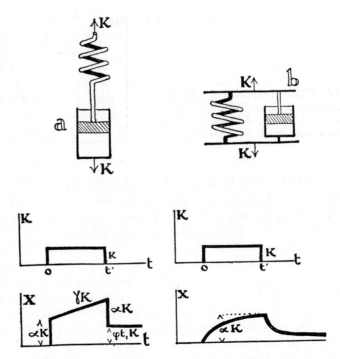

Fig. 17   Elastic and plastic properties: (*a*) coupled in series,
(*b*) coupled in parallel connection. *a* represents a Maxwell
fluid, *b* a Kelvin body.

the slow flow of the piston, which equals φtK in the time interval t.
On unloading, the strain αK is recovered while the permanent strain
remains. This arrangement therefore represents a particular kind of
elastic viscosity, which is the characteristic property of what are
called "Maxwell fluids." When the two elements are coupled in parallel, the stretching of the spring is prevented by the slow motion of the
piston, and during the motion, the force acting on the piston is diminished by the portion absorbed in stretching the spring. Hence the
curve is steeper at the start and flattens out to the horizontal. When t
is made long enough, the total tension equals αK. On unloading, the
reverse process takes place. This system represents a strongly retarded
elastic strain which is sometimes called elastic flow, and materials
having this property are called "Kelvin bodies." The two systems can
also be combined in one arrangement (Fig. 18 and the accompanying
diagrams). First we notice an immediate strain of $\alpha'K$ in the upper
spring, followed by the constant strain velocity of φ_1K per second and
by the gradual strain of the spring α_2 retarded by the piston φ_2. The
velocity is therefore larger than φ_1K at the beginning and eventually

becomes $\varphi_1 K$. On unloading, the permanent strain still equals $\varphi_1 t_1 K$. This combination of pistons and springs gives a picture of the combinations of elastic strain with an elastico-viscous flow, such as we have already described as a typical deformation of ductile materials and rocks under high confining pressure. By adding a new unit representing the strength as a yield limit, we could complete the picture and obtain what is called in rheology a "Bingham solid." In this way we may illustrate a wide range of possible elastic and plastic behavior.

We must emphasize, however, that all our deductions from experimental data are extrapolations in time. Neither the absolute value of the strength nor the fact of a constant plastic deformation velocity can be ascertained with enough accuracy in the laboratory. This is due to the fact that the time interval of an experiment, even if it lasts more than a year, as has been tried, is too short for the purpose. I shall again refer to this uncertainty when we have examined the experiments themselves.

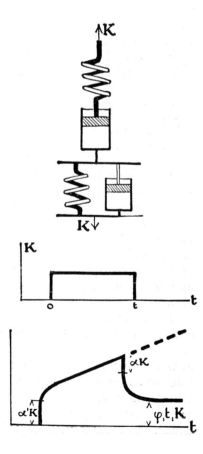

Fig. 18 In-series and in-parallel connections combined, illustrating the property of Bingham solid.

MECHANICAL PROPERTIES OF
UNCONSOLIDATED SEDIMENTS

The physical properties of unconsolidated sediments are rather different from those of cemented rocks. Since many deformations in surface sediments occur before consolidation, it will certainly be advantageous to understand their peculiarities. During the progress of lithification we might get intermediate stages between soft rock and loose sediments.

The principal difference between unconsolidated sediments and solid rock is that the first are essentially a two-phase aggregate, water and mineral grains.

If we consider only two sediments clay and sand, we shall cover more or less the whole range of present-day sediments. The difference between clays and sands is due principally to two factors, the difference in grain size and the kinds of grain. Sands may be considered as a simple two-phase aggregate of rounded and hard grains resting on one another, with a liquid phase filling the pore space. Clays, on the contrary, have flat, flexible grains surrounded by a water film and therefore not in contact with each other, the pore space beyond the water film being also filled with water.

In loose sediments we can distinguish:

1. Dense packing of grains touching each other
2. Loose packing of grains touching each other
3. Honeycomb texture
4. Flake texture

In the first two subdivisions each grain is a structural unit; in the second two a group of grains is the structural unit. In the honeycomb texture a large pore is surrounded by a group of grains, and in the flake structure the walls of a large pore are built up by a honeycomb texture of small grains. The honeycomb and flake textures can exist only in superficial clays and silts, and they cannot stand up to any large load of covering sediments. Nevertheless, in sandstones which are loosely or even densely packed, we find large pores whose walls are formed by many grains. The pore volume of sands is determined to a very large extent by the manner of sedimentation, and it cannot be changed appreciably by subsequent loading. Loose packing may be expected when large volumes of sand are rapidly deposited in water or in wind-blown sand on the surface. Deposition of moist sand in large volumes on the surface invariably results in very loose packing. When, on the contrary, the sand is laid down gradually in water, as in the ordinary natural process of sedimentation, a dense packing is obtained. Once the sand is deposited as sediment, the packing cannot be altered by pressure; it remains virtually incompressible. A sand with a wide range in its grain size can clearly attain a much more dense packing than a sand of more uniform grain size.

The ground or rock pressure σ_g at a depth h is built up from two kinds of pressure, first the weight of the grains, transmitted from grain to grain, σ_k, and the hydrostatic pressure σ_w, equal to the weight of a column of water of that height,

$$\sigma_g = \sigma_K + \sigma_W$$

When we apply a shearing stress to an uncemented sand layer under normal stress σ, we find, in the case of loosely packed sand, that a volume decrease occurs when strain takes place; but in the case of densely packed sand, we obtain volume increase (Fig. 19).

The relationships between stress, strain, and density for loosely and densely packed sands are illustrated in Fig. 19. Curve a in Fig. 19A shows that, in a loosely packed sand, at first, a continuously increasing level of stress τ is needed to produce failure as strain progresses; this increase stops at the point where the corresponding curve a in Fig. 19B shows that volume changes, accompanying the strain, cease.

This increase of τ is due to a small initial movement causing the grains to settle more compactly, and therefore an increased deformative stress is necessary to keep the shear moving. A densely packed sand must first undergo a little loosening, and the shearing stress therefore necessarily increases beyond the steady-state value (curve

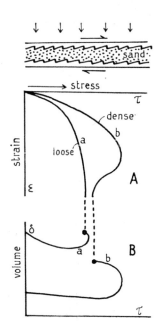

Fig. 19 Shearing stress τ/strain ϵ diagram for (A) a loosely and (B) a densely packed sand. (*After Keverling Buisman, Grondmechanica, published by permission of Waltman, Delft, 1940.*)

b in Fig. 19*A*). At the same time the density decreases. Thus both loose and dense sands reach a constant strain velocity with roughly the same density and require the same shearing stress after this density has been obtained. This value is called the critical density D_k (Fig. 20). The critical density depends to some extent on the normal pressure σ.

When a loosely packed sand mass $(D < D_K)$ with water-filled pores is subjected to a shearing stress, the sand will tend to settle in a denser state, but to accomplish this it must get rid of a certain volume of water. When the water cannot escape immediately, the hydrostatic pressure increases and the grain pressure necessarily decreases by the same amount. Because of this drop in the grain pressure the sand enters the zone of the critical density (compare Fig. 20, where *A* moves toward *B*), where a lower shearing stress suffices for deformation. With the original shearing stress, a lower normal grain stress, and a higher hydrostatic pressure, the motion already started accelerates and sometimes attains catastrophic proportions. There are many examples of such happenings in loosely packed sediments even on a very slight slope—landslides, for instance. With a densely packed sand this danger does not exist. The action of a shear stress tends to increase the pore volume, thereby causing a decrease in hydrostatic pressure and an increase in grain pressure. Hence the shearing stress must further increase to make continued movement possible.

The porosity of clay can be much greater than that of sand; this is principally due to the fact that its sliverlike grains do not touch, but are surrounded by a water film.

Fig. 20   Critical density field between loosely and densely packed sand.

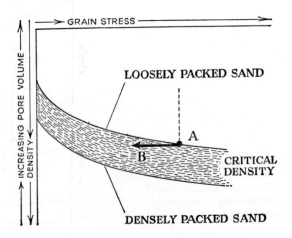

Table 3

	Upper Limit or Liquid Limit	Lower Limit or Plastic Limit	Plasticity Index
Fat clay	65.4	27.6	37.8
Lean clay	51.7	24.6	27.1
Loam	23.3	14.1	9.2
Loess	30.4	24.9	5.5

Most of the intergranular motion in clays is restricted to the films around the grains, the so-called "tough" water. The transition from the "tough" water to the free water of the pore space is gradual. The distance from grain to grain in a typical clay is of the order of 300 Å, and the closer the grain surface is approached, the "tougher" becomes the water. It is this "tough" water that gives clays their plasticity. When too much water is added to a clay it starts to flow; too little, and it will break when kneaded. The difference of the volume percentages of the water which determine these upper and lower limits of the clay sediments is called its plasticity index.

It is obvious that clays, which may contain as much as 80% of water and in which the grains do not touch, are much more susceptible to compression than sands. But the compressibility is again a function of the rate at which the water is disposed of, and therefore of the permeability, which in clays is small. The change in the grain pressure in a clay after a load has been added is therefore to a large extent dependent on the time that has elapsed since loading.

The compaction of clay has been studied in great detail by civil engineers and architects, in particular in Holland, because building on a clay soil is equivalent to loading the clay with the weight of the building and will always result in compression of the clay and sinking of the building. The enormous amount of settling of large buildings in Mexico City, built on saturated loose lacustrine volcanic tuff deposits, is of the same character. The experimental data are therefore numerous, and observations of settlement over time intervals of tens and hundreds of years are sometimes available. There is no essential difference, moreover, between loading with a large building and loading with more sediments, and so the results of investigations in soil mechanics are directly applicable to problems of sedimentation. It has been ascertained that we must make a distinction between two kinds of compaction:

1. Direct compaction (or primary consolidation)
2. Secular compaction (or secondary consolidation)

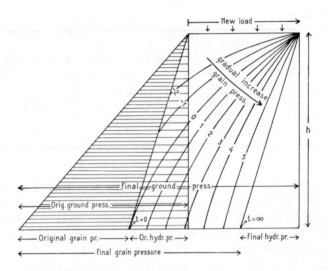

Fig. 21 Development of hydrostatic and grain pressure by loading. (*After Keverling Buisman, Grondmechanica, published by permission of Waltman, Deft, 1940.*)

The direct compaction is due to the escape of the free water, and the secular compaction is due to the slow pressing out of the "tough" water. Both processes are hindered by the low and decreasing permeability of the clay.

When a clay is loaded with a weight of P g/cm², the ground pressure at a depth h will be increased by the same amount. This additional pressure is initially transmitted by the pore water (which sets up a hydrodynamic pressure) rather than by the intergranular pressure. By the gradual escape of water the load p is slowly transferred from the water to the grain skeleton; Fig. 21 demonstrates this process. The grain pressure is hatched; the hydrodynamic pressure is left unhatched. The time t_0 is taken at the moment when, at the depth h, the grain pressure starts to increase. The isochrones 1, 2, etc., illustrate the distribution of the ground pressure between the grain and hydrodynamic pressure at the time t_1, t_2, etc. Similarly, the isochrones -1, -2 show their distribution before the moment t_0. Complete settling will be reached only after $t = \infty$. The degree of compaction at a particular moment is dependent on both the compressibility and the permeability.

The fact that quick loading produces a decrease of grain pressure is demonstrated, for instance, in quicksands. The weight of the person stepping on the sand is carried by the water column; the sand grains, just touching before the loading, lose their mutual loading weight; and the slightest disturbance causes the whole soil to become a fluid in which the load sinks down. This quicksand principle is also thought to be involved in the origin of mud volcanoes, where slow mud streams flow to the surface through a fracture or other opening in the overlying sediments. In that case the original loading might very well be due to a lateral folding pressure. The impermeability of the sediment prevented the escape of water to the surface, so that the clay has become a mud again. Similar mud streams have also been encountered in drill holes, often putting a conclusive end to all drilling operations. In Chap. 18 we shall again refer to this quicksand principle as being perhaps responsible for gliding tectonics.

It has been demonstrated that after this so-called direct compaction, a stable condition has still not been reached. In the compaction diagram of Fig. 22, we do not get the curve *a*, as should follow from the above-mentioned considerations, but the curve *b*.

It has been proved that after this direct adaptation of the clay to the new load, retarded by the low permeability, the compaction continues, although more slowly. This secular compaction is probably due to the pressing out of the "tough" water and is a logarithmic function of the time. The specific secular compaction of a clay a_s is the compaction per kg/cm² per cm thickness of the clay in the time intervals of 1–10, 10–100, 100–1,000 days, etc. It varies from 1 to 5%. With a value of $a_s = 3\%$ and a direct settling of 10%, a clay with 30% water would be compressed 25% in three centuries per kg/cm² load. A layer 10 cm thick would be reduced to 7.5 cm. The experiments have always been executed with small loads; there is little doubt that the compaction does not increase linearly with increasing loads, but little is known about this relation.

I shall return to compressibility from the point of view of elastic and permanent deformation when we consider other experiments later, but there is no doubt that a small part of the compaction is elastic.

Fig. 22   Direct (*a*) and secular (*b*) compaction curves by loading of clay sediment.

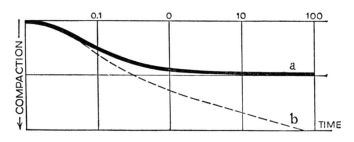

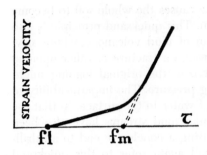

Fig. 23   Viscosity curve for clay.

In experiments on plastic deformation of clay it has been proved that the strain of clay follows the so-called Bingham formula

$$D = \frac{1}{\eta} (\sigma - \gamma)$$

(and Fig. 23). The viscosity η has a linear relation with the water content, and f_m, the strength, increases with a lower water percentage.

Table 4

Per Cent of Water in Clay	η, Poises
50.5	0.31
52	0.23
55.5	0.20
55.6	0.16

Beneath the strength there exists a differential viscosity, again with a lower limit (fl in Fig. 23). The threshold value f_m for clay with 50% water lies somewhere between 10×10^2 and 15×10^2 dynes/cm².

The experiments with clay give us valuable insight into its behavior in tectonic processes. Its capacity for flowing under increasing load explains many features of gliding—and diapiric—tectonics.

Chapter 3

Strain of Rocks in Laboratory Experiments

After the principle of oblique shearing due to a normal stress had been established by Napier (Hartmann), and had been introduced into geology by the experiments of Daubrée (1878), the matter rested there for a long time.

Bucher (1921) applied the principle again and explained joint systems with it, while Mead (1920) made some very clear experiments in which the relation between folding and faulting direction is admirably expressed; but no fundamentally new material was adduced. Mohr (1914), Anderson (1951), and many others have pointed out that, besides the shearing stress, the normal stress on the shearing plane plays an important role; Anderson and Jeffreys (1936), moreover, drew attention to the fact that a fault is not only a static problem, but also a dynamic one, and that the stress conditions are therefore necessarily altered after the birth of a fault (or fold).

In the meantime the elastic and plastic behavior of rock material under stress has been extensively studied by many investigators, among whom special mention should be made of Griggs (1936, 1939a), Goguel (1943), Handin and Hager (1957, 1958), and Griggs and Handin (1960), the last giving full references to modern work.

Thus we see that, ever since the beginning of this century, laboratory experiments have been made on the behavior of rock specimens under varying stress conditions. All of them have some bearing on tectonic processes of rock deformation, and most of them have been performed with this problem in view.

The imperfection of our knowledge of the mechanism of rock deformation has also been demonstrated by them all. We are at present, nevertheless, in a position to put forward, tentatively at least, a few fundamental properties for several varieties of rock under stress.

The earlier experiments on rock deformation were always performed with a growing stress under high confining pressure. Some of the specimens were wetted, but most of them were dry. It was soon found that the specimen must be jacketed with rubber or copper in order to prevent the surrounding high-pressure fluid from penetrating and exploding it, although later experiments of ductile flow with interstitial fluids have been made. The results were plotted in a stress/strain diagram, and certain features of the curves obtained were regarded as representing fundamental physical properties of the rocks in question. However, as soon as the time element was introduced, it became clear that the rate of increase of stress had an important influence on the measured results, and the earlier type of experiments with a quickly growing stress therefore became valueless as a means of measuring fundamental physical properties in rocks in relation to tectonic processes.

This means, unfortunately, that in order to measure one physical property, such as the elasticity limit under a certain pressure, one has to perform a whole series of experiments, each lasting considerable time, instead of one experiment taking a few hours. I do not think that there is any way of overcoming this obstacle to a thorough investigation of rock behavior under stress.

In addition to that difficulty, to which I shall refer again later, it has become clear that we must not only distinguish between elastic and permanent yield to stress, but must also recognize that there are several modes of permanent plastic, and elastic yield, and even transitory phases where the deformation is both plastic and elastic.

To complicate an already involved matter, the behavior of rock specimens which are wet is different from that of dry ones, and their final rupture may be due to quite different processes, so that even the notion of strength has to be revised.

ELASTIC AND PLASTIC FLOW

In order to be able to discuss these complicated matters, we must first define the terms we shall use. Fundamentally, an elastic yield is characterized by complete recovery after unloading. Since hardly any elastic yield is instantaneous but always shows retardation, the recovery is never immediate, and one must wait a considerable time after unloading to observe whether any of the deformation is permanent or not. The retardation of recovery is called the hysteresis. When retardation and hysteresis are large, it becomes difficult to distinguish between elastic and permanent deformation, but the final criterion is undoubtedly that an elastic strain is related only to the stress, whereas a permanent strain is also related to the time the stress is applied.

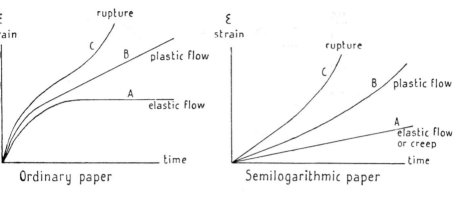

Fig. 24 Strain/time curves of elastic (*A*) and plastic (*B*) deformation and rupture (*C*) of a rock specimen by constant load on ordinary and on semilogarithmic paper.

Therefore, in a strain experiment with a constant load, the elastic deformation is characterized by a gradual decrease of the strain velocity, leading finally to a standstill of the process, while a permanent (or plastic) deformation goes on indefinitely with a constant strain velocity (Fig. 24).

In curve *A* the strain ceases to increase and becomes zero after a certain time; in curve *B* the strain continues and reaches a constant strain velocity. With higher stresses, curves like *C* have been obtained, in which, after a certain period of constant strain velocity, an increase which eventually resulted in rupture was observed. Plotted on semilogarithmic paper, the curve *A* becomes a straight line and curve *B* curves upward. Good examples of elastic flow were given by Griggs (1939a) when he made an experiment lasting 550 days on a dry specimen with a constant stress of 1,400 kg/cm^2 and no extra confining pressure. He obtained a perfect elastic flow for the whole of the 550 days (Fig. 25). A similar result is given by his experiment on alabaster (Griggs, 1940; Fig. 26).

Because the plastic yielding is always accompanied by a permanent rearrangement of particles of the rock, whereas elastic yield means only a temporary rearrangement, the limit between the two modes of deformation is essentially a limit between a nonimpaired and an impaired rock and might be called the "strength." I prefer, however, the term "elasticity limit," as a less ambiguous term.

Above the elasticity limit we enter the field of permanent deformation, or the plastic field. In experiments it has been observed that when the stress is further increased, rupture of the specimen will occur and the specimen disintegrates. Griggs called this threshold value the "ultimate strength," which, however, is not a well-defined

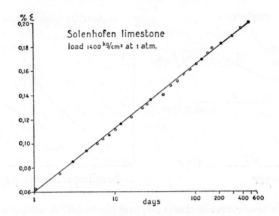

Fig. 25   Strain/time diagram of stress experiment
on Solenhofen Limestone, load 1,400 kg/cm²,
confining pressure 1 atm. (*After Griggs, 1939.
Published by permission of the University of
Chicago Press.*)

Fig. 26   Strain/time diagram of experiment on dry alabaster specimen
with 420 kg/cm² stress at 1 atm elastic flow. (*After Griggs, 1940. Published
by permission of the Geological Society of America.*)

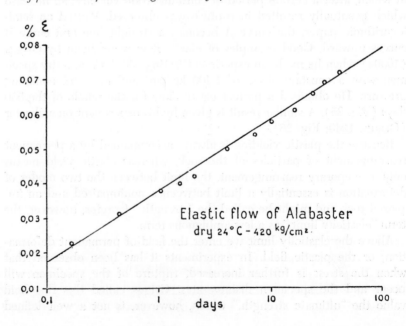

physical property and depends on nonessential circumstances of the experiment. Nevertheless, some kind of upper limit to the plastic field probably exists.

A good example of permanent deformation is given by the stress/strain diagram of Fig. 29, showing experiments on marble by Griggs (1936).

When we make a series of experiments under nonvariable conditions of (1) kind of rock, (2) environment, (3) confining pressure, and (4) constant stress, our definitions of these terms become as follows: an elastic flow is characterized by the fact that the strain velocity becomes zero (on semilogarithmic paper the curve becomes a straight line), whereas plastic, or permanent, deformation is characterized by an unlimited constant strain velocity. Within the field of plastic flow we shall have to distinguish a field where the elastic stress is still an important factor, the field of elastico-viscous flow, and a field of higher stress where it is of little or no importance, the field of plastic flow. We shall see that most folding processes take place in the elastico-viscous flow field.

The elasticity limit is the highest stress with which a zero strain velocity can be maintained after an initial elastic flow. Rupture indicates disintegration of the specimen. It occurs above the rupture limit of stress and is initiated in the experiments by an increasing strain velocity. The different fields and their limits are schematically shown in Fig. 27. Originally, the strength of a material was defined as the load

Fig. 27   Schematic strain/time diagram showing different fields of deformation.

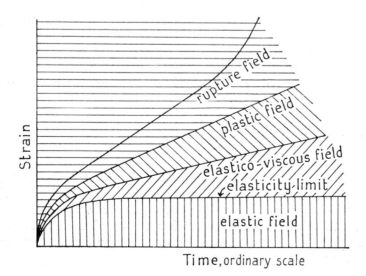

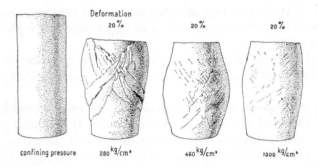

Fig. 28   Ductility limit demonstrated by deformation
experiments on marble with increasing confining pressure.
(*After Paterson, 1958. Published by permission of
Geol. Soc. America.*)

under which the material cracked and disintegrated. This definition had
been borrowed from the engineers concerned with testing building
material. The experimental definition of strength was determined by
increasing the load (or the tensile stress) and observing the point at
which the first crack appeared. In this way a "crushing strength" and
a "tensile strength" were determined.

In experiments with increasing confining pressure it was found
that, below a certain confining pressure, the specimen cracked and
disintegrated and it behaved in a brittle fashion; but under higher
hydrostatic pressures, the same material could be deformed smoothly
and it had become ductile. Many experiments have been made to
define this ductility limit of the confining pressure (e.g., Paterson,
1958), and its existence has already been indicated by theoretical
considerations with the help of the Mohr circle (Figs. 13 and 14).
This ductility limit also shows very clearly in the appearance of the
deformed specimen (Fig. 28). However, this limit is also dependent
on the rate of strain, which in all experiments is of course much larger
than in most tectonic events.

TIME FACTOR INTRODUCED INTO EXPERIMENTS

In the classic experiments performed by Adams and Nicholson (1901,
1912), von Kármán (1911), Böker (1915), and later by Griggs (1936),
a rock specimen under varying confining pressures was submitted to
an increasing stress; the moment when the initial small elastic strain
changed into a larger plastic strain was found by constructing stress/
strain diagrams (Fig. 29).

Invariably, the experimenter, in order to prevent rupture, had to raise the confining pressure above a certain limit, and this adjustment from the brittle to the ductile state caused a higher yield point. This yield point under high confining pressure was called the elasticity limit. It varies with temperature and confining pressure and is at the same time the brittle-ductile transition of Fig. 30 (H. C. Heard, 1960, in Griggs and Handin, 1960). Griggs repeated the experiment of Fig. 29 with limestone and introduced pauses in the rise of the stress (Fig. 31), an experiment repeated by Robertson with the same result (Robertson, 1955, and in Griggs and Handin, 1960, p. 229). These experiments showed that during the pauses and long before the original elasticity limit was reached, small permanent deformations took place. Evidently this gradual flow had been masked in the earlier experiment by the rapid increase of stress and its elastic strain. Moreover, this experiment clearly showed that the rate of strain became greater for each successive pause at a higher stress level. From the stress/strain curve given by this experiment, a strain/time curve and a stress/strain velocity diagram (Fig. 32) can be derived. Figure 32 shows that, with stresses of 47,000, 62,500, and 78,000 lb/in.², constant velocities were attained and that the highest stress of 96,000 lb/in.² led to rupture. The stress/rate of the strain curve shows that the relation between stress and strain velocity is not a straight line, but is governed by a differential viscosity, where the viscosity increases when the stress diminishes. The velocity curve apparently

Fig. 29   Stress/strain diagram of a series of experiments on marble with increasing confining pressure. (*Reproduced from Griggs, 1936a. By permission of the University of Chicago Press.*)

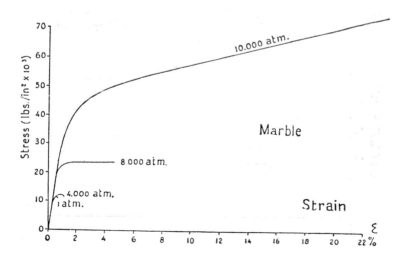

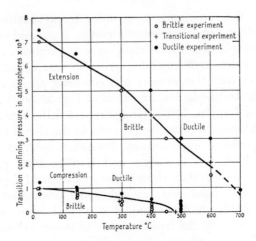

Fig. 30 The ductility limit by changing temperature and confining pressure for Solenhofen Limestone. (*After Heard,* 1960. *Published by permission of Geol. Soc. Am.*)

reaches a zero value at approximately the rupture point of 1 atm confining pressure, but the experiment was obviously not sufficiently detailed, the earlier pauses being too short, to be sure about this point. Neither does the viscosity curve tell us much about the velocity of strain and the viscosity at higher levels of stress, the duration of the pauses being too short and the increments in stress being too large. It appears probable, however, that the curve will eventually become a

Fig. 31 Stress/strain diagram of experiment on Solenhofen Limestone with pauses in increase of stress. (*Reproduced from Griggs,* 1963a. *By permission of the University of Chicago Press.*)

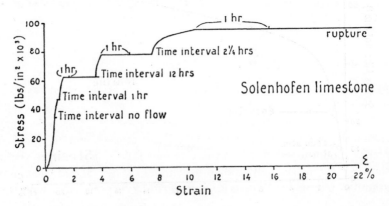

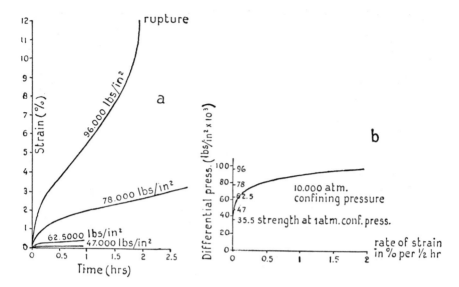

Fig. 32   (*a*) Strain/time diagram and (*b*) stress/rate of strain diagram derived from Fig. 31.

straight line with a small constant angle, or in other words, that above a certain stress the viscosity becomes constant.

The field where the viscosity is still differential is no doubt the field of elastico-viscous deformation, where both elastic and permanent deformation are active, in the sense that Burgers (1935) gave to it, i.e., an elastic strain which is taken over by small translations and thus eventually transformed into a permanent deformation. We may expect that the elastic deformation is no longer possible above a certain stress limit, and all deformation is directly of a permanent character, characterized by a constant viscosity. This field, where the strain velocity curve has become a straight line, can be termed the plastic field, and its lower limit, the plasticity limit (Fig. 27).

MODES OF DEFORMATION

Even the first series of experiments, those of Adams and Nicholson in 1901, showed that there are two quite different ways in which limestone yields to stress, one by *intergranular* slip planes causing a cataclastic texture with shattering of the crystal edges along those planes, and the other an *intracrystalline* failure, the calcite crystals showing intensive polysynthetic twinning. They found that intergranular motion prevailed in quick-loading experiments, whereas a very slow increase of load facilitated the twinning mechanism, particularly in the presence of water. Later on von Kármán (1911) showed that low confining pressure favored intergranular motion and high confining pressure, intracrystalline slip. These results were confirmed by Griggs in 1938 when he showed that a single calcite crystal showed much less strain than either limestone or marble under the same conditions of rather rapid loading under high confining pressure. Apparently, under these conditions, much of the yield in limestone had an intergranular character, whereas the calcite crystal showed only twinning and translation along intracrystalline slip planes. Intergranular slip is the most important mode of deformation in sandstones, accompanied by considerable crushing, as was shown by experimental work. Undoubtedly, this is due to the extreme brittleness of quartz (I. Borg et al. in Griggs and Handin, 1960, pp. 133–192).

Very extensive research on this subject of twinning and translations in single calcite crystals has been done by Turner, Griggs, and Heard (1954). Their work showed rather conclusively that twinning occurs only on the rhombohedral planes [01$\bar{1}$2] and translations are restricted to [10$\bar{1}$1] planes.

When a specimen is oriented with respect to the directed pressure so that the twinning planes are in the attitude receiving maximum stress, the resulting stress yield point is relatively low, reduced by as much as a factor of 20 compared with the result when the orientation of the specimen favors deformation along the cleavage planes. Temperature also affects the stress-yield-point values for both twinning and translation deformation. Unfortunately, we cannot attach too much value to the numerical value of the yield point because all experiments have been performed with a quickly growing stress, and we know that in such experiments the real yield point is not revealed. Recrystallization played a minor role, if any, in these experiments, even in those with high temperatures.

In addition to the intracrystalline and intergranular motion, it has been demonstrated that solution and recrystallization on intergranular slip planes are an important factor in the deformation of soluble substances such as gypsum, salt, and possibly limestone, as well. Griggs (1940) performed experiments using alabaster with a load of 205 kg/cm^2, first in a dry state, later in water, and finally in a HCl solution (Fig. 33). The dry specimen very soon reached its maximum strain, whereas with the water-jacketed specimen the strain became 0.6% in 20 days, and with a HCl solution, even 0.5% in 10 days. In both cases the stress of 205 kg/cm^2 was too high, and rupture occurred after some more days of accelerated rate of strain. Figure 34 (after Griggs, 1940) demonstrates once more that in experiments

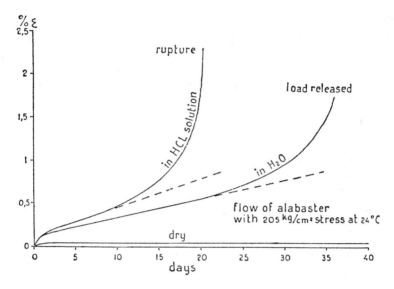

Fig. 33 Strain/time diagram of experiment on alabaster, wetted specimen, with 205 kg/cm² stress at 1 atm confining pressure. (*After Griggs, 1940. Published by permission of the Geological Society of America.*)

with water-jacketed alabaster specimens the rate of deformation is also dependent on the load.

In some instances the solution-and-recrystallization type of strain becomes a factor of some importance. Goguel (1943), for instance, demonstrated that a gypsum aggregate specimen showed irregular motion along 45% slip planes, which were recemented during the experiment. The experiment was made with a confining pressure increasing from 100 to 500 kg/cm² and a stress above 500 kg/cm² for the plastic-flow experiment (Fig. 35).

Experiments with Solenhofen Limestone have shown that unjacketed, water-saturated specimens require a higher confining pressure than dry-jacketed specimens to bring about the transition from brittle to ductile behavior. This implies that the water content retards the plastic deformation, in opposition to other experience, but it is not known whether this would also apply at much slower, more natural strain rates.

Recrystallization has also been observed in experiments on Yule Marble (Griggs et al. in Griggs and Handin, 1960, p. 21) when the deformation was done at low temperatures and the specimen was heated afterward in its strained condition to 500°C and higher. This annealing recrystallization produced unoriented new crystals, like

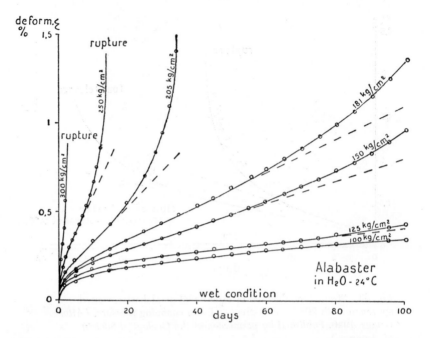

Fig. 34   Strain/time diagram of experiments on alabaster, wetted specimen, with varying load at 1 atm confining pressure, plastic flow and rupture. (*After Griggs,* 1940. *Published by permission of the Geological Society of America.*)

porphyroblasts in metamorphic schists, which are also regarded as produced by an increase of temperature after deformation. Syntectonic recrystallization was also realized (*ibid.,* pp. 90–97) at 100°C, with oriented calcite crystals as a result. With a lower strain rate this kind of recrystallization occurs at lower temperature, simply because more time for this process is available. The strain was very high in these experiments, 500 to 1,000% extension.

There is still another kind of deformation which has to be taken into account, namely, compression. Goguel (1943) made several experiments in which the strain was undoubtedly mostly due to simple compression, that is, to the elimination of the pores. He even demonstrated that sedimentary rocks not previously subjected to tectonic stress showed a much greater compressibility than those taken from a folded region.

Compression is always a finite motion and will therefore always show a strain/time curve of the character of an elastic flow, even when the process in itself is permanent. Goguel (1943) made an ex-

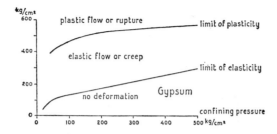

Fig. 35 Stress/confining pressure diagram of stress experiments on gypsum (*After Goguel*, 1943. *Published by permission of Service de la Carte Géologique.*)

periment on a soft homogenous Miocene marl which showed such a curve (Fig. 36).

The strain was mostly due to the confining pressure, which equaled 500 kg/cm². An Eocene limestone experiment by the same author showed the transition from compression to shear. Up to about 12% the strain was chiefly due to compression. After that critical value had been passed because of a higher load, slip planes were formed and finally resulted in rupture (Fig. 37).

Griggs performed an experiment on mudstone in which the limit of compressibility was reached with a 2½% strain for 144 days. Up to about 2% strain the specimen showed a logarithmic elastic flow curve,

Fig. 36 Linear and semilog strain/time diagram of experiment on marl, with a load of 380 kg/cm² and 500 kg/cm² confining pressure. (*After Goguel. Published by permission of Service de la Carte Géologique.*)

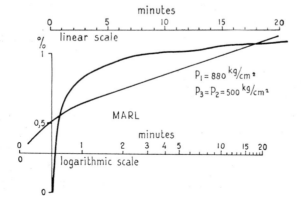

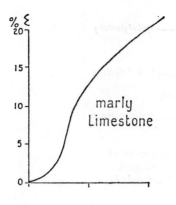

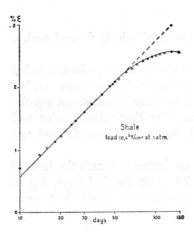

Fig. 37   Strain/time diagram of experiment on an Eocene marly limestone. (*After Goguel. Published by permission of Service de la Carte Géologique.*)

Fig. 38   Strain/time diagram of experiment on Conchas Shale, load 10.4 kg/cm², confining pressure 1 atm, showing compression only. (*After Griggs, 1939. Published by permission of the University of Chicago Press.*)

but then slowed down very rapidly to zero between 2¼ and 2½% strain (Fig. 38).

Since compression shows essentially the same strain curve both in terms of strain velocity and a limit to strain, it is clear that there is no possibility of distinguishing elastic and plastic-elastico-viscous flow by means of only the strain curve. The definition of elastic deformation remains based on the recovery of strain after the removal of stress.

THE INFLUENCE OF THE CONFINING PRESSURE AND TEMPERATURE

Experiments by Handin and Hager (1957–1958), where a strain rate of 1% per minute was imposed in triaxial dry tests on different rock types, showed that shales and slates are weaker than limestones up to confining pressures equivalent to 10 km depth, although lower strain rates cause a considerable decrease in strength at all temperatures

(Griggs et al. in Griggs and Handin, 1960). Therefore, not too much value can be attached to the numerical values of this rather obvious relationship between pelites and limestones.

In general we may say that the experiments with constant loads show that the elasticity limit of motion along shear planes is raised by increasing the confining pressure, a result which is in perfect accordance with the results of experiments where the strength was measured under a gradually increasing load.

The experiments by Robertson (1955) give numerous examples of this characteristic property (Fig. 30). Although all rock types that have been tested show considerable decrease in strength with increasing temperature (up to 800°C) and an increase of strength with increasing confining pressure, the combined effect of these factors with increasing depth of burial is different for different rock types. The tests on quartz crystals failed completely to achieve ductile deformation under any conditions (Griggs et al. in Griggs and Handin, 1960), and in accordance with this result all experiments on quartzite or sandstone (e.g., Maxwell and Borg et al. in Griggs and Handin, 1960) show cataclastic intergranular deformation.

Experimental investigation into the behavior of rock in a stress field has taught us many important principles but also leaves us with many queries.

We may assume that in tectonic processes in general the stress only slightly exceeds the threshold value of the resistance, and since the longest of our experiments lasted less than two years, there can be little doubt that all the experiments have failed to approach dynamic similarity with natural processes. The numerical values obtained in the experiments are therefore probably valueless; nevertheless, the principles which they established may be applicable to a large degree. The most important feature is doubtless the necessity to distinguish between finite processes such as compression and elastic deformation, on the one hand, and permanent deformation, on the other.

The permanent processes in nature are all of the viscous-elastic type except when very high temperatures lead to extensive recrystallization or a very incompetent rock like salt comes under high pressure. It has become very clear that in this viscous-elastic deformation there always is slip on regularly oriented planes or just between grains and that both intergranular and intracrystalline slip may act simultaneously.

In the next chapter we shall see that the results of the experiments cannot as yet be applied with any certainty to explain the characteristics of different fold or fault types. There is still a wide gap between our experimental and field experience, which we can bridge only with hypotheses.

Chapter 4

Experimental Tectonics

In Chap. 3 we made the acquaintance of a set of experiments which investigated certain physical properties of rocks but did not try to imitate actual tectonic processes. This latter kind of experiment has often been performed ever since the beginning of the nineteenth century (James Hall, 1813). In most cases the experiments tried to imitate the final shape of tectonic disturbances such as a fold, fault, or joint pattern, and sometimes deductions were made on the history of the event. Their contribution to our tectonic knowledge is very real, although, as we shall learn when we analyze their results, it is decidedly limited in its scope.

THE SCALE MODEL

Tectonic experiments, like all other kinds of scale-model experiments, are beset from every side by pitfalls and obstacles which prevent a close resemblance to natural processes.

Most experiments on folding have been made in rectangular boxes, with one of the shorter sides acting as a moving block and the opposite one acting as a buttress. When pressure is applied by the moving block, the contents are pushed a certain distance toward the stationary end. Both the sides and the bottom, however, exert a friction on the moving material, causing a decrease of stress away from the moving block. The obvious result is that, in all these experiments, the folding is initiated next to the moving block, and only after this first fold has been strongly compressed does further buckling take place (Fig. 39). In nature, of course, with a much larger lateral extension of the fold, this frictional influence is much smaller or practically nonexistent, and a belt of folds develops simultaneously. Lubricating the bottom and walls of the box helps somewhat, but does not eliminate the fundamental error.

Another difficulty is the confining pressure. The initial fold tends to

54

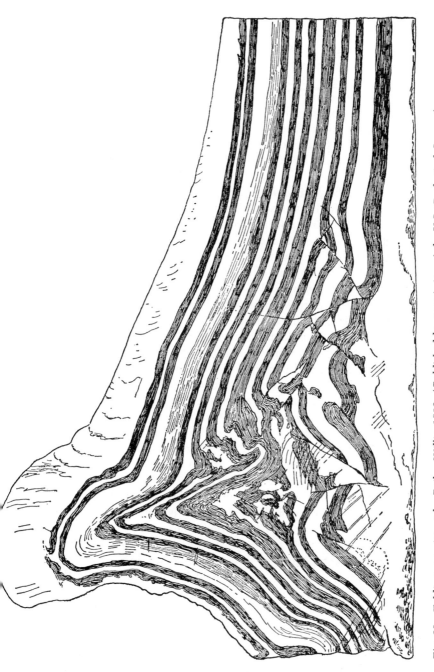

Fig. 39 Folding experiment by Bailey Willis, 1893. (*Published by permission of the U.S. Geological Survey.*)

rise vertically much higher than natural folds, and various expedients have been invented to imitate a load: Bailey Willis (1893), for instance, charged his test material with lead shot. The difficulty lies in the fact that gravity is as strong in the experiment as in nature, whereas the mass of the scale model is so much less. Loading with heavy material is only a very poor substitute.

The main obstacle, however, is the extreme difficulty—if not the impossibility—of achieving dynamic similarity in the scale model.

Most of the theoretical subject matter of scale models has been treated adequately by King Hubbert (1937), whom we shall follow here.

Theory of the Mechanical Scale Model. To imitate in the laboratory a fold or fault as observed in nature we must necessarily reduce its scale both in time and in size. Since our purpose is to learn something about the forces that produced the structure, we are not content with a simple model; we wish to reproduce its development, from a supposed initial form, usually a horizontal layered sequence, to the observed distorted shape. We know that we cannot use common rock material for this purpose because, when we try to deform it within a reasonable time, it will be shattered or broken by the stress we are forced to apply. It is therefore necessary to use some material other than rock in order to reproduce a fold or even a fault. The reduction of the time scale, and perhaps of size as well, necessitates the use of material with "reduced" physical properties. The relation of the reduction factors for each of these properties has been worked out theoretically, and every scale model ought to comply with the theory; otherwise it is impossible to draw reliable conclusions from the results. This principle is much used in hydrodynamic and aerodynamic laboratories, where scale models are constructed and the effects observed.

The basic theory can be formulated thus: the reduction factor of all material properties of the scale model is prescribed by the dimensional formula of their mechanical quantities.

Every property such as length, strength, force, etc., is measured by appropriate combinations of three fundamental units: mass M, length L, and time T, and their "dimensional formula" represents this combination. Thus a velocity is represented by L/T, which means a length divided by time, and a force by ML/T^2, which means a mass multiplied by a length and divided twice by time, and so on. From the fundamental reduction factors, or model ratios (l for length, m for mass, and t for time), the reduction factors for every mechanical quantity can be deduced by using them in the same combination in which they occur in the dimensional formula of that quantity. Thus in the scale model, the velocity must be l/t times the original velocity, and the force must be ml/t^2 times the original force. This law enables us to deduce the strength which the material of a certain construction ought to have from the support we had to give it in the scale model in order for it to withstand a measured stress, provided that all the mechanical properties of the model were correct.

In making models to imitate tectonic processes we are as yet not so much concerned with measuring mechanical properties as with simply understanding how each process works, and we can therefore be content with certain approximations. But the fundamental principles must be obeyed; otherwise we should not have the slightest guarantee that a real similarity has been achieved.

The most important mechanical properties have been assembled in Table 5, together with the ratios that must exist in a true model. The value of mass is avoided in all ratios by use of its relation to density, $d = m/l^3$.

In column (2) of this table we have assumed that the similarity as regards the forces is satisfied by the forces due to inertia, ML/T^2 ($=DL^4/T^2$), but all scale models are also subject to gravity, and therefore acceleration, L/T^2, must equal unity. Hence L and T would no longer be independent ratios. When, however, our scale model is not concerned with high velocities but is a slow-working process, then the inertia becomes almost equal to zero, and gravity remains the only force of account in our experiment. In such a case l, t, and m become again independent ratios and the acceleration = l/t^2 can be

Table 5

(1)	(2)	(3)	(4)
		Model Ratio	Model Ratio
Property	Model Ratio	Disregarding Inertia	d = 1
Length	l	l	l
Time	t	t	t
Density	d	d	1
Area	l^2	l^2	l^2
Volume	l^3	l^3	l^3
Velocity	l/t	l/t	l/t
Acceleration	l/t^2	l/t^2	l/t^2
Force	dl^4/t^2	dl^3	l^3
Strength, stress	dl^2/t^2	dl	l
Strain, angle	1	1 ·	1
Elastic modulus	dl^2/t^2	dl	l
Viscosity	dl^2/t	dlt	lt

factored out from all the general model ratios of stress, strength, etc. [column (3) of Table 5].

In scale models of tectonic features the reductions in length and time are important, while those in density are unimportant because we can hardly find a material that weighs less than one-third of rock; hence we may take d as equaling 1, and the ratios we then have to comply with are listed in column (4) of the table. By this process of elimination of factors which are unimportant in our kind of scale models, we have arrived at the simple condition that all such static material properties as strength and elasticity must be reduced with the length-reduction factor; the stress we have to apply ought then to be about l times smaller than the stress in nature. As soon as the model is slowly deformed, however, we have to take into account the time factor, and in order to maintain mechanical similarity, the viscosity must be reduced with the factor lt.

Let us demonstrate this with an example. A scale model of a fold of the whole crust of the earth is desired:

Strength of crust = 10^6 g/cm^2
Thickness of crust = 3×10^6 cm
Viscosity of crust = 10^{22} poises

The reduction factors l and t for an orogenic process would be $l = 10^{-5}$ and $t = 10^{-9}$, if we assume that a cake of 30 cm thickness, deformed in a few hours, can represent an orogenic process lasting a million years. The mechanical properties of the material we want to find must therefore be:

Strength $10^6 \times 10^{-5} = 10$ g/cm^2
Viscosity $10^{22} \times 10^{-5} \times 10^{-9} = 10^8$ poises

which would mean the strength of a very soft material like butter with a viscosity of that of pitch at 20°C, a combination which is perhaps difficult to find. When the same experiment represented the folding of a limestone bed of 3 m thickness, strength 10^5 g/cm^2, and viscosity 10^{21} poises, the material ought to have had, assuming that the folding of the limestone bed took 100,000 years, the following properties:

Strength $10^5 \times 10^{-1} = 10^4$ g/cm^2
Viscosity $10^{21} \times 10^{-1} \times 10^{-8} = 10^{12}$ poises

This is even more difficult to match with a well-known material.

These examples also demonstrate how easily we can be many orders of magnitude off in scale-model experiments because we have no reliable data on the length of time of a tectonic process and the strength or viscosity of the material.

There are obviously other unavoidable difficulties. For instance, the size of the sand grain or clay mineral cannot be reduced in the same way as the length of the scale model, nor can the different modes of deformation, which I have distinguished in Chap. 3, be introduced in the model material. There are clearly many more discrepancies which cannot be avoided.

Scaling down the viscosity is especially important in fold imitations because viscosity controls the strain rate caused by the combination of compressive stress and gravity. There are many fold imitations, however, where a void developed naturally in the core of the anticline, an impossibility in nature. But when the material used was weak enough to prevent this void at the bottom of the cake, it would not form a fold, but was compressed without folding.

In any experiment where the purpose is the generation of a set of faults or shear planes, it is obvious that, once these planes have been created, any succeeding movement will favor those planes (Chap. 10, Fig. 81). Therefore the important moment of the experiment occurs when the shear plane is generated and not the subsequent movement. Hence the viscosity does not enter into the fault problem. Only the strength and the elastic stress field are determining factors, and a material of about the right strength, such as soft clay, will suffice for this kind of experiment, notwithstanding the fact that its viscosity has an incorrect value. This is one reason why most fault experiments are better imitations than fold models.

Moreover, we have at our disposal a means of studying the relation of the scale model to the large structure in the quite common occurrence in nature of microstructures, a means which has seldom been fully utilized.

Relation of Minor Structures to the Tectonic Experiment. Any geologist will know, from his own experience, exposures which show minor structures that are exact replicas, including many details, of major structures (compare, for instance, Chap. 11, Figs. 116 and 117). In these folds or faults nature performed the experiment with the same material and in the same time interval, but on a very much smaller scale, and achieved perfect similarity, infinitely better than any clay cake could ever yield. Evidently size reduction does not play the predominant role which the scale-model theory prescribes. There are two reasons for this apparent contradiction.

First, the shape of a fold or the orientation of a fault is purely a matter of relative lengths, or in other words, a matter of angles and not of lengths themselves. The relative proportions of lengths, a strain, and an angle are all dimensionless, and therefore independent of any length-reduction factors applied to strength or strain properties.

Second, any later internal movement will naturally follow the shear planes, and therefore the final shape of the structure of a rift valley, for instance, is wholly determined by the orientation of the original fault planes.

The fact that the similarity between minor folds and major folds is so striking is now clear: the shape is independent of the size. Because the minor folds were reproduced under the same confining pressure as the major folds, the material had the same state of ductility and therefore the same relation between strength and viscosity and between tensile and compressive strength, and therefore the same shape. Not only does the contradiction between theory and observed facts disappear, but in the clear similarity we find a proof that the shapes of both microstructures and macrostructures originate in the same combination of elastic and permanent deformation. In the large fold and the small one, the shape is governed by an elastically bent layer, whose thickness is measured in tens of meters in the case of the large fold and in tens of millimeters in the case of the microfold; and the same is true for fault structures.

In the case of a permanent deformation the scale model is concerned with the relation between strength and viscosity or with compressive and tensile strength, and the correct relation can be achieved either by raising the confining pressure, which, as we have seen in Chap. 3, changes a brittle material into a ductile one, or by lowering the strength and viscosity of the material. In the imitative experiment the second course is followed; in the microstructures, the first.

Notwithstanding all this, such experiments fail completely in dynamic similarity because in nature the deformative stress in most cases exceeds the strength by only very little, so that deformation is extremely slow, but in the experiments this difference is much larger, since the experimenter wants to see the result himself. He will never be able to overcome the difficulty that the scale model can never realize, within the span of a lifetime, a similarity to the natural relation of stress/strength or stress/rigidity or any other elastic property. What the experimenter can do, and what he succeeded in doing, is to achieve a similarity in shape or orientation of shear—or fracture planes—by just guessing the physical properties of his scale-model material. The complete lack of dynamic similarity prevents any but superficial deductions from the experiments. A good proof of this conclusion is the fact that not one single experiment has ever succeeded in imitating similar folding with the development of cleavage. The successful tectonic imitative experiment has a great value as illustrative material and may elucidate something about the probable succession of different movements, but it never can teach us anything new.

THE EXPERIMENTS

To review all the more important experiments would lead us too far, and they will, moreover, be more appropriately described together with the tectonic phenomena they illustrate. I will mention here only those types of structure which have been illustrated experimentally and the degree of success achieved.

Fault Structures. Fault structures have been imitated very successfully by a number of experimenters, among whom H. Cloos (1930, 1932) has been the most prominent. In several series of experiments with clay cakes he obtained exact replicas of the Rhine Valley rift, with its set of normal and antithetic faults (cf. Chap. 10, Fig. 81). His best experiments were made with soft clay mounted on a rubber sheet which could be stretched. By introducing nonhomogeneities into the clay cake, i.e., more solid parts with less water flanked by soft parts with more water, he succeeded in locating the normal faults in the softer portions, thus indicating that the location of a rift valley might be influenced by nonhomogeneities in the earth's crust, such as granite bodies.

Wrench faults have been successfully imitated by H. Cloos (1929–1930) and Riedel (1929) (Chap. 11, Fig. 103). Both experimenters succeeded in showing the formation of tension cracks oblique to the vertical shear plane.

Thrust faults are less satisfactorily imitated. Many folding experiments have shown a development of thrusts in the later stages of experiment, but the usual low-angle thrust fault of an asymmetric anticline has never been convincingly imitated. This failure is probably due to the fact that gravity plays an important role in nature, but not in the experiment, because deformation is too rapid in the latter (Lohest, 1913; B. Willis, 1893; Kuenen and de Sitter, 1938).

Fold Structures. Fold structures have been imitated by numerous experimenters, with varying success. Many experiments illustrate different kinds of deformation (Figs. 105 to 107) with rubber plates, a pile of paper, and some soft plastic matter. All of these illustrate some characteristics of folding, but none of course shows the combination of the different types which is typical of a normal folding process in nature. Moreover, neither cleavage, nor schistosity parallel to the axial plane (a common characteristic of natural folds), nor joints have ever been imitated successfully in a fold. Also, the spontaneous concentric shear planes in a nonorientated medium (unstratified), which are a predominant feature in almost all folds of nonmetamorphic rocks, have been reproduced only once, by Kuenen and de Sitter (1938; Chap. 13, Fig. 108). The folding experiments in general are therefore rather unsatisfactory, and can be used only by isolating certain characteristics as illustrative material. The reason for this relative failure of folding experiments must be sought in the impossibility of achieving the right relation between deformative stress and the elastic properties or the strength of the material, as has been explained in the foregoing discussion. Further experiments should concentrate on cleavage and on concentric folding of unstratified material.

Diapiric Structures and Disharmonic Folds. The experimental imitation of salt domes has been very successful. Escher and Kuenen (1929), Nettleton (1943), and many others have succeeded in creating typical diapiric structures, always accompanied by flow structures in the extrusive mass. The success is no doubt due to the fact that in this kind of structure in nature the stress also greatly exceeds the resistance of the material. Disharmonic structures, on the contrary, are apparently very difficult to imitate, although their mechanism is closely related to diapirism. We may presume that this is again due to the impossibility of retaining the right relation in the experiment between the stress and the strength and, most of all, the viscosity. Perhaps very slow experiments, lasting months or years, could succeed.

Joint Patterns. Joint patterns (cf. Chap. 9) have been successfully imitated by a great number of experimenters, beginning with Daubrée (1878). They conform to natural patterns to a high degree, although they are not as diversified. The success is without doubt due to the fact that the only requirement for the scale model is to imitate an orientation, which is of course a dimensionless thing. Unfortunately, the experimental joint patterns of homogeneous models have often been used to interpret those found in folded layers or other non-homogeneous situations with which they can have little in common.

Chapter 5

Rock Behavior in Tectonic Processes

COMPETENT AND INCOMPETENT ROCKS

The terms "rigidity" and "brittleness" have been much used, as antitheses of "plasticity," to designate certain physical properties of rocks and in discussion of rock deformation. We have seen in the foregoing paragraphs that the complexity of the physical properties of rocks is far too great for such a simple terminology and that some rigid or competent rocks become plastic under relatively low confining pressure and stress.

"Hardness" and "softness" are terms indicating the resistance of rocks to weathering. But the two sets of terms are sometimes unconsciously regarded as synonyms. This is unjustified. Goguel (1943), for instance, has shown that marly limestone has a stronger resistance to deformation than pure limestone, whereas it weathers away more easily.

Still, there is undoubtedly a great difference in behavior, in tectonic processes, between the competent type of rock and the plastic, or incompetent, type. This is particularly noticeable in disharmonic folding. Considerable work on the theoretical background of the origin of cracks, fissures, and folds in rocks is progressing steadily since Griffith (1925) started it with his theory of rupture. Griffith's theory starts from the point of view of brittle material in elastic strain condition. Ode (1960) starts from the assumption that the material is purely ductile. Jaeger (1960) and Paterson (1958) also studied shear failure experimentally and theoretically.

Folding in layers of different elastic and viscous property has been studied theoretically and experimentally by Biot (1961), Biot, Ode, and Roever (1961), and Currie, Pamode, and Trump (1962), with results which are to some extent quite convincing. The experiments

63

and theoretical considerations proved the independent behavior of competent layers in an incompetent surrounding and a direct relation between thickness and wavelength of their folds.

Conditions in nature are, however, so much more complex than they have been assumed to be in these theoretical considerations and in the accompanying experiments that we certainly have to await further developments in this branch of research before their results become applicable to natural conditions.

All sedimentary sequences are built of layers of different physical properties. Rigid rock types alternate with plastic ones. As the tectonic stress grows, it reaches an intensity below the elasticity limit of the rigid rocks, but is beyond that of the weaker plastic rocks. At this stage the rigid rocks may have undergone some elastic deformation, the plastic rocks being kept in place by the strong adjacent beds. As the stress increases further, it will eventually reach the elastic limit of the rigid layers, and the inhomogeneous layered sequence will start to fold, but at this point the stress is of course far above the elasticity limit of the plastic layers.

When deformation of the rigid rock sets in it is therefore entirely governed by the elastic stresses which still exist in the folded sheet. The weaker rocks follow the shape taken by their sturdier neighbors, and their own elastic stresses have no appreciable effect.

Hence the distortion of rock under deformative stress is determined by two factors, namely, (1) its anisotropy and (2) its elastic, or plastic, state. Either of the two factors may be dominant, or they may be combined in a certain pattern.

Before discussing why a certain rock type has become deformed in a certain way, we shall have to relate the experimental data concerning stress, strain, and viscosity to the types of deformation that we observe in the field or under the microscope.

We have seen that experimental data on rock distortion indicate that we must distinguish between five main modes of deformation:

1. Compression into a smaller volume, a finite process
2. Creep or elastic flow, a deformation with a logarithmic time/strain curve, which therefore becomes infinitely small for long periods
3. Elastico-viscous flow, where the elastic strain is gradually replaced by permanent deformation
4. Plastic flow, with a more or less constant, but slow, strain velocity for a minimum stress increase
5. Rupture, with, at the beginning, a high constant strain velocity which eventually increases and leads to fracture of the specimen

The mechanism of deformation in these five modes is not yet well understood, but we know that certain mechanisms are typical for certain modes. Solution and recrystallization, for instance, is certainly a flow phenomenon.

In fold and fault tectonics it is obvious that compression into a smaller volume can play a part in the initial stage only. It may perhaps determine the location of a future fault or of the crest of a fold, but during the actual process of folding, compression ceases to operate.

Nor can elastic flow, since it is a finite process and therefore of strictly limited extension, be an important factor in folding. It is possible, of course, that in well-stratified rocks, where each member can be folded elastically and independently of its neighbors, the curvature of the folds can reach measurable dimensions, but in general we can assume that the stress will rise beyond the elasticity limit and that the field of pure elasticity will be passed.

We then enter into the elastico-viscous flow field, where the elastic strain is slowly and continuously replaced by permanent strain.

The elastic stresses in an elastically folded sheet are parallel to its surface—tensional at the outer arc and compressional in the inner arc of the fold. Inside the sheet these stresses result in shearing stress parallel to the surface which causes shear planes to develop on the flanks of the fold (Fig. 40).

As soon as one of these shear planes has been formed, the original sheet is divided into two elastically folded sheets. During further folding the process repeats itself continuously, so that the elastic state of the rigid rock is never lost. This process of splitting up the original layer into more and more independent arcs allows continuous further bending without increasing the stress.

Another kind of deformation, in which the influence of an elastic strain is much less obvious, is a flattening process. By the rotation of randomly oriented mica flakes and growth of new mica in planes perpendicular to the stress, a fissility is produced which has been called stress cleavage.

Fig. 40   Elastic stress in bent sheet leads to concentric shear planes.

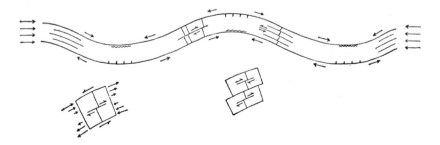

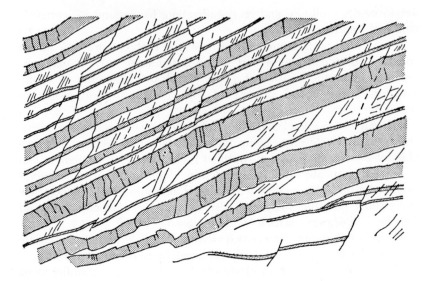

Fig. 41   Fracture cleavage in shale, rotational joints in sandstone, drawn from photograph of Ordovician rocks near Aberystwyth, Wales.

In cleavage folding the thin slices of rock between the cleavage planes are called microlithons.

In an alternation of layers of different composition the deformation of the competent layers often has a different character from that of the incompetent ones (Fig. 41).

Minor folds and even microfolds in such a sequence often show concentric folding of the competent layers in the cleaved surrounding incompetent rock. This fact proves that when the interval between stress level and the yield value of the rock is small, concentric folding begins, and by increasing the stress, the fold type changes from concentric to cleavage. Accordion folding and shear-cleavage folding are apparently intermediate stages between the two principal types of concentric and stress-cleavage folding.

From the foregoing reasoning it follows that in folding processes it is not the absolute value of the elasticity limit of the whole complex which is the most important factor, but the relative competency of the different rock types and the highest elasticity limit of the most competent rock. There are other factors, however, which certainly operate as well.

In the first place it is quite possible that the rate of increase of the deformative stress is important. If this rate is small, the relaxation of the elastic deformation soon absorbs its acceleration, and the stress remains constant as soon as it has reached a value only a little above the elasticity limit. When, on the other hand, the rate of stress increase is greater, the acceleration is not absorbed as quickly by the yielding of the rock, so that the value of constant stress will not be reached until the stress has risen somewhat higher above the elasticity limit of the most competent rock, and the deformation may then be of a different character altogether. If we assume that concentric folding corresponds to a minimum interval between stress and elasticity limit and that planar shear corresponds to a somewhat larger difference, then cleavage could simply indicate a higher acceleration in the rate of increase of the deformative stress.

Second, the influence of the depth of burial of the rocks (i.e., the confining pressure) is certainly an important factor. It raises the elasticity limit, changes some rigid rocks into ductile rocks, and thus influences the relative competence of the different rock types.

Third, temperature, and in particular thermal action in relation to regional metamorphism, may change the whole picture. A rise in temperature has, in general, the function of weakening the resistance of the rock material and, perhaps more important, of the differences in competence of the rocks.

Finally, the fluid content of the rock, already proved important in the experimental work, also makes itself felt in nature. The fluid content may be either the original connate water in the sedimentary rocks or an addition through regional metamorphism at depth. In many metamorphic processes this original water content is thought to play a decisive role in activating the recrystallization of new minerals (scapolite in limestone metamorphism by means of salt water, for instance), and Griggs (1940) showed in his experiments that water, and an acid solution to an even higher degree, accelerate recrystallization in limestone. The quantity of water liberated by the regional metamorphism of a body of pelitic rocks is enormous. In addition to the chemical functions, these fluids might simply act as a lubricator.

Summarizing, we can state that the factors that determine the reaction of rock to stress depend on:

1. Its anisotropy
2. Relative competency of its component members
3. Elasticity limit of the most competent rock
4. Rate of increase of the deformative stress
5. Confining pressure
6. Temperature increase with depth and in regional metamorphism
7. Fluid content, either connate or intrusive

We are now confronted with the difficult task of relating these different influences to actual observed rock textures. The observations on the rock specimens of the experiments are not a good guide, because we can rest assured that in our haste to achieve a result in the laboratory we always let the stress climb far too high above the resistance limit, even when we wait 5 years, as Griggs did in some experiments. They served us very well in establishing the principles which are involved, but are certainly not representative of natural circumstances.

From general considerations we can, however, infer some directions along which our thoughts may travel. First of all, it seems extremely probable that concentric folding, with its elastically induced shear planes parallel to the bedding and its tension cracks on the anticlinal hinges and rotational joints, is typical of the smallest possible excess of stress over the elasticity limit. On the other hand, we can reasonably suppose that flow structures like those of salt in salt domes, or marble flow structures in metamorphic limestone, and even flow structures in gneisses are typical of the largest interval between resistance and stress.

Hence it seems reasonable to suppose that planar-shear and stress-cleavage deformation is an intermediate stage with an intermediate interval between resistance and stress that is more plastic in character but is still influenced by elastic stress. Figure 42 represents this reasoning in diagram.

This view is confirmed by the fact that, in an alternation of rigid competent rocks and ductile incompetent rocks, rigid rocks such as sandstone fold concentrically and incompetent shales show cleavage (Fig. 41). And in diapiric structures the very incompetent gypsum, anhydrite, or salt, together with shales and marls, flows through cracks in the concentrically folded upper layers.

Summarizing our experience of fold mechanics, we may construct Table 6. In this table the sequence of deformation from top to bottom

Fig. 42   (A) Increasing stresses d_1, d_2, and d_3 cause a succession of concentric, cleavage, and flow folding in one type of rock. (B) The same stress can cause concentric, cleavage, and flow folding in three different types of rock.

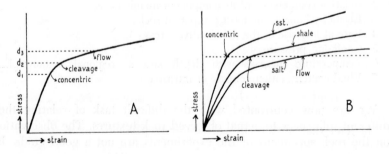

Table 6

Compression	Finite process	No folding
Elastic bending	Finite process	Slight folding
Elastico-viscous folding	{ Continuous process	Concentric folding Cleavage and schistosity
Flow	Continuous process	Flow structures

indicates either a sequence of rocks with decreasing elasticity limit deformed by the same stress or a sequence of the same rock deformed by an increasing stress (in other words, an increase of the interval between the stress and the elasticity limit), but with the proviso that many kinds of schistosity (and flow in metamorphic rocks) require a rise of temperature.

INFLUENCE OF DEPTH

Unfortunately, we have very little comparative data on the influence of an increase of confining pressure with depth on different rock types such as limestone, sandstone, shale, siltstone, etc.

The early experiments of Griggs (1939, 1940) on limestone, marble, and alabaster have been amplified by experiments on basic rocks, sand and sandstone, slates, etc., and several minerals, described in Handin and Hager (1957–1958), Griggs and Handin (1960), and in Robertson (1955). Goguel (1943) has tried systematically to get comparative data on different rock types, but he succeeded only partially, because so many other factors became involved.

The most important result without doubt is that Goguel clearly distinguishes between the behavior of three rock types:

1. Gypsum and salt, which are apt to show considerable solution recrystallization, even when the samples are comparatively dry.

2. Limestones, in which the deformation is apparently mostly due to intergranular slip, but which have a much higher elasticity limit and smaller strain velocity (higher viscosity) than gypsum and salt. With higher confining pressure we may expect intracrystalline slip.

3. Sandstone, which is characterized by the fact that the internal angle of friction and intergranular slip are important factors. The strain velocity and the elasticity limit are strongly influenced by the confining pressure.

Both in sandstone and limestone deformation under extreme circumstances, solution and recrystallization has proved to be an important factor.

The fact that an increase of confining pressure has a different in-

Table 7

	Shallow Depth, up to 2 km	Great Depth, below 2 km
Competent	Impure limestone	Sandstone
	Pure limestone	Impure limestone
	Sandstone	Marl
	Marl	Pure limestone
	Clay-shale	Clay-shale
Incompetent	Salt-gypsum	Salt-gypsum

fluence on different kinds of rocks indicates that the relative competency of rocks changes with depth.

With a compressive stress of 600 kg/cm^2 at a shallow depth of 1 km, for example, we may expect flow in shales and salts, but only elastico-viscous flow in limestones and sandstones.

One question remains, to which we must now return, after our consideration of rock behavior in natural folds.

The experimental data could not definitely indicate whether a rock really has a lower limit of strength beneath which no other deformation than elastic bending is possible or whether this limit is only apparent and created by the increasing value of the viscosity with low stress. The question has some importance, for flow experiments of long duration using relatively low stresses have shown that the absolute strength of rocks was originally greatly overestimated. Some geologists (notably Gignoux and van Bemmelen) have assumed that, at great depth, rocks would flow under any stress condition. Others, like Goguel and me, insist that a real strength is much more probable because we know that large mountain masses do stand up for a considerable time; more important, because longer time and larger masses are concerned, is the fact that the continental platforms can stand stress on their edges for hundreds of millions of years. Moreover, rockbursts in deep mines or tunnels prove that an elastic strain is permanently present at deeper levels. Hence we may conclude that even the differential viscosity of rocks has a real zero point, a threshold value, which we may call the strength, or elasticity limit.

For a folding process the question is not very important, because, with a rising stress, even an apparent strength would have the same effect as a real threshold value.

Chapter 6

Rock Distortion and Rock Fracturing

Under this heading are assembled a number of phenomena produced by rock deformation which are visible to the unaided eye in an outcrop or hand specimen. They fall into two classes: (1) rock distortion and (2) rock fracturing.

In rock distortion, certain components of the rock, of which the original shape is known either beforehand or by reconstruction, are distorted either by minute shear planes or without any visible shearing. Distortion of fossils, ooliths, pebbles, and thin layers falls in this class. As rock distortion is mainly restricted to cleaved or schistose rock deformation, we shall treat only some of the phenomena here and refer the reader for more information to Chap. 21.

In rock fracturing, the production of angular rock fragments, sometimes accompanied by recrystallization or by development of schistosity, provides evidence of the great stress to which certain zones of the rock mass were submitted.

ROCK DISTORTION

Pebbles and Boulders. The pebbles in conglomerate beds which have suffered the effects of an orogenic phase often show clearly how they have been deformed. They may be flattened by a multitude of minute shear planes or along a few cracks, and in both cases give us valuable information about the direction of stress in that locality. The flattening is often parallel to the bedding plane, but in other cases it is oblique or perpendicular to it. If we assumed that the original shape of the pebbles was a sphere, we could establish their average flattening and its orientation. This assumption is never quite warranted, however, since even nondistorted pebbles are almost invariably triaxial ellipsoids, deposited in a position in which the shortest ellipsoid axis is perpendicular to the bedding. The measured relation is therefore almost certainly a maximum when the flattening lies in the bedding plane, and a minimum when it lies perpendicular to that plane. Moreover, the pebble very often represents a piece of hard rock embedded in a softer medium and therefore reacts differently to the stress field from its matrix. Thus the flattening of the pebbles may not be representative of the distortion of the whole conglomerate bed. Although the actual amount of flattening is only a rough approximation of that of the whole bed, the orientation in space of the plane of maximum shortening is always an important fact and worth recording. In most cases the flattened pebbles lie in the schistosity plane of the surrounding rock. Brace (1955) measured a flattening varying from 50 to 80%; Oftedahl (1948), one varying from 10 to 90% over a large area; and Flinn (1956), a flattening of less than 60%. The elongation and flattening of the pebbles could be correlated in each case with the orientation pattern of the quartz grains of the pebbles and with the prevalent tectonic stress field as derived from the general structure and the schistosity, proving that pebble deformation is a valuable asset for a stress-direction and deformation analysis. Whether the longest axis of elongation of the pebble lies in the direction of movement (a axis) or perpendicular to it (b axis) is often a matter of discussion, and the decision is not easy to make.

Ooliths. In the case of the distortion of ooliths, the objections against the exactness of measurements of pebbles disappear. A limestone oolith has almost the same composition as its matrix, the limestone itself, and in addition it is formed as a sphere. An oolitic limestone is therefore an ideal subject for the study of internal deformation. A very complete study of distorted oolitic limestones has been made by E. Cloos (1947b). The South Mountain section of the Appalachian orogeny, which Cloos analyzed, is reproduced in Fig. 43. The most striking of his conclusions is that the average elongation axes of the ooliths, measured in many hundreds of slides, are parallel to the axial plane of the recumbent folds and the cleavage; their disposition changes with that of these latter planar features, from a SE dip to a vertical position, going from SE to NW. It would carry us too far to follow Cloos exhaustively; we shall deal only with some of the most important details of his methods and results.

The cleavage is well developed in the stronger deformed portions of the structure (above 20% distortion as measured on the ooliths) and shows a clear lineation in the direction of movement. The a and b axes are therefore well defined. In order to measure the exact distortion of the ooliths, two slides of an orientated sample specimen have to be made, one in the ac plane and one in the ab plane. When r is

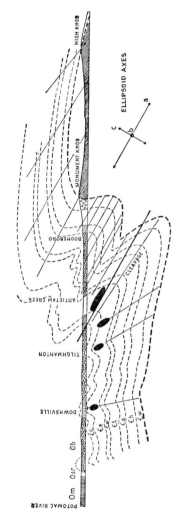

Fig. 43 Section of South Mountain folds with direction of oolite extension in *a* axis. (*After Cloos, 1947b. Published by permission of the Geological Society of America.*)

the radius of the original sphere and a, b, and c the three axes of the ellipsoid, and assuming that the volume has not changed by distortion,

$$\tfrac{4}{3}\pi r^3 = \tfrac{4}{3}\pi abc \quad \text{or} \quad r = \sqrt[3]{abc}$$

From this formula first r and then the extension of a and b and the reduction of the c axis can be calculated.

For explanation of the terms a, b, and c axes, see Chap. 7. b is in general the fold axis, a the direction of extension. a is perpendicular to b, and c is perpendicular to the ab plane.

The average extension in b, measured in 124 specimens, was less than 8%. There were occasional high values of b extension, but the low average was judged to justify making slides in only the ac plane and assuming the b extension to be zero in order to save time.

By measuring the orientation of the a direction in relation to the bedding plane, the thickening of the strata can be deduced from the extension in a throughout the fold. The results indicated that the standard section of the Cambrian of this region, measuring almost 12,000 ft in thickness, has to be reduced to less than 6,000 ft.

Both cleavage and extension showed a fanlike arrangement in all the folds (Fig. 44), opening toward the anticlinal hinge. In the upper limb of a recumbent fold the degree of extension is usually less than in the lower limb.

Conclusions of a more general nature will be made in Chap. 7, but it can be seen that this study of a distortion of a rock constituent of which the original shape was known beforehand is of the utmost importance.

Fossil Distortion.   Fossil distortion offers the same possibilities as oolith distortion, but is much more difficult to measure because of the more irregular shape of fossils. The distortion of fossils has long been recorded, but almost exclusively in Paleozoic rocks (Sharpe, 1847; Haughton, 1856; Rutsch, 1948; Breddin, 1956). This is due to the fact that most Tertiary folding is of the concentric type, in which all movement is parallel to the bedding plane and mostly concentrated on shaly or marly intercalations. In fact, it is astonishing how fossils involved in concentric folding can escape all distortion. Even in strongly folded sedimentary sequences in a vertical position one can find perfectly well preserved upper bedding planes of limestones full of undistorted fossils.

Apparently, the concentric shear leaves such surfaces alone and is concentrated within the shale or marl beds.

On the other hand, the paucity of fossils in many Paleozoic rocks is often due to the intense cleavage. It is not only that the rock no longer splits along the bedding plane on which the fossils lie; the fossils

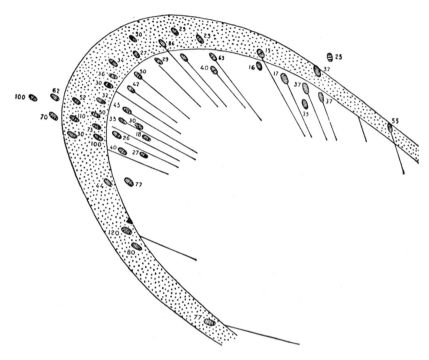

Fig. 44   Recumbent fold with oolite flattening and thickening in the anticlinal hinge. The numbers indicate the flattening in percentages. (*After E. Cloos,* 1947b. *Published by permission of the Geological Society of America.*)

themselves are also often totally destroyed. This is particularly true of fragile fossil remains such as graptolites. A typical example of this influence of cleavage on fossil content is found in the Paleozoic chain of the Pyrenees: fossils occur only in the northern and southern marginal zones where the folding is of the concentric type; the axial zone, where cleavage folding predominates, is almost completely barren. One of the best surveys on the subject of fossil distortion dates from 1847, by Daniel Sharpe. Fossil distortion in relation to cleavage and bedding was studied, and the observed flattening of the fossil in a plane parallel to the cleavage proved that cleavage represents a stress perpendicular to the cleavage. Moreover, the comparison of fossil deformation in flat and steeply inclined beds with cleavage proved that folding preceded the cleavage foliation.

In order to measure the deformation of a fossil, the original shape and the relation between certain dimensions, i.e., length and breadth, must be known, but if these are not well known, a comparison of these measured relations on many specimens on the same surface, in particular of two specimens with a 90° different orientation, can give

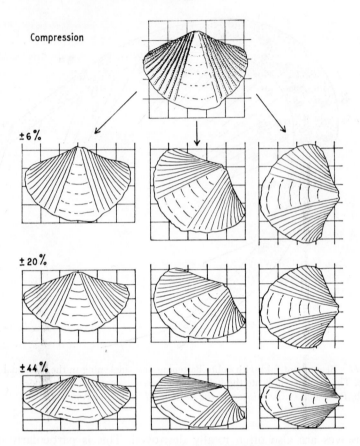

Compression

±6%

±20%

±44%

Fig. 45 Distortion by optical means of a brachiopod in different orientation to the stress. (*After Breddin*, 1956. *Published by permission of Deutsch Geol. Gesellsch. Hannover.*)

the solution (Breddin, 1956). The change of an original 90° angle between base and median line of a brachiopod can also give the necessary information (Fig. 45). The simple mathematics of this method has been explained by Breddin (1956) and Gräf (1960), the latter working mostly on *Goniatites*. Breddin found a lengthening of an axis parallel to the strike of the Rheinische Schiefergebirge varying from 10 to 50%, going from the northern border zone toward the center.

Of particular interest is the direct connection of the deformed fossils with the local folding mechanics of the beds in which they are contained. This problem, tackled by Sharpe in 1847, has been studied by Kurtman (1960) on crinoid stems of a section of the Rheinische

Schiefergebirge. He found that the grade of deformation is dependent on the lithology, and therefore on the resistance to deformation of the enclosing rock. In general, the elongation lies in the direction of the cleavage, but not always; sometimes there is better correlation with a joint system. Evidently a broad field of detailed research is still open.

ROCK FRACTURING

Rock fracturing by tectonic processes can simply be called "mylonitization," and the shattered rocks called mylonites. But if the fracturing is not accompanied by slickensiding or intense cleavage or recrystallization, the term "brecciation" is generally preferable, and the shattered rocks are termed tectonic breccias.

Mylonites, in the strict sense, are rocks which show strong lamination and in which the original constituent particles have been pulverized and have then disappeared in the general crushing of the rocks. When this process of crushing advances still further, there is recrystallization, or a kind of fusion. The rocks are then termed "ultramylonites."

The particular type of brecciation, or mylonitization, which is developed is, of course, greatly dependent on the nature of the rock, the depth below the surface, and the stress field. In crystalline rocks, fracture planes will immediately show lamination, since the shearing motion will take advantage of the mica flakes and curve around the quartz and felspar crystal. To rupture the rock, the shearing stress must be much greater than the stress which will rupture sedimentary rocks. Rock fracturing in granites and other massive crystalline rocks will therefore always take the form of mylonitization. The superficial mylonites of crystalline rocks show strong lamination and chloritization of all dark minerals. The rock can become so soft that one can crush it with the fingers. Going down into the earth's crust, the mylonitization will be accompanied by more and more pulverization. The quartz and felspar minerals will be gradually crushed and appear as a vitreous matrix in which their uncrushed fragments appear as porphyroclastic elements on a dark background (Fig. 46). The extreme form of ultramylonitization has been reached when the matrix appears as a glasslike substance and the porphyroclasts have diminished to a diameter less than 0.02 mm (Staub, 1928). The ultramylonite material may be injected into tension cracks. When the injections attain considerable dimensions, they are termed "mylonite dikes," or "pseudo tachylite" (Shand, 1916; A. L. Hall and G. A. F. Molengraaff, 1925; Bearth, 1933).

The developments in sedimentary rocks are analogous. The most superficial fracturing is described as tectonic brecciation. In all

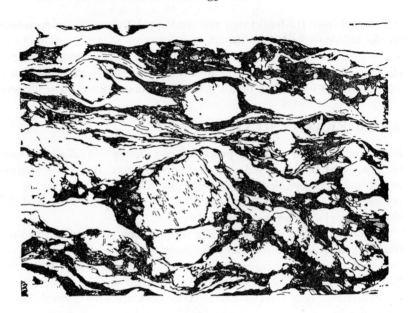

Fig. 46   Mylonite in tonalite Adamello massif, Carisolo, northern Italy.
White patches are felspars, white zones are quartz; dark zones consist
of dark minerals (biotite, etc.). (*After Malaroda, 1946. Published by
permission of Istituto di Geologia, University of Padova.*)

classifications of breccias, these tectonic breccias are distinguished
from sedimentary breccias (cf. Norton, 1917; Reynolds, 1928; Leuchs,
1933), but their field characteristics are very similar. Breccias of this
kind are frequent in limestones, which are brittle rocks when near the
surface. The result is a zone full of angular limestone fragments in a
finer limestone matrix, very like a primary sedimentary breccia. When
the intensity of movement and the depth increase, the limestone becomes more and more plastic, and the final stage is a marble mylonite
such as is found, for instance, at the base of thrust sheets. When the
movement is no longer concentrated on limited surfaces but becomes
general, we find that the whole limestone has been marmorized.

In shaly rocks, crush zones are often developed as clay streaks, and
when shales or marls alternate with limestones, the clay may lubricate
the fault plane even where it crosses the limestone. At the surface
such clay streaks can seldom be found, but in artificial exposures in
mines or tunnels they are frequently encountered. Mylonitic and
fracture zones in both igneous and sedimentary rocks are great
sources of danger in tunneling. They are very often water conduits,
and the whole crushed rock may start to flow into the tunnel if pre-
cautions are not taken immediately.

Mylonitic zones in igneous and metamorphic rocks have a far greater importance than in unmetamorphosed sedimentary rocks, for they are often the only traces that the tectonic stress has left. They are difficult to detect, however, because erosion has often taken advantage of the disintegration of the rock along the mylonitic zones, and river courses mask their presence.

Other phenomena of distortion like boudinage, parasitic folds, mullions, etc., will be treated in Chap. 21.

Chapter 7
Structural Petrology

Our analysis of theoretical and experimental evidence in the preceding chapters has resulted in the conception that almost all rock deformation takes place in the elastico-viscous field, where the deformation is a slow process of replacement by slip of an elastic form leading to a permanent shape. The most common form is the fold, which can be either of the concentric type or the stress-cleavage type or one of the intermediate types such as accordion folding and shear cleavage.

In stress-cleavage folding the cleavage plane is parallel to the axial plane of the fold and its intersection with the bedding plane is consequently parallel to the fold axis (see also Chap. 21). Moreover, minor folds, many of microscopic dimensions, often develop, with their axes also parallel to the main axis.

A good outcrop gives the mapping geologist the opportunity to measure these features as lineations, which provides valuable information about the structure of the region.

Another kind of lineation, also frequently parallel to the folding axis, is given by the oriented growth of new minerals in regionally metamorphosed rocks. In order to assess the relation between such rock textures and the stress field, the science of structural petrology has been developed. The work of Sander goes back to 1911, and his new textbook of 1950 lists some 350 studies on this subject. Since then the influence of the methods of structural petrology on structural geology has grown enormously and has become a normal tool in the hands of the structural geologist.

The basic concept of the whole science is that, by measuring statistically the preferred orientation of minerals in deformed rocks in relation to cleavage, fold axes, and other structural lines, it is possible to find a simple relation between stress and strain. This objective has certainly not yet been realized. That there is some relation, nobody doubts, but extensive research has shown that it is very complex.

80

Statistical compilations show that the simple theoretical background of strain phenomena is inadequate to explain the observed orientations; they demonstrate emphatically that the reaction of the mineral grains to strain varies greatly. The systematic orientation of rock particles can frequently be measured without the help of the microscope, and one often gets a much clearer picture from megascopic study than from microscopic analysis. It should also be remarked that in many cases in which microscopic analysis gives a clear picture, simple observation of the rock exposure *in situ* would have also given the desired information, though not in the same detail, since the orientation of the quartz or calcite grains remains hidden.

Notwithstanding the practical shortcomings of petrofabric methods, our knowledge of the variety of preferred orientation has been much advanced, its terminology has entered our vocabulary, and some of its results have deepened our insight considerably. Here we can treat the subject only in a superficial and inadequate way, since it needs a full textbook to explain its methods and results. (For fuller information see the textbooks of Sander, 1930 and 1950; Knopf and Ingerson, 1938; Fairbairn, 1942 and 1952; Turner, 1948.)

The theoretical background of structural petrology is the same as that for the deformation of all solids, as treated in the foregoing chapters. Deformations are termed *affine* when they result from movement on a single set of parallel planes with equal direction and equal differential velocity on thin parallel layers of equal thickness. *Nonaffine* movement occurs when the direction and velocity of movement are unequal and the parallel layers are of unequal thickness. Nonaffine movements are much the most common, and create folds; affine movements are typical of the flanks of accordion folds. Both are generally described in textbooks on structural petrology as movements along shear planes oblique to the deformative stress. We have seen, however, that this kind of shear plane is rather rare in naturally deformed rocks; neither the concentric shear planes, nor the slaty-cleavage shear planes, nor the planar shears of accordion folding belong to this class. But in experiments, oblique shear is very common.

The textbook explanation of oblique shear leading to ordinary slaty cleavage or schistosity points out that the two original sets of intersecting rupture shear planes rotate as the flattening of rock proceeds; that when they finally arrive at a dead point not far away from a position perpendicular to the stress, a new set is formed, and that this will rotate in turn. The observed single set of shear planes is represented as a kind of accumulation of dead oblique shear planes all rotated toward the 90° position. Other explanations for the preferred slip on one plane have been advanced, but none of them give an adequate explanation of the great preponderance of only one schistosity or cleavage plane in nonmetamorphic and in metamorphic rocks. Our assumption of an elastico-viscous flow and consequent elastically defined slip planes in one set only provides a more logical relation between stress and deformation. This does not mean that oblique shear along two sets cannot occur; many metamorphic schists show them clearly, and the common type of augen gneiss is possibly one of the kinds of rock which is generated by this type of shearing. Besides the slip on one set of shear planes, or on an intersecting set of slip planes, with its accompanying lineation in the slip direction (the *a* axis), one can expect rotational movement around axes perpendicular to the slip movement. All kinds of microfolds with accompanying mullion or rod structures can be formed, with a common orientation parallel to the fold axis (*b* axis). This is particularly true of rocks in which the original bedding or stratification remains a prominent factor during the process of tectonic deformation, in rocks with fracture cleavage, for instance.

The preferred orientation may be due to two different processes: on the one hand, to tectonic deformation or reorientation of the minerals, and on the other, to secondary growth of new minerals or extension of old minerals in preferred directions of minimum resistance. It will often be impossible to distinguish the two phenomena in thin sections.

THE PETROFABRIC METHODS

They are ideally directed toward the correlation of the megascopic structure with the microscopic data of mineral orientation. Much confusion has been caused by the assumption of general laws about these correlations without adequate investigation. The correlation has to be made statistically, since a structure may be clearly seen in the field as a single entity, whereas orientation data must be built up from a large number of readings, especially if the latter are to form a reliably representative sample of the whole structure. This may be very clearly seen if we try to imagine the number of dip and strike readings that would be necessary to define a fold as fully as a map and section, and even a field sketch, do. Frequently it is found necessary to subdivide a fold into different sections in order to obtain interpretable results. This subdivision is a very important step, statistically, because it allows a great opportunity for bias to affect the result, but also theoretically, because it implies that the internal deformation of the folded layers may vary throughout an essentially homogeneous fold.

Petrofabric data are usually presented on a Schmidt net, in structural work normally taken to be the equal-area projection of the lower hemisphere of a unit orientation sphere. All measurements are represented by points at the intersection of linear orientations with the unit hemisphere, planes being located by the attitude of the perpendicular to them, their poles. The use of the equal-area projection allows the construction of frequency or density contours to illustrate the preference for various orientations.

When no other information on fold axes, etc., is available, the supposed direction of tectonic transport is called the *a* axis, which coincides with the slip direction on an *s* surface or with maximum elongation of particular rock particles (ooliths, for instance). Perpendicular to it one can distinguish the *b* axis, which is the axis of internal or external rotation or the intersection of bedding and slip planes. In general, it will coincide with the fold axis. The *c* axis is perpendicular to *a* and *b*. All the movement usually takes place within the *ac* plane. As the *a* and *b* axes can often be determined only after extensive microscopical study with the universal stage, a tentative scheme is established first, and this may later be rotated until the desired coincidence between mineral orientation and elongation and the supposed tectonic directions has been established. There is no doubt that this procedure may be misleading, for the relation one is looking for may thus have been introduced into it beforehand.

Once the tectonic axes have been provisionally fixed, the orientations of the crystallographic properties of the minerals are measured— the optical axes, cleavage, twin lamellae, etc., separately for each mineral—and are plotted on the equal-area net, in which the *a*, *b*, and *c* axes are taken as coordinates. In order to bring out the pattern of preferred orientation, the axes and poles of crystallographic orientation are counted within circles of 1% standard area, covering the whole net. With the help of density contours and by shading areas of equal density, the maxima are made easily legible (Fig. 47).

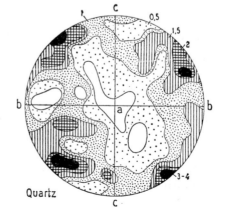

Fig. 47 Incomplete preferred reorientation of quartz optical axes, rhombic symmetry. (*After P. Niggli, Gesteine und Minerallagerstätten, vol. 1, 1948. Published by permission of Birkhäuser Verlag, Basel.*)

SYMMETRY OF PREFERRED ORIENTATION PATTERN

The link between the observed pattern of the preferred orientation and the mechanics of deformation is forged by the symmetry of the pattern, which has proved to be a reflection of the internal tectonic movement. The kinematic interpretation may be wrong in many cases, because our theoretical and practical knowledge of what really happens is certainly inadequate; nevertheless, the identification of symmetry remains a fact.

Three kinds of symmetry are observed in the orientation patterns:

1. Triclinic symmetry, or absence of any plane of symmetry. It is typical of flow structures without preferred direction of internal movement or of two succeeding deformation phases which were not parallel.

2. Monoclinic symmetry, with one plane of symmetry, which in most cases can be identified with the plane of schistosity or shear cleavage.

3. Orthorhombic symmetry, with three mutually perpendicular planes of symmetry, which is in agreement with stress cleavage.

The measurements are carried out on a variety of minerals, mainly mica, quartz, felspars, hornblende, and calcite, and on easily recognizable crystallographic properties such as the cleavage of micas, the optical axes of quartz and hornblende, and the twinning planes of felspars and of calcite. Often the orientation diagrams of different minerals in the same slide have different symmetries; for instance, mica flakes are generally more or less parallel to the main slip plane (*s* plane) of schistosity, showing a monoclinic symmetry, but the quartz grains are inclined to this plane, showing an orthorhombic symmetry. The explanation is often difficult and sometimes very dubious. It is generally believed that quartz is the most mobile of all the minerals and the most apt to be reorientated. The fact that the mica and quartz diagrams have different symmetries is therefore often ascribed to a later reorientation of the quartz. Another solution of the contradictory symmetries of these two minerals can be drawn from our experience of microfolds, in which we often notice that several kinds of deformation can coexist in the same microstructure. In Chap. 13, Fig. 116, we see a clear example of this. Oblique shear, flow cleavage, drag folds, concentric folding, and still other types of internal deformation are clearly shown to have acted simultaneously in the same fold, doubtless because most of the internal deformation was influenced both by an elastic stress field and by a permanent stress field. Or if objections are raised to the complete simultaneity of the different modes of distortion, it would not invalidate our assumption of coexistence if these modes followed one another in a

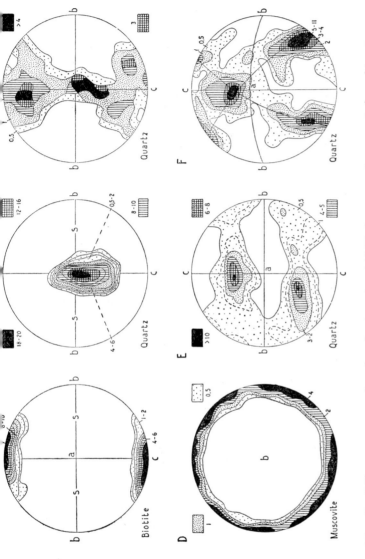

Fig. 48 Different patterns of preferred orientation. (*A*) Biotite axes maximum vertical to schistosity plane. Garnet schist from S. Valpurga d'Ultimo. (*B*) Quartz axes maximum parallel to *a* axis in granite mylonite, Odenwald. (*C*) Girdle of quartz axes in *ac* plane. Quartzite from the eastern Alps. (*D*) Girdle in *ac* plane of muscovite cleavage. Mica schist from Schimborn. (*E*) Two small girdles of quartz optical axes. Granulite from Saxony. (*F*) Two crossing girdles of quartz optical axes. Granulite from Finland. (*After P. Niggli, Gesteine und Minerallagerstätten, vol. 1, 1948. Published by permission of Birkhäuser Verlag, Basel.*)

quick succession within the same folding process. Both assumptions, simultaneity and quick succession, have the same result—different modes of deformation coexisting in the same fold and due to only one folding process. We therefore consider it quite possible that one mineral reacts to the flattening, and another to the rotational, or oblique shear, both in the course of the same process of distortion.

The preferred orientation minerals can assume either of two patterns: maxima (m) or girdles (g). There may be several maxima in one section; several girdles are much less common. The maxima are often enclosed in a girdle pattern (Fig. 48).

SIGNIFICANCE OF PREFERRED ORIENTATION PATTERNS

Turner (1948) gives a very useful compilation of the significance of the orientation patterns in terms of tectonic or growth structures, which we shall follow here in a slightly modified form (Fig. 49):

I. A concentration of poles in one maximum m.
   a. Presence of a single set of s planes, the pole of which coincides with m, commonly shown by (001) of mica either because of growth in a plane of least resistance or for mechanical reasons; common for (001) in mica and (01$\bar{1}$2) of calcite (I$_A$).
   b. Presence of a single set of s planes within which m coincides with direction of slip. Very common in quartz (0001) (I$_B$).
   c. Presence of a b axis whose pole coincides with m, either for mechanical reasons or because of fabric growth of prismatic crystals in that direction; (001) in hornblende, for instance (I$_C$).
II. An arcuate girdle of concentration in a great circle. The measured optical directions tend to fall within a plane surface.
   a. The same case as in I$_A$, but the single set of s planes has been folded; the fold axis is then the axis of the girdle (001) in mica and chlorite, (01$\bar{1}$2) in calcite, (0001) in quartz (II$_A$).
   b. Intersection of several sets of s planes in a line coinciding with the axis of the girdle (b axis); (001) in mica and chlorite, (01$\bar{1}$2) in calcite, (0001) in quartz (II$_B$).
   c. The same case as in I$_A$ or I$_B$, but the faces or cleavage parallel to the axes of the prismatic minerals, and not the axes themselves.
   d. Growth of elongated crystals with their longest dimension (e.g., 001 in hornblende) orientated at random in a plane of minimum resistance to growth, which coincides with the plane of the girdle (II$_C$).
III. A girdle which is *not* a great circle, but a small circle of the sphere of projection. The measured optical lines thus tend to lie on the surface of a cone (III).

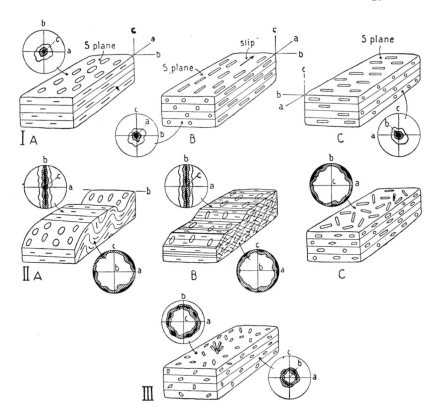

Fig. 49 Preferred orientation patterns of different structural features. For explanation see text.

  a. The measured optical direction makes an angle with the crystal face orientated in *s*. This is essentially the same case as Iᴀ, except that some optical angle, and not the crystal faces, is measured, as, for instance, the (0001) axis of calcite, which is orientated in the *s* plane according to its (01Ī2) faces. The diameter of the ring is then 52°.
  b. The *b* axis is an axis of rotation, the pole of which coincides with the center of the ring. Quartz diagrams very often show this arrangement.

With all these possible orientation diagrams in mind it is usual to distinguish, in accordance with Sander, between S-tectonites and B-tectonites.

S-tectonites are those in which a single well-developed planar schistosity is characterized by lack of any pronounced lineation. Elongated crystals are absent or inconspicuous. In consequence, the preferred orientation diagrams are mostly of the type of IA, a single maximum, or sometimes of the type of III, a single "cleft girdle." The rocks which have been marked by a single slip movement or are flattened without prominent lineation belong to this S category.

B-tectonites are those rocks whose fabric is characterized by a linear parallelism of elements to the *b* axis. There is generally some external evidence of rotation of individual crystals or layers, as in the types Ic and IIA; *ac* girdles are typical of the *B*-tectonites. When the rotation is clearly indicated, they are sometimes classified as *R*-tectonites. A *B*-tectonite is, then, the result of intersecting planes. Notwithstanding the very detailed method of analysis of preferred orientation in metamorphic rocks, of which only the broadest outlines have been sketched in the foregoing discussion, the interpretative value is still doubtful. We shall learn in the course of our descriptions of structures that hardly any deformation of rocks in slightly metamorphosed zones (epi- and mesozones) is simple. In an accordion fold, for instance, the flanks form *s* planes parallel to the bedding, but in the axial planes we find flexural slip combined with planar slip and recrystallization along the *B* axis. In cleavage folds we often find a combination of *s* planes parallel to the axial plane and flexural slip along the bedding planes. It is possible that in deeper metamorphic zones the orientation pattern becomes more simple through the preponderance of flow, but in this case we might also expect to get more lineation in the *b* axis and even unidirectional flow. The method has one great advantage over any megascopic measurements in that it reveals the orientation of quartz, calcite, and felspar, which is not observable without the use of the universal stage. A great disadvantage from which the whole petrofabric method has suffered is the fact that it has been first applied to structural problems which could not be solved otherwise. The interpretation of its results could therefore not be tested or checked against other tectonic data.

In my opinion the interpretational problems can be solved only by careful fabric studies of structures whose major features and microstructures are both well known beforehand. The tendency to depend on deformation experiments in the laboratory in order to find the solution is to my mind a wrong road; for the same reason that megascopic imitation experiments will always fail in dynamic similarity, we have not the slightest guarantee that the experiment arrives at an identical structure by the same path as in nature.

PART TWO

Comparative Structural Geology

Introduction

When we leave the theoretical and experimental study of the deformation of rocks and direct our attention to the facts observed in nature, we meet with great difficulty in applying our former findings to our later observations.

This discrepancy is due to a different approach to the subject matter. The experimental study was mostly concerned with the mechanics of inner deformation, on the scale of the rock grain, or of the rock sample, whereas ordinary tectonic study in the field is mostly concerned with the shape of a structure on the scale of major folds or faults, the latter scale being at least 100,000 times the former. No wonder that a chasm exists between the two points of view.

This chasm has been bridged to a certain extent by the imitative experiments, whose important results we have already indicated, and by the science of structural petrology. This latter subject, however, cannot reveal any tectonic feature unless a recrystallization of the grains has taken place, and in most unmetamorphosed rocks there has been no such thing. Nevertheless, the methods of structural petrology have been applied with considerable success to megascopic features of rock distortion.

This difference in approach to the study of the tectonics of metamorphic rocks and of the nonmetamorphic sedimentary cover reflects a fundamental difference in the way the rocks yielded to the stress condition, in the "basement" and in the "sedimentary blanket." Each division has its own structural characteristics, due in the first place to an increase of temperature downward. Hence we must distinguish between "basement tectonics" and "sedimentary-cover tectonics." Obviously, there must exist a roughly horizontal plane, or a transition zone, between the two modes of deformation, separating the basement from its sedimentary cover. When this plane coincides with a pronounced break in the nature of the rocks, such as the break between the folded Hercynian basement and its Mesozoic cover in most Tertiary mountain systems in Europe, this feature then becomes by far the most important structural factor. Often, however, the division plane is not provided with such a prominent and predestined horizon, and a transition zone is developed. In the first case, that of a clear-cut boundary plane, we find totally different tectonic shapes above the plane and below; such superficial structures have been called "plis de couverture" (superficial folds), in contrast with the large-scale warping of the basement, which has been called "plis de fond" (deep-seated folds) by Argand (1916). The structural features in its lowest reaches comprise the structural features of metamorphic rocks.

The plane which separates the superficial fold from its basement is the plane of "décollement," which we can translate as a basal shearing plane, or plane of detachment. The production of this phenomenon is not only due to the difference in the mode of rock yield to stress with increasing depth, but is also inherent in all concentric folding processes, independent of depth or temperature. It is an essential consequence of the geometry of the superficial concentric fold, as we shall explain later. Minor basal shearing planes do, therefore, almost invariably develop in the vertical range of superficial folds. There are, then, three factors which tend to separate the upper sedimentary cover from a differently folded substratum: first, the increase of hydrostatic pressure and temperature; second, the nature of the rocks; and third, the geometry of the concentric fold. In the case of the European example already quoted, a Mesozoic cover on a Hercynian basement, the effects of the three factors often more or less coincide on a single level, but elsewhere there is frequently no such coincidence, and less obvious structural features develop.

Structural geology describes the deformations which result from the action of stress conditions in the earth's crust, as we can observe them at the surface and at depth. Our depth of penetration below the surface is not very great, since the deepest mines reach only some 2,000 m and the deepest boreholes useful for structural purposes do not reach more than three times that depth. On the other hand, the greatly variable depth of erosion due to uplift of portions of the earth's crust gives us the opportunity to look at structures which were originally buried beneath great masses of other rocks.

It is obviously impossible for one geologist to see and judge with his own eyes a sufficient number of typical structures, and he is obliged to draw heavily upon published reports. But in the majority of cases the published sections and maps are interpreted representations of observed facts and not the facts themselves and are therefore strongly charged with the subjective views of the observer. By using these data indiscriminately, we should probably arrive at a classification of different schools of thought instead of a systematic classification of structural features. Hence it is most important to use only those sections which are fully factual, those in which subjective interpretation plays a minor role.

We can find the kind of data we need in the deep ravines of mountain systems, and also in artificial exposures produced by mining.

We shall start our survey with faults of different kinds, since they represent the less complicated features of deformation, and proceed to simple folds, in which we shall again observe many different kinds of faults. Finally, we shall try to penetrate somewhat deeper into the relation between sedimentary history and structural features and into the relation between structures of different classes.

Chapter 8

Origin of Faults

Faults are an extremely common feature in all deformed strata, and even in unfolded strata, if we regard joints as very small faults. In our theoretical and experimental studies we found that nearly all deformation can be considered as movement along shearing planes; that its effects may be either invisible or healed by recrystallization or visible as planes along which either small or comparatively large translations have taken place. In the majority of cases, faults are simply such shearing planes along which a great deal of deformation has been concentrated. The total slip along hundreds of thousands of small closely packed shearing planes can alternatively be concentrated on one plane, parallel to the small ones, with a hundred- or thousandfold larger motion and with the same overall result. When the shear planes are small and numerous, we speak of plastic deformation and "folding," or "flexuring"; when there are a few large shearing planes, we call the deformation "rupture" and speak of faults. There is no fundamental difference, however, between "rupture" and "plastic" deformation, between "faulting" and "folding." In the next chapter, where faults are compared with joints, we shall see that all transitions between folding and faulting do actually exist in nature.

CLASSIFICATION OF FAULTS

According to Anderson (1951), the three main types of faults, (1) normal, or tension, faults, (2) thrust faults, and (3) tear, or wrench, faults, differ only in the varying orientation of the three principal stresses in relation to the earth's surface.

All three are shear planes, of which the acute angle is intersected by the largest principal stress and which are parallel to the median principal stress. When the median principal stress lies in the horizontal plane, we get either thrust planes, when the largest stress is also in the horizontal plane (Fig. 50B), or normal faults, when the largest stress

94

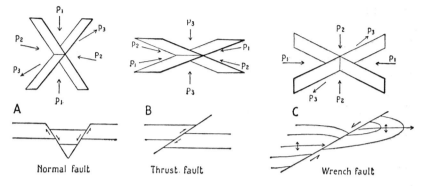

Fig. 50 The origin of faults. P_1 = largest, P_2 = median, and P_3 = smallest principal stress.

is vertical (Fig. 50A). When the median stress is vertical, we get wrench faults (Fig. 50C). In general, a stress condition in the upper part of the earth's crust will be a tangential pressure, or tension. A tensional stress in a horizontal direction will represent the smallest principal stress, and the largest stress will result from the weight of the rock acting in a vertical direction. The result will be a normal fault. In the case of a horizontal tangential pressure we can find either wrench faults, which result in an extension in the horizontal plane, or thrust faults, which mean an extension in a vertical sense. Hence, according to this simplified reasoning, we might expect thrust faults near the surface and wrench faults at depth. So far this reasoning does not indicate why in one case we find folds and in another case thrust or wrench faults and why normal faults have no apparent counterpart in fold tectonics. The latter query is easier to answer. When a tensional stress in a horizontal direction is applied, the confining pressure is also lowered, and we have already seen that rupture in the sense of movement along a single plane is more easily performed with low confining pressure. We have seen that this is due to the fact that the normal stress on the shearing plane is decreased to such an extent that the cohesion of the grains is completely lost as soon as the motion starts. A tension stress will therefore nearly always produce a normal fault or tension crack and very rarely anything else.

It is more difficult to understand which factors determine the preference for a fold, a thrusted structure, or wrench faulting. First of all, the three modes of deformation are often mixed up in nature. When there is thrust faulting in the superficial layer, there is usually folding as well, inseparably associated. Wrench faulting and folding are often similarly associated. In general, we find that really big wrench faults and some thrust faults originate in the basement and are features which penetrate deep into the earth's crust, whereas smaller faults of both kinds are closely connected with folding in the sedimentary blanket. There are, however, wrench-fault patterns which are more or less independent of folding, and we may presume that in those cases there actually existed a tensional stress in the horizontal plane. Yielding in a horizontal direction thus replaces ordinary folding by wrench faulting. Folding along vertical axes might be produced instead of wrench faulting in such circumstances, but it appears to be extremely rare in the superficial sedimentary layers. It may play a much larger role in the dynamo-metamorphic field.

The classification of faults in normal, thrust, and wrench faults is more or less theoretical. When a fault is mapped in the field, even when the separation of homologous elements on both sides can be mapped, we still often do not know to which of the three types it really belongs. What we often can ascertain is the apparent separation, determined by the relative position of two homologous elements. Therefore a fault in the field ought to be classified in the first instance as an apparent wrench fault (strike slip) or dip-slip fault; the latter may be either a thrust or a normal fault (Mason Hill, 1959).

The actual movement of the blocks can be controlled by observing the striations on the fault surfaces. In simple cases all striations on normal or thrust faults ought to have a dip-slip orientation, and on wrench faults, a strike-slip orientation. Actually, deviations are often observed, and usually are attributed to later movements on the fault plane. Obliquely plunging striations can be due to a gradual rotation of the stress field, as has been demonstrated by A. Williams (1958) in his survey in the Midland Valley of Scotland.

Joints interest us mainly as a general expression of the stress field to which the rocks have been submitted, but besides the orientation of the joint pattern and eventually the striations on the planes due to slip, there are patterns visible on the joint surfaces, of which the feather, or plumose, fracture pattern is most frequent (Hodgson, 1961). The feather fracture occurs most frequently on shear joints and is certainly the result of spreading of the crack through the rock from the axial zone outward (Fig. 51). On the fringe of the feather, on top and bottom of the competent bed in which the joint has developed, the fracture plane has developed in a set of small echelon joints. It is a typical example of the fact that even in the case of a simple fracture without movement on the plane, we have to take into account that fracturing is a dynamical process and not instantaneous (Roberts, 1961).

In order to relate, as far as possible, our theoretical reasoning and observed phenomena in our study of faults, we shall first discuss the joint and fault patterns which have been observed, and then proceed

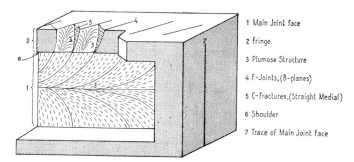

1 Main Joint Face

2 Fringe

3 Plumose Structure

4 F-Joints,(B-planes)

5 C-Fractures,(Straight Medial)

6 Shoulder

7 Trace of Main Joint Face

Fig. 51 Feather or plumose structure developed on a joint plane. (*After Hodgson, 1961. Published by permission of the American Journal of Science.*)

to normal and thrust faulting and wrench faulting. Flat thrusts will be treated in a separate chapter, after we have considered fold mechanics.

THE STRAIN ELLIPSOID

Rock deformation has often been described both by the deformation of a unit square and by that of a unit circle. By inserting the circle in the square, as in Fig. 52, we get both of them at the same time. The kind of deformation indicated in Fig. 52A is then called "pure shear," and that of Fig. 52B, "simple shear." The ellipses are congruent in both cases, which shows that the final shape cannot indicate the kind of deformation that actually took place. Because the simple shear is accompanied by a rotational movement of the strain ellipsoid, it is also called simple rotational shear. In Fig. 52C, the identity of the different modes of deformation has been illustrated so far as the resulting shapes are concerned.

A normal stress will always create a shearing stress, and whether the actual deformation takes place by pure or simple shear, the shape of the deformed object is identical. The rotation in Fig. 52B is an apparent one, a displacement of the unit in space only, and does not imply any particular mode of internal deformation of the rock nor any peculiarity of the stress field. The strain ellipsoid is nothing but a simple graphic way of demonstrating the geometric consequence of a deformation and has no physical meaning.

All this does not mean that there is no difference between simple and pure shear, but only that the final shape of any unit particle of rock cannot inform us about the mode of deformation. Pure and simple shear have no definite significance concerning the mode of deforma-

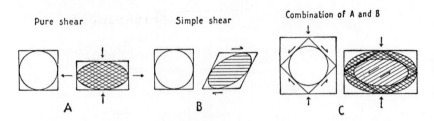

Fig. 52   The strain ellipsoid. (*A*) Pure shear; (*B*) simple shear; (*C*) combination of *A* and *B*.

tion; they may mean, for instance, only that in pure shear both possible shear planes have been active, and in simple shear, only one set. On the other hand, pure shear might mean a fluid or a purely plastic deformation involving extension in only one direction and compression in the others, without any shear planes.

Hence the use of the strain ellipsoid in structural problems is often misleading, even in structural petrology, where schistosity planes are sometimes visible planes of movement, since we do not know beforehand whether such planes represent real shear planes. Goguel (1952, p. 36) has pointed out that the principle arrived at by Becker (1904), in which the two intersecting circular sections of an ellipsoid are regarded as planes of no deformation, and hence as possible schistosity planes, is erroneous because these planes are not fixed planes in the material slowly rotating during deformation. The use of Becker's principle in structural petrography is therefore also erroneous. Any plane parallel to the median axis of an ellipsoid passes through the stage of a circular section, but that section is equal to one of the original sphere only when the length of the median axis remains constant. Even then, such section is not a rotating fixed plane in the material, but a transitory stage between shortening and lengthening.

Chapter 9

Joint and Fault Patterns

The relation between joint patterns and stress direction has often been investigated, but that between joints and faults has received much less attention. It has nevertheless been assumed in general that there is a certain relationship.

Both joints and faults are believed to have a common origin in deformative stress acting during a folding phase and must therefore be closely related. The nature of this relation, however, has seldom been ascertained. In general, the belief prevails that there is a gradual transition from joints with no motion along their faces, through joints with a small motion, to small faults, and then to large faults.

THE RELATION BETWEEN JOINT AND FAULT PATTERNS

The Heidelberg school of joint investigation (Salomon, 1911, 1925, 1927), for instance, tried originally to prove the compressive origin of the great Upper Rhine rift valley by extensive joint surveys on both its sides. It failed completely in its purpose, but gave us valuable general data. In the later surveys of this group the original purpose was abandoned. Most of the joints proved to be vertical, one group with horizontal and another with vertical striation, but there were none consistently dipping away from the rift and showing dip striation. This extensive survey therefore more or less proved that there is no relation between the great rift faults, which have since been found to be normal faults heading toward the rift valley, and the joints on both sides of the trough.

Another instance in which this relation was the subject of a survey is work by Kwantes (in Sax, 1946), in the South Limburg coal field of the Netherlands.

This report tells us that the NW direction of the major post-Carboniferous faults (Chap. 10, Fig. 71) is *not* represented in the joint dia-

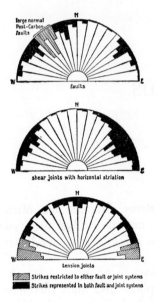

Fig. 53 Strike frequency diagrams of faults and joints in the South Limburg coal field. (*After Sax, 1946. Published by permission of Geologisch Bureau, Heerlen.*)

grams of the Carboniferous rocks and that several maxima of the tension-joint diagrams, in particular the E-W one, are *not* represented in the fault pattern (Fig. 53). Other directions, noticeably of N 60° W and N 55° E, are maxima in both the fault and shear-joint patterns of the Carboniferous rocks. The survey was extremely extensive. The faults were measured from the colliery production maps, and the joint survey was carried out in several mines by trained geologists. We may conclude that the shear joints and the majority of the fault directions are both due to the folding stress of Late Carboniferous origin. Some tension-joint directions, probably of the same age, are not duplicated by a corresponding set of faults, however, and the Mesozoic stress or tension, causing the major NW-SE trending faults, although active at several distinct periods from the Triassic onward to Recent times, did not cause a joint pattern in the older rocks. This result accords with the negative result of the Heidelberg survey.

A joint survey of the lignite field of Cologne by Wölk (1937) gives quite another picture (Fig. 54). The Miocene lignite layer, more than 30 m in thickness, is exploited in open-cast pits and shows excellently developed and very long joints in regular sets. The general geology is very well known, thanks to the numerous boreholes and open workings of the lignite, and shows a pattern of normal faults which have a general NW-SE trend, but often deviate from this direction, thus joining and then separating again. The general result of the survey showed that the joints are very consistently parallel to the nearest normal fault, whatever its strike may be. When the field of observation is situated between two main faults of different direction, both directions are represented in the joint pattern. The joint surfaces are plane and cut through irregularities of the strata. Their hade is steep, and they usually occur in two perpendicular sets, of which one is predominant and parallel to the nearest fault. It is a curious fact that the number of joints does not increase near the fault.

There can be no doubt about the conclusion that the joints are due to the same stress conditions as the normal faults. During the faulting, the lignite layer carried very little overburden, and this fact may possibly explain the steep dip of the joints. The other member of the

Fig. 54 Joints parallel to normal faults in Miocene lignite of the Ville lignite field near Cologne. (*After Wölk*, 1937. *Published by permission of Zeitschrift der Deutschen Geologischen Gesellschaft.*)

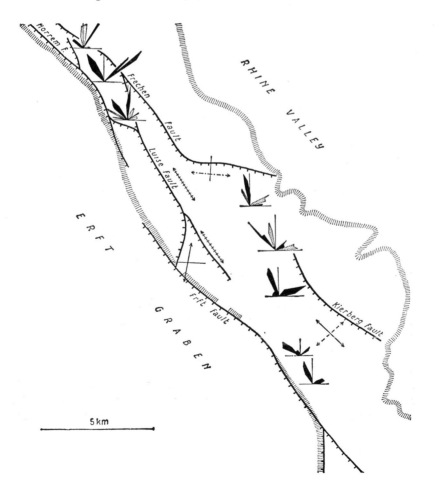

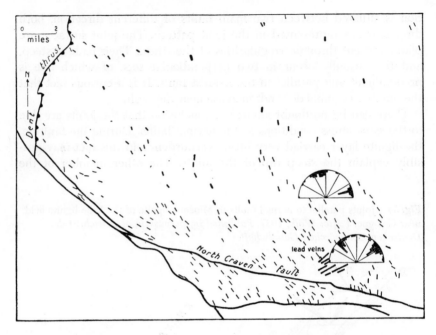

Fig. 55 Joint patterns in the Great Scar Limestone. (*After Wager,* 1931. *Published by permission of the Geological Society of London.*)

conjugate set, perpendicular to the joints parallel to the faults, indicates that a tensional stress parallel to the faults also existed. As the joint frequency is independent of the faulting, it seems probable that the joints were formed at the very beginning of the stress condition.

The outcome of this survey is in direct contradiction to that of the South Limburg coal field, where no joints are related to the normal faults. This is most probably due to the fact that the Carboniferous rocks were already folded, cemented, and generally lithified before the faulting started, whereas the Miocene lignite was still a very soft rock.

In the survey by Wager (1931) on the Great Scar Limestone of Craven, we have another valuable contribution to our knowledge of the relation between regular joint patterns and tectonic features. The limestone is cut by two sets of joints nearly at right angles to each other; one of them is parallel to lead veins, which are common in this region. The sets of joints again perform a swinging motion in the field of observation (Fig. 55). The frequency diagrams of different parts of the region all show the same two perpendicular sets. In some places the joints, which are generally straight and perpendicular to the bedding plane, are joined by "en échelon" gash (tension) joints, filled by calcite. The gash joints make an angle of 45° with the main joint sets. The whole area is limited in the south by the North Craven fault and in the west by the Dent fault, the latter being a thrust. The compressional stress direction of N 55° W is fixed by this Dent fault thrust. This direction bisects one of the angles between the joints, which can therefore be regarded as normal shear joints. The western portion of the North Craven fault, parallel to one of the joint sets, is most probably a tear fault.

In this example of joint pattern we again find a close relation between compressional stress and shear-joint direction, but we notice a rigorously perpendicular system of two sets, and not the acute angle found in many other instances.

THE RELATION BETWEEN JOINT AND FAULT PATTERNS AND FOLDING

Often a distinct relation between folding and a fault pattern can be established, in particular when good aerial photographs are available.

In such a set of vertical aerial photographs of an adjoining anticline and syncline in eastern Algeria, a pattern of very small faults, which can be compared with a joint pattern, can be observed in two limestones which respectively form the axial arc of two adjacent and parallel structures. The synclinal limestone is obviously much younger (Eocene in fact) than the anticlinal limestone, which is of a mid-Cretaceous age. In the syncline the foraminiferal limestones form the top of a table in a reversed relief; in the anticline a hard limestone crops out. Their stratigraphical distance is some 1,500 m (Fig. 56). The most striking feature of the fault patterns is that both show a double maximum, with an intervening angle of 20° in the anticline and 35° in the syncline, but orientated differently in relation to the axis.

From this example of fault and joint patterns it follows that, on the one hand, small faults discernible in favorable circumstances on aerial photographs are almost certainly orientated in some way in relation to the direction of the principal folding stresses.

According to the theory of Mohr and Anderson, shearing planes, either faults or joints, may develop in planes parallel to the median stress direction and making an acute angle bisected by the largest stress direction, whereas tension joints, or fissures, will be orientated parallel to this largest stress and perpendicular to the smallest stress.

This theory gives us a ready answer to the question of why sets of differently orientated small faults developed in the anticline and syncline mentioned above. In the anticlinal arch of a competent limestone layer we may expect a local tensional stress in the outer arc perpendicular to the axis. This would therefore be the direction of small-

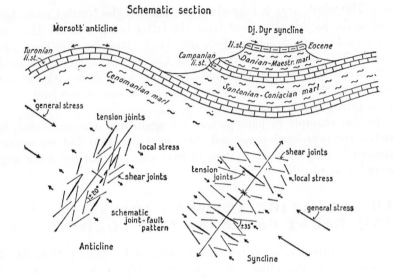

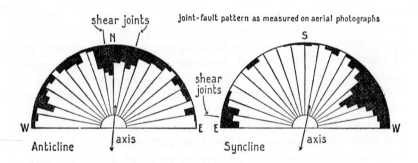

Fig. 56 Origin of fault patterns in adjoining anticline and syncline, adopted from aerial photographs of adjacent structures in southeast Algeria, with fault strike frequency diagrams.

est stress, with the overburden constituting the median stress, and the largest stress parallel to the axis (Fig. 56). In the syncline we may expect, on the contrary, a local compression in the direction perpendicular to the axis. In both cases a set of shear joints develops, at an acute angle bisected by the largest stress, but differently orientated in relation to the axis direction. In this very simple case in Algeria we found remarkably good agreement between theory and practice, but in general the agreement is much less obvious and the joint pattern or fault pattern much more complicated. Joint surveys from tectonically complicated areas are mostly far too complex to allow any trustworthy interpretation, although this has often been attempted. But when we consider regions which are almost unfolded, the patterns are much more simple and show obvious relations to known tectonic features. The survey by Parker (1942) in central and northern New York and northern Pennsylvania (Fig. 57) shows a very marked consistency of pattern, slowly swinging from the NNW in the central portion of the surveyed area to the NNE in the eastern portion, in close relation with the bend of the Appalachian fold axes but independent of local variations in the individual folds. Parker distinguishes three sets of joints, all of them perpendicular to the bedding plane. Set I is a double set with an average intervening angle of 19° (varying from 13 to 26°) swinging round from N 30° W in the west to N 10° E in the east. Set II is somewhat less regular, but perpendicular to the median line of set I. Set III seems to be independent of the other two for it does not follow the swinging motion clearly exhibited by sets I and II, and it has an average direction of N 60° E with a very small deviation of the median value. (It varies only from N 50° to 65° E.) The joints of the compound set I are remarkably plane; they slice clearly through hard concretions in weak strata and pass without deviation through extreme cross-bedding, etc. They are obviously shear joints.

The surfaces of the joints of set II are, on the contrary, curved and irregular, with a rough, torn appearance, and must be regarded as tension joints.

Tentatively, I would explain the compound set I of shear joints as normal shears caused by the main stress direction which bisects the very small angle of 20° between the two components. Set II, being perpendicular to this stress direction, cannot be a normal set of tension

Fig. 57 Map of strike frequency of joints in central and northern New York and northern Pennsylvania. (*After Parker, 1942. Published by permission of the Geological Society of America.*)

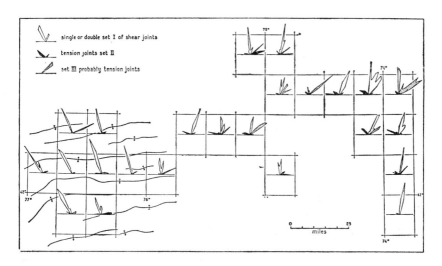

joints (which ought to be parallel to the main stress direction), but may perhaps be regarded as due to tensional stress produced by an elastic release of the compression. Set III may be due to a later (or earlier) stress direction of unknown quality. The main conclusions which may be drawn from this survey are:

1. The angle between the two components of a compound set of shear joints may be very small (20°) and is intersected by the main stress direction.

2. A set of tension joints perpendicular to the main stress may develop as an effect of elastic release of the compression.

The examples we have quoted have been taken from rather simple cases. In a survey of the fracture pattern of a complicated structure, we are always confronted with sets so variably oriented that the interpretation and the derivation of stress fields from the orientation of the pattern become doubtful. A typical example of such a study has been given by Spencer (1959) in his work on the Precambrian of the Beartooth Mountains.

Many investigators, including Deenen (1942), who made a very extensive and detailed survey of jointing in a coal mine, have concluded, from the fact that all joints are orientated to the plane of stratification instead of to the horizontal plane, that the joints were originated before the folding. In other words, they found that their picture of the joint or fault frequency became intelligible only if the strata were rotated to their original horizontal position. In my exposition I have presumed, on the contrary, that many of the joints are due to the folding itself, and hence are formed continuously during the folding. This difference arises because Deenen, and those who share his view, assume that the deformative stress is invariable in direction and always in the horizontal plane only; whereas there is ample evidence in favor of the view that during folding there are elastic stresses always necessarily orientated to the upper and lower limits of the deformed sheet or mass of rock, independent of its position in space.

In order to check this assumption we made a joint survey of the well-known "Sleek Stone," an asymmetric anticline (one flank dipping at 90°, the other at 25°) exposed in the coastal cliffs of western Pembrokeshire, near Broad Haven. This anticline has the great advantage of showing excellent jointing on the surface of one and the same bed, from one flank into the other.

The net result of the survey was that:

1. The joint system is very much dependent on the lithological character of the rock; a massive sandstone, a graywacke, and a sandy shale, each has its own type of jointing, with characteristic frequency and direction.

They have some major directions in common, but in general the angle of intersection of a conjugate set is different for different kinds of rocks.

2. Some joint directions are early features in the structure; this is proved by the fact that in the sharp anticlinal hinge they show curved faces, obviously bent along with the bed that contains them.

3. Some joint directions which occur near the axis do not occur in the gentle flank.

4. The simple relations between joints and stress which we could discern in some of the examples quoted earlier cannot be established in this strongly folded structure.

5. Although in limited areas of a few square meters the joint systems are very regular, this regularity disappears as soon as the area under consideration is enlarged to 100 or 200 m².

Quite another approach to this problem of the relation between the joint pattern and folding has been made by Harris et al. (1960), who tried to establish a criterion for the joint frequency. In a survey of moderately folded regions in Wyoming, a distinct relation was established between the lithology and thickness of the beds and the joint frequency; the fracture density is greater in the thinner beds and in the more brittle rocks. By comparing the different lithological units with one "datum" bed, the thickness and lithology factors can be established and a frequency factor can be calculated for each point of observation. The isofracture lines can then be drawn on a structural map, which give the general result as shown in Fig. 58. It was obvious from this survey that the fracture frequency was closely related to the curvature in a cross section, and therefore to the folding.

Of particular interest also are the fracture patterns in Precambrian rocks, like the Canadian shield, of which Blanchet (1957) gave us beautiful examples. Obviously the fracture pattern here has no relation to the tectonics of the Precambrian rocks, and it has sometimes been proposed that these cracks are due to the tidal motion of the earth's crust, in particular because the pattern has been propagated distinctly upward into the sedimentary rock or the glacial drift cover. In a regional study of the Colorado Plateau, Hodgson (1961) thinks it is proved that here also no relation can be established between any tectonical stress field which originated the flat monoclines and the fracture pattern.

When we try to summarize the results of our short review of joint and fault patterns, we find that we are confronted by very contradictory conclusions. On the one hand, a distinct relation between folding and fracturing has been established in several cases, but on the other hand, joints occur as well independently of the established tectonical stress field. Sometimes a relation between major faults and the joint pattern is evident; sometimes it can be proved there is no relation. It

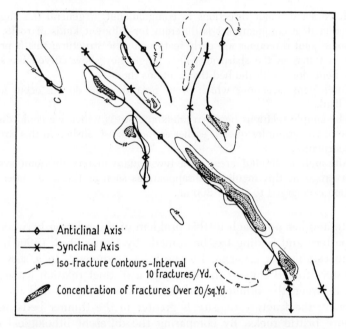

Fig. 58   Isofracture map, Sheep Mountain anticline, showing
maximum fracture concentration on anticlinal axes. (*After
Harris, 1960. Published by permission of the American Association of Petroleum Geologists.*)

is certainly true that lithified rocks always show jointing, whether
they are folded or not, but even unfolded rocks may have been submitted to a tectonic stress field, with no other result than a fracture
pattern.

I will try to summarize the results of these joint surveys on very
gently folded competent layers, which we have reviewed.

In the first place, we must distinguish between shear joints and
tension joints; each type can be recognized in the field by its special
characteristics. Further, we have found that there are shear joints
due to a general stress direction and others due to local stress conditions, as in the anticlinal and synclinal axial regions. The intervening
angle between two sets of shear joints may vary widely; the minimum
we found was 15°, the maximum almost 90°. The difference may
simply be due to differences in rock properties or to the weight of
the overburden, but on the other hand, it may merely indicate that
two quite different kinds of shear joints exist. Tension joints may
develop either parallel to the compressive stress or as an elastic release
perpendicular to it. Here also we must distinguish between local and
general stress direction.

THE RELATION BETWEEN JOINT AND FAULT PATTERNS AND STRESS

As we have seen in Chap. 8, Anderson (1951) distinguishes three main types of faults: normal or tension faults, thrust faults, and tear or wrench faults, which differ only in their different orientation in relation to the horizontal plane. The same classification can be applied to joints, with the important addition of tension joints, which would find their equivalent in the fault system as fissures or gash fractures. All three kinds of faults mentioned by Anderson are shear faults, making an angle varying from 15 to 45° with the largest principal stress; the tension joints, or gash fractures, which we encountered in several examples are parallel to the largest principal stress. Because they have no motion along their faces, they are generally not considered as faults, but they are frequent in joint diagrams and play an important role in ore deposits.

Let us consider what kind of joints (and faults) we might expect in a moderately folded limestone.

At first the sheet of rock is in the simple stress condition of Fig. 59. We find *shear joints* making an acute angle with the deformative stress, and *tension joints,* parallel to this stress.

In the next stage we might expect the *secondary stress condition,* caused by elastic bending of the sheet as described earlier, which will cause a set of shear joints with their acute angle bisected by the anticlinal axis and tension joints parallel to the axis (Fig. 56).

Besides these secondary shear and tension joints, the elastic state of stress in the bent sheet is apt to create still another system. When we consider a block on the flank of a bent sheet we find opposite stress directions on the upper and lower surfaces, a couple on the other faces necessarily compensating for the rotational effect of the first couple, as sketched in Fig. 60. These frictional shear joints are parallel to the anticlinal (or synclinal) axis.

Finally, we might perhaps expect *release tension joints* after the stress has vanished, as was suggested by the tension joints in the Parker survey in New York. They will be either parallel or perpendicular to the axis, depending on whether they release the main or the

Fig. 59   Shear joints and tension joints in an unfolded sheet of rock.

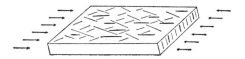

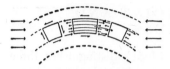

Fig. 60   Shear joints due to elastic bending of a sheet of rock.

secondary stress. We have not yet considered the possible shear joints or faults which make an acute angle with the stratification plane. Since the main stress is always directed parallel to the bedding plane in an elastically bent sheet, they might cause thrusts or normal shear joints making an angle of more or less than 45° with the bedding plane.

If all these possible joints or small faults were formed in one and the same structure, they would appear diagrammatically as shown in Fig. 61, where the normals to the joint planes have been plotted in a stereographic projection instead of in a frequency diagram. If the anticlinal axis had a distinct plunge and the survey had been made on the longitudinal curvature of the crest, the picture would have been much more complicated; even in this rather simple case, the distribution of the joint planes becomes so general that a slight deviation of the shear angle from 30° would result in a continuous girdle around the circumference and another one perpendicular to the first. It would then obviously be impossible to distinguish between the joints by means of their position. In nature we seldom find all kinds of joints in the same outcrop, but as soon as we combine too many outcrops in one diagram, the fact that we are apt to find continuous girdles can be explained by the multitude of possible joints and need not be due to a varying stress direction. Difference of joint patterns from one outcrop to the next may also be due simply to a difference in the lithology

Fig. 61   Stereographic representation of possible joints in an anticlinal structure.

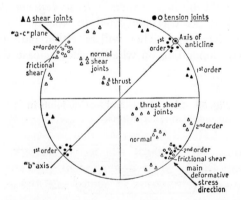

of the rocks, one lithology being preferred by one kind of joint, the other by another. As I have mentioned before, only very simple cases, where elastic bending has not played a preponderant role, give reliable results.

EXTENSION AND RELEASE FRACTURES, DIKES, VEINS, AND SILLS

All the fault types and most of the joint types which we have considered up to now have been shear faults. Normal, wrench, and thrust faults differ only in their orientation to the horizontal plane or their relative movement. There exists, however, a distinct group of faults and joints which are characterized by the fact that their origin is not a shearing movement but the widening of a tension crack, parallel to the largest principal stress and normal to the smallest principal stress.

We have already made their acquaintance in our survey of joints, where we distinguished shear joints from tension joints. A wide-open tension crack can hardly exist at depth, and is always infilled with some material, either an intruded foreign rock or a recrystallized component of the surrounding rock. The widening movement is relatively small. The two walls commonly move no more than some tens of meters from one another at most; some dikes, however, have thicknesses measured in hundreds of meters.

The origin of tension cracks can be twofold. They may be a direct consequence of the deformation in the form of a dilatation parallel to the largest principal stress, or a secondary consequence of the deformation, through an elastic dilatation in a plane perpendicular to the principal stress. It is only rarely that these two modes of origin can be distinguished, and elastic dilatation has rarely been mentioned as even a possible explanation. Some of the joint patterns we examined strongly suggest, however, that it is much more frequent than was originally supposed. Personally, I feel inclined to accept this explanation, particularly for parallel dike swarms.

Dike Swarms. E. M. Anderson (1951) discusses the problem at great length. To establish the right kind of stress field with a minimum stress direction in the horizontal plane, in order to get vertical tension fissures, he presumes a radial vertical stress exerted by a rising magma. His most convincing example is the Tertiary Mull Swarm (Fig. 62), which spreads from a center which is occupied by ring dikes on the Island of Mull and extends into the Southern Uplands to the south and into the Hebrides in the north. About the origin of the ring dikes themselves there can be little doubt. Their concentric arrangement makes a definite *center of stress* an almost essential assumption. That

Fig. 62   Tertiary dike swarms in Scotland. (*After Richey, 1939. Published by permission of Oliver & Boyd Ltd.*)

this can be due only to a push from below by a rising magma in a kind of volcanic vent is equally likely. The arrangement of the dike swarms, originating from the Mull and Skye centers, is a very convincing argument for the close relationship between the ring dike and dike swarm phenomena. The very fact, however, that ring dikes and dike swarms differ in their outer shape suggests that they originate in different kinds of stress fields, though these must obviously be closely related. It is true, as Anderson pointed out, that it is more probable that the filling of these long cracks, sometimes 400 km in length, with igneous rock did not take place from below, upward, but by lateral filling from the center outward. Perhaps the simplest way of conceiv-

Fig. 63   Paleozoic dikes in Scotland. (*After Richey, 1939. Published by permission of Oliver & Boyd Ltd.*)

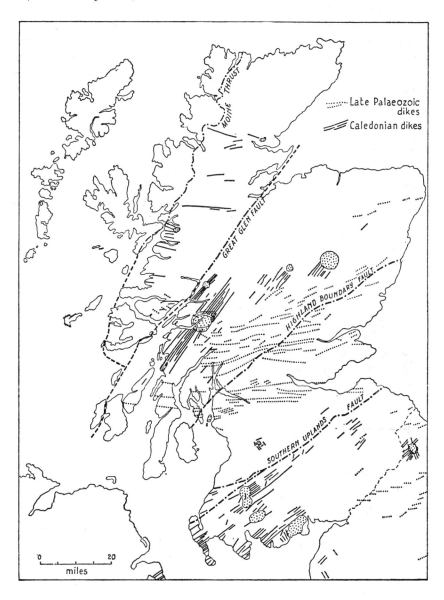

ing the ring-dike system and the dike swarm in one stress field would be to presume a lateral tension in the WSW-ENE direction, with points of incipient failure at various places, of which the upwelling magma immediately took advantage, producing first the ring dikes and, immediately afterward, a parallel fissure system perpendicular to the general tension. The ring dikes are then the expression of a secondary and momentary stress field, touched off by the rupture of the crust, just as the weight of a single person on an ice-covered lake can touch off the cracking of the ice in long and almost straight cracks running from shore to shore.

The Tertiary dike swarms of Scotland are not the only evidence of cracking of the crust. The Caledonian orogenic belt of this country runs NE-SW, with the Moine thrust as its most striking structural feature. The Caledonian dike system runs parallel to the main folding axis. This direction suggests that the dike formation is due to an elastic release of the NW-SE compression.

The Hercynian (Armorican) stress finds its most spectacular expression in the great wrench faults, with a NE-SW trend: the Great Glen fault, the Highland Boundary fault, and the Southern Upland fault. The direction of these wrench faults and other structural evidence from the Upper Paleozoic strongly suggest that this folding phase was due to a N-S compression. The Hercynian dikes trend E-W, perpendicular to compressive stress, again suggesting that they are due to an elastic release of the compression (Fig. 63).

In view of these conclusions on the orientation of the dikes in rela-

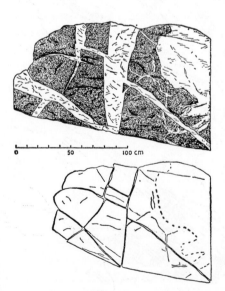

Fig. 64 Demonstration of dike material filling up fissures. (*After E. Niggli*, 1953).

tion to the Caledonian and Hercynian stress fields, a similar relation suggests itself for the NNW-SSE Tertiary dike swarm, e.g., a tension in a perpendicular direction due to elastic release of an ENE-WSW compression.

Apart from dike swarms, nearly all intrusive granites—in particular, those of the late orogenic type—are accompanied by dike intrusions, showing a much less regular pattern, although preferred directions are generally noticeable. The cracks they fill are most probably due to the pushing of the granite itself, and very often a detailed scrutiny of the walls of the dikes can prove that they have simply moved apart. Small notches or other specific rock characteristics can sometimes be matched in the opposite walls. This was demonstrated very convincingly by E. Niggli (1953), who cut out a dike shown on a photograph and joined the fragments of the host rock again in their original position (Fig. 64).

There are many other examples where dike intrusion can be directly related to a tension field without the mechanism of elastic release. A particularly convincing instance has been given by Wager and Deer (1938, 1947) from East Greenland. A basalt blanket covers a metamorphic series and is bent in a flexure along the coast, along a stretch many hundreds of kilometers in length. The axis of the flexure lies along a smooth curve which follows the run of the coast. This flexure is accompanied by a dike swarm which is most intimately connected with it (Fig. 65). Not only does it follow the flexure most faithfully, but it is also restricted to the convex bend of the flexure and absent in the concave part. There is, moreover, a direct relation between the frequency of the dikes and the maximum curvature in the flexure. When the dip is 55°, more than 100 dikes per mile across the structure are found; when the dip is only 12°, the swarm contains only some 20 dikes per mile; and where the dip decreases to 7°, only a few dikes are observed. The dikes themselves dip approximately perpendicular to the lavas. The position of the dike swarm in relation to the flexure

Fig. 65   Dike swarms from East Greenland coast. (*After Wager,* 1938.)

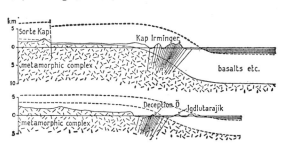

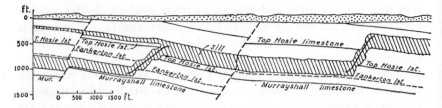

Fig. 66   Stirling dolerite sill. (*After Macgregor, 1948. Published by permission of Her Majesty's Stationery Office.*)

strongly suggests that the dikes fill tension fissures due to bending of the earth's crust along the coast. The flexure causes a maximum structural difference in level of at least 8 km.

Sills.   A sill is a sheet of igneous rock injected parallel to the bedding. All the great sill complexes of the world consist of basaltic rocks, dolerites, etc. An interesting system occurs in the Anti-Atlas, where its close relation with a dolerite dike 120 km long is clearly established. The intrusion of the dike and sills is earlier than the slightly folded margin of the Sahara craton, and can be dated as very early in the Upper Carboniferous. Sills occur at different horizons ranging from the Cambrian to the Devonian. Because of the lack of vegetation and deep erosion of the country, it is sometimes possible to see, in a single outcrop, the transition from dike to sill. On the southern slope of the Djebel (mountain) Saghro, in the eastern part of the Anti-Atlas, for instance, one can follow the dike intrusion in the Lower Cambrian, rising and causing considerable and violent disturbance in the otherwise extremely even bedding just before it turns into the sill. From the moment the sheet assumes a quasi-horizontal position between the thick sandbeds, all evidence of disturbances disappears. Apparently the vertical crack which was followed and caused by the ascending dolerite magma did not extend through the whole series toward the surface; the ascent was stopped, but the intrusive mass possessed sufficient pressure to cause violent disturbances before it found its way between the sandstone.

That the transgression of a sill can take advantage of existing faults is proved by the Stirling dolerite sill (Macgregor, 1948) of the Midland Valley, Scotland (Fig. 66). In the mine workings the sill repeatedly changes its stratigraphical position by following some of the normal faults of this coal field.

The preference of a dike intrusion for either a subvertical or a subhorizontal extension is evidently due to a particular property of the postorogenic stress field. Dolerite dikes are always characteristic of nonorogenic or specifically cratonic conditions (the Karroo Formation in South Africa, for instance), where epeirogenic lateral tension is a frequent occurrence (rift valleys). During its ascent the dike meets less and less vertical stress, and at a certain stage its own upsurge may turn the scales so that the median and smallest principal stresses, which hitherto were orientated, respectively, in the vertical and horizontal sense, change places. It will then make a sharp bend from the vertical to the horizontal and intrude itself between the layered beds at the appropriate horizon.

Veins. Veins differ from dikes in that their emplacement is certainly a long and complicated process. It is true that in dikes, also, a succeeding series of intrusions can sometimes be observed, proving that the same stress field reigned for a long time, but more generally only one kind of rock is intruded, probably in one single process. In metalliferous veins, where the filling has a hydrothermal character, successive phases can almost invariably be deduced from the mineralogical sequence, by the evidence of one kind of mineral systematically corroding another. Evidently such processes are comparatively slow. This is a warning that faults, which in a tectonic sense are often regarded as sudden occurrences, may also in fact be the result of slow processes. The complete integration of faults in the folding movement, which we shall consider later on, leads to the same conclusion. Veins, in common with dikes, are often orientated perpendicular to the smallest stress direction. In other instances, however, veins obviously follow oblique shear planes, even intersecting shears, and ore shoots on the intersecting lines of shear planes are a frequent and well-known phenomenon. This latter fact can readily be understood, for even when the movement of the blocks separated by the intersecting shear planes is small, there will always be a zone of crushing and tension on the intersecting line (Fig. 67), and this will be favorable for hydrothermal intrusion or recrystallization. Veins on the shear planes themselves are less easily understood, but unless the shear is very regular and planar, every irregularity will cause a certain crushing and widening of the fracture. Moreover, the vein emplacement is often not only the filling of a void, but also a replacement by metasomatism, facilitated by the crushing of the host rock.

This explanation, however, is not entirely satisfactory in view of the great frequency of veins along oblique shear. The problem is presented in a more trenchant form by the pattern of clastic dikes of the Big

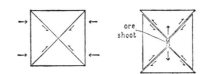

Fig. 67 Ore shoot on the intersection of shear planes.

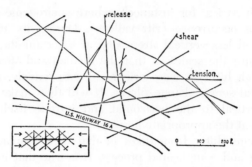

Fig. 68   Clastic dikes of the Big Badlands of
South Dakota. (*After Smith*, 1952.)

Badlands of South Dakota (Smith, 1952; Fig. 68). According to
Smith's description, there can be no doubt that the filling of the cracks
with volcanic ash, sand, silt, and clay proceeded from above and not
from below. Hence they must have presented open fissures at some
time or other. The pattern clearly represents a conjugate set of shear
planes, intersected by a main tension phase parallel to the stress, and
other tension joints perpendicular to this stress. The main tension joint
bisects the acute angle of the intersecting shear joints very accurately.
All the planes are filled with clastic material. From this picture it is
obvious that the fissure system is due to a uniform stress field and its
elastic release. The elastic release not only originated the secondary
set of tension cracks perpendicular to the original stress, but also
opened up the shear joints. This mechanism of elastic release explains
satisfactorily the filling up of shear joints or fractures with vein
material and makes intelligible the fact that very often only one
direction of a conjugate set is favored by metalliferous ore deposition.

Chapter 10

Upthrusts and Downfaulting

Thrust faults and normal faults are both dip-slip faults, both are due to vertical movements of the crust, and it often is difficult to decide from the field evidence whether a block has moved upward or a rift has dropped downward. Therefore they will be described in one chapter. Nevertheless, there is a fundamental genetic difference between upthrust and downfaulting, because the upthrust has some characteristics of a compressional stress field and the downfaulting those of a tensional stress field.

CHARACTERISTICS OF NORMAL FAULTS

Normal faults occur in relation to folding and independently of other structures. The first group will be treated in Chap. 14. The independent normal faults can belong to large structural features, e.g., the rifts, or can be of much smaller size and belong to a simple fracture system. The hade of major faults is an extremely important factor from a technical point of view, for instance, in the collieries of the South Limburg coal field, since these faults form the boundaries of the individual fields of exploitation. In addition, the probable position of the fault at depth is a matter of considerable anxiety to the mining engineer, since serious water trouble may be expected in its vicinity. Hence a trustworthy prognosis of the positions of the fault planes with increasing depth is, apart from its theoretical interest, a matter of considerable economic value. In textbooks, the dip of large normal faults belonging to rifts is stated to vary from 45 to 90° but values between 65 and 70° are stated to be most frequent. The only dip actually measured that Cloos mentions in his textbook (1936, p. 407), is one of 55° observed in the Loretto tunnel near Freiburg im Breisgau. Elsewhere Cloos (1936, p. 274) remarks, concerning this same measurement, "Von diesem einzigartigen Querschnitt wird jede künftige Diskussion des Rheingrabens, ja der groszen Brüche der Erde

Fig. 69   Normal faults in South Limburg coal field exposed at different levels. (*After Dikkers and Patijn*, 1944.)

überhaupt auszugehen haben." I quite agree with Cloos that such artificial outcrops in tunnels, borings, mines, etc., are more valuable to our problem than surface outcrops in general, since the latter are mostly too small in the vertical sense to yield satisfactory and trustworthy measurements of the general dip of the fault. Even better than the measurements in the Loretto Tunnel are those of some sections published by Dikkers and Patijn (1944); (Fig. 69) and Rutten (1943), all on the limiting step faults of the Roer Valley rift in the South Limburg collieries. Rutten measured in the Coal Measures in one section a hade of 60° and in another, one of 50°. Dikkers measured in four of his sections angles of 50, 60, 57, and 65°. These important measurements are very accurate, for all of them are founded on two or more determinations of the fault plane, in drifts or in underground boreholes, at least 100 m apart in vertical distance.

The torsion-balance survey of the great faults of the Roer Valley

Fig. 70   Torsion-balance section across normal fault (Feldbiss) in South Limburg coal field. (*After Zijlstra, Geologie en Mijnbouw, N.S., vol. 6, 1944.*)

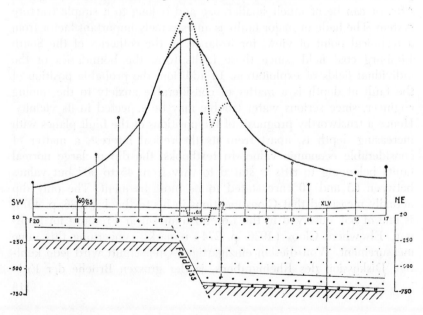

rift revealed that flat dips predominate, particularly when the throw is large (de Sitter, 1947); (Fig. 70). Let us consider this particular rift in more detail. The Roer Valley rift is the deepest rift belonging to the extensive system of NW-SE faults, which reaches from the Belgian Campine in the west far into the Ruhr coal field in the east (Fig. 71), and from Bonn on the Rhine to s'-Hertogenbosch in the north of the province of North Brabant of the Netherlands. Its continuation farther northward is surmised, but has not been ascertained. The fault system probably originated at the end of the Permian and had a maximum period of activity between the Lower Jurassic and the Cretaceous and another period of activity in the younger Tertiary. A detailed description of the gravimetric survey can be found in de Sitter (1947), the tectonic structure of the South Limburg coal field in Sax (1946), that of the Ruhr coal field in Kukuk (1938). Together these give a complete

Fig. 71 Fault pattern of Lower Rhine embayment. (*After de Sitter, 1949; and Ahorner, 1962*).

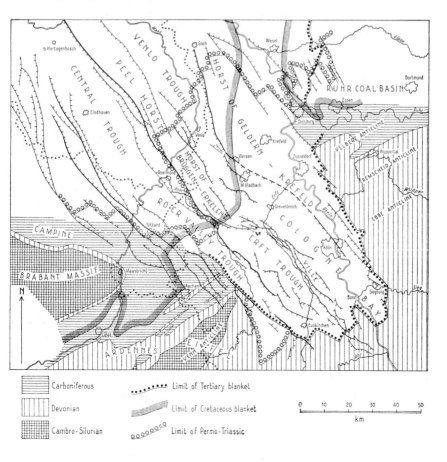

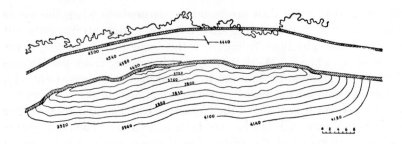

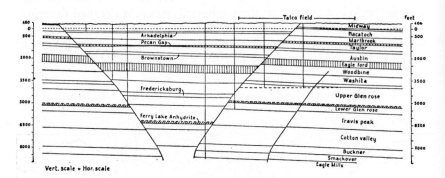

Fig. 72 Talco oil field, Texas, map and section. (*After Shelby*, 1951. *Published by permission of the University of Texas.*)

bibliography of the whole area. The faulting is due to lateral tension and must be connected with the Upper Rhine Valley rift. Locally, it is closely connected with the repeated uplift of the older ENE-WSW Variscan orogenic belt of the Armorican Mountains, of which the Ardennes form a portion, cutting it almost perpendicularly. The maximum total throw of the Roer Valley rift is perhaps some 2,000 m, and it is filled with some 900-m-thick series of Triassic and Lower Lias, perhaps 200 m of Upper Cretaceous, some 300 m of Lower Tertiary, and 600 m of Upper Tertiary (depending, of course, on where these thicknesses are measured, since the throw of the fault decreases in a southern direction). These numerical values of the thicknesses are somewhat conjectural, however, as no drill hole in the rift has penetrated much beyond the younger Tertiary. The data are derived from drill holes on the fault steps along the border of the fault troughs, from quantitative calculations of numerous gravimetrical sections, and from general geological considerations. All the fault-dip measurements which could be made arrived at the same result, i.e., of dips less than 70° and more than 40°. Kukuk (1938, p. 337) reports that the normal faults of the Ruhr coal field have a hade of 50 to 70°, but that the flatter dips are to be found in the less folded regions to the north and the steeper dips in the zone of the steep anticlines and synclines in the south, where the throw is, moreover, much smaller; i.e., the throws decrease as the dips increase from north to south. The same is true for the South Limburg coal field, where it was observed that the larger the throw, the flatter the dip. I do not think that Carboniferous folding has anything to do with the dip of these normal faults (as Kukuk suggested), but believe instead that the dip simply decreases with increasing throw from both extremities toward the center of a normal fault.

For this aspect we shall review a region in southern Arkansas where the extremities of the fault are better known than in the Ruhr district. We find here several oil fields which show an oil accumulation against a normal fault, e.g., the Fouke, Nick Springs, Stamps-Lewisville, and Fray oil fields. Each of them shows a doming effect against the normal fault, which has a dip of 45 to 55°. The same feature of a half dome limited at one side by a normal fault can be observed in nearly all the fields of the Mexia fault zone, to which we shall refer further on. Perhaps the best developed half dome of this type is the Talco oil field in Texas (Fig. 72; Shelby, 1951). I do not think that the doming ought to be regarded as a folding phenomenon due to a compressive stress separate from the faulting. On the contrary, the two features belong to one and the same tensional stress field. The development of even a normal fault is not due to a static stress condition; it is a dynamic process during which the stress conditions necessarily change in consequence of the very effect they produce. We may expect the initial stress condition to be more or less homogeneous along a certain horizontal distance (Fig. 73a). For some reason or other the shearing process starts at one point (P in Fig. 73a), and soon a small normal fault has developed. It has been shown by E. M. Anderson (1951) that the shearing stress is variable along the shearing plane, being maximum at its edges and minimum at the starting point P.

In order to allow the fault to develop, either both lips of the fault

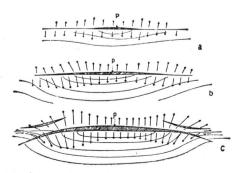

Fig. 73 Development of normal fault.

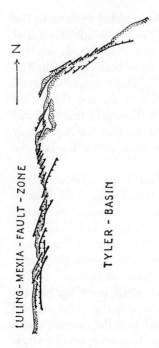

Fig. 74 Mexia fault zone from tectonic map of the United States. (*Published by permission of the U.S. Geological Survey.*)

must move, one upward, the other downward, or one is stationary and the other moves. The result is half a dome as figured by the contour lines in Fig. 73*b* and *c*. The process is represented in a horizontal plane, but if we regard it as we ought to do, as a three-dimensional process, we should probably see that the stress condition at the edges no longer conforms to the original condition, but that horizontal stresses along the fault planes have developed as a result of the doming effect at the center. It therefore seems very probable that the edge conditions may cause both a steepening of the original 45 to 70° dip of the normal fault plane and its splitting up into several divergent smaller faults—so-called "splays." These splays are very frequent at the extremities of large rifts, as Cloos has pointed out (Fig. 83).

Fig. 75 The hade of the Mexia faults. (*After Lahee, 1929. Published by permission of the American Association of Petroleum Geologists.*)

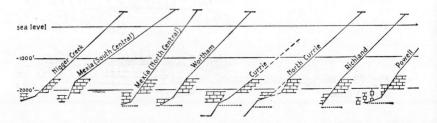

Table 8. Dip of the Mexia Faults in Eight Oil Fields

Oil Field	Dip of Fault Plane, deg	Maximum Displacement, ft.
Nigger Creek	43	500
Mexia (South Central)	35⎫	550
Mexia (North Central)	53⎭	
Wortham	46	600–650
North Currie	42	395
Richland	45	450–500
Powell	51	650
Average	45	

A very thoroughly explored fault zone is the Mexia group of faults (Fig. 74) in Central Texas, against which, in a number of formerly important fields, oil has accumulated. The dip of the main fault planes can be measured very accurately by joining the surface outcrop of the fault with the numerous points at which the fault has been crossed by the drill holes (Lahee, 1929). In his paper, Lahee assembles the dips of fault planes of eight oil fields (Fig. 75); they vary from 35 to 53°, with an average of 45° (Table 8).

Actually, the dip of the faults varies from the extremes of 16° to 63°, being steeper in the brittle Austin Chalk, less steep in the soft Eagle Ford Shale, and steeper again in the Woodbine Sandstone. In Fig. 76, a typical section through one of the oil fields, these particular features are evident. The nature of the rock has apparently a great

Fig. 76 Section through Mexia fault. (*After Lahee*, 1929. *Published by permission of the American Association of Petroleum Geologists.*)

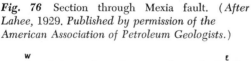
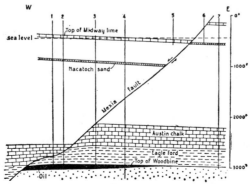

influence on the hade of a normal fault, and we may imagine that, in a particular incompetent layer of sufficient thickness at greater depth, the fault will be lost altogether when the tension diminishes downward or is replaced by another stress condition. This is in perfect accordance with the experimental evidence, by which we learned that the angle between the shear plane and the largest stress direction depends on the nature of the rock and the hydrostatic pressure. Near the surface we may expect higher dips than at depth.

TILTING OF STEP BLOCKS AND ANTITHETIC FAULTS

Large normal faults are often accompanied by so-called antithetic faults, which hade toward the main fault and therefore away from the main rift valley. They appear clearly in some of Cloos's experiments (Fig. 81) and are particularly well developed along the Rhine rift. They have been explored in great detail in the Pechelbronn oil field. The average dip measured on three sections by Haas and Hoffmann (1928), containing some 15 faults (one section is represented by Fig. 77), is 49°, varying from 43 to 57°. On a more recent map by Schnaebele (1937), dips of 40 to 60° appear. This author says: "Leur inclinaison est en général de l'ordre de 50°, mais peut varier de 40 à 65°."

Sometimes the whole graben structure is more like one major fault, with one or two accompanying antithetic faults, as in the Hessische Graben belonging to the Saxonic faulted area, which has been treated extensively by H. Stille and F. Lotze and their students in the series of *Geotektonische Forschungen*. The schematic section of the Egge rift from a paper by Martini (1937) (Fig. 78) is here reproduced. In many outcrops faults with hades of 50° and less were measured (cf. Lemke, 1937, pp. 39 and 40). These narrow rifts, often not more than 1 km wide, are not supposed to be formed by two equivalent faults, but by one major fault, with a rather flat hade and one or more antithetic secondary faults, as in Fig. 78.

Fig. 77 Section through Pechelbronn oil field, with faults antithetic to main rift fault. (*After Schnaebele, 1937.*)

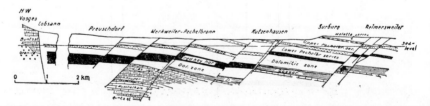

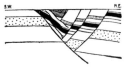

Fig. 78 Section through Egge rift, showing small antithetic faults. (*After Martini,* 1937.)

Fig. 79 Tilting of blocks: (*a*) Planar step faults, no tilting; (*b*) curved step faults with tilting; (*c–d*) development of antithetic faults due to curved shape of main fault.

In the Pechelbronn section, the tilting of the blocks is well demonstrated. This feature is very common, and is regarded as quite a normal phenomenon accompanying step faults. But it does not occur on the steps of the Roer Valley rift. The tilting is easily understood when we realize that a block is limited by two faults, and that its relative movement along these two faults is contradictory. The two shearing stresses together form a couple which will give a rotational motion to the block. Whether the couple succeeds in tilting the blocks or not will be, on the one hand, a matter of fortuity and depends largely on the nature of the rocks involved (incompetent rocks will allow more scope to this motion than will competent rocks) and, on the other hand, a question of the shape of the fault—a downward flattening of the fault will facilitate the rotation better than will a straight and invariable dip (Fig. 79*c*).

Goguel pointed out that the antithetic faults accompanying a single normal fault plane are a result of the somewhat curved shape of the main fault, because further slipping down of one block would result in a gap at the surface and this is filled up by antithetic blocks (Fig. 79*c*). We might conclude that the forming of antithetic blocks and of tilted step blocks are alternative solutions of the same problem of tectonic forces: both indicate a flattening of the hade of the main fault with increasing depth.

FAULTS OF THE BASIN AND RANGE FAULT SYSTEM

Tilting is very pronounced in the faulted Basin and Range system of the Great Basin of the Rocky Mountains. In central Utah the Wasatch Mountains and the Oquirrh Range have been faulted after folding.

The faults are true gravity faults limiting tilted blocks. Their dips can be measured with some accuracy in this bare hill country. The Oquirrh Range has been mapped by Gilluly (1932), and the following excerpt is from his paper:

> An additional point of interest in connection with the frontal faulting of the Oquirrh Mountains is the prevailing steep dips of the fault-planes. Fourteen measurements of dip were made, either on bedrock fault surfaces or by the 3 point method, in places where the topographic relief of the country traversed by the faults was sufficient. The measurements range from 40°–64° and average 57°. The West Mercur fault changes in dip from 40°–60° within a mile. . . .

The Wasatch Range has been mapped by Eardley (1933) and is also a tilted fault block. The net slip on the major fault planes ranges from 2,200 to 2,600 m. Two dip observations indicated a dip of 50°W. The following excerpt is from Eardley's paper:

> Two parallel faults of the Basin and Range orogeny cross the mouth of North Canyon. An old prospect hole follows down a silver gouge on the eastern of these two faults, just north of the canyon. The foot-wall is the fault-plane. The dip, definitely defined, is 50°W. At the mouth of Santaquin canyon the trace of the main fault is seen in the south wall and, if the writer's interpretation is correct, measures about 50°W . . . which facts add additional weight to the conclusion [of Gilluly] that the main faults of the Basin and Range orogeny in the vicinity of the Wasatch Mountains dip about 50°–55°.

A general review of the Basin and Range faults has been given by Nolan (1943). The eastern limit of the faulted part of the Great Basin is formed by the Wasatch fault. Farther west we find the faulted Oquirrh Range, the Stansbury Range, and the Cedar Range, each of them another tilted fault block of some 20 miles breadth. The western limit is the great normal fault which limits the tilted Sierra Nevada block to the west. A typical range in the north-central part of the province is the Ruby and Thumboldt Mountain Range (R. P. Sharp, 1939). All these faults have undergone recurrent motion, usually in the same sense. In the Basin range one can distinguish five periods between the first (late Middle Miocene) and the last (Late Pleistocene to Recent) phases, a recurrence which is very similar to the recurrent motion on the Roer Valley rift faults. In the case of the Roer Valley rift there are several periods in the Permian and Triassic, followed by opposite thrusting movements during the Upper Cretaceous, and then normal movement again at several times from the Miocene to the Recent.

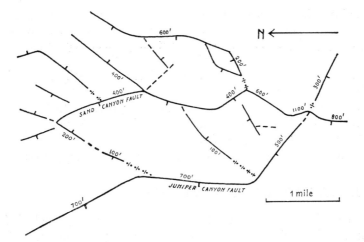

Fig. 80   Fault pattern at Juniper Canyon, Basin and Range
province, south-central Oregon. (*After Donath, 1962. Published
by permission of the Geological Society of America.*)

In central Oregon the late Tertiary basalt flows have been broken
up by a fault system which has been analyzed by Donath (1962).
There is a typical and prominent conjugate set of vertical faults intersecting in an angle of 55°, probably representing an oblique shear set
which later, because of elastic release, became reactivated by vertical
movements (Figs. 80 and 68).

Without doubt, the best exposed normal fault faces which have
become known are the Death Valley and Panamint faults in southern
California. Noble (1926) gives a vivid description of these huge fault
scarps. The two faults are so very similar that they may be regarded
as twin features with a common origin. They form two escarpments
some 60 km long and 40 km apart and are roughly parallel. The following excerpt is from Noble's paper:

The escarpments are exceedingly rugged, bare, sloping rock-surfaces that
rise abruptly from the valley floor. At most places the profile of this
rock-surface exhibits three elements, at the base a small vertical cliff
or set of cliffs at some places over 30 m high, at other places absent.
This cliff marks a recent vertical fault. . . . Above the small vertical
cliff the escarpment rises several thousand feet in an extraordinary huge
sloping surface whose angle of slope averages 35°. This surface is scored
by innumerable parallel ravines which run straight down it to the valley.
These gullies are deep, straight and acutely V-shaped. One would like
to call it a fault face. Above the gullied surface the slope of the escarpment becomes much gentler, changing to about 25°. Wide valleys with

broad mouths open out at the top of the 35° slope, and the topographic forms become relatively subdued and rounded. The relatively mature topography above this rock face is then the pre-fault topography.

The rocks which compose the rock faces are chiefly Precambrian gneisses and schists, crushed and sheared to a virtual fault gouge. The shearing planes in this crushed material are parallel to the slant of the rock face. The date of the normal faulting is probably Early Quaternary. The trace of the faults on the map is exceedingly irregular in detail, and their escarpments have a roughly zigzag pattern.

THE GREAT RIFT SYSTEMS

In the earth's crust we find large and very long zones which have repeatedly been disturbed by large-scale normal faulting alone, forming horsts and rift valleys. The most famous example is the African rift zone, extending 6,000 km from south to north and accompanied by volcanoes, which reaches the Red Sea graben and is continued in Palestine and the Lebanon. A second, with the same direction, is the Upper Rhine graben, which, with a detour round the Alps, reaches the Rhone graben and can be followed northward until it is lost in the Roer Valley rift, in the Westphalen Ruhr coal-basin* faults, and in the Hessische graben. The latter is often thought to extend below the North German plain into the Oslo rift.

It is true that compressive stress perpendicular to the fault strike has been proposed for the African fault zone, the Upper Rhine rift, and the Basin and Range province, but these views have never gained much support, and their arguments have been proved insufficient. In every instance in which sufficient data were available, it has been proved that the faults hade toward the down-thrown block, and the mechanism therefore represents a broadening or a stretching of the surface, and not a compression. The problem of the origin of the rift has been illustrated by H. Cloos (1929–1932) by a series of experiments with clay cakes, and very convincing imitations of a rift valley were obtained. Cloos carried out several experiments: first, with a clay cake mounted on two boards which were drawn apart; second, with an inflated rubber balloon at the base of the clay cake; and finally, with a rubber plate which was stretched (Fig. 81). The balloon best imitated his theory that the rift valley was due to an arching of the Rhine shield, while the other two experiments simply illustrated a stretching mechanism. With the rubber balloon the upper layer of

---

* The Roer Valley rift and the Ruhr coal field are named after two different rivers although they are pronounced exactly alike in Dutch and German, the Roer being an affluent of the Meuse, the Ruhr of the Rhine.

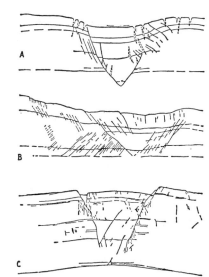

Fig. 81 Three experiments imitating normal faulting. (*A*) Clay cake mounted on two boards; (*B*) clay cake mounted on stretched rubber plate; (*C*) clay cake mounted on inflated rubber balloon. (*After H. Cloos, 1930.*)

the clay cake is stretched much farther than the bottom. In all three instances we find a very good imitation of rift valleys in general, with their limiting step faults and other peculiarities. Very often the lips of the rifts are raised, and this is certainly true, as Cloos pointed out, for the Upper Rhine Valley and the Red Sea. This fact was the basis of Cloos's theory connecting the rift with the arching of the Rhine shield. The same observation led Taber (1927) and, in the beginning, also Cloos (1929), independently, to the theory that the inward sloping normal faults of a rift are the boundaries of a trapezium-shaped block of the earth's crust, which by virtue of its shape will become depressed into the heavier substratum in which it floats (Fig. 82), whereas the borders of the trough will rise on account of their shape. The hypothesis is very attractive, but has the disadvantage that the mechanism can be applied only to major fault troughs where the faults are sufficiently far apart to reach this substratum. With a width of 30 km the limiting faults could just reach the substratum, but smaller troughs and horsts would not come into contact with it. The Lower Rhine fault system, for instance, consists in part of a close succession of much narrower alternating horsts and rifts (Fig. 71), all of which have exactly the same character as the larger ones. To make a distinction between the larger and the smaller rifts would be illogical. Moreover,

Fig. 82. Experiment demonstrating tilting of floating blocks. (*After Taber, 1927*).

the raising of the lips of the rifts is definitely *not* a feature of the Lower Rhine faulting. Other great rifts such as the Upper Rhine Valley rift or the Red Sea rift approximate this outline much better. The two theories, arching and hydrostatic equilibrium, are not, however, mutually exclusive. When the doming effect is too small for the faults to reach the substratum, the hydrostatic readjustment is impossible. When, on the contrary, the substratum is reached, an extra amount of sinking may occur in the trough and the lips of the bordering high will be warped up. In that case the formation of the trough might be accompanied by volcanic activity along its boundaries. In a later paper, Cloos (1932) has given a very convincing analysis of the doming of the Rhine shield (Fig. 83). He regards the arching of the shield as the direct cause of the downfaulting of the Upper Rhine

Fig. 83   Rhine shield with Upper Rhine rift valley. (*After Cloos,* 1936.)

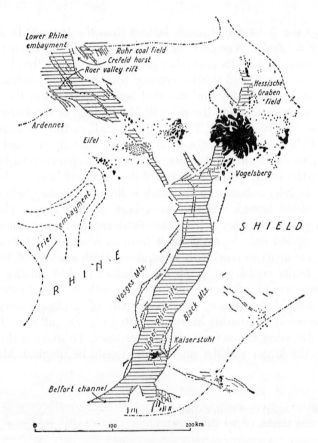

graben. He considers that the stretching of the upper arc of the dome, and indeed the filling up of the rift structure, started in the Oligocene, contemporaneously with a major diastrophism in the Alps. He agrees that in detail there may seem to be many anomalies and difficulties, but points out that the intricate older structure of the shield must have interfered with the regularity of the phenomenon. The main objection against his conception is that, in the Lower Rhine fault region, the Upper Cretaceous unlift is distinctly prior to the Late Oligocene and Miocene downfaulting. This may be answered by assuming that there was no faulting during the first stages of doming, but that the fault troughs were formed only in the later stages, when the crust finally gave way. Another objection to Cloos's theory is the fact that the Upper Rhine rift does not end against the Jura Mountains near Basel, but sends out a branch which connects it with the Rhone Valley rift by way of the Belfort channel (de Sitter, 1939b). The doming is therefore partly a circum-Alpine phenomenon, partly a N-S-directed dome perpendicular to the Alpine folding, and partly a posthumous Variscan doming. As far as the Lower Rhine embayment is concerned, we can say that it is due to a tension force, following a compressive doming effect, acting on the NW flank of the uplifted Variscan orogenic belt, which is crossed by an approximately N-S secondary axis of positive movement.

From the Mid-Atlantic rift little is known yet except that a rift valley exists, 5 to 10 miles wide, on the center of the Mid-Atlantic Ridge (Hill, 1960). Nearly all earthquake epicenters of the Atlantic Ocean are concentrated in the central rift, and all the rocks that have been dredged up are of basaltic character and are probably of Tertiary age. Again we find here the combination of a large bulge with a narrow rift on its top (Chap. 26).

The African rift system consists primarily of two branches, an eastern (Gregory) rift, continuing through Ethiopia to the Red Sea rift (Mohr, 1962) and the larger and more prominent western rift, with the great lakes of Rukwa, Tanganyika, and Albert, converging near the top of the Nyassa rift. Its history is certainly complex and long and reaches into modern time because earthquakes still occur along its borders (Fig. 84).

The throw and situation of the faults are determined largely by morphological effects, among which the youngest are naturally most prominent. In the Gregory rift, for instance, the offset of Quaternary volcanic rocks is clearly visible in the field and beautifully expressed in aerial photographs (Baker, 1958). Offset of aplanation surfaces, presumably of Jurassic, Cretaceous, and Tertiary age (Dixey, 1946; James, 1956), gives the interpretation a basis.

The discussion of whether these features are of a tensional or com-

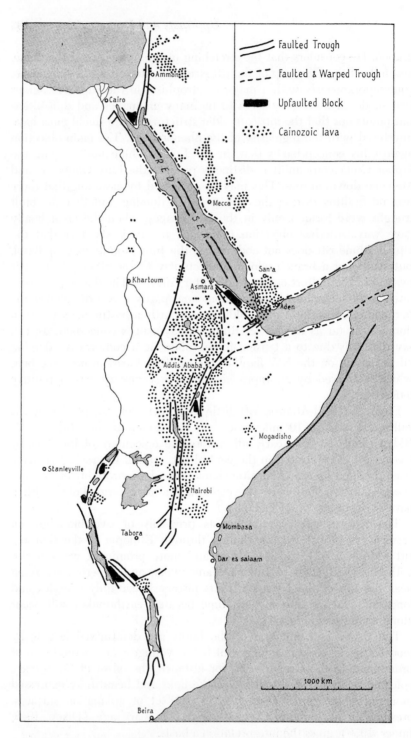

Fig. 84 The African rift system. (*After P. A. Mohr, 1962. Published by permission of University College Addis Ababa.*)

pressive origin has centered around the African rifts. It was started
by Bailey Willis (1936), who advocated the thrusting of two adjoining
blocks, pressing down the rift valley. The numerous proofs for normal
faulting as origin for rift valleys, brought forward in the preceding
paragraphs, must suffice here. It is true that none are derived from the
African rifts, and they are not mapped in detail, except that I personally saw a beautiful outcrop of a mylonitic zone exposed in the
eastern scarp of the Rukwa rift dipping with some 45° toward the lake,
that is, toward the rift. The discussion of negative gravimetric anomaly
observed over the rifts is interesting. It was started by Bullard (1936)
in favor of compression, contradicted by Vening Meinesz (1950) and
Goguel (1957, 1958).

It is interesting to note that in an analysis of seismological data
from the western rift by Sutton and Berg (1958) the first motion
studies indicated that dip-slip movement, presumably normal faulting,
is much more consistent with the actual fault strikes than strike-slip
motion.

In contrast with the African rifts, the Red Sea rift shows a positive
gravimetric Bouger anomaly (Girdler, 1958), centered on a narrow,
central, deeper rift zone. The Red Sea is considerably wider, though,
than the African rift, and it seems probable that intrusion or upwelling
of heavier basic rocks from the substratum, combined with the lack
of a thick light sediment infilling, causes this positive gravity anomaly,
in the presence of a positive magnetic zone.

In almost all rift sections the bordering faults are often drawn as
step faults, but the downfaulted block as a solid unit, principally
because nothing is known about its structure. In the Rhine Valley rift,
however, extensive geophysical exploration and drilling has revealed
that the whole block has been folded and is broken up in strips (Fig.
85; Andres, 1959). A similar pattern of faults in a downthrown rift
block is revealed in the young volcanic rocks filling up the western
rift in Central Africa (Baker, 1958).

In all these rifts, the Roerdal, Upper Rhine, and African rifts, it has
become abundantly clear that the present downthrow is the result of
a lengthy affair of repeated faulting over a long period. In the Upper
Rhine rift this has been worked out in detail by Murawski (1960),
with the result that a basin probably preceded the actual faulting and
that the activity in the different branches can vary considerably.

I shall try to summarize our experience of normal block faults.

A normal fault can have a slip from a few centimeters to many
kilometers. There is some evidence that the dip near the surface may
be greater than at greater depth. In general, it varies from 45 to 70°,
but in some instances dips of even less than 45° have been ascertained.
Normal faults are always due to a tensional stress, and they represent

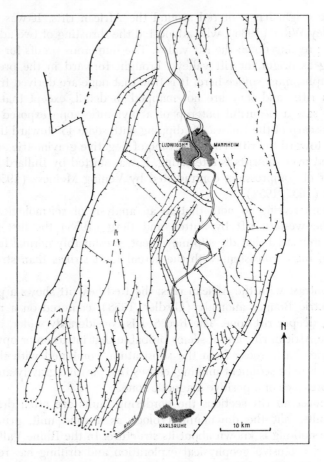

Fig. 85 Southern part of Upper Rhine rift with complicated
fault structure in downthrown block. (*After J. Andres and
A. Schad, 1959. Published by permission of Industrie
Verlag von Hernhausen.*)

a shearing plane parallel to the medium principal stress, which is
situated in the horizontal plane, and make an acute angle with the
largest principal stress, that of gravity, the least principal stress
direction being the direction of tension. The nature of the rocks also
influences the dip, which is flatter in soft incompetent layers than in
brittle competent horizons. There seems to be a correlation between
the maximum slip and the dip of the fault, the dip being flatter at the
maximum and steeper near the edges of the fault, where the dip slip
is probably partly replaced by strike slip. Normal faulting often shows
an en échelon arrangement, which may be due either to the over-

lapping of different faults of the same origin and direction or to a surface expression of a deep-seated shearing movement, making an acute angle with the normal fault direction. The width of the blocks between the steps varies greatly and may be anything from a few meters up to scores of kilometers. There is no apparent correlation between the amount of slip and the width of the steps or any other feature. Both tilting of the steps and antithetic faulting are probably due to the flattening of the fault face downward. The origin of tensional stress may vary greatly; we know of long tension zones, local tension zones, tension zones oblique to shearing, and many other types of origin. Individual normal faults have the same characteristics, whatever their cause. Step faults are very common, and antithetic faults are often observed.

There are many normal faults, closely connected with individual folds, which have nevertheless the same characteristics as the block faults, but these will be described in connection with folding. On the other hand, there is generally no direct genetic connection between belts of folding and normal faulting; this is logical, since the stresses which might be expected to produce them are diametrically different.

UPTHRUSTS AND BLOCK FAULTING

While large normal faults are typically independent of folding, and wrench faults show frequent transitions to folding but are still often independent, thrust faults, on the contrary, are usually closely connected with the folding process. This difference in the relation between folding and the three principal classes of large faults is readily understandable when we realize that the orientation of the three principal stresses in thrusting and folding is the same, the plane of the largest and smallest principal stresses being vertical, the plane of the median and largest principal stresses being horizontal. Both folds and thrusts show an expansion in the vertical direction and a shortening in the horizontal direction.

Before we treat low-angle thrusts, which form an integral part of asymmetric folding, we shall consider a smaller, but important, class, the so-called upthrusts, which are features more or less independent of folding.

Upthrusts.   The upthrust is a rather steeply dipping reversed fault (greater than 60°), which develops most frequently in massive crystalline rocks of the basement. The same kind of movement in stratified rocks would give rise to flexuring or other kinds of asymmetric folding, as, for instance, in monoclines (Chap. 14). Upthrusts are found, therefore, near or in the stable shields of the continents, but they are also particularly frequent on the borders of the great folded mountain

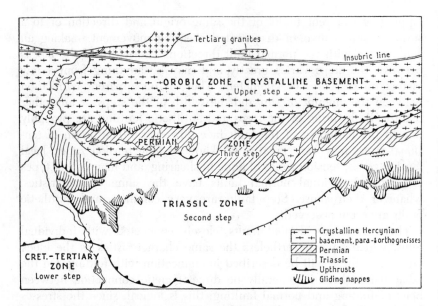

Fig. 86 Schematic map of the Lombardy Alps, showing longitudinal blocks limited by thrust faults. (*After de Sitter,* 1949.)

chains, where the central part has been pushed over the subsiding marginal troughs. We find this latter situation, for instance, in the Lombardy section of the southern Alps (Fig. 86).

The general structure of the Bergamasc Alps (de Sitter, 1949; Dozy, 1935; Zijlstra, 1941) consists of a series of longitudinal blocks, separated by upthrusts and strongly pressed together along these thrust zones.

To a certain degree each block is characterized by rocks of a particular age: the southern and lowest block, by Triassic limestones; the middle block, by Permian clastic and volcanic rocks; the northern and highest block, by crystalline schists, gneisses, and granites. The Orobic fault which separates the northern crystalline block from the Permian zone is one of these big thrust faults which flattens out toward Lake Como in the west and is accompanied by a whole series of similar thrusts to the south. The two sections of Fig. 87 are taken from the western and eastern parts of the Orobic zone, where the upthrusts are very frequent and form an imbricate structure.

These faults are not particularly straight, their surface outcrop resembles those of normal faults, and they often replace one another en échelon. Mylonite zones are frequent and often very thick. Their dip below the higher block can be ascertained only when the topography is sufficiently pronounced.

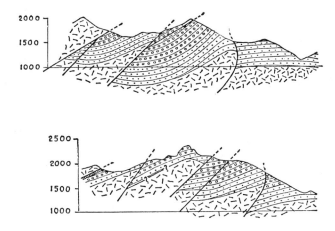

Fig. 87   Two sections through Orobic zone of the Lombardy Alps, showing imbricated structures. (*After Zijlstra, 1941.*)

Very often the nature of upthrusts is masked when sedimentary rocks are involved. On the southern border of the High Atlas, for instance, the Upper Cretaceous presents a series of vertical flexures which limit blocks of almost horizontal strata (Fig. 88), but I think there can be little doubt that in the basement we should find a series of thrust faults similar to those in the higher parts of the Bergamasc Alps. The same kind of structure has been described in the Pyrenees (Destombes, 1948; de Sitter, 1949).

The above-mentioned examples of upthrusting in the border zone of an orogene has led Beloussov (1959, 1960), with the evidence offered by the Caucasus Mountains, to stress the importance of vertical movements in the development of an orogene. The principles that vertical upward motion of a block causes inclined thrusting around its borders has been demonstrated by Russian experiments, quoted in Beloussov (1960) and by Sanford (1959). Apparently, these border thrusts can

Fig. 88   Simplified section through southern margin of High Atlas in Morocco.

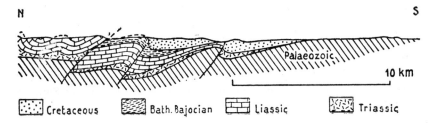

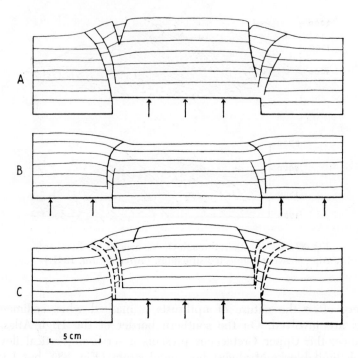

Fig. 89   Upthrust structures. Experiments with sand material.
(*After Sanford, 1959. Published by permission of the Geological
Society of America.*)

become quite flat. In this respect the study of uplifted blocks in
nature becomes particularly interesting.

One of the most accurately studied and very typical uplifted blocks
is that of the Beartooth Mountains in the middle Rocky Mountains
(Foose et al., 1961). It is a roughly rectangular block of some 40 by
80 miles of Precambrian rocks standing high above the surrounding
plains. The block is bounded on all sides by faults with important
vertical throw (Fig. 90). The uplift of some 1,000 m of the block was
accompanied and succeeded by horizontal movements resulting in
thrusting and secondary wrench faults. The boundary faults steepen
downward and may become flat thrusts in their upper reaches, a structure similar to that observed along the Osning fault in Germany (Fig.
305). There can be no doubt that the uplift of this block is closely
connected with the subsidence of the Bighorn and other basins (Fig.
298) of Laramide age.

The fact that the steep vertical thrusts flatten out upward and
outward is a puzzling phenomenon. It has been shown by Sanford
(1959) with experiments (Fig. 89) to be principally due to a branch-

ing of the fault upward, demonstrating the wider distribution in space of the deformation away from the origin of the fault. In such a case the flattening of the thrust is not due to a primary horizontal stress, but is a secondary effect of a vertical movement. This conception has been applied by Osterwald (1961) to the whole front of the Cordilleran foreland, where vertical movements of the rigid basement block are thought to have caused folds in the overlying sedimentary rocks, in particular along the line separating the thick geosynclinal sequence from the thin cover on the foreland.

Although purely vertical upthrusting can certainly originate very flat thrusts in the upper layers, it is doubtless going too far to ascribe all tectonical deformation to phenomenon related to vertical movements as van Bemmelen and Carey do.

Besides thrust faults of considerable throw, every tectonized region contains numerous small faults (less than 5 ft throw), which cannot be mapped on the usual scale of geological maps and appear only on mining maps. A statistical review of all the small faults in one of the South Limburg coal mines revealed that the average dip of small thrusts is 22° and that of small normal faults 63° (Fig. 91). The average dip of small normal faults is in good agreement with the dip of large normal faults, but the thrusts are decidedly of low-angle type, and not of steeper upthrust type.

Fig. 90   Major tectonic features around upthrusted Beartooth Mountains. (*After Foose, 1961. Published by permission of the Geological Society of America.*)

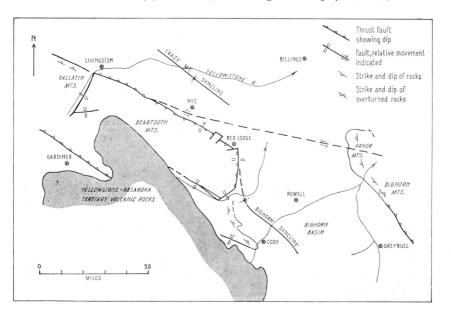

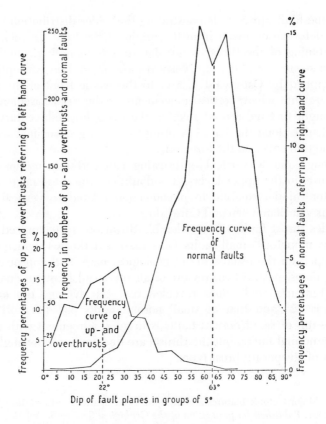

Fig. 91   Statistical frequency curves for small faults in
Willem-Sophy Colliery, South Limburg, Netherlands. (*After
Sax, 1946. Published by permission of the Geological
Bureau, Heerlen.*)

The average angles that these small faults make with the largest
principal stress (27° for the normal faults with a vertically directed
stress and 22° for the thrust faults with a lateral stress) differ only
slightly, and we may presume in this case that the thrusts are due to a
tectonic compression, and the normal faults to a dilatation of the
elastic release type. From this evidence we may perhaps conclude that
the steep upthrusts, certainly different in origin from the low-angle
thrusts, are not due to a simple lateral compression acting in the
horizontal plane, but to a differently orientated stress field, a vertical
upthrust. As we have remarked already, big steep thrusts are characteristic of the marginal areas of mountain chains and the uplifted
central massifs of crystalline rocks. Evidently such uplift implies in
itself a radial force.

Chapter 11

Wrench Faults

Different terms have been applied to these faults; in American usage we find "rifts" and "strike-slip faults" denoting the larger ones, and "tear-faults" used perhaps more often for the smaller ones. In English terminology "wrench faults" is the common term; "transcurrent faults" was proposed by Anderson in the first edition of his book (1942), but in the second edition (1951) this author reverted to preference for the term wrench faults.

The wrench fault is a shearing movement along a vertical plane. We can distinguish between sinistral and dextral faults; when the observer views a fault plane, motion on the distant side will appear either toward the left (sinistral) or toward the right (dextral).

In considering the phenomenon of wrench faulting we enter a domain in which many more complications arise and in which the pattern of the faults is much less simple and comprehensible than in that of normal faulting.

We shall find, however, the same general occurrences, e.g., very large faults, fault belts, and small faults of different kinds, many of them connected with folding.

Wrench faults are definitely due to a compressive stress. They are vertical, and hence we can state that the median principal stress is vertical, the largest and smallest stresses lying in the horizontal plane. It is logical to presume that wrench faults belong essentially to the unflexible portion of the earth's crust, the so-called crystalline basement, for instance. They are certainly not restricted to these portions of the earth's crust, however, since we also find them in highly mobile belts where individual blocks have moved in relation to one another.

The analysis of large earthquakes indicates that many more fault traces are due to wrench faulting, in particular round the Pacific, than was thought before (Scheidegger, 1963; Allen, 1962).

As regards the larger wrench faults, it is for several reasons extremely difficult to prove anything except their strike, and relatively few are definitively determined as wrench faults. First of all, they often change laterally into thrust faults; since both thrusts and wrench faults are due to lateral compression, this would be expected. Second, their outcrops are often deeply weathered and therefore covered by alluvial deposits, even when the slip is comparatively small. Very often they have been regarded, and perhaps still are, as normal gravity faults, for a vertical component of the motion is never altogether absent and is often locally important. Moreover, it is often almost impossible to decide whether the shift of homologous elements on both sides of the fault, when such can be recognized, is due to vertical or horizontal motion or both.

We shall study wrench faults by means of some well-known examples.

EXAMPLES OF WRENCH FAULTING

The Great Glen Fault of Scotland. In my description of the Great Glen wrench fault, I shall follow the paper by W. Q. Kennedy (1946), who made a special study of this fault.

The Great Glen fault intersects Scotland from coast to coast with a singular straightness and has a major effect on the topography of the region; there is a string of lakes along its eroded outcrop. Wherever this outcrop can be studied, the line of disruption is marked by a broad belt of crushed, sheared, and mylonitized rock up to 1.5 km in width. The ultimate products of the dislocation metamorphism are flinty-crush rocks and true ultramylonites.

The deep erosion along the fault, the true depth of which is masked by a filling of glacial sediments (sometimes more than 100 m) and by water (depth of Loch Ness 50 m), is doubtless due to this shatter belt. Although circumstances nowhere permit a factual measurement of the dip, it is obvious from the rectilinear character of the fault that it cannot deviate much from the vertical. Moreover, many subsidiary fractures, branching out from the main fault zone, are definitely vertical; some of these have, however, been proved to be steep thrust faults.

Kennedy advances very convincing arguments for a horizontal displacement along the fault of more than 100 km; the argument is chiefly based on the correlation of corresponding geological structures on either side of the fault.

The Moine Schists on both sides of the fault show a central zone of migmatite in whose center we find intrusive granites, the Strontian Granite on the NW side of the fault and the Foyers Granite on the SE side. When the northwest block is shifted 107 km to the northeast along the fault plane (as in Fig. 92), the two granite masses become

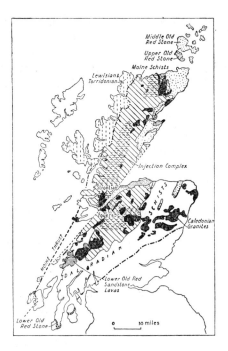

Fig. 92   The displacement along the Great Glen fault in northern Scotland. (*After Kennedy*, 1946. *Published by permission of the Geological Society of London.*)

Fig. 93   The Strontian and Foyers granites joined. (*After Kennedy*, 1946. *Published by permission of the Geological Society of London.*)

one mass, the migmatite zones correspond neatly, and the different metamorphic zones of the Moine Schists, the kyanite and sillimanite zones principally, form continuous belts. In addition, the characteristics of the two granite masses are very similar, each being a half dome truncated by the fault. Together they would form a typical granite stock with an outer tonalite zone around a center of porphyritic granodiorite, penetrated by a somewhat later intrusion of a fine-grained biotite-granite with typical structural features which would join admirably (Fig. 93).

By shifting the northwest block to its original position, we can even find the continuation of the famous Moine thrust plane, southeast of the fault in a thrust plane on the island of Islay. Finally, there are many parallel wrench faults north and south of the Great Glen fault, several of which have been proved to possess slips of 3 to 5 km in the same sinistral sense as the main fault.

Its continuation in northern direction to Shetland has been studied by Flinn (1961). On this island a N-S-striking crushed fault zone separates two regions of different structure which must have been active later than Lower Old Red Sandstone, in agreement with the Great Glen fault in Scotland, where the age of the main lateral movement falls in the Upper Old Red Sandstone or Lower Carboniferous period.

The main characteristics of this great wrench fault are its strictly rectilinear character, its wide shatter belt, containing true mylonites, its vertical position, parallel wrench faults of much smaller slip, and oblique thrust faults merging into the lateral shearing on approaching it. Although its age is Upper Paleozoic, seismic disturbances along its course still occur quite frequently.

The Great Glen fault (Chap. 9, Fig. 63) was most certainly due to a north-south lateral compressive stress at the beginning of the Hercynian folding and runs parallel to the grain of the Caledonian structure; this latter perhaps provided a zone of weakness of which the fault took advantage.

The San Andreas Wrench Fault, California. The fact that the San Andreas fault of California is such a widely known structural feature is no doubt mainly due to the great earthquake of Apr. 18, 1906. It also has a great influence on the topography of the region, which is marked by the very recent movements along its face.

We possess in an article by Taliaferro (1943) an excellent study of the San Andreas fault, which is based on intimate knowledge of the field characteristics along 80 km of its length and of the earlier literature. Since then many parts of the fault zone have been studied in detail, and it has become to some extent the "type" for wrench faulting.

Figure 94 presents the main faults of this region. The San Andreas fault can be traced for more than 800 km. At both ends it branches into two "splays" (the Hayward fault of San Francisco and the San Jacinto fault in the Peninsular Range). Such splays are a common feature of the extremities of all kind of faults, not of wrench faults alone (Fig. 73).

The fault may be divided into two portions, a northern one with NNW direction from the Tejon Pass northward, belonging to the structural field of the coast ranges, and a southern portion striking southeast of the Tejon Pass. The southern part is a structural feature of the Basin and Range province. At the junction of the north and south branches of the fault, the Garlock fault branches off from the San Andreas fault.

Although the two portions are certainly one fault now, their earlier history may have been quite different; they may only recently have been united into one fault zone. The northern branch has been studied

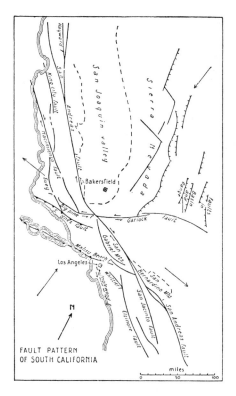

Fig. 94 The fault pattern of southern
California with the San Andreas fault.

most closely. It runs parallel with the western limit of the San Joaquin
Valley basin, but is itself not the limit. As Taliaferro describes it,
it is very close to the large Eocene normal fault which really limits
this basin, but seldom coincides with it. This earlier fault is always the
boundary between crystalline basement complex and Mesozoic sediments, whereas the San Andreas is either wholly within the crystalline
rocks or in the Mesozoic rocks, except where it cuts through younger
Tertiary formations. There is no doubt that its present major features
were formed by Plio-Pleistocene disturbances. It cuts the late Middle-
Pleistocene thrusts and other tectonic features, which can actually be
traced at the other side of the fault. Nearly everywhere along the
San Andreas fault there are attendant physiographic evidences of
recent shift, such as true sag ponds, offset ridge and drainage lines,
etc. For example, the Castle Mountain thrust, 15 km east of Parkfield,
which brings Franciscan (Jurassic) rocks above overturned Miocene
and Pliocene, can be traced northward until it becomes entangled

with the San Andreas, 20 km NW of Parkfield, and for about 5 to 6 km the two cannot be separated because of the very acute angle of intersection. However, 25 km NW of Parkfield the thrust is found back to the west of the San Andreas fault and can be followed for another 25 km before it is lost. There is abundant evidence of recent movement along the thrust in the section where it intermingles with the San Andreas. Taliaferro mentions several similar Middle Pleistocene structural features which are traversed by the San Andreas fault. Nowhere is its post–Middle Pleistocene dextral horizontal slip larger than some 3,000 ft, as measured by the offsetting of drainage lines and such recent features.

The degree of movement during the April, 1906, earthquake amounted to some 4 m through a distance of 435 km along the strike. The time occupied by the movement was but a few seconds.

The Pleistocene San Andreas rift, therefore, may be a very prominent and long feature, but it is certainly not a large one. According to Taliaferro, the supposed branches, or "barbs," are actually earlier faults formed by a different type of movement, with the probable exception of the Hayward fault. This is certainly true for the San Andreas fault movement as compared with earlier Tertiary tectonics, but whether or not it already existed in the Jurassic is more difficult to prove.

Bailey Willis (1938a,b) succeeded in finding an independent proof of the orientation of the main stress direction that caused the fault. In a quarry in the Logan Granite near the fault trace he made a careful analysis of the joints, and concluded that they were caused by a stress direction of N 15° E. Bucher arrived independently at the same conclusion in a study of the same quarry.

Further northward, north of San Francisco, the San Andreas fault can be followed quite accurately along the coast (Higgins, 1961) until it definitely runs into the Pacific, where the Mendocina fault trace hits the continental shelf.

The southerly branch of the San Andreas rift, in particular where it traverses the San Gabriel Granite basement, is less well known. It has been described chiefly by Noble (1926), Bailey Willis (1938a,b), Nolan (1943), Wallace (1949), and Crowell (1952). We find the same features as in the northern portion—a remarkable straight fault line, numerous offsets of topographical features, evidence of uplift rapidly varying from one side of the fault to the other, and repeated evidence of upwarped blocks in the fault zone itself, but unfortunately no definite proof of large-scale strike slip by homologous elements on both sides of the fault. The shift of stream channels amounted to 25 km, that of terrace deposits possibly to as much as 10 km.

The splays of the southern extension of the San Andreas fault are numerous; the San Jacinto, Elsinore, and San Gabriel faults each had their function at some time of the total displacement. For the San Gabriel fault Crowell (1952) proposed some 33 km post-Miocene displacement by comparing anorthosite-bearing conglomerates at one side of the fault with an anorthosite mass at the other side some 33 km away. This argument was not considered conclusive by Paschall and Off (1961), who advocate a dip-slip movement for this fault, indicating how difficult it is to find conclusive evidence for the real throw of a large fault.

The problem of the total strike slip of the San Andreas fault has been taken up recently by Hill and Dibblee (1953). These authors consider the possibility of a pre-Cretaceous age for the fault and of recurrent movements in the same sense at different periods up to the present. The cumulative effect would amount to a 580-km offset. The older phases are obviously difficult to prove, but the younger ones seem very probable. They conclude a displacement of 16 km since the Pleistocene, on the ground of an offset of a particularly Pleistocene facies, and of 370 km since Late Eocene time.

Analysis of the 1906 earthquake and of geodetic surveys since 1850 led Reid (1911) to suppose that elastic deformation slowly built up until the strain became too great and a sudden movement along the fault relieved the strain. Since then very accurate geodetic surface measurements across the San Andreas fault at a particular point have shown that slow creep at an annual rate of 1 cm does take place along the fault line (Steinbrugge et al., 1960).

For several wrench faults the actual displacement caused by seismic shock has been measured. In the case of the April, 1906, San Andreas earthquake, the maximum displacement was 6 m, and not more than 450 km of its total length of 850 km is believed to have been in motion.

In 1857 displacements of over 10 m took place in the Tejon Pass region along a distance of 330 km. During the earthquake of 1868 in the San Francisco area, strike-slip displacements reached 3 to 4 m, and in the recent earthquake of 1940 in the Imperial Valley, displacements averaged about 1 m over a length of 70 km.

The Tarma fault in Japan (Otuka, 1933), 26 km in length, showed a displacement of 2.7 m during the earthquake in 1930.

There would obviously have to be very many such earthquakes to obtain the great displacements which have been inferred from geological evidence. The Great Glen fault would have needed some 20,000 earthquakes within a relatively short period to reach its present displacement. This is not unreasonable in view of the present frequency of earthquakes in active seismic zones.

The post-Nevadan Californian geosyncline, originally simply parallel to the Sierra Nevada, became split up by a N-S-trending stress

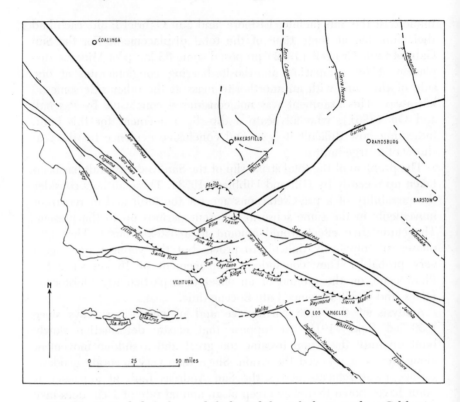

Fig. 95   Sinistral, dextral wrench faults and thrust faults in southern California. (*After Hill, 1954. Published by permission of the California Department of Natural Resources, Division of Mines.*)

field. This stress created the many small E-W-trending basins, the San Joaquin, Santa Barbara–Ventura, and the Los Angeles basins, which show the peculiar transverse position which coincides with the flat S curve of the San Andreas fault. The whole set of structures in this region between Los Angeles and Bakersfield gives an almost perfect expression of the deformation pattern that can be expected from a single stress field: oblique sinistral wrench faults, the Garlock and Big Pine faults; dextral wrench faults, the San Andreas and San Gabriel faults; overthrusts perpendicular to the stress, some overthrusted to the north, the Pleito thrust, some to the south, the Frazier and Pine Mountain thrusts; and then the above-mentioned basins (Fig. 95; Hill, 1954).

The Valganna Fault.   This fault lies between the lakes of Lugano and Maggiore. We find here an elongated dome with a steep overthrust north flank striking NE and a much flatter south flank. In the center of the dome the crystalline schists of the basement rock and overlying Permian volcanics are exposed, the flanks being formed mostly by Triassic limestone (Fig. 96).

The fault line itself has again given rise to a deeply eroded valley, dividing the core of the dome into two portions. The stress direction is given by the straight line of the steep north flank, which has a strike of N 60° E. The main stress had, therefore, a direction of N 30° W. The Valganna fault, with a strike of N 3° W, makes an angle of 27° with the main stress direction. The fault increases very rapidly in importance from north to south. The main result of the strike movement is that, east of the fault line, the south flank of the dome is somewhat steeper than on the west of the fault, and consequently, although the movement was actually a strike slip, the net observable result is largely vertical, increasing rapidly southward. At its southern extremity the fault curves sharply to the west, where the Triassic limestone is thrust over the Cretaceous.

The opposite extremity also curves into a steep thrust, and the crystalline basement is pushed upon the Permian extrusive rock. The fault is most probably accompanied by another parallel one which runs in the valley floor, for the offsetting of the northern thrust fault is much bigger than the visible offset on the eastern slope of the valley. As a result of the two thrusts at its extremities, the fault is given an

Fig. 96   The Valganna fault of the Lombardy Alps. (*After de Sitter*, 1939c.)

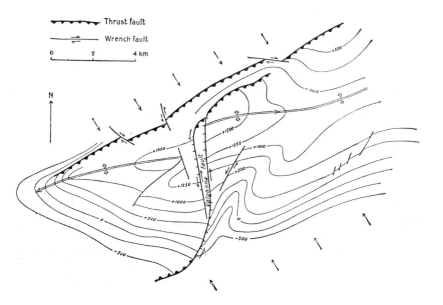

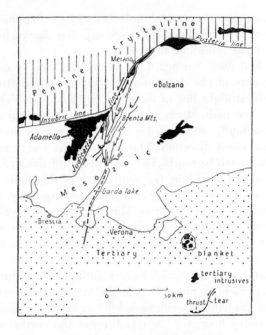

Fig. 97   Map of the Brenta faults in the
Lombardy Alps. (*After Trevisan,* 1939.
*Published by permission of University of
Padua, Istituto di Geologia.*)

S shape, which we often observe elsewhere and which always has
the same origin, a combination of thrusting and a wrench movement.

The fault demonstrates very clearly the close connection between
the production of a wrench-fault origin, vertical movements, and
thrusting and folding.

Although its origin is certainly typical of that of a vertical shear
fault with a horizontal slip, most of the actual motion is vertical because of the thrust at its front. The Valganna fault represents a type of
wrench fault which is often referred to as a basculating, or torsion,
fault, and its origin can easily be misunderstood when only a portion
of the fault is open to accurate mapping or when its dip cannot be
ascertained.

The Brenta Mountains Set of Wrench Faults.   This very interesting
set, in the western Trentino district of the Lombardy Alps, has been
described by Trevisan (1939).

The Lombardy Alps are separated from the vertical root zone of
the Penninic nappes by the well-known Insubric, or Tonale, line, an
E-W fault zone of a character which I shall describe further on. In the

eastern part of the Lombardy Alps we find the Tertiary batholith of the Adamello Mountains, bounded at its northern limit by this Insubric line and at its eastern limit by another large fault line, the Judicaria line, which is itself a wrench fault that shifts the Insubric line in a NE direction (Fig. 97). The continuation of the Insubric line in an eastern direction along the slip is called the Pusteria line. No detailed data have as yet been assembled about the major wrench fault, the Judicaria line, but a set of nearly parallel faults east of this line in the Brenta Mountains has received more attention. The principle of the movements was very clearly demonstrated by Trevisan (Fig. 98). Again, as in the case of the Valganna fault, we find the remarkably close connection and transition between overthrusting and wrench faulting, here accompanied by an en échelon arrangement of the latter. Some of the wrench faults are vertical, but many are inclined to the west; this is probably due to the fact that some of their movements still had a thrust character, although the striation on their faces was always horizontal. In this case it is impossible to deduce the direction of the largest principal stress from the accompanying fold strikes. First, there is not much folding in the very strong limestone blocks; and second, the tectonic history is so complex that one well-determined folding stress cannot be defined.

The Dead Sea Rift. As described by Quennell (1956, 1958) the Dead Sea rift is a large wrench fault with 107 km displacement reached in two stadia, the first of 62 km in the Miocene and the next of 45 km started in the Pliocene and still proceeding, demonstrating exactly the opposite effect of the Brenta faults. The original faults followed an arcuate pattern as in the Brenta, but the movement was opposite (Fig. 99) and voids were created instead of overthrusts. The voids are represented by the deep holes of the Dead Sea and of Lake Tiberias. In this case the main stress direction is given by the trend of adjoining folds and by arching of geomorphic planation surfaces. Some fifteen homologous elements have been recognized on both sides of the rift by Quennell, but with such a large shift such comparisons are not always convincing. A pre-Tertiary shift of 100 km has been well established, but it seems probable that later movements were of the normal type, and there is good evidence that the western Jordan

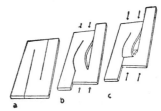

Fig. 98 Diagram explaining the origin of the Brenta faults. (*After Trevisan, 1939. Published by permission of University of Padua, Istituto di Geologia.*)

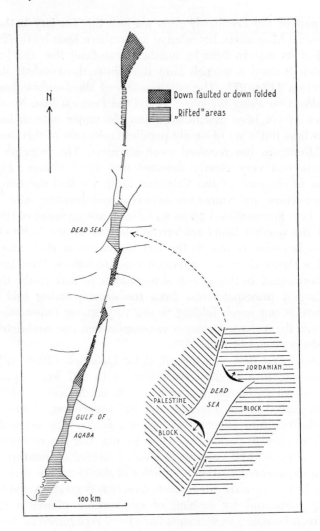

Fig. 99 Jordan fault with the Dead Sea rift. (*After Quennell, 1956. Published by permission of International Geological Congress, 1956, Mexico.*)

fault is a normal fault (de Sitter, 1962a). The same principle of voids being created by wrench faulting has been proposed by Kingma (1959) for a set of en échelon–arranged wrench faults in the North Island of New Zealand.

The Jura Mountains Set of Wrench Faults. Perhaps the most famous of all is the set traversing the numerous folds of the Jura Mountains (Heim, 1919). The four largest are given in Table 9.

Table 9

	Strike Direction	Angle with Fold	Angle with Stress Direction	Maximum Net Length of Slip
Salève fault	N 40° W	70°	20°	1 km in 50 km
Dôle-Champagnole fault	N 20° W	60°	30°	1–1.5 km in 40 km
Vallorbe-Pontarlier fault	N 9° W	55°	35°	10 km in 45 km
Montruz fault	N 10° E	50°	40°	0.5 km in 1.5 km

Together with many smaller ones (Fig. 100), these faults form an outstanding example of a regular and constant tectonic feature. Their strike swings from N 40° W to N 10° E, together with the arc of the Jura folds; but their swing is rather greater than that of the arc because the intersecting angle between fold and fault strike diminishes toward the east, together with the decrease of the thickness of the strata involved in the folding, and consequently the depth of the

Fig. 100   The Jura folds with their wrench faults. (*After Heim, 1921.*)

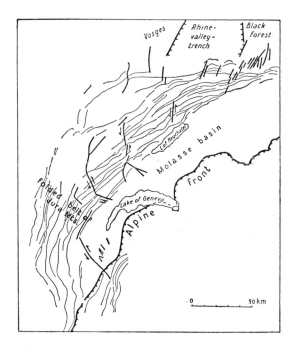

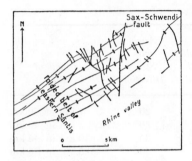

Fig. 101   The Sax-Schwendi fault system in the Säntis Mountains.

basement. The same stress direction which caused the folds obviously caused the wrench faults. Why this stress-fault angle increases from 20 to 40° from west to east is not yet quite clear. At their extremities the wrench faults either disappear in one of the longitudinal thrust faults of the folds or branch off in several splays. They originated, without any doubt, during the folding process, for left and right of the fault the folding is not quite the same. A fold may be much more accentuated and steeper at one side than at the other, or there may be two folds instead of one with similar differences.

Although these wrench faults can be adequately explained as a consequence of the folding stress, it is equally true, as Heim (1919) pointed out, that the original arc of the whole Jura belt of folds would promote lengthening of the arc as folding proceeded, and lengthening would be facilitated by the formation of the diagonal wrench faults. Relatively speaking, the theory advanced by Kraus (1951), that the folding movement was not an outward-directed motion from the upper crust, but an inward motion of the basement, a kind of underflow, expresses exactly the same thought; there is no fundamental difference between the two concepts.

The Sax-Schwendi Fault. This fault, in the Swiss Säntis Mountains, is certainly one of the most famous wrench faults in a folded belt. The Säntis belt is in itself a strongly folded flat-lying overthrust mass which has probably glided down for some of its way; but the folding and fault tectonics are to all appearances perfectly similar to ordinary folding and faulting.

The eastern portion of the Säntis Mountains has been particularly disturbed by a set of diagonal wrench faults; of these the largest is the Sax-Schwendi fault (Fig. 101). It is most spectacular in its appearance. Where it cuts the steep anticlinal limestone ridges its brecciated fault zone has given rise to depressions; the anticline has been shifted in front of a syncline and is mirrored in the lake which it formed. The brecciated fault zone is sometimes very narrow, less than 1 m, and at other places some tens of meters. It is 8 km long, and the sinistral strike slip varies from 500 to 800 m. The numerous striations on the fault faces have a dip of 12 to 15°N, roughly parallel to the dip of the gliding plane.

To the west of the Sax-Schwendi fault we notice a swarm of similar but much smaller faults, which together occupy a triangle with its base to the north and apex to the south. The apical angle is about 50°, and the bisectrix, the assumed stress direction, runs N 21° W, whereas the strike of the folded belt is N 123° W. The wrench-fault group originated in a very late phase of the folding, for the homologous folds on either side of the faults are in general of the same structure, but not of the same intensity, except in the northern anticlines. It is quite possible that during the gliding an obstruction in the substratum caused a slight deviation of some 10° in the general stress direction, and hence in that of the wrench faults themselves.

The Ruhr Coal Basin Wrench Faults. Very similar to the Sax-Schwendi fault are the wrench faults in the strongly faulted Ruhr coal basin south of Bochum (Fig. 102). Here, however, only one set of faults is developed, while in the Säntis Mountains both sets are pres-

Fig. 102   The wrench faults of the Bochum area of the Ruhr coal field. (*After Kukuk, 1938. Published by permission of Springer-Verlag, Berlin.*)

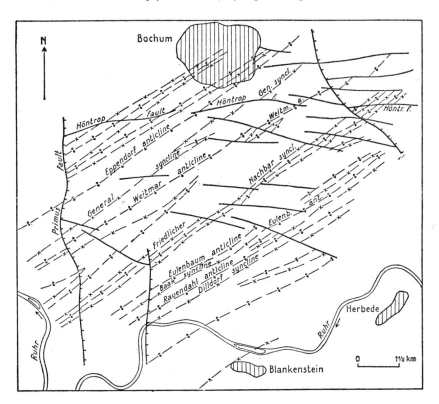

ent. The faults belong, again, to a very late phase of the folding stress, or are simply postfolding.

It would be wrong not to mention one of the greatest wrench faults which have so far been suggested. For western New Zealand, Wellman (1956) suggests a 300-mile displacement along an Alpine fault parallel to and to the west of the New Zealand Alps, on the evidence of similar structures and rocks on different sides of the fault in the northern and southern extremities of South Island. Kingma (1959) is of a different opinion, and considerable work will obviously have to be done before the suggestion becomes an established fact, but it is a fascinating concept. Such large wrench faults as the Great Glen, the San Andreas, the Atacam in Chili, the Philippine (Allen, 1962), and the New Zealand faults are not far removed from the great fundamental faults, which I cover in Chap. 12.

CONCLUSIONS AND EXPERIMENTAL DATA

Experiments on wrench faulting have revealed some interesting facts which may quite well have a certain bearing on natural belts of faults.

The clay-cake experiments by Riedel (1929; Fig. 103) showed that, in a plastic medium such as wet clay, a shearing motion originating at the bottom had a tendency to propagate itself upward, in a wedge-shaped zone widening toward the surface. The first cracks that were observed made a 45 to 47° angle with the shear plane and were obviously tension cracks (gash fractures) which rotated during the movement, the angle increasing to 50 or 60°. New cracks with a 45° angle were then formed, and these in their turn rotated in accordance with the shearing movement.

The tension cracks were parallel to the principal normal stress that can be derived from the applied shearing stress.

During the process there developed at the surface a zone of shear, containing vertical shearing planes making an acute angle of 10 to 15° with the shearing stress. The reason for the origin of these shear planes is not at first apparent. However, since they did not develop immediately, but only when a distinct shear zone in the plastic mate-

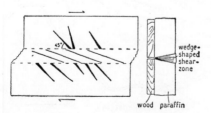

Fig. 103 Diagram explaining Riedel's experiment.

rial had developed, the shear planes must belong to the dynamic process. It seems probable that in a less incompetent medium a clear-cut shear plane would have developed. The observed wedge of shearing with diagonal shear planes is an intermediate stage between very incompetent flow and very incompetent shear.

R. W. Brown (1928) performed a series of experiments on wrench faulting by mounting a block of paraffin–petroleum jelly mixture on two wooden bases which were moved horizontally in opposite directions. When the paraffin blocks had a uniform composition, the tear fault between the wooden blocks simply expanded through the paraffin block to the top, but when several paraffin layers were applied, some less competent than the others, it happened that the tear fault did not penetrate a particular incompetent layer; this was simply contorted, and the higher competent layers showed a complicated set of wrench, normal, and thrust faults combined with folds.

One case in which deep-seated wrench faulting has been assumed to explain another kind of faulting at the surface is that of the belts of en échelon normal faults in Osage and Creek Counties, Oklahoma (Fath, 1920). The normal faults have the same function and direction as the gash fractures of Riedel's experiment. It is true that Fath's explanation has not been accepted by either Sherrill (1929) or Melton (1929). Melton found that the strike of normal en échelon faults coincides with a very constant shear-joint strike, but since the latter is vertical and normal faults have a dip of 50 to 65°, they cannot have the same origin. Nevertheless, it is quite true that the kind of torsional motion due to unequal vertical movements of the basement which was suggested by Sherrill could explain the normal faults as well, and is actually less hypothetical than a deep-seated wrench fault. It is equally true that the typical alignment of the faults in narrow N-S striking belts may be due to the fact that the faults are observed or developed only in particularly brittle strata which outcrop in the belts. Still, the Fath hypothesis has not lost its originality and appeal, and I should also like to apply it to the set of normal faults which are together called the Mexia fault belt, in Texas (Chap. 10, Fig. 74).

When taken together the examples of wrench faults I have selected give a fairly complete picture of the characteristics of this kind of faulting; for convenience, these characteristics are repeated below:

1. The fault outcrop is usually remarkably rectilinear.
2. The dip differs little from the vertical.
3. There is apt to be a fault breccia, mylonite, or even ultramylonite, along the fault line.
4. In general, their topographic expression is excellent even when the shift is small.

5. The shift along the fault may vary from a few centimeters to hundreds of kilometers.

6. When the main stress direction is known from an independent source (e.g., fold direction), the angle is normally less than 45°.

7. The length may vary, from very small faults to faults many hundreds of kilometers long.

8. Very often either they merge into thrust faults, making an oblique angle with their own strike at their extremities, or thrust faults merge into the wrench fault along their course.

9. At the extremities, splays which differ little from the main strike are often formed.

10. The wrench faulting generally belongs to a later phase of a folding process.

11. The vertical throw along the fault varies very much, either because synclines abut upon anticlines, and vice versa, or because some independent vertical warping occurred.

12. There is no preference for sinistral or dextral faults.

13. An en échelon arrangement is not common, but in general the wrench faults are accompanied by many smaller parallel faults of the same character.

Chapter 12

Great Fundamental Faults

Besides the normal faults and wrench faults, described in the foregoing chapters, and the thrust faults, which will be described in Chap. 15 after we have considered folding, there are certain great fault lines which do not fall clearly into any of the classes mentioned above. They represent great cracks in the earth's crust; and either the multiple movements which have occurred along them have obliterated their original character, or they never had the characteristics of one of the distinct classes.

Some of these fault lines, all belonging to major mountain chains, have been investigated in fairly great detail. As typical examples we shall consider the Insubric-Tonale-Pusteria fault zone of the Alps and the North Pyrenean fault zone of southwestern France.

THE NORTH PYRENEAN FAULT ZONE

Let us first consider the simpler North Pyrenean fault line (de Sitter, 1954; Fig. 104). It runs roughly WNW-ESE and separates the axial zone of Paleozoic rocks, intruded by granites, from the North Pyrenean zone where Mesozoic rocks, often surrounding secondary Paleozoic domes, are predominant. The fault zone obviously separates a down-warped northern zone from an uplifted central zone south of it. The fault zone itself is almost everywhere marked by Mesozoic rocks dipping at 90°—limestones and pelites, often highly metamorphic and accompanied by intrusions of basic and ultrabasic rocks. When the fault zone runs between a Paleozoic dome like that of the St. Barthélemy or of the Trois Seigneurs massifs and the axial zone, it invariably consists of crushed, vertical Mesozoic strata. There can be no doubt that the zone was already formed at an early phase of the Alpine folding process, for the nonmetamorphic Upper Cretaceous rests unconformably on the crushed metamorphic rocks of the Lower

161

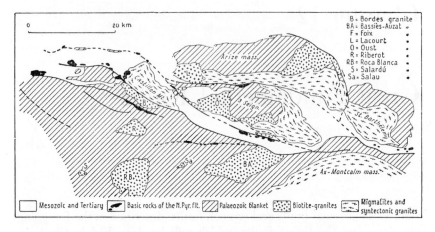

Fig. 104   The fault pattern along the North Pyrenean fault zone in the central Pyrenees.

Cretaceous. But the history of this fault goes back further than the phase of post–Lower Cretaceous folding. Along the tear-fault line from Foix to Tarascon, the St. Barthélemy massif was shifted some 7 km to the southeast, and thrust over the plunging nose of the Trois Seigneurs massif, the latter being shifted, at the same time, some 9 km to the west. This double shift produced a basinlike depression, around Tarascon, in which the Trias has a much more pronounced evaporite facies than it has elsewhere (Zwart, 1954a). This proves that here, at least, fault movements were already active at the beginning of the Mesozoic. The slow transgression of the Mesozoic on the tilted block of the St. Barthélemy massif confirms this hypothesis (de Sitter, 1954). On the other hand, the fault line from Auzat to Biella and farther west cuts obliquely through the Late Paleozoic structures. Hence the horizontal movements to which I referred must belong to a late tectonic phase of the Hercynian orogenies, post-Westphalian but pre-Triassic.

We can follow the history of the fault line still further back. At present it separates the integrated Hercynian axial zone from the dissected North Pyrenean zone (Chap. 32, Fig. 282). It also forms a line separating a North Pyrenean differentiated facies of the Devonian from an axial nondifferentiated facies. It is even possible that it acted as a facies boundary line in the Ordovician.

Hence we know that in the Upper Paleozoic, and perhaps earlier, a narrow mobile zone of the earth's crust came into existence, which became a distinct fault line at the end of the Hercynian folding, and was rejuvenated in the first phase of Laramide folding.

Its horizontal extension is probably much greater than the present Pyrenees. It probably extends westward into the Asturian-Cantabrian Mountains, and to the east it possibly links up with the Insubric line of the Alps.

The metamorphism of the Lower Cretaceous and Jurassic rocks is of a peculiar kind—the limestones have been scapolitized—and it is accompanied by the intrusion of numerous small stocks ranging from ultrabasic peridotites to gabbros (ophites) (Zwart, 1954b). These basic magmas cannot be regarded as an initial magmatic phase in the development of the Pyrenean geosyncline, since we cannot call the Lower Mesozoic of the Pyrenees a geosyncline, but they certainly indicate that the fault penetrated very deep into the crust and reached the basic substratum. We are justified in calling the fault zone a fundamental feature because of its great lateral and vertical extensions and its long history of activity.

THE INSUBRIC LINE OF THE ALPS

The next compressive zone to which I should like to call attention is the Insubric-Pusteria line (Cornelius, 1930). This line of dislocation is one of the major features of Alpine structure and one of its most enigmatic ones, as demonstrated by the fact that different authors have ascribed to it most diverse interpretations. It has been described as a normal gravity fault, sometimes with the northern limb and sometimes with the southern limb warped down, as a thrust fault, and even as a "Verschluckungszone," a zone in which by a process of "downward sucking" a large slice of surface rocks has disappeared, as a "Narbe" (i.e., a deep scar) of some unknown orogenic origin and as a wrench fault.

Structurally, it is a most important line (Fig. 276). In the terminology of Staub (1924) and many others, it represents the boundary between the "Dinarides" and the "Alpides," which are sometimes translated by "Africa" and "Europe," a rather fanciful terminology which teaches us very little about its function (de Sitter, 1947a).

Along its most prominent portion, the stretch between Lake Como and the Tonale Pass, it actually constitutes the boundary between the vertical roots of the lower and middle East Alpine thrust sheets in the north and the crystalline Orobic mass in the south (Cornelius, 1930). The latter is simply a block of the basement rock of the southern Alps, with a few remnants of its Permian cover in a more or less horizontal position (Chap. 10, Fig. 86). The rocks on each side of the line of dislocation are crystalline schists, but in the Tonale zone to the north of the fault the metamorphism is of a much higher order than that south of the fault. Along the fault line we can recognize long narrow slivers of Triassic and Permian rocks, and the fault plane itself is characterized by strong crushing and mylonitization. It is followed by the great valley of the Valtellina, and hence is usually covered by alluvial deposits. Both north and south of the fault there appear large granite intrusions, the Adamello in the southeast and the Bergello Granite in the northwest. They were intruded, to all appearances, after the dislocation came into existence, and they do not cross it.

The main feature of the Insubric dislocation line is therefore its extremely fundamental character from a structural point of view. It certainly penetrates very deeply into the earth's crust and has given access for granites and probably for basic rocks (Ivrea zone) to reach the surface, but it certainly is not a normal gravity fault, although large vertical movements have taken place along its plane.

Toward the east, it is displaced northward by a great tear fault, the Judicaria line (de Sitter, 1947a), and it continues much farther eastward as the Tonale-Pusteria line. Toward the west, it first curves southward and then disappears beneath the Tertiary sediments of the Po plain. Whether it reaches the Mediterranean and whether it links up with the North Pyrenean fault are matters of conjecture. In its known and exposed course it is not generally accompanied by intrusions of basic rock, unless, as is quite possible, one regards the thick basic rock mass of the Ivrea zone as an Alpine intrusion (E. Niggli in Cadisch, 1953). Like the North Pyrenean fault zone, it is marked geophysically by a pronounced gravimetric maximum, perhaps indicating a basic rock mass of considerable width intruded into the sialic crust.

It is difficult to find equally well known examples of similar dislocation lines which separate two structurally different units over long distances within the same mountain system. With some hesitancy I cite the serpentine belt along the western border of the Piedmont system of the Appalachians and the line separating the western gneisses from the eastern granites in Scandinavia (Chap. 33, Fig. 291). The latter is also accompanied by a long belt of basic rocks, the hyperite belt. The last two fundamental faults are both characterized by the fact that they separate two units with a difference in metamorphic state: in the Appalachians, highly metamorphic schists are separated from recognizable Paleozoic strata, and in Sweden, katazone gneisses from granites. The same is true for the Insubric line, but less obvious for the North Pyrenean dislocation. All four show an accompanying belt of ultrabasic rocks. The two last zones, characterized by serpentine belts, have also been regarded as compressed geosynclinal belts with an initial magmatic phase. In our present state of knowledge it is impossible to decide whether they really represent such a geosynclinal belt or whether they are comparable with the Pyrenean and Insubric lines.

Another very important fault line of fundamental significance is, for instance, the line that separates the Sahara craton from the Atlas mountain chains along its northern border (Chap. 35, Fig. 303). It is characterized by big facies differences on each side, by enormous movements, by great unconformities, and even occasionally by rather modern volcanoes.

There are evidently long fundamental cracks in the earth's crust penetrating the whole upper crust and characterized by frequent movements. They occasionally constitute a way of access to the surface for basic or granite magma. Their particular tectonic function at a particular moment in geological history entirely depends upon the stress field prevailing at that moment. They may facilitate radial displacements, or they may act as wrench faults or as great zones of compression, as the stress field dictates. They often accompany the great orogenic belts of the earth and are always parallel to the grain of the mountain chains to which they belong.

Chatper 13

Principles of Folding

FOLDING AS A SHEARING PHENOMENON

Geological experience has taught us that folding is the most common form of distortion of the predominantly layered arrangement of the various rock types that make up the upper layers of the earth's crust. But whereas faulting is easily understood from a mechanical point of view, folding of such apparently brittle material as rocks is a baffling problem which has occupied the minds of geologists since the earliest observations. In Chaps. 2 and 3 we learned that under increased confining pressure such brittle material does become ductile. Another approach to this problem is the imitating experiment, whose weaknesses we explained in Chap. 4. By way of illustration, Kuenen and de Sitter (1938) made a series of folding experiments with different materials to show different possibilities of deforming solid or half-solid cakes into folded structures.

The purely elastic fold is illustrated by the bending of a squared rubber plate (Fig. 105). The internal deformation of the material can be judged by the distortion of the squares, showing flattening parallel and perpendicular to the bedding plane. We tried to illustrate the purely plastic fold with a weak paraffin cake floating on warm water (Fig. 106). The incipient deformation was a simple thickening of the cake, which would certainly have continued without folding if we had not added an irregularity to the structure, a small load of petroleum jelly. Folds developed on both sides of this small irregularity. Folding began earlier when the compression was accelerated, but again the initial process was a simple thickening. The distortion of the squares indicates that the more rapid deformation caused some elastic resistance, since the squares then show the same stretching and compression pattern as in the rubber plate. No shear planes could in any way be produced in this kind of material. In order to illustrate the con-

 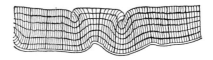

Fig. 105 Folder rubber plate. Deformation of original squares indicates their elastic deformation.

Fig. 106 Thickened and folded weak paraffin cake floating on water.

(*Both after Kuenen and de Sitter,* 1938)

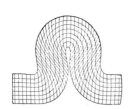 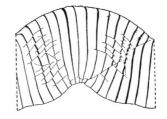

Fig. 107 Folded pack of paper sheets, illustrating pure concentric folding.

Fig. 108 Folded unstratified clay cake with spontaneous concentric shear.

(*Both after Kuenen and de Sitter,* 1938.)

centric folding of layered sediments, a pack of paper sheets was folded (Fig. 107). The distortion of the squares was now quite different. As I was personally convinced that this concentric folding is also the predominating principle, even when stratification does not predispose the material to this mechanism of folding, Kuenen tried different materials and other conditions, and finally succeeded in folding an unstratified clay cake in this way (Fig. 108). Concentric shear planes, parallel to the bottom and top of the cake, were spontaneously formed. The conclusions from this series of experiments will be drawn further on, but one conclusion is obvious: except for the last experiment with spontaneous concentric shear, none of the experiments show any convincing analogies with natural folds in rocks so far as their internal mechanism is concerned.

Concentric and Planar Shear in Folding. From microtectonic and theoretical considerations we can conclude that there are only three fundamental modes of folding:

1. Concentric folding
2. Cleavage folding
3. Flow folding

All the endless variation of tectonic features and shapes can be explained by different combinations of these three processes.

Van Hise's old classification into parallel and similar folds still holds good, since parallel folding is synonymous with concentric folding, and similar folding is always associated with some kind of cleavage.

In cleavage folding we are always confronted with the problem of how much of the distortion is due to flattening of the rock and how much to differential slip along the cleavage planes. When the slip is important, the difference with flow folding becomes vague, but personally I am convinced that flattening is the most important mechanism in ordinary cleavage folds.

Concentric Folding. The process of concentric folding, often called flexure folding, primarily and of necessity the reaction of a layered mass to compression, is certainly due to the secondary stress field originating in the incipient elastic deformation stage, with compression in the inner arc and tension in the outer convex arc. When a thick sedimentary series is folded in this way it is understandable that the bedding planes will act as planes of movement, but the process would be impossible if a thick homogeneous layer could not follow the same process. The experiment of Fig. 108 proved that even in that case pure concentric folding can develop. This problem has also been investigated theoretically by Ramberg (1961). From the experiment of Fig. 108 and Ramberg's considerations it follows that the concentrically folded mass must be thick in relation to the wavelength of the fold. This thick mass, reacting as a unit to the stress, can either be a thick sequence of layered rocks or one particular layer of rock.

Cleavage Folding. In contrast to pure concentric folding, where the relative movement of particles during folding takes place along or parallel to the bedding plane, are the different kinds of cleavage folding where the plane of movement is at an angle to the bedding and the bedding plane consequently gets stretched. This secondary plane of movement is the cleavage, or schistosity, plane. There are many different kinds of cleavage, but they all have in common that the movement plane is planar unless it has been refolded. We distinguish three genetically different types of cleavage: (1) concentric cleavage, (2) oblique, or shear, cleavage, and (3) axial-plane cleavage. Besides this subdivision, there are a profusion of purely descriptive names, like slaty cleavage in slates, flow cleavage in phyllites, schistosity in schists and gneisses, and fracture cleavage, having a larger interval than slaty cleavage. In analyzing the deformation process it is important, in the first instance, to establish the relation between the cleavage and the fold with which its formation was connected, and in the second place, great care must be taken in this analysis because of the multiplicity of folding phases that are now being discovered everywhere in cleaved rocks.

Concentric Cleavage (Fig. 109A). Concentric cleavage occurs parallel to or at a very acute angle to the bedding, having in some places steeper, and in others shallower, dips than the bedding. The folds in which it is found have a basically concentric form, although it is clear that any deformation related to planes at an angle to the bedding must allow a departure from the strict concentric form. This cleavage may have the form of a fracture cleavage, or shaly parting. In fact, there is the possibility that much of the "bedding-plane" slaty partings observed may be of this origin, and flat-lying schistosity was perhaps initiated as bedding-plane cleavage. Being derived, via the fold, from the bedding of the sequence, such partings are reliable indicators of the structures to which they belong, but, being a derivative, may be considerably influenced by other factors. It is believed that concentric cleavage is also a flattening process.

Oblique Cleavage (Fig. 109B). Oblique cleavage can also occur in the incompetent beds of the concentric-fold type, and then generates the so-called pencil shales, shales which fall apart in long (up to 30 cm), mostly four-sided pencil-sized rocks. They are due to a conjugate set of oblique shear planes. Actually, they sometimes also cut through the competent beds.

Another kind of oblique shear occurs in relation to thrusting and is simply the distribution of oblique shear over a large number of parallel shear planes instead of concentration on a single surface.

Axial-plane Cleavage (Fig. 109C). Axial-plane cleavage is the most common and most important kind of cleavage and seems to be a purely flattening process. Compression of the rock sequence by an approximately horizontal stress field has resulted in flattening perpendicular to the stress and extension vertically, since this may be assumed to be the direction of least stress. These structures do not necessarily imply any appreciable movement on the planes, which are merely part of the process by which argillaceous rocks in particular

Fig. 109 Cleavage folding. (*A*) Concentric cleavage; (*B*) oblique cleavage; (*C*) axial-plane cleavage.

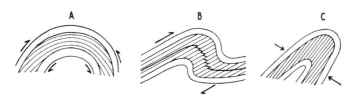

deform in the elastico-viscous field. Pure flattening cannot, of course, form folds from exactly planar layers, and it has to be assumed that at least a certain amount of concentric folding preceded all cleavage folds. The amount of flattening has been calculated in certain cases, using contained fossils, oolites, and pebbles, as discussed in Chap. 20. Flattening is accompanied by mica recrystallization, although the parallel arrangement of the mica is partly due simply to rotation into the cleavage plane by the flattening of the rock.

Flow. Flow is a kind of distortion, in which a fixed orientation of shear planes to a stress direction is lost. The internal movement itself is no longer orientated, but can take any direction, with the result that it can no longer be represented adequately in a section and there is no parallelism of the fold axes. It is typical of very weak rocks like salt, or of very high confining pressures or high temperatures as in migmatites, and is the only true plastic deformation of rocks. Flow of rock does not necessarily mean that the material acts completely as an ordinary fluid; in most cases it is laminar flow, with distinct shear planes between lamellae of different size.

Combinations of cleavage and concentric folding in different types of mixed folding are very common, showing that the two main kinds of folding are not very far removed from each other in a mechanical sense.

There are also many transitional stages between the principal folding types. A common one is that a competent rock member, a quartzite, for instance, folds concentrically and the shales show axial-plane cleavage. Sometimes one part of the fold has a concentric character, the flanks, for instance, and another part, the hinges, shows cleavage, as in accordion folds. A very good analysis of the difference between

Table 10

Characteristic	Concentric Folds	Kind of Fold		
		Axial-plane Cleavage	Schistosity Folding	Flow
Synonyms	Parallel or distance-true	Similar	Similar	Irregular
Position of planes of movement	Curved parallel bedding plane	Planar, steep-dipping	Planar, flat-dipping	Curved
Position in earth's crust	Superficial	Superficial and deep	Deeper level	Deeper level
Typical of rock	Competent	Incompetent	Metamorphic	Weak
Faults	Many faults, related to folding	Fewer faults, related to main stress field	Upthrusts	None
Detachment plane	Common	Possible, but not necessarily	None	
Secondary folds	Rare	Common	Common	Common

minor concentric and cleavage folds from actual exposures has been given by Ramsay (1962).

The relation of the folding types with increasing intensity are:

$$
\left.
\begin{array}{l}
\text{Concentric folding} \\
\text{Concentric cleavage}
\end{array}
\right\} \text{Parallel folding}
$$

$$
\left.
\begin{array}{l}
\text{Oblique cleavage} \\
\text{Accordion folding} \\
\text{Axial-plane cleavage} \\
\text{Flow}
\end{array}
\right\} \text{Similar folding}
$$

In Table 10 some characteristics of different fold types are assembled, but the table is far from complete.

DETACHMENT ALONG A BASAL SHEARING PLANE (DÉCOLLEMENT)

Without doubt, the concept of the basal shearing plane has been one of the most fruitful thoughts in the realm of comparative tectonics. It teaches us that a superficial cover may have been deformed, for one reason or another, independently of its substratum. Argand distinguished clearly between "plis de couverture," folds belonging exclusively to the superficial cover, and "plis de fond," where the substratum took part in the folding process. Since Buxtorf advocated the thesis that the folds in the Mesozoic rocks of the Jura were folded independently of their crystalline basement, and glided on the very incompetent anhydrite layers of the Triassic, this concept has gained in weight, and superficial folds have been called simply "Jurassic" folds (Fig. 110). The process of "décollement," which means the detachment of the upper cover from its substratum, is the fundamental concept which lies at the base of all thrusting, gliding, and diapiric structures and is equally important for the understanding of most of the tectonics of superficial folding.

It would be erroneous, however, to presume that the phenomenon of detachment is necessarily, or even ordinarily, restricted to one surface. On the contrary, we may safely assume that in a thick stratigraphical column several horizons are very often prospective horizons of detachment, and it depends largely on the relative incompetency of the several lithological units, which build up a sedimentary cover, as to whether one or more will act as detachment layers or not. It is obvious, for instance, that the extreme incompetency of the salt-bearing clays of the Upper Triassic in Europe and North Africa has determined the tectonic style in several independent fold systems, since it has repeatedly acted as the preferred detachment horizon. But when another suitable incompetent layer is present, as, for instance, the

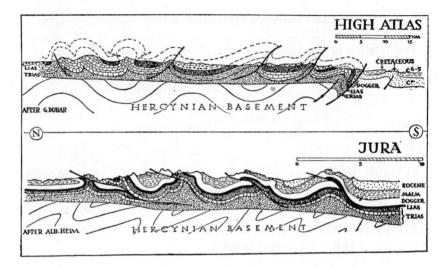

Fig. 110 Décollement, or detachment along basal shear plane. "Jurassic" folds in Jura Mountains and in High Atlas. (*After Heim, 1921, and Dubar, 1952.*)

Lower Malm clays of the western Pre-Alps, this may locally play an equally important or even a predominant role.

The effect of the detachment is such that the series of rocks above the detachment layer moves and takes its shape more or less independently of the underlying series. In the case of gravity-gliding tectonics, for instance, the underlying series is not deformed at all. Only the cover has glided down and eventually, but not necessarily, has been folded under its own weight on arrival at the base of the preexisting slope. On the other hand, the presence of a detachment layer may mean only that the shortening is concentrated in a fold at one position in the series above the layer, rather than in the series below it. Or in other circumstances it may facilitate deviations from pure concentric folding, as, for instance, when lack of space due to the high curvature in the core necessitates the crumpling of either an anticline or syncline. The selection of the detachment surface depends mainly on the contrast between the competencies rather than on absolute values. Locally, a shale between thick limestones (and at greater depth even a limestone between thick sandstone series) may act as a detachment plane. Nevertheless, we mostly find that one special horizon such as the gypsiferous marls and the cavernous dolomites of the Lower Triassic of the southern Alps, covered by thousands of meters of Lower, Middle, and Upper Triassic limestones, acts as a basal shearing plane over a large area. It is adopted both by gravitational gliding sheets moving from north to south and by ordinary thrust sheets moving from south to north. And even when no perceptible displacement can be ascertained, the same horizon of cavernous dolomite has been found to be strongly brecciated, again demonstrating some movement along this plane.

Another very striking example of such a universal detachment horizon is represented by the Silurian black-shale horizon of some 100 m thickness lying between the Ordovician neritic facies and the Devonian limestone-shale facies of the Pyrenees (Chap. 31).

THE SIZE OF A FOLD

I have enlarged somewhat on the function of the basal shearing plane because it is a fairly universal factor in folding processes, not restricted to concentric folding. In concentric folding, however, a basal detachment is more common, and its presence also determines the size of the fold. In its most simple shape the concentric fold consists of one regular arc, with its center in the core of the fold, flanked at both sides by two similar synclinal arcs, with centers above the surface, as in Fig. 111.

It is obvious that below the center O the principle of concentricity can no longer be sustained; nevertheless, the volume of the triangle below the last concentrically folded bed is still the same as in its unfolded shape. We may assume that the strata in this triangle have been shortened by faulting or crumpling. The lower, straight boundary of the fold is the basal detachment plane of the fold. Referring to Fig. 111, we see that the breadth of the fold at any stage of the folding is then determined, from the very beginning, by the thickness of the

Fig. 111 Development of a basal detachment plane at the bottom of a concentric fold.

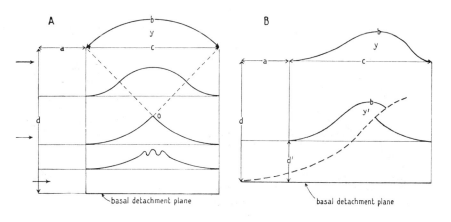

sedimentary blanket. As no appreciable compression of the rock into a smaller volume is possible, the volume of rock above the originally horizontal top surface must equal the total volume of the shortening in a horizontal direction. This is also true for any other originally horizontal surface. In a vertical section,

$$y = da$$

where y = surface of rock above original horizontal surface
   d = thickness of beds below that particular horizon
   a = total shortening

a can be measured as the difference between the present distance between two cores of a syncline c and the length of the folded layer b, and y can be measured on the section (Fig. 111A).

This is equally true for any other concentrically folded layer, even when thrust or other faults occur, as in Fig. 111B, where $y = d(b - c)$ and $y^1 = d^1(b - c)$.

The wavelength of the fold at any stage of the folding is therefore dependent only on the thickness of strata involved in the folding, e.g., the folding depth d. Thus we see that the position of the particular incompetent layer at the bottom determines the size of the fold. This makes it possible to calculate the depth of the detachment surface. The area above the surface and the shortening can be measured on a section, and the depth is their quotient, $d = y/a$. The theory can be checked by measuring different adjacent sections, in the Jura Mountains, for instance, and the result is surprisingly good, the difference in the calculated depth of the basement being only about 6%.

The relation between thickness and size of folds is also very well illustrated by Fig. 112, where two very similar overthrust folds from the western and eastern Jura Mountains are drawn on the same scale; in the Reculet section the same strata are considerably thicker, and hence the fold wavelength is larger than in the Lägern section.

Fig. 112   Comparison of Reculet and Lägern folds, both from the Jura Mountains.

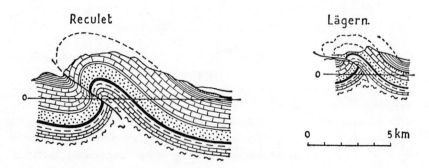

Because the wavelength of a fold is determined beforehand by the thickness of the strata, the initial location of one crest can determine a whole belt of folds. The location of the first fold is still arbitrary and probably depends on irregularities in sedimentation.

R. W. Brown (1928) has shown experimentally that the location of folds in younger unconformably overlapping rocks is strongly influenced by the structure in older strata. In his experiments, renewed compression in the same direction, after deposition of the younger unconformable strata, resulted every time in a fold in the younger strata directly overlying the older structure. This conclusion, moreover, is in agreement with the observation that, during the same cycle of sedimentation, recurrent folding accentuates, almost without exception, the first formed structures and seldom creates new ones in other positions.

This principle cannot be applied, however, when a complete detachment of the basement takes place. In that case it is principally sedimentary features which predispose some regions as the sites of the first folds. In particular, the edges of competent strata determine the location of the anticlinal axes, as is shown by many parts of overthrust faults, where we find this kind of wedge exposed (cf. Fig. 113 and Chap. 15, Figs. 137 and 143). It is evident that other kinds of prominent irregularities, lenses, for instance, will have the same capacity of locating a fold. Cleavage folds are necessarily preceded by concentric folds, so that their wavelength tends to be fixed beforehand by this initial folding stage. But since cleavage folds are very apt to develop secondary folds, this regularity may be destroyed. To some extent their amplitude may be influenced by the thickness of particular layers, mainly through the effect of these on the initial concentric fold.

THE DIRECTION OF FOLDING STRESS

A process of geological deformation is no laboratory experiment, and we can try to read the direction of the deformative stress only from the orientation of fold or fault structures. From a general point of view the problem is not difficult to solve. One of the principal stresses is always assumed to be necessarily vertical, because the surface of the earth with gravity perpendicular to it is by far the most important plane of discontinuity that enters into the stress field. In the horizontal plane, we can determine the largest principal stress as either bisecting the acute angle of a set of tear faults or, better still, as perpendicular to the longer axis of folding or to the strike of the thrust planes.

It is, of course, inconceivable that a fold making an oblique angle with the major stress should be formed, unless some local factor of disturbance is present and makes the major stress deviate from its regional direction. This factor of disturbance must be determined before the deviation can be assessed.

Since this process of determining the direction of the main stress is simple, controversies seldom arise, except on minor points or if the evidence is contradictory.

Great difficulties and long discussions have, however, arisen from a very simple misconception: that a stress field can be divided into an active one in one direction and a passive one in the opposite direction. All discussions, and they are very numerous, as to whether the "push" is from the north or from the south, whether there is an underthrust or an overthrust, whether there is a buttress or an active moving block, are irrelevant. Each and every observed displacement is relative to the next block only, and never absolute in relation to the center of the earth. We have no means whatsoever of determining which part has actually moved in relation to the earth's center and which has remained stationary. This applies only to tangential movement; in all radial movements we might expect some evidence of the actual direction of movement because the sea level may sometimes be expected to remain stationary, or at any rate to have a limited radius of action, and gravity necessarily acts only downwards in the vertical. Colloquially, we may talk of an "overthrust," and may imagine the upper flank to have been "pushed" over the lower flank, but exactly the same structure would have been formed if the lower flank had been pushed under and the upper flank had been stationary. This applies just as well to a simple thrust anticline as to the whole Alpine structure. When Ernst Kraus (1951) advocated an underthrust from north to south of the foreland below and toward the center of the Alpine chain, as compared with the classical way of expression, by which the Alps advanced from south to north over and on their foreland, he merely used different words to say exactly the same thing. In order to illustrate this fact, we can advance several examples where the direction of movement in the upper and lower portions of a structure in the same section is opposite. In a section of the Bergamasc Alps (Fig. 113) we see an "upthrust" from south to north and an overthrust, cutting it off at the top, directed from north to south. In this case it is true that some of the north-to-south movement is probably due to gravitational gliding.

The Tarra structure, southwest of Lake Maracaibo, offers another very clear example. In its northern portion the anticline has a steep, largely overthrust eastern flank, but in the south it is the west flank that is considerably steeper than the east flank. It is quite possible that in the lower levels (Chap. 15, Fig. 143) below the eastward-thrust structure we still may find a westward-thrust structure.

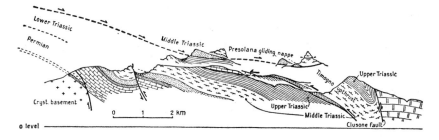

Fig. 113 N-S section through Bergamasc Alps, showing combination of N-S and S-N movements. (*After de Sitter,* 1949.)

In German literature the asymmetry of folding structures, the "Vergenz," is often used as an indicator of the thrust direction (Stille, 1924a). In the border zone of a mountain chain, for instance, we often find an outward-directed thrust movement of the upper layers; the "Vergenz" is centrifugal. In such a case it is the emergence of the central block which caused the asymmetry.

This is not only true when we think of an asymmetry in a cross section, but also on the map. An island arc is no proof of an active push against the concave side and a buttress on the convex one; neither has a wedge "penetrated" as an "active" block in resistant medium.

Even in structures due to gravity gliding it is immaterial whether we think of a sedimentary cover gliding down or a rising block.

Once this has been clearly understood we may revert to the classical expressions: overthrusting, or pushing folds against buttresses, or letting one portion of the crust advance, or any unidirectional term.

DEPTH OF EROSION

In the following chapters I shall describe many different shapes of fold structure and shall try to classify them according to their peculiarities. All our information about their shape, however, is derived, in the first place, from a relatively thin section of the crust, that exposed on the surface, and second, from the knowledge which the drill or tunneling has brought us. But a large portion of the fold seen in a section is interpretative—either in the air, representing the upper portion carried away by erosion, or in the subsurface, below the reach of the artificial exposures. The manner in which the section is completed is largely a matter of the experience of the geologist concerned, and he prefers to take his examples from the surrounding structures on the just assumption that they will have a similar structural history and similar physical properties. He will be confronted immediately, how-

ever, with the difficulty that all the structures in the neighborhood
are laid bare by erosion to about the same level and thus give him
little information about either the deeper or the higher structural
levels. He will have to look elsewhere for information, but then he
will perceive that, in a more deeply eroded country, the structures do
not resemble his original ones, and he will not know how to conjoin
higher structural features with deeper ones. When we think, for instance, of the complicated superficial structures in the Lower Fars
Series in Iran (Fig. 114), we see that it would be quite impossible to
construct the structure of the Asmari Limestone from the surface data
alone. Here the interference of a basal shearing plane at the top of
the limestone makes construction impossible.

In Fig. 115 we can compare an ordinary section through a Jura
fold with one north of Thüringen. In the Jura the folds appear as a
series of broad anticlines in Upper Jurassic limestones with relatively
narrow synclines, whereas in Thüringen we find narrow compressed
anticlines with broad sweeping synclines. The comparison suggests
that the lower part of the section of the Jura anticline may be completed by taking account of the data from Thüringen, and vice versa.

When we think of an overthrust anticline where the upper flank is
still well preserved, as, for instance, in the Tarra folds (Venezuela),
or the Turner Valley structure (Canada) (Chap. 15, Figs. 143 and
146), we can understand that it would be difficult for any tectonician
to draw this kind of structure if erosion had carved it away to a level
1½ km deeper. We should have found at the surface a relatively broad
belt of vertical strata, certainly faulted, since several members of the
stratigraphical sequence were missing, but there would be no indication that there had originally been a large overthrust.

Consequently, we often find apparently different kinds of folding
described as separate types, although in reality they merely represent
different levels of the same type of folding. Only very wide experience
can in some degree guard us against this fallacy.

Fig. 114 Section through Iranian oil fields. (*Slightly altered, after Lees*, 1953.
Published by permission of the Oxford University Press.)

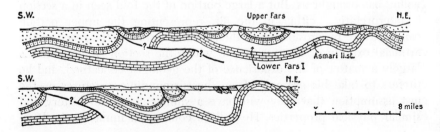

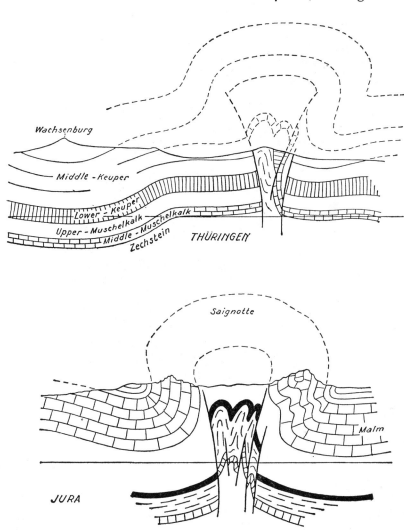

Fig. 115 Comparison of Jura section with Thüringen section.

MINOR FOLDS

In Chap. 4 attention was called to the fact that minor folds and micro-folds show the same shape and characteristics as large structures. This feature is clearly demonstrated, in particular, by parasitic folds on the flank of a larger structure (Chap. 22). Here I want to point out that we find replicas on a small scale of all kinds of large structures.

Fig. 116 Microfold in limestone with chert bands,
Devonian, Valle de Aran, Spanish Pyrenees.

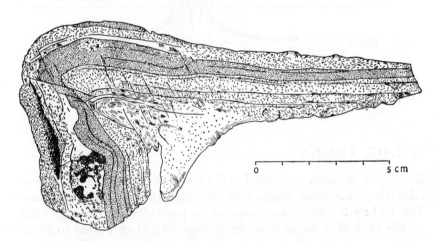

Fig. 117 Overthrust in microfold, metamorphic limestone, Ordovician,
Pyrenees.

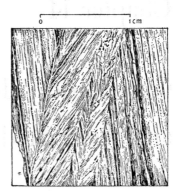

Fig. 118   Accordion fold in Ordovician
schists from Vicdessos Valley, Pyrenees.

Figure 116 is an anticline in a hand specimen in which chert bands
with rotational joints represent the competent member and limestone
with flow lines represents the incompetent member. The fold is of a
similar type, with occasional faults parallel to the axial plane, small
parasitic folds, and oblique shear planes of a late date.

In Fig. 117, also a hand specimen, an overthrusted anticline has developed which can be compared with the structures of Fig. 186, which
are about 10,000 times as large.

In the next chapter the similarity between concentric folds in
hand-specimen size (Fig. 123) and outcrop size (Fig. 124) and large-
sized folds will be demonstrated again.

A comparison of Fig. 118 with Fig. 226 in Chap. 22 shows that accordion folds have the same character under the microscope as on a
60-m-high cliff.

The importance of these similarities lies in the possibility of studying the details of a complete fold and the relation between them
without the disadvantages of incomplete exposure inherent in large-
sized structures.

Chapter 14

Concentric Folds
and Associated Faults

In the previous chapter I explained that concentric folding is one of the guiding principles in folding processes inasmuch as incipient folding usually involves the elastic deformation of the most resistant and rigid rocks. I shall dwell at some length on the development of concentric folds, because other types of fold can often be regarded as derivatives from the fundamental concentric principle.

THE DEVELOPMENT OF A CONCENTRIC FOLD

The birth of a simple fold can be imagined as taking place at a single point, which later becomes the culmination of the fold in both the cross section and longitudinal section. The axis of such a fold may be horizontal for some distance, but it will always show an axial plunge, eventually, at each end. Since the compressive force is acting perpendicular to the fold axis, there will, in general, be no tensional stress in that direction, but perpendicular to the stress direction and parallel to the fold, tension due to the arching of the axis may be expected. The size of the fold is determined, first, by the total thickness of strata involved in the particular fold, and second, by its rigid, elastically deformed members. Hence the incompetent members simply have to follow the prescribed shape, which they will do passively when no extra stress becomes involved. A consequence of this is that the upper, soft, nonconsolidated part of a stratigraphical sequence which has to follow the elastically determined shape of lower strata may have another stress condition different from that of the intermediate layers, and different again from that of the basal layers.

In Fig. 119 three stages are constructed in the development of the

182

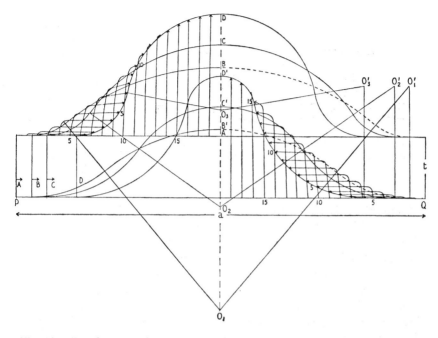

Fig. 119 Development of a concentric fold. For explanation see text.

most simple imaginable shape of a concentric fold. This simplification does not, however, invalidate the conclusion for more complex forms.

By drawing lines joining the numbered points on the original horizontal surface and its subsequent positions, we get the trajectories of these points in space. We notice that each point starts with a vertical motion and then suddenly turns to a horizontal direction. Hence, at each stage, there are in any one anticline two marginal blocks moving inward and one central block moving upward (Fig. 120); the latter narrows down to a small wedge in the course of the process. The relative motion of one point to the next on the same bedding surface is therefore practically negligible during almost the whole of the process, except at the precise moment when the upper point is still moving upward but the lower one turns to its horizontal stage. If we join the points at which this occurs on different surfaces, we obtain a line slanting toward the center of the structure. Such a line of turning points obviously represents a possible break in the smoothness of the motion, and these lines are therefore potential faults (Fig. 120). We find during folding that the centers of the anticlinal curvature (O_1, O_2, O_3 in Fig. 119) move upward, and those of the synclinal curves move horizontally inward. In its upward course the anticlinal center moves much more quickly than the strata themselves, since the radius

concentric fold

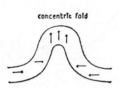

diapiric fold

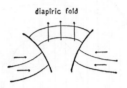

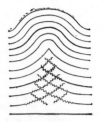

Fig. 120   Horizontal and vertical movement in a concentric fold, leading to diapirism.

Fig. 121   Lack of space in the core of fold.

of curvature is shortened simultaneously. Hence its position in the stratigraphical succession wanders from one layer to the next. In Fig. 121 we can see that as soon as this center has passed any particular horizon, the latter surface can no longer fold in the same concentric fashion and maintain its original length; in other words, at the base of each fold with a definite basal shear plane there is a layer which, because of lack of space, can no longer be folded concentrically. This layer may be expected to thicken in the core of the fold during the folding process. Besides the fact that the increasing curvature cannot be concentrically followed by an increasing thickness of bottom strata, we also find that whatever the exact shape of the fold, the narrowing of the upward-moving axial wedge causes an increasing lack of space in the core of the fold.

This lack of space in the core of the anticline creates a tendency to broaden the wedge of upward thrust within the center of the fold or for a breakthrough by faulting; both actions involve disturbance of the concentric mechanism. In the second case, where faulting occurs we get complications such as overthrusts or diapiric structures, which will be described later. In the first case we shall find a flat-topped broad anticline with steep flanks, a so-called "boxfold."

At the top of the fold the softest layers are not actively concerned with the folding. They follow the shape prescribed by the more rigid competent beds below. They may therefore show all the characteristics of tension on the anticlinal crest, or of crumpling in the syncline, both in cross section and in longitudinal section. Hence, in an ordinary concentric fold, we can distinguish three zones: a lower zone, broken and compressed; a large middle zone which has been folded concentrically; and an upper zone with tension faults and other adjustments (Fig. 122).

From this standpoint, the supposed tensional stress on the crest of a fold is limited to the most superficial layers, and may even be altogether absent if the stratigraphical sequence has no particular com-

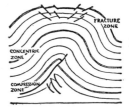

Fig. 122 Zoning on a concentric fold.

petent series in its middle portion. The relative scarcity of longitudinal tension faults on the crests of anticlines is thus explained.

Nevertheless, it is undoubtedly true that in an elastically bent sheet the concentric shear planes are restricted to the flanks, the crest showing tension cracks and the core crumpling. In Fig. 123 the tension of the zone of maximum curvature has resulted in the filling up of wedge-shaped cracks by recrystallized quartz. It seems logical to suppose that the quartz is not derived from the sandstone next to fractures, but from this inner curvature where the pressure is greatest. The fold of Fig. 123 is a microfold; we find the same phenomenon in folds which are some hundred times larger, of the size of a big cliff, as, for instance, on the South Wales coast (Fig. 124). The tensional cracks and the wedge-shaped recrystallization zone probably originate in most cases during the latest phase of folding, and sometimes actually after the folding, as release tension cracks. It is improbable that folding would continue in the same strictly concentric fashion if the ten-

Fig. 123 Crestal tension fractures in a microfold. Carboniferous sandstone-shale alternation from East Asturia (Spain).

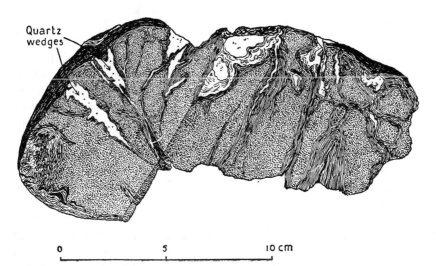

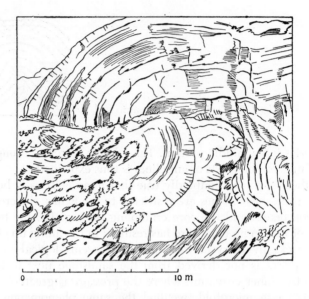

0   10 m

Fig. 124   Crestal fractures and thrust in a minor fold
of Carboniferous sandstone, Millstone Grit; cliff near
Amroth, South Wales.

sion fractures existed long before the process stopped; the width of
the cracks, moreover, is usually very small in comparison with the
total curvature.

The slip on the bedding plane has been checked in the field by
Nabholz (1956) in the typical concentrically folded Jura folds. Striation on limestone bedding planes, but also on joint planes related to
the folding, proved to be more irregular than expected, demonstrating
the complex nature of the process.

We have seen that during the advanced stages of concentric folding
an active role is played by the incompetent bottom layers, which
have a tendency either to break through the core or to broaden the
anticline. In both cases we get a tensional stress even on the crest of
the fold. The faults that are characteristic of the upper incompetent
top layers may penetrate much deeper in this advanced stage, inter-
rupting the concentric folding of the intermediate, concentric layer,
and may eventually link up with the complications in the core (cf.
Figs. 126 and 128). In ground plan, folds, and concentric folds in
particular, generally have an elongated shape, the crest being much
longer than it is broad, but the relation of length to width may vary
considerably. We find all variations, from domes which are nearly
round, and short or brachyanticlines, to very elongated structures.
There are many domes which are supposed to have been formed, not

by tangential pressure, but by radial pressure, caused, for instance, by deep-seated salt domes, such as those in the Texas embayment. As far as I know there has never been an adequate answer to the question of why, in one case, we find a system of parallel elongated anticlines and, in another, a group of domes and short anticlines with varying strikes. The explanation might lie in irregularities in the sedimentary pattern or in succeeding folding phases.

The faults which accompany ordinary concentric folding can be divided into two groups, those of the upper zone and those of the lower zone. The group of the lower zone is apt to break through the concentric zone to the surface and give rise to thrust-faulted and diapiric structures, which will be described in their own chapter. Those of the upper zone can be subdivided into:

1. Longitudinal crest faults
2. Cross-faults and flank faults
3. Diagonal tear faults

These will be described in the following sequence of examples.

LONGITUDINAL CREST FAULTS

The Three Kettleman Hill Domes. These domes are situated near the western border of the San Joaquin Valley basin. Their closure is in the Pliocene San Joaquin shales. The structure is slightly steeper toward the west, in accordance with the general thinning of the strata in that direction toward the basin border. On the map of the central part of the dome (Fig. 125) we notice a whole set of longitudinal normal faults, with throws which are seldom more than 100 ft, as shown in the cross section. The origin of this set of faults is undoubtedly the tension of the outer arc of the fold, typical of the upper portion of the fold.

Because the longitudinal faults converge downward, embracing small grabens, they cut one another out not far below the present surface. We may surmise that we then enter the better-consolidated and therefore concentrically folded part of the fold. Similar longitudinal crest faults are numerous since they characterize, for instance, several other oil fields: Quitman oil field, Wood County, Texas; Sand Draw oil field, Fremont City, Wyoming; La Paz oil field, Maracaibo district, Venezuela, and also the large broad Waubach anticline of the South Limburg coal field.

La Paz. Here the crestal faults (Fig. 126) penetrate very deeply into the core of the structure, and the original crestal trough has probably been accentuated by thrusting at a later stage.

The Quitman Oil Field. This has an exceptionally well developed set of normal crestal faults (Fig. 127) dipping at 45 to 50° and cutting

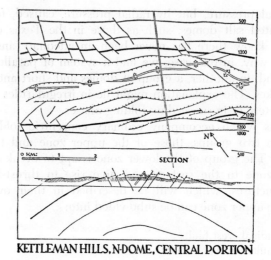

KETTLEMAN HILLS, N-DOME, CENTRAL PORTION

Fig. 125 Crestal faults in central portion of
Kettleman Hills, North Dome, California.
(*After Woodring and Stewart, 1934. Published
by permission of the U.S. Geological Survey.*)

one another out at depth. The Quitman faults also penetrate deeply
into the structure—below 6,000 ft—into the Lower Cretaceous. These
beds cannot be regarded as the soft passive cover of the fold. The
stretching must have another cause, and we may presume that there
has been upward pressure by the incompetent bottom layers.

This need not surprise us, since the Quitman structure is situated
in the same trend as the Opelika and Van oil fields, both considered to
be domes above deep-seated salt plugs. Salt is evidently the best

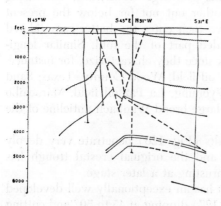

Fig. 126 Section through La Paz
fold, Venezuela. (*After Caribbean
Petroleum Company, 1948. Published by permission of the American Association of Petroleum
Geologists.*)

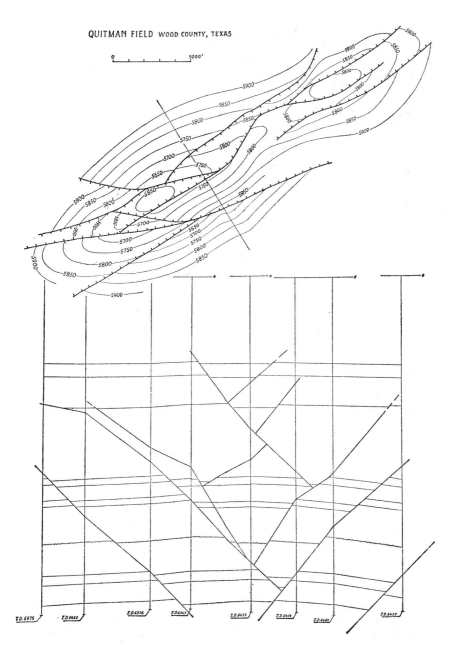

Fig. 127 Quitman oil field, Texas; map and section, showing crestal faults. (*After Smith, 1951. Published by permission of the University of Texas.*)

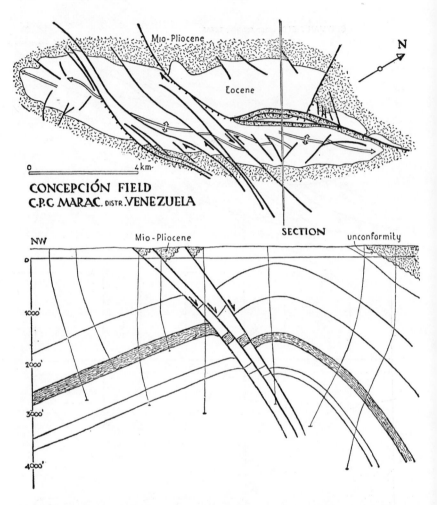

Fig. 128   Concepción oil field, Venezuela; map and section, with crestal faults.
(*After Caribbean Petroleum Company, 1948. Published by permission of the
American Association of Petroleum Geologists.*)

incompetent basal-shearing bed and is particularly active when it
is in a condition of high stress.

   The Concepción Structure of the Maracaibo District, Venezuela
(Fig. 128).   This provides another curious example of crestal faults,
which in this instance curve into diagonal faults. Downward, the
crestal faults merge into the bedding plane at a depth of about 6,000
ft and produce relative motion along the bedding planes, just the
opposite to that which folding would have caused. The folding of
Concepción was accomplished in two stages, a post-Eocene phase and
a post-Miocene phase, with erosion in between, so that the Late

Tertiary cover rests on older rocks in the center of the dome rather than on the flanks. The faults obviously belong to the younger phase. No doubt the crestal region broke through when the second folding created a new anticlinal axis, slightly shifted to the east. The crestal faults are then due in this case to action quite different from ordinary crestal tension. The fact that the northern portion of the field is far more prolific in oil than the southern half corroborates the hypothesis that, after the post-Eocene folding, the top of the structure was in the northern area and that the post-Miocene folding subsequently created the present higher culmination in the south.

The Newport-Inglewood Anticlinal Belt of California. This belt (Chap. 20, Fig. 198), on which numerous oil fields are located, shows a longitudinal crestal fault in its southeastern fields, i.e., in Seal Beach, Long Beach, and Huntingdon oil fields. Faulting is often complex; nevertheless, one continuous fault, with a block downthrown to the northeast, is a consistent feature in these structures. The fault is very steep, almost vertical, and the throw increases downward (Fig. 129). Reviewing the literature on the structural features of the Inglewood belt, Reed and Hollister (1936) conclude that the fault line has probably a deep-seated origin, in the basement, and that motion took place along it at various tectonically active periods during the Tertiary. Either directly or indirectly the folded structures are supposed to be

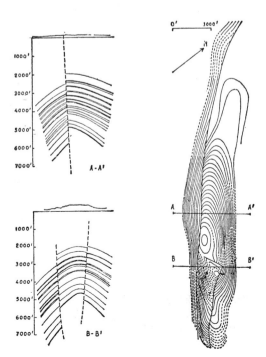

Fig. 129 Crestal faults in Long Beach oil field, California. (*After Stolz, 1943. Published by permission of the California Division of Mines.*)

due to the fault in the basement. It seems probable that the later movements along the fault have been partly horizontal (Chap. 19).

CROSS-FAULTS

Almost every anticlinal structure is accompanied by a host of faults, particularly where the anticlinal axis plunges. All these faults have a

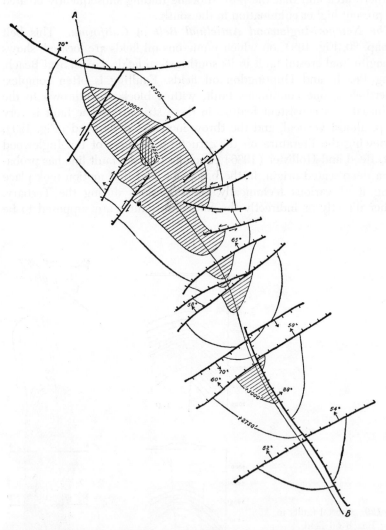

Fig. 130 Elk Basin oil field, with cross-faults and diagonal faults. (*After Bartram*, 1929. *Published by permission of the American Association of Petroleum Geologists.*)

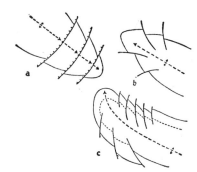

Fig. 131   Perianticlinal faults. (*a*) Ordinary normal tension faults; (*b*) stretching by wrench faults; (*c*) compression shear in convex arc and stretching shear in concave arc.

common origin in the stretching that results from the three-dimensional shape produced by uplift. The simplest kind of fault is the normal cross-fault, perpendicular to the axis, which results from the stretching of the longitudinal arch of a culmination in the anticlinal axis. This tension parallel to the fold axis occurs because the low points of the axis remain fixed in place, unlike synclinal axes, which are crowded closer together as folding progresses. The Elk Basin oil field (Bartram, 1929) is a classic example (Fig. 130). The majority of the faults hade toward the culmination point, and their maximum throw is near the crest. They die out in the flanks, where the structure contour lines become parallel, because there the longitudinal tension disappeared.

Usually, the cross-faults are accompanied by sets of flank faults, which die out both toward the crest and farther down on the flank. A peculiar set of faults very often occurs in the plunge of an anticline. We might call them perianticlinal faults. In general, one can distinguish two kinds of perianticlinal faults: those which have the effect of "drawing out," to lengthen the nose, and those which are connected with a curvature of the perianticline (Fig. 131*c*).

The "drawing-out" faults (Fig. 131*a* and *b*) have the same origin as the normal cross-faults. The anticline, which grows during folding from its center outward, causes longitudinal stretching which can translate itself by wrench faults in the flanks, as sketched in Fig. 131. A very good example may be quoted from the structure of Mene Grande (Fig. 132) in Venezuela and of Lake Bisteneau in Louisiana. The movement along the fault faces has been partly horizontal and partly vertical, since the blocks were in motion during the folding and not afterward; they are typically syntectonic, since they merge into the fold by dying out toward its axis. Many anticlines are slightly curved in ground plan as a result of a slight asymmetry in their cross section, the curve being convex toward the steep flank (Fig. 131*c*). This is easily understood if we again imagine the structure as the result of the dynamic process, starting at the center and growing in height and

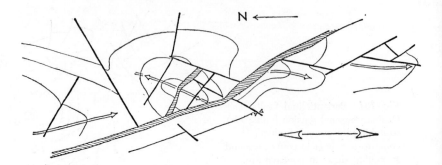

Fig. 132 Map of Mene Grande oil field, Venezuela. (*After Caribbean Petroleum Company, 1948. Published by permission of the American Association of Petroleum Geologists.*)

in length at the same time; the culmination will move forward slightly more than the perianticlines.

This curvature in the perianticline causes two kinds of faults, one due to compression in the inner curve, the other to stretching in the outer curve (Fig. 131*c*). A particularly clear example of this kind of compression faulting can be seen in the southern perianticline of the Kettleman Hills Middle Dome, where both kinds of faults are repre-

Fig. 133 Perianticline of Kettleman Hills, Middle Dome, California. (*After Woodring and Stewart, 1934. Published by permission of the U.S. Geological Survey.*)

KETTLEMAN HILLS M.DOME

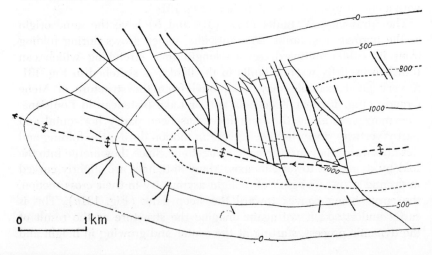

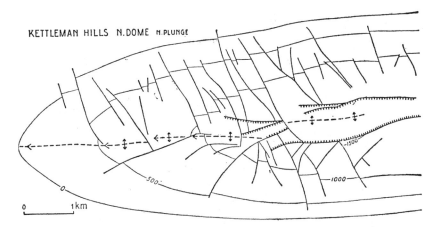

Fig. 134 Perianticline of Kettleman Hills, North Dome, California. (*After Woodring and Stewart, 1934. Published by permission of the U.S. Geological Survey.*)

sented (Fig. 133). We also find the same kind of faults in the northern perianticline of Kettleman Hills North Dome (Fig. 134), where the stretching in the west flank is partly due to "drawing-out" faults and partly to curvature stretching. The eastern perianticlinal flank is characterized by curvature-compression faults. The same stretching can also be effected by normal faults alone. This is proved by the plunge of the Wilmington (California) perianticline (Fig. 135). The majority of the diagonal flank faults which we frequently encounter in the flanks of anticlines, even opposite a horizontal portion of the axis, can be considered as older perianticlinal faults of the types described above. During the longitudinal growth of the anticline, the anticlinal plunge is gradually pushed outward, leaving its faults to adorn the flanks of the later horizontal axis.

The fact that a perianticlinal fault is frequently found to merge into another kind, a normal cross-fault, for instance, can easily be understood when we realize that the growth of the structure is a dynamic process and not static. The faults as well as the fold grow and extend; faults may meet and merge into one another, especially since, during the process, their extremities are the scene of maximum stresses. The two stress fields will merge even before the faults have joined. The normal longitudinal crestal faults are the last to come into existence, because they belong to the anticlinal, and not to the perianticlinal, stage. This is clearly illustrated by the two examples given above of Kettleman Hills North Dome and Middle Dome where crestal faults are lacking in the perianticline (Figs. 133 and 134) but are present on the crest (Fig. 125).

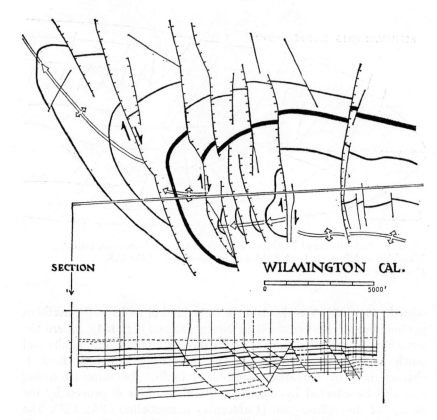

Fig. 135 Perianticline of Wilmington oil field, California; map and section. (*After Winterthurn, 1943. Published by permission of the California Division of Mines.*)

If I were to extend this review of the characteristics of concentric folds to a further stage, we should perceive that all kinds of other complications set in when anticlines become very steep. We should enter the domain of thrust, diapiric, and pinched anticlines. These will be treated in separate chapters.

MONOCLINES

The faults treated in the foregoing paragraphs are all induced by folding, but in some cases the folding is due to faulting in the basement. Clear examples of this interaction are the monoclines, anticlinal structures with one very broad and flat flank and one very narrow and steep flank, more like a flexure. This feature is thought to indicate a tilted block in the underground, with the sedimentary strata warped

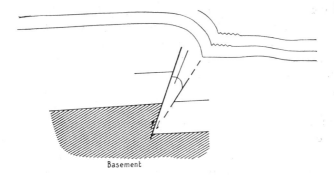

Basement

Fig. 136   Monocline. A steep flexure above a basement thrust.

over the vertical throw of the fault. It is typical of these structures that the syncline next to the steep flank is a sharp nick without any thrust plane. Faults do occur inside the structure very near the anticlinal axis.

Monoclines are typical of cratonic conditions, the Colorado Plateau, for instance, or in the Negev Desert of southern Israel (Fig. 136) (de Sitter, 1962a). When one approaches a cratonic shield from the basin, ordinary concentric folds change into monoclines having the same axial trend and presumably due to the same compressive stress field. Therefore it is probable that the basement fault is an upthrust, and not a normal fault. Moreover, it is very improbable that in a tensional stress field the surface layers would not be broken by normal faulting.

CONCENTRIC FOLDS AND OIL ACCUMULATION

Concentric folds are preeminently the realm of oil and gas accumulations. The oil which is driven out of its pelitic mother rock by compaction, as a suspension in water, enters a more permeable psammitic layer and is trapped in it by another overlying pelite. The droplets of oil in the reservoir rock are too large to enter the narrow capillaries of this rock above, and are left behind as the water continues its upward travel. This process implies that the porosity of the rock was not too much impaired by the tectonic processes which tilted the reservoir bed and caused the oil to travel to the highest position it could reach. In this respect it is interesting to remember that Goguel (1943) succeeded in demonstrating in the laboratory that a folded rock has lost a considerable percentage of its porosity in comparison with its unfolded condition. We may expect, therefore, that the liberation of oil from its source rock can take place in two stages. First, the compaction stage lasts for long periods of continuous loading as sediments accumulate. The compaction drives the connate water and its oil content out of the fine-grained source rock and into the sands or limestones, with their larger pores. Second, the original slope of these reservoir rocks toward the center of the basin will encourage accumulation of oil in the basin margin, a process facilitated by the fact that the center of the basin will have a more pelitic facies than its shores. Sand tongues will reach from the margin toward the basin, and differential compaction will increase the original depositional slopes.

This period of accumulation will fade out as compaction slows down in the course of time. It will be reactivated, however, if there is subsequent folding which compacts the pelites again, and the whole process of liberation, lateral migration, and accumulation will be repeated. It seems improbable that a second folding phase will start a new cycle of accumulation, since the compression of the rocks is certainly a finite process.

The repetition of the process of oil migration and accumulation explains why it is possible to find oil accumulations both in unfolded marginal rocks of a basin and in folded rocks of the same age in the center of the basin, as occurs, for instance, in the San Joaquin basin of southern California. On the other hand, a well-known reservoir rock, like the Cretaceous Woodbine Sand of the Texas embayment, is often locally barren in structures that can be proved to have belonged to a second folding phase which occurred after the migrating oil had reached the older structures.

Vertical migration of oil is relatively rare, and when it does occur, the much smaller secondary accumulation above the original pool is generally filled with a so-called "freak oil," a much lighter derivate from the original oil, which can apparently pass upward although heavier oil is trapped. Faults can act as oil conduits, as is proved by oil-filled fault breccias, for instance, but they serve much more frequently as oil traps. The perianticlinal faults, and particularly those that cross the anticlinal axis, often retain the oil behind them. A well-known and spectacular example of such traps is offered by the Elk Basin oil field (Fig. 130) situated in the axis of the Bighorn basin.

Strong folding and even large overthrusting do not prevent the accumulation of oil. Oil accumulations are known in the lower flank of overthrust anticlines such as the Tarra anticline in Venezuela (Chap. 15, Fig. 143) and even in nappelike structures such as the old Borislaw field in Poland.

As soon as the deformation has the character of cleavage folding, oil can no longer be expected, since the compression has been too severe. This is probably one of the major reasons why accumulations, in Paleozoic time, are restricted to those regions where there has been no later deformation.

Any review of the tectonic shapes of oil accumulations would comprise the whole gamut of concentric fold structures and their faults, besides a number of pure fault structures (Chap. 10, Figs. 72 and 74) and diapiric structures and domes; the latter will be treated in Chap. 17.

Chapter 15

Low-angle Thrusts

The flat overthrust developing into a thrust sheet and a nappe along a basal detachment plane is such a spectacular phenomenon in the structural development of the Alpine type that it merits treatment in a separate chapter.

ASYMMETRIC FOLDS AND LOW-ANGLE THRUSTS

Asymmetry of folds is a very common feature, which always originates because of irregularities in the structure of the basin.

The two irregularities which are the most frequent causes of asymmetry are (1) wedging out of the folded series and (2) original differences of altitude between two flanks of the same fold.

When a sedimentary series wedges out toward the basin border, and later compression originates a concentric fold on this thinning portion of the basin margin, the two flanks of this structure are no longer equal; the sedimentary series of the flank nearest to the basin border are thinner than those of the opposite flank. As the radius of curvature is a direct consequence of the thickness of the sedimentary series involved in the folding, the flank facing the border will have a shorter radius and will therefore be steeper than the opposite flank (Fig. 137).

Fig. 137 Asymmetric fold on basin margin due to thinning of sedimentary series.

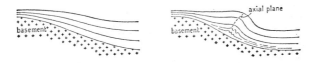

Fig. 138   Asymmetric fold on basin margin due to
higher elevation of basin border.

In this case we have assumed that the surface was horizontal, but
it often happens that, in the first stage of compression, the basin
borders have been elevated and that a considerable slope toward the
basin center has been established. In that case further lateral compression may result in an asymmetric anticline where the steep flank
is facing the basin center (Fig. 138).

The two examples here advanced are the most simple forms of
asymmetric structures, where the whole sedimentary series is folded in
one structure and the basement is thought to have been completely
passive. It will often occur that a detachment plane is formed below
a conspicuous competent member of the series, and when either the
whole series or that particular competent member is wedging out, the
same effect, i.e., an asymmetrical anticline, will be produced in the
upper fold (Fig. 139). What happens to the lower series, below the
detachment plane, will remain hidden to the field geologist; in Fig.
139 I presumed it was folded higher up on the basin border. It is often
observed that the fold is located on the thin wedge of the competent
member as a disharmonic structure; this is probably due to isolation
of the topmost series by means of the detachment plane below this
competent member.

When the basement itself is involved in the folding, we may get
quite different structures, mostly unpredictable and therefore often
misinterpreted. The axial plane of a concentric asymmetric anticline
necessarily hades away from the steep flank, and the axis of the fold

Fig. 139   Asymmetric fold due to thinning of
competent member of sedimentary series and
located above its thin wedge.

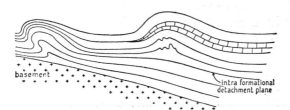

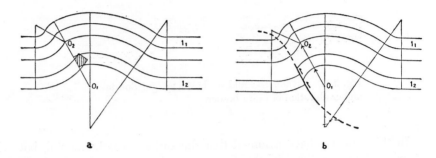

Fig. 140   Origin of thrust fault in asymmetric anticline.

is therefore displaced toward the flatter flank. In drilling for oil this displacement has to be taken into account, and the construction of the section from surface dips assuming pure concentric folding will indicate the displacement (Fig. 140).

Construction along those lines will reveal that, at a certain depth, pure concentricity is no longer possible unless we suppose that the sediment can be compressed in a smaller volume, which is evidently possible to only a very small extent. The shaded part in layer l_2 of Fig. 140, for instance, represents the volume of that layer which has been omitted in the section construction. Obviously, this cannot be a true representation of the real fold, and this lack of space, due to the geometrical impossibility of maintaining concentricity downward results in the breaking through of layer l_2 before this stage of folding is reached. In Fig. 140b a much more probable construction has been drawn, showing the origin of a thrust fault in the steep flank of the asymmetric anticline.

The frequency of asymmetric and overthrust anticlines in folded regions shows that they are closely associated. It can often be observed that the two merge into one another laterally. We shall find the overthrusts in the structurally highest area of a fold, since it is the most strongly compressed portion. Laterally, the slip along the thrust diminishes and finally disappears into a simple steep flank, or splits up into tear faults which cross the anticline diagonally. The Jura Mountains, for instance, show many examples of the transition of a thrust-faulted anticline to an asymmetric one.

The development of the thrust has been explained by Albert Heim (1921) as due to attenuation of the middle limb of a recumbent fold (Fig. 141). His conception was derived from the tectonic features of the Säntis Mountains. Buxtorf (1916), on the other hand, studying the tectonic conditions of the Jura Mountains, concluded that a flat reversed fault gradually develops into a thrust-faulted anticline. The

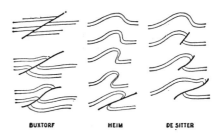

Fig. 141 Origin of thrust faulting according to Buxtorf, Heim, and de Sitter.

BUXTORF   HEIM   DE SITTER

same conception of the origin of flat thrusts prevails with the geologists of the Westphalian coal basin (Kukuk, 1938, p. 138).

Besides these contradictory conceptions, a third possibility is here presented, i.e., the development of a thrust fault in a much earlier stage of folding than Heim observed and a much later phase than Buxtorf and Kukuk presume, as explained above.

As we have seen, the first phase of the steep reversed longitudinal fault in an anticline will originate in the core of the structure; its location is solely due to the relative position of the center of major curvature and is independent of the actual dip of the flank, but depends on the breadth of the steeper portion of this flank. Figure 142*a* represents a very flat structure—an oil-bearing anticline in Java, which, however, has at the surface a narrow zone of steeper dips, with a maximum of 26°. This relatively "steep" flank, in a structure with flanks dipping mainly at 3 to 6°, develops downward, as revealed by drilling, into a very steep flank with broken strata, etc., as shown in the section. The steep dips are encountered only below the center of curvature of the steep part of the flank. The formation consists of hard limey sandstones and soft marls and shales, a well-stratified formation.

Figure 142*b*, a section through the Lok-Batan oil field of the Apsheron Peninsula, gives an example of a further stage of a thrust

Fig. 142 Development of a thrust fault in an asymmetric anticline exemplified by three structures: (*a*) Nglobo (Java); (*b*) Lok Batan (Apsheron Peninsula); (*c*) Kampong Minjak (Sumatra).

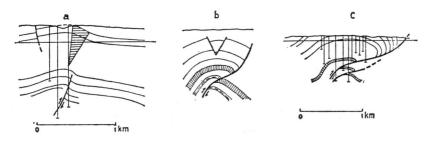

structure. A really vertical zone is not yet present; neither has the thrust movement become great.

In Fig. 142c, a section through the old Kampong Minjak (oil village) oil field of Sumatra, a still further advanced stage of thrusting is revealed. The original S-shaped thrust which provided an obstruction to further movement has been flattened by means of a second lower thrust. We see very clearly the development of a broad apex in the overthrust flank arching over the buried center of the structure, a feature which we shall also find in much larger overthrusts.

The few examples advanced to illustrate the growth of a thrust plane all depend on the assumption that an overthrust anticline is a typical superficial structure. This assumption is substantiated by the fact that thrust and asymmetrical anticlines are favored by the existence of a particular incompetent layer at the base, above the basal shearing plane, in which the thrust plane is lost. When no single outstanding basal shearing plane exists somewhere at depth, then the amplitude of structures may vary, and each may have taken up a different incompetent layer as its basal shearing plane; and the thrust planes may run for considerable lengths above one another before they eventually unite at a lower level.

Very much also depends on the distribution of competent layers in a folded sequence of strata. When there is mainly one thick competent layer, it will to a large extent control the amplitude of the folds; and when there are two or more outstanding competent horizons, each of the layers may have its own influence. In the Tarra anticline (Colon district, eastern Venezuela) we find two competent horizons. The upper one is a thick, occasionally oil-bearing arkosic sandstone of Eocene age, which shows an overthrust to the east (Fig. 143). Below that, the Cretaceous limestones apparently show an overthrust in the opposite direction. This structure is not revealed in one section, but in the prolongation of the anticline toward the south. In Fig. 143 the two phenomena have tentatively been combined.

In this respect it is of interest to recall a structure which Fallot (1949) described, in the western Alps, as a subcutaneous thrust (Fig. 144); in this the independence of the upper and lower parts of a series separated by a thick incompetent bed is clearly demonstrated.

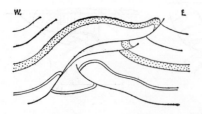

Fig. 143 Overthrust of Tarra anticline, Colon district, Venezuela, completed with deeper structure revealed in the southern extension of the same anticline.

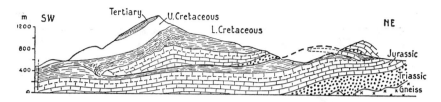

Fig. 144 Intercutaneous thrust in Royce structure, western Alps. (*After Fallot, 1949. Published by permission of the Director, Laboratoire de Géologie de la Sorbonne, Paris.*)

The sequence of Fig. 142*a* to *c* illustrates the growth of the overthrust from the inconspicuous original shape to the developed shape of the ordinary overthrust anticline, and the upper part of the Tarra anticline section demonstrates its possible further development.

Thrusting of the type of the Tarra anticline is quite a common kind of structure. We find it, for instance, in the section of the Sarrebrück anticline (Fig. 145), the upper part of which has been well explored by coal mining, and in the Turner Valley oil field (Fig. 146). The development of the Turner Valley structure as figured by Link (1949) again shows the location of a fold on a wedging-out member of the series, a limestone (Fig. 147). These thrust structures in the Foothills belt of the Canadian Rocky Mountains, of which Turner Valley is most prominent, are extremely complicated, and it seems doubtful that every thrust plane originated in its own asymmetric anticline (Fox, 1959). The presence of the Mississippian limestone at 2 to 4 km depth and of a preferred detachment plane in the Devonian below it certainly is the controlling factor, but it seems that, once a thrust plane, originating in an asymmetric anticline above, cut through this limestone, further compression favored the development of numerous thrusts in the upper layers, all originating in this once established

Fig. 145 Sarrebrück anticline with thrust fault. (*After Pruvost, 1934.*)

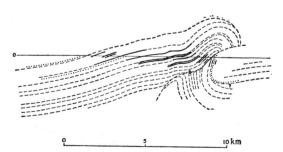

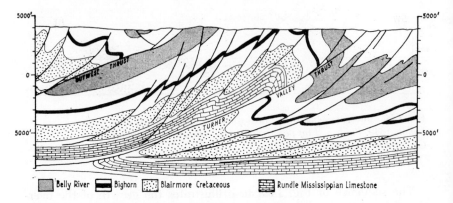

Fig. 146   The Turner Valley thrust in the Foothills belt of the Canadian Rocky Mountains. (*After Fox, 1959. Published by permission of the American Association of Petroleum Geologists.*)

limestone thrust. In this kind of thrust-faulted anticline the actual bending of the strata stops as soon as the thrust plane cuts through them in the course of its extension upward and downward during folding. Once it has, in its downward course, reached the basal detachment plane, the folding stops altogether, and the rest of the compression is wholly taken up by the thrust movement. Extreme cases of such

Fig. 147   Development of Turner Valley structure. (*After Link, 1949. Published by permission of the American Association of Petroleum Geologists.*)

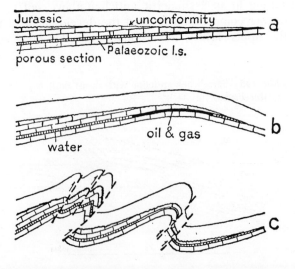

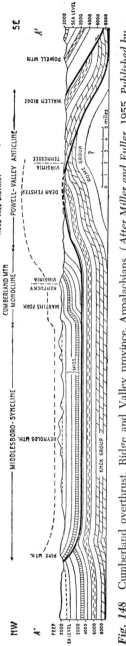

Fig. 148 Cumberland overthrust, Ridge and Valley province, Appalachians. (*After Miller and Fuller,* 1955. *Published by permission of the Virginia Geological Survey.*)

thrust structures are found in the Valley and Ridge province of the Appalachians. Its best-known structure is perhaps the Cumberland thrust, Virginia (Fig. 148; Miller and Fuller, 1955; Wilson and Stearns, 1958).

In this section we observe that the Cumberland thrust plane reaches its basal detachment plane just below the Mississippian and stays in the same horizon for 20 miles; it then cuts obliquely down to a lower detachment plane, a shale in the Cambrian Rome Group. It seems probable that it is forced down by the next thrust plane, the Wallen Ridge thrust. The structure of thrust sheets stacked like roof tiles, as Wilson and Stearns represent them, can be compared with the succession of thrust faults of the Charleroi coal basin as Kaisin, Jr. (1947) figured them (Fig. 149), and the incipient stage of the Helvetian thrust sheets was probably similar (cf. Chap. 18, Fig. 186).

A very interesting feature is the fact that the amount of forward slip in the frontal anticline of the Pine Mountain is very small indeed (1 or 2 miles), as compared with the breadth of the thrust sheet (20 miles), and that the slip increases backward to some 8 miles in the Powell Valley anticline. This last feature proves again that the thrust started at depth and at the back where the throw is largest and gradually advanced toward the front where the throw is smallest. Where the thrust plane cuts stratigraphically upward in the thrust sheet from the Cambrian to the Mississippian naturally, it also cuts upward in the autochthonous, as revealed in the Powell Valley anticline.

The S shape of the thrust plane is prominent only in the first stage of the thrust, when it is still more or less parallel to the curved axial plane of the asymmetric fold. Later thrusting has to obliterate the curve, and therefore we often find intermediate blocks and crushed zones along the later thrust plane.

Development as sketched above and illustrated by many examples is not the only possible result of further compression on an asymmetric thrust anticline. When the folds are closely packed, without broad synclines, and when they are well developed before the thrust plane breaks through, the front of the upper thrust mass soon abuts upon the

Fig. 149   Charleroi coal basin thrusts. (*After Kaisin, Jr.,* 1947.)

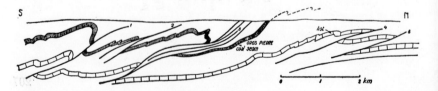

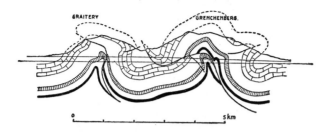

Fig. 150 Graitery-Grenchenberg structure. (*After Buxtorf, in Heim, 1921.*)

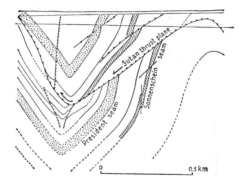

Fig. 151 The folded Sutan overthrust, Ruhr coal field. (*After Kukuk, 1938. Published by permission of Springer-Verlag, Berlin.*)

next fold, and no further thrusting is possible. Further compression is then continued again by folding, the thrust plane being folded together with the original fold. A well-known example of this development is that of the Graitery-Grenchenberg tunnel section in the Swiss Jura Mountains (Fig. 150). The original S shape of the thrust plane is now more pronounced by further folding.

The same kind of development is found in the Ruhr coal field, where the famous Sutan thrust has been severely folded in the later stages of compression (Fig. 151), and also in many of the low-angle thrusts of the Liège coal basin.

FLAT PLANAR THRUST PLANES

Although the early-stage overthrust has been illustrated by many examples in the preceding paragraphs, we must not forget that Buxtorf's

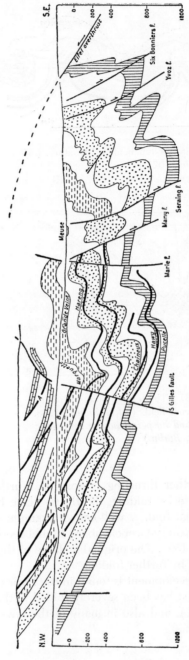

Fig. 152 Numerous low-angle thrusts in the Liège coal basin. (*After Humblet, 1941, and Ancion, 1948.*)

hypothesis, that the overthrust anticline originated in an unfolded flat overthrust, was based on substantial evidence.

In both the coal fields of Limburg and Liège and in the Canadian Rocky Mountains foothills, extensive and extremely flat thrusts have been revealed. They are often in no way connected with any individual folds. The thrust movement can easily disappear from sight by running into a bedding plane. These very flat thrusts possibly represent nothing more than the prolongation of anticlinal thrusts back from the anticlinal front which have been carried away by erosion, but there is no direct supporting evidence for this hypothesis. They are frequent in the Liège coal field (Fig. 152), where it is certain that they belong to a very early stage of the folding process, since they have been folded after the thrust movement.

COMPOSITE WEDGES

In this respect it is interesting to turn our attention to a feature of faulting in the calcareous Apennine ridges which has been demonstrated by Beneo and Migliorini (1948). The most typical section is that of the Montagna del Morrone (Fig. 153), and the resulting structure has been called a "composite wedge" by Migliorini. The structure is characterized on one side by low-angle thrusts over a subsided basin; these become steeper toward the center and change their character from thrust faults to normal faults, on the other side of the ridge. Because the thick rigid limestone, never covered by much sediment, was near the surface, it did not fold, but became faulted. The schematic section of Fig. 154 shows that the whole structure can be seen as a compression phenomenon due to an inclined stress field. One could imagine that the departure of the stress from the horizontal by some 30° could be due to loading by a large mass on one side of the basin or to the subsidence of a basin at the other side. This also happens on the internal side of a marginal trough; the Liège coal basin is an example. A simplified section (Humblet, 1941), corrected for its south-

Fig. 153 Triassic to Middle Miocene limestones overlain by Tertiary and Pleistocene clastics (in black). Montagna del Murrone composite wedge. (*After Migliorini, 1948. Published by permission of Società Geologica Italiana.*)

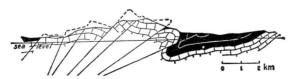

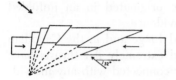

Fig. 154 Composite wedge due to inclined stress field. (*After Migliorini, 1948. Published by permission of Società Geologica Italiana.*)

ern part with the help of Ancion's section (1948; Fig. 152), shows that the structure of this basin is peculiar. In the gentler northern part of the basin, where it rests on the flank of the Brabant massif, we find the succession of six flat thrusts which have been mentioned above; and in the south, in the deepest part of the basin, we find a few normal faults. Still farther south, the Eifel fault is a low-angle thrust with a large throw, along which a large overthrust mass passed over the Cointe anticline and onto the southern border of the coal basin in front of it. I think this conflicting appearance of flat thrusts in the north and steep normal faults in the south could be regarded as analogous to the composite wedges of Migliorini, as a *set* limiting a series of upthrusted central wedges. The tilting of the stress could arise from the extra loading of the thrust mass above the Eifel fault. It is significant that the axial planes of the sharp folds in the southern part of the basin also indicate that the principal stress had this inclination to the horizontal. We should commit a serious error if we imagined the complicated structure of the Liège basin to be the result of one stress field caused by a lateral stress which originated the Eifel thrust. On the contrary, we must view it as a slowly developing process, in which the stress, moving the advancing main thrust sheet, first caused the flat overthrust in the north; later, when the loading began to make itself seriously felt, the sharp folds; and lastly, near the end of the process, the normal faults in the south. This sequence is proved by the fact that the flat overthrusts are folded and that the normal faults cut through the folds. Nevertheless, the final configuration of the basin seen as a whole is the result of one stress field slowly rotating from a slightly inclined to a more strongly inclined position.

Chapter 16

Disharmonic Folds

GENERAL CHARACTERISTICS

Disharmonic folding is a general term, giving expression to the observation that the continuation of a fold downward is often neither concentric nor similar. Its most extreme form is found when a fold dies out downward very quickly and thus forms a "wrinkle" above an undisturbed flat surface. In such a case we clearly have a detachment horizon; the beds above the undisturbed horizon have been folded independently of their basement. Between this extreme case of disharmony and the case of a fold in which only a slight difference in shape can be noticed between two overlying beds, all transitions exist. In the course of our descriptions we have already met with quite a few instances of disharmony.

The bed in which the disharmony between the overlying and underlying bed has been effected is always an incompetent member in relation to its wall and roof. In this incompetent bed the mechanism of folding is different from that in the competent members—flow in the case of salt-bearing beds; crumpling, faulting, or cleavage folding in the case of ordinary shales or clays.

The lateral shortening of the underlying less disturbed bed must necessarily be more or less equal to that of the overlying sequence of beds. It may either be folded more intensely elsewhere or it may be folded along cleavage planes and thus compressed in another way within the same section. Lack of sufficient exposures usually makes it difficult to decide between these possibilities.

We have already seen, in Chap. 14, that concentric folding inevitably leads to detachment, and therefore to disharmonic folding. And as the erosion has to cut deep down into the structures in order to reveal its disharmonic nature, the Hercynian folds, being more deeply eroded, show disharmony more often than do Tertiary structures.

THE RUHR COAL DISTRICT

Disharmonic folding is often developed on the flank of a concentric structure. In Fig. 155, a thrust on the flank of a concentric anticline, the Wattenscheider structure, has its origin in one of a set of oblique shear planes which developed at a late stage in the folding process. Where this thrust plane cuts the Hugo and Robert seams at the top of the anticline, we perceive an extra wrinkle which preceded the thrust (bed *c* in Fig. 155). The thrust plane cuts very obliquely through the left-hand flank. In other instances it often stays in one particular bed and thus takes part in the concentric folding in the flank. In such cases one can say that the direction of slip along the bedding in the flank, due to concentric folding, cuts through the anticline instead of following its curvature. This will happen when the folding has advanced so far that the flank has a dip equal to or higher than 45° and the bedding slip planes in the flank happen to coincide with the potential oblique-shear direction, oblique to the general lateral stress (see also concentric cleavage, Chap. 21). In this way a small disharmonic fold appears, for instance, at the apex of a major fold (Figs. 155 to 157), or even sometimes on the flank (Fig. 158).

A perfectly analogous case is represented by the section in Fig. 156, where the same kind of structure is found in a syncline. The disharmony is somewhat more pronounced than in Fig. 155. The numerous oblique fault planes of this section are parallel to a set of minute shear planes which are oblique to the detachment plane of the disharmonic fold; the latter coincides with the bedding plane of the upper structure. The thickening of the strata on the crest of the disharmonic fold is of the oblique-cleavage type which we call chevron

Fig. 155   Thrust in the flank of the Wattenscheider anticline, Ruhr coal district. (*After Kukuk, 1938. Published by permission of Springer-Verlag Berlin.*)

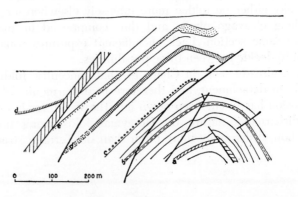

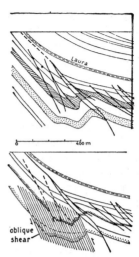

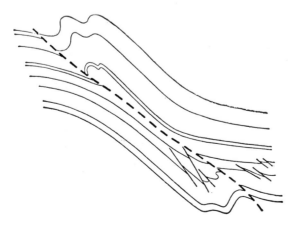

Fig. 156 Thrust in flank of syncline, Gelsenkirchen syncline, Ruhr coal district. (*After Böttcher, 1925, in Kukuk, 1938. Published by permission of Springer-Verlag, Berlin.*)

folding (Chap. 22). With the flattening of the dip toward the synclinal axis, the position of the oblique shear faults also becomes flatter. We shall find this same phenomenon in Chap. 22, Fig. 234, where the formation of a basal shear plane as a thrust plane causes a reorientation of the stress direction parallel to this plane, which in its turn causes shear oblique to the thrust plane. In this case the several thrust planes actually disappear in the shale beds below the Katharina seam. This structure has given rise to a supposition that the folding of the lower series below the Katharina seam took place before the deposition of the upper beds and that the upper beds are unconformable on the lower beds. This fact (no such unconformity existing elsewhere)

Fig. 157 Hypothetic upward completion of synclinal thrust of Gelsenkirchen syncline.

supports the view that the section shows only a particular kind of disharmonic folding, and no unconformity.

The necessary shortening in the upper beds, Laura-Zollverein, could have taken place by disharmonic folding on top of a thrust plane in the same stratigraphic position, but higher up the structure. The thrust movement would be concentrated, for both structures, on the same thrust plane, and the two disharmonic folds would compensate each other as sketched in Fig. 157.

A very similar disharmonic fold, exposed in the shafts of one of the Dutch collieries (Fig. 158), shows the development on the gentle flank of an anticline.

In Fig. 159 another kind of disharmony is represented, arising not by the prolongation of slip along the bedding beyond its proper place, but by the formation of an accordion synclinal fold, dying out upward against a gentle flank. The axial plane of this fold is accentuated by an axial fault plane of the kind that we shall find also in accordion folds (Chap. 21), and the mechanism by which it dies out is clearly demon-

Fig. 158   Disharmonic fold exposed in shaft of Willem-Sophy Colliery, South Limburg coal field. (*After Sax, 1946. Published by permission of Geologisch Bureau voor het Mijngebied, Heerlen.*)

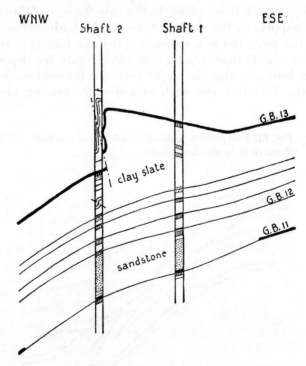

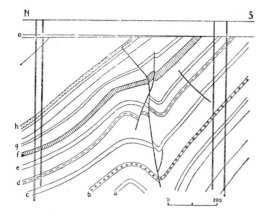

Fig. 159 Disharmonic fold in Grubenfeld, Holland, Ruhr coal district. (*After Böttcher, 1925, in Kukuk, 1938. Published by permission of Springer-Verlag, Berlin.*)

strated by the presence of secondary faults. We can regard this fold as an example of one of the many means by which the lack of space in the core of an anticline is solved, the anticline in question being a much larger structure situated farther to the south.

THE ANTHRACITE COAL BASIN OF NORTH PENNSYLVANIA

All the detailed sections of this basin give numerous instances of disharmonic folding. In the section in Fig. 160 we observe that the beds *b*, *c*, and *d* have been folded independently of bed *a*, which reflects the sharp anticline of the upper beds only very faintly. The shales between beds *a* and *b* have acted as a detachment horizon and have thus given the upper beds the opportunity of folding independently of the lower beds.

On the other hand, compression in the upper beds must be compensated elsewhere by an equal compression in the lower beds. This is illustrated by Fig. 161, in which the same detachment horizon has allowed the lower bed *a* to make a much sharper fold than have the higher beds. Without detailed field observations it is impossible to decide what kind of shearing took place in the intervening shale bed, but in the anticlinal and synclinal folds, concentric folding has been preserved to some extent.

In general, disharmonic folding represents a possibility of transition from one kind of folding to another and from one fold shape to an-

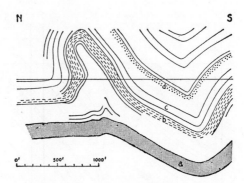

Fig. 160 Disharmonic folding in Anthracite
basin of Pennsylvania. Upper beds in extra
disharmonic fold. (*After Darton,* 1940.
*Published by permission of the U.S.
Geological Survey.*)

other. It is very difficult to predict from surface observations whether
disharmony can be expected or not, but one can safely assume that
in a concentric structure either faulting or disharmony will set in at
a certain depth. Whether the disharmony will be distributed over
several incompetent layers or be concentrated on a single one is
unpredictable, unless one has information from adjacent structures.
Although disharmony is not restricted to concentric folding, it is more
obvious here than in cleavage folding. As cleavage deformation is
generally preceded by concentric folding, disharmony occurs also in
this similar type, as, for instance, in the Pyrenees, where the highly
incompetent Silurian slates separate structures of completely different
character in the Devonian from those in the Ordovician (Chap. 31).

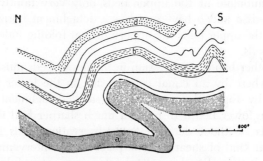

Fig. 161 Disharmonic folding in Anthracite
basin of Pennsylvania. Lower beds in extra
disharmonic fold. (*After Darton,* 1940. *Published
by permission of the U.S. Geological Survey.*)

Chapter 17

Diapiric and Collapse Structures, Domes, and Cauldrons

In this chapter I propose to describe two opposites: diapiric structures, which are formed by pressure acting upward from below, and collapse structures, which are formed by different sorts of caving in due to voids below the surface. They have one thing in common, however, their circular shape, due to a peculiarity of their stress field. In this the lateral forces are equal and unvariable, and the active force is vertical and either positive (upward) or negative (downward). It is true that many diapiric structures are not circular. This happens when the horizontal stress field is not homogeneous, but has been changed and orientated by a folding stress. Nevertheless, even the oblong diapir is due to a vertical stress.

Because many domes are due to a deep-seated diapir they are described in this chapter. They could, however, have equally well been discussed in connection with ordinary plunging anticlines, of which they are an extremely short variety.

Collapse structures are either connected with volcanism, as cauldrons of different kinds and cryptovolcanic structures, or are due to solution of salt or limestone at depth.

DIAPIRIC STRUCTURES

In Chap. 13 we saw that every concentric fold finds more difficulty in maintaining its concentric habit as folding progresses. There is less and less space left in the core of the fold, occupied by its basal incompetent layers. The solution of the difficulty is either a broadening of the fold or a breakthrough in the flanks. Broadening is often checked both by the weight of its own arc and by the proximity of the next fold. The breakthrough is therefore the normal consequence in ad-

219

vanced folding. The asymmetric breakthrough is a thrust fault. In this chapter we shall get to know its symmetrical form, the diapir. The diapiric structure is characterized by the expulsion of the core of the anticline through the crest of the fold and, as such, is an example of two horizontally moving flanks in contrast with a vertically moving crestal wedge (cf. Chap. 14, Fig. 120). The lines joining the turning points from vertical to horizontal movement turn into fault planes leading toward the core of the anticline, and the block contained between these faults is pressed out. This action is realized only in nature when the bottom layers are extremely plastic; this can be understood when we consider that only a fluid, or, as in this case, an extremely plastic material, is able directly to transform a lateral stress into hydrostatic pressure.

This mechanism of diapirs due to folding is, however, not the only cause of upward breakthrough of plastic material. The other cause is the simple load of sediments overlying the plastic layer; this can cause an upwelling because the specific density of salt is much smaller than that of ordinary rock material and because a local thinning or removal of the load, by erosion, for instance, will allow the plastic material to be pressed out.

It is of course impossible in most cases to judge how much of the movement is due to one or the other factor; whether a slight folding started the movement or whether hydrostatic adjustment was the primary cause. Let it suffice to say that the upwelling of the lower plastic layer can often be connected with both folding and hydrostatic movement. The Hannoverian salt-dome region (Fig. 162) gives a good example of diapiric salt domes where the gravitational effect preponderates.

A clearer insight into the problem of the origin of the diapir can be obtained when the incipient stage of these structures is studied. Some sections from the northeast part of the Netherlands, wholly based on a seismic reflection survey for oil prospection, are helpful (Fig. 163). Four stages are represented by four different sections. In the first section we perceive hardly any deformation of the horizontal succession of Permian (Zechstein) salt, Jurassic, Cretaceous, and Tertiary rocks.

In the second section the upper boundary of the salt bed is distinctly wavy; this is reflected in the base of the Albian (Lower Cretaceous), but not in the base of the Tertiary. It indicates that the movement took place before the deposition of this last formation.

In the third section the structures become more pronounced. In the fourth section a distinct dome has been formed. The base of the Jurassic is slightly unconformable, and so is the base of the Portlandian; the base of the Lower Cretaceous has a stronger uncon-

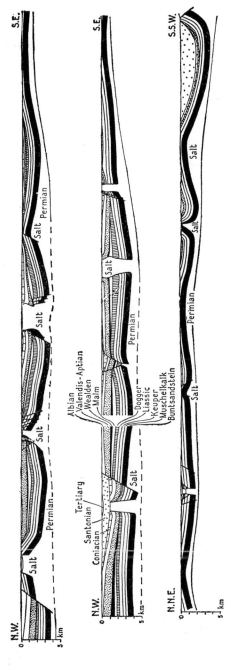

Fig. 162 Three sections through Hannoverian salt-dome region. (*After Roll, 1949.*)

DIAPIRIC STRUCTURES

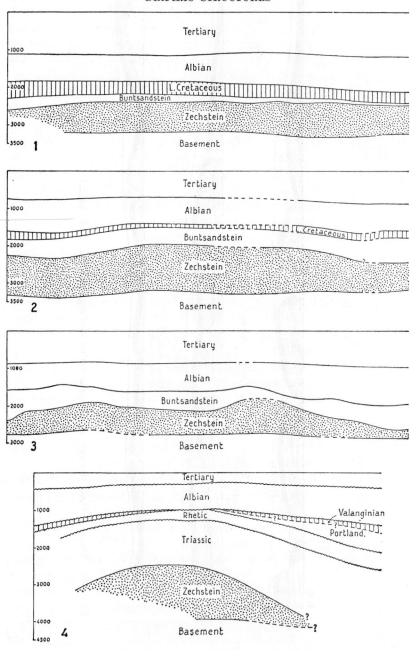

Fig. 163 Incipient salt-dome structures revealed by seismic exploration in the northeast Netherlands. (*Unpublished. Reproduced by permission of Nederlandse Aardolie Mij., Oldenzaal.*)

formity; and the strongest unconformity is found at the base of the Albian. The base of the Tertiary is horizontal. On the flank, the Zechstein Salt thins to almost nothing, proving that quite a volume of salt has flowed toward the dome. (The third section shows the beginning of the effect of flow.) The repeated unconformities throughout the Mesozoic prove that the movement was more or less continuous, but with a distinct maximum in the Lower Cretaceous. Once it was initiated at the close of the Trias, probably by a very slight tectonic movement, it continued slowly by itself, and was reactivated by a pre-Albian folding phase. Some subsequent slight hydrostatic rise is discernible, but the movement stopped before the deposition of the Tertiary, probably because of the lack of salt within the synclinal regions. In these sections it never attained true diapiric character.

The same problem has been studied by Trusheim (1957) in the German plain, also mostly from seismic data. This author even proposed the term "halokinesis" for purely gravitative salt tectonics. It is the absolute value of the thicknesses of the salt layer and its cover and their relation which form the main factors in the salt-dome structures. When the salt or its cover is too thin, the process never starts. The limiting factors for these thicknesses are roughly a 1,000-m overburden on 300 to 500 m salt, but such values are only applicable when no tectonization takes place.

Once it has started in a thick sequence, a chain of reaction sets in. By the first flow of salt toward the first initial salt cushion, or pillow, the gravitative equilibrium is broken up and adjoining pillows are formed, each gradually growing until the salt has been altogether squeezed out from the synclinal rims. In the depressions sedimentation continues, and their load intensifies the process. The tilting of the cover can result in fractures on top of the dome, which allow extrusion of the salt, and true diapiric salt domes are formed. According to Trusheim, no lateral tectonic force intervened at all; the intricate minor structures are due to this purely gravitative salt-flow process. Depending on the thickness of the original salt deposit, pillows can develop in domes, and these in salt walls, the latter reaching lengths of over 100 km (Trusheim, 1960).

It has been proved by Richter-Bernburg (1959) that the location and arrangement of the domes and walls are certainly influenced by the original location of the salt basins and by faults in the basement so that Trusheim's halokinesis is not wholly atectonical.

In the salt-dome region of southern Iran (Harrison and Falcon, 1936) the flow of salt of Cambrian age is supposed to have been started by volcanic activity, breaking up the blanketing sediments and forming the conducts for the salt extrusion (O'Brien, 1957). Each of these salt domes is accompanied by basaltic rocks either in blocks swimming in the salt or by ring dikes around the salt plug (Wolf, 1959).

In the Gulf Coast region numerous salt domes of a purely gravitative diapiric character have been formed, some penetrating to the surface, some still deeply buried. A thinning of the stratigraphic units on or near the domes as compared with the normal thicknesses is very common, showing that the upwelling process lasted a long time through the Cretaceous and Tertiary during the sedimentation. The age and depth of the original salt layer are unknown in this region, because it is beyond the reach of drill holes. Sometimes the salt is on the border of its piercement pillar accompanied by very plastic shale of deep-sea origin.

The shape of the folds in the salt domes, caused by the flow, has been studied in detail in salt mines both in Germany (Richter-Bernburg, 1955) and in the Gulf Coast (Muehlberger, 1959) and can be seen on the aerial photographs of arid regions like Iran (Gansser, 1960). These folds have in common that the older and lower parts of the salt layer occur in the center, the younger layers on the sides, of the piercement pillar. Further, the majority of the folds have a vertical axis, but their orientation is quite random. Their shape is very plastic;

Fig. 164 Flow structures in salt. (*After Muehlberger, 1962. Published by permission of Houston Geological Society.*)

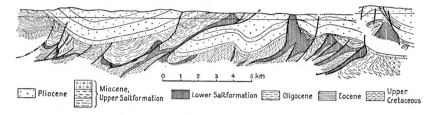

| | Pliocene | | Miocene, Upper Saltformation | | Lower Saltformation | | Oligocene | | Eocene | | Upper Cretaceous |

Fig. 165 Section through South Romanian oil fields. (*After de Raaf*, 1953. *Published by permission of the Oxford University Press.*)

nowhere are the folds crossed by faults. In the flanks of the folds considerable thinning has taken place, and thickening in the hinges. More competent anhydritic layers are either broken up in small pieces or show a most remarkable extreme parasitic fold pattern (Fig. 164).

The section by de Raaf (1953 in Fig. 165) gives us a good example of the complicated history of the Rumanian region. In this southern branch of the Carpathian arc a strong pre-Pliocene phase of folding formed many thrust anticlines, in which the salt-bearing Lower Miocene acted as a lubricating horizon for the thrust planes. After erosion, and deposition of the Pliocene, renewed compression rejuvenated some of these structures, with the result that some of the thrusts reached the surface again (Ocnita). These thrusts are always accompanied by Miocene salt. The compression left some of the other structures undisturbed, and in some cases reactivated only the salt diapir itself (Ochiuri oil field). In the Gura-Ocnitei oil field we find typical normal crest faults due to a pressing up of the salt core, the type we have already encountered in Concepción oil field, Venezuela (Chap. 14, Fig. 128). The whole Rumanian section gives an excellent example of the supple kind of folding that prevails in such flysch sediments in a marginal trough, but in this case the folding is intensified by the presence of salt-bearing beds.

An instructive example of rim synclines surrounding residual domes is found in a group of diapiric anticlinal structures in eastern Algeria, (Fig. 166). The Ouenza, Bou Khadra, and Jaber anticlines each possess an extensive diapiric core of gypsum and salt-bearing red shales and marls. The arrangement of these three anticlines and their plunges leaves a large basin between the Ouenza and Jaber structures. The margins of the anticlines are sharply depressed as a consequence of the salt flow toward the anticline, and the central basin is thus surrounded by a depressed rim, and consequently stands out as a circular residual dome. The Djebel Def dome is totally different in structure from all the other structures in the area. It is characterized by the ab-

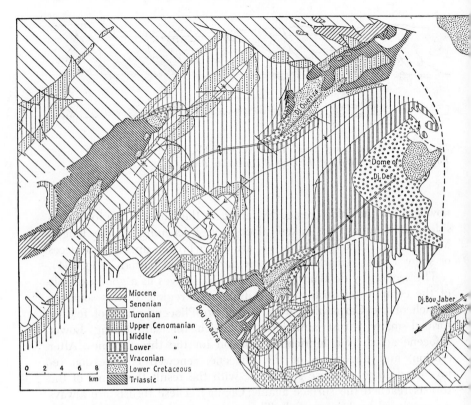

Miocene
Senonian
Turonian
Upper Cenomanian
Middle   "
Lower   "
Vraconian
Lower Cretaceous
Triassic

0 2 4 6 8
        km

Fig. 166 Djebel Def, circular dome structure between diapiric anticlines eastern Algeria.

Fig. 167 Barbers Hill salt dome, Texas, showing overhang of caprock. (*After Judson, Murphy, and Stamey, 1932. Published by permission of the American Association of Petroleum Geologists.*)

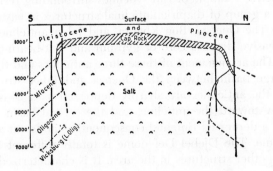

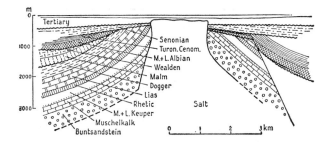

Fig. 168 Stöcken-Lichtenhorst salt dome. (*After Schlüter.* 1949).

sence of faults, by gentle dips, and by its circular slope and flat crest, whereas the truly anticlinal structures are just the opposite, with steep flanks, diapiric cores, many faults, and elongated shape.

When salt-dome structures of the static type are relatively closely packed, their synclinal rims will also leave a flat, domelike structure between the domes.

The salt flow toward the dome continues until the salt formation in the rim is exhausted. On the top of the salt dome and along its flanks, as far as it rises above the ground-water level, solution of the salt sets in. With solution of the salt, accumulation of insoluble residues commences, and these in their turn are submitted to chemical

Fig. 169 Reitbrook dome, section. (*After Behrmann,* 1949.)

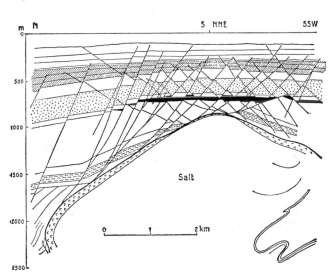

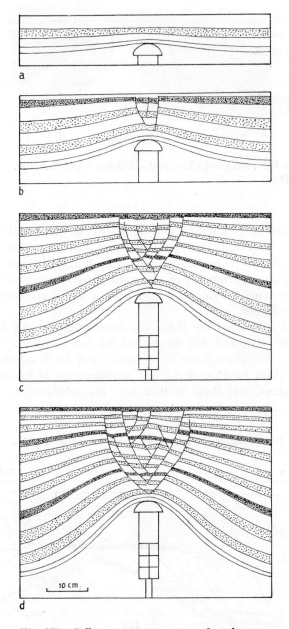

Fig. 170   Collapse structures on top of a salt
dome demonstrated by experiments. (*After Currie,*
1956. Published by permission of the American
Association of Petroleum Geologists.)

changes, so that anhydrite, gypsum, limestone, and sulfur form a caprock, often showing an overhang (Fig. 167).

Structurally, all salt domes show marked upward bending of the surrounding beds against the salt stock, often accompanied by faulting (Fig. 168). In the static type of dome the upward bend and its faults are due to the presence of the salt; in the folded type both the bending and the faulting may be primary.

Fig. 171 Hawkins oil field, structure map. (*After Wentlandt*, 1951. *Published by permission of the University of Texas.*)

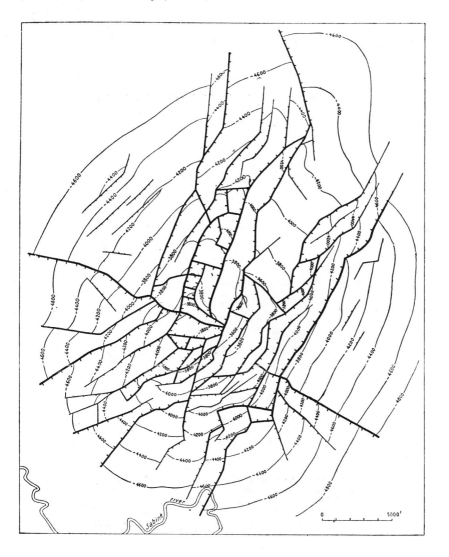

The beds above the salt dome, when they are preserved, are domed, and therefore stretched, by the push from below, and often show an intricate pattern of normal tension faults, such as those on the Reitbrook dome (Fig. 169) in Germany. A similar structure is the Hawkins dome in Texas (Fig. 171), where the fault pattern has a more radial arrangement. Both kinds of faults, normal tension faults and radial tear faults, are typical of this kind of structure. The intricate fault patterns, as in Figs. 169 and 171, have been imitated experimentally by Currie (1956), who demonstrated that if the sedimentation continues during the slow gravitational salt-dome development, the collapse structure above the dome spreads upward, but the earliest faults remain on the outside. It is also very clear that the doming of the salt results not in a horst structure, but in a graben structure in the sedimentary layers above it, because of the stretching of the surface (Fig. 170).

Fig. 172   Perianticline to the diapiric Bou Khadra structure.

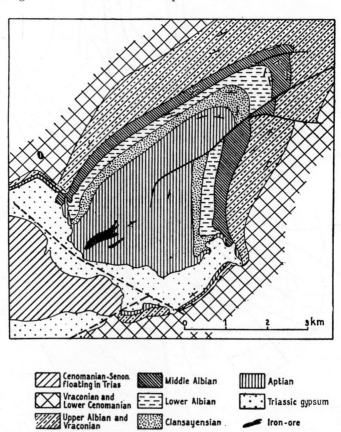

Cenomanian-Senon. floating in Trias

Vraconian and Lower Cenomanian

Upper Albian and Vraconian

Middle Albian

Lower Albian

Clansayensian

Aptian

Triassic gypsum

Iron-ore

Such faults can be compared with those we find on a plunging anticline. These perianticline faults have already been explained, in Chap. 14, and the same explanation is applicable to domes. Normal and radial faults can occur together on both types of structures. They then form intricate patterns, and their intersections pose complicated geometrical problems.

Longitudinal crestal faults curving into the flank as shown in Fig. 172 are typical of the perianticline of diapiric structures. These faults are almost vertical and have a vertical throw diminishing toward the plunge and flank. They are due to the uplift caused by the rising salt in the center of the structure and are neither normal tension faults nor wrench faults. They are also present in the plunge of the equally diapiric Ouenza structure shown in Fig. 166.

COLLAPSE STRUCTURES

The largest and most spectacular kind of collapse structures are the calderas, or cauldrons. Although the origin of the voids which caused their collapse may differ, the various calderas are all ascribed in some way or other to the formation of an empty space in the center of a volcanic structure. Williams (1941) distinguishes five types:

1. Krakatau type, collapse following explosions of pumice and ash
2. Kilauea type, collapse following rapid effusion of lava
3. Katmai type, produced by a combination of internal solution, pumice explosion, and avalanching of crater walls
4. Cryptovolcanic type, subsidence following subterranean explosions with little or no escape of magma at the surface
5. Glencoe type, collapse due to subsidence of magma in magma chamber

Many calderas are probably due to a combination of several of these mechanisms.

Cauldrons. In the true calderas, types 1 to 3, the volcano itself is not completely destroyed. The crater walls still form the circumference of the structure. Their history is often very complicated; recurrent explosions, new volcanic vents, etc., abound. The subsidence of the center is generally depicted in sections by inward-sloping normal fault lines, and since there often is evidence of step faulting, tilting of the steps seems to be common. Nevertheless, factual evidence about this inward slope is mostly lacking, and it seems doubtful, for the smaller calderas, at least, that the slope really exists, for it would hinder subsidence in these circular structures.

Cryptovolcanic Structures. Cryptovolcanic structures are known in many parts of the world. They are circular and occur in cratonic

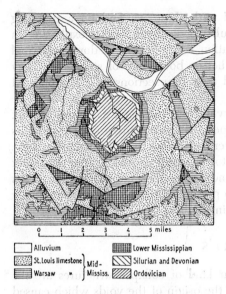

0   1   2   3   4   5 miles

☐ Alluvium
▒ St. Louis limestone ⎫ Mid -
☰ Warsaw   ⏺ ⎭ Mississ.
▦ Lower Mississippian
◫ Silurian and Devonian
▨ Ordovician

Fig. 173 Wells Creek basin, Tennessee. (*After Bucher, 1933. Published by permission of the
Tennessee Department of
Conservation.*)

regions among flat-lying sediments or in the crystalline basement. They are related to alkaline gas-rich magma typical of this sort of environment and "can be considered as products of abortive attempts to blast diatremes" (Williams, 1941, p. 300). Sometimes the surrounding sediments have been domed before the collapse, as in some of the structures described by Bucher (1933) from the United States (Fig. 173) and by Monod (1954) from the Sahara. Probably, the doming was due to a preliminary rise of the magma along a diatreme, followed by collapse and subsidence.

The cryptovolcanic structures of the Oslo rift, described by Ofte-dahl (1952, 1953), are characterized by a narrow vertical ring dike injected along a circular boundary fault (Fig. 174). As suggested above, such a vertical position of the boundary fault seems more logical than an inward slope.

The Scottish ring dikes and cones have been mentioned already, in Chap. 9. Their origin is aptly described by Anderson (1936) and has been sustained by Billings (1943), although some divergence of opin-ion exists on the mechanism. Anderson presumes that in a magma chamber of circular shape the magma column oscillates in height, pushing upward and subsiding and causing tension cracks in the sur-rounding rock and collapse. The ring dikes generally dip steeply out-ward or are vertical; only a few dip inward. The cone sheets of the Scottish systems, on the other hand, dip at about 45° inward and, if projected downward, meet at a focus 4 to 5 km beneath the present surface. They are much less frequent than ring dikes. The geometry of the system indicates that the cone sheets originate in the upward push of the magma, and the ring dikes in the collapse of the caprock after its withdrawal (Fig. 175). The exact mechanism seems to be different in various systems, and it remains curious that the faulting of domes, with its radial pattern, is not reproduced in the ring-dike systems. Perhaps the deeper level of erosion of these latter systems can explain this anomaly.

Collapse Structures due to Solution and Mining. Collapse structures are common in all limestone-covered areas and in those that are underlain by salt-bearing beds. Hundt (1950) devoted a book to the subject. He gives numerous examples of collapse in empty spaces created by solution of limestone, gypsum, and salt. The most interesting examples are perhaps those collapse zones in which swamps came into existence in Tertiary times, creating channel-shaped and round lignite bodies.

In coal mining the collapse above an extracted coal seam and the

Fig. 174 Baerum cauldron. (*After Oftedahl, 1952.*)

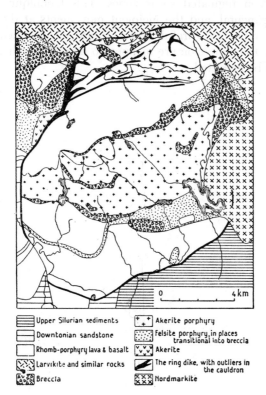

Upper Silurian sediments

Downtonian sandstone

Rhomb-porphyry lava & basalt

Larvikite and similar rocks

Breccia

Akerite porphyry

Felsite porphyry, in places transitional into breccia

Akerite

The ring dike, with outliers in the cauldron

Nordmarkite

0   4 km

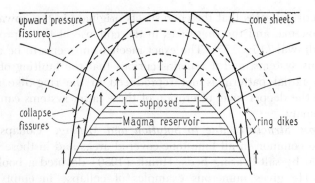

Fig. 175   Ring dikes and cone sheets. (*After Anderson,
1936. Published by permission of the Royal Society
of Edinburgh.*)

damage it causes to buildings, etc., at the surface have led to the development of a special branch of technical science. This has advanced so
far that, by the regulation of the underground extraction of coal, surface collapse can be kept under control so that buildings are let down
gently between regulated shear zones. This technique is of course
highly experimental, and the incipient movements at the surface are
detected by repeated, careful, and accurate measurements. Zones of
dilatation and compression are mapped to determine where and when
collapse can be expected.

Chapter 18

Gravitational Gliding Tectonics

Since the birth of the science of structural geology, geologists describing particular phenomena observed in the field have explained certain structures as the result of gliding down an inclined surface. However, the great impetus that the discovery of large thrust masses gave to structural geology, and the resulting prominence that has been given to lateral compression as the origin of these thrusts, have to a large extent caused structures rightly ascribed to gliding to be overlooked or misinterpreted. Modern thought has taken up the concept of gliding again and has applied it with much success to the great nappes of the Helvetian type in Switzerland and to the flysch nappes of both the western and the central Alps.

At the same time, however, another school of thought has developed which emphasizes the fluidity of rocks under high confining pressure, as observed in laboratory experiments, combined with the obvious uplift that every mountain system has undergone. It attempts to explain all tectonic features by the influence of gravity on elevated parts of the earth's crust. In this view, the positive and negative vertical movements are caused by hypothetical processes at great depths, and all horizontal movements are due to sliding downhill, even those in the deeper parts of the crust.

Thus two concepts of gliding have developed, one chiefly concerned with superficial features, the other with deeply buried parts of the earth's crust. Unfortunately, though they originally sprang from widely different considerations, they have mingled when they met at the surface of the crust, and heated arguments have resulted.

They ought to be kept separated, however, and each judged on its own merits. We are here concerned mostly with observable aspects of structural geology, and not with theoretical arguments about their deep-seated cause and origin.

The idea of gliding tectonics was hatched in Grenoble by Gignoux (1948) and Schneegans (1938), in Lausanne by Lugeon and Gagnebin

(1941), and in Rome and Florence by Beneo (1956), Merla (1951), Migliorini (1933, 1936), and others, more or less simultaneously, though it had been present in the mind of many geologists before.* Gravitational gliding tectonics may be understood as embracing all phenomena where gravity has been the cause of movement of relatively large and coherent superficial portions of the earth's crust. In this sense it does not include all such movements as landslides or slumping. Starting from a single pebble rolling down a slope and increasing gradually the mass of the dislocated material gliding down, we should be able to establish a continuous scale ending with nappes of the Helvetian type. We shall observe, however, that in this scale the smaller masses have a chaotic aspect, as in landslides, and that the larger the mass, the more coherent the structure. Also, the larger the mass, the smaller the dip of the gliding surface need be.

Incompetency of certain members of stratigraphic sequence plays an important role, e.g., salt beds or, more frequently, particularly plastic shales. A large mass of highly incompetent strata can slide down, developing a chaotic structure, even picking up and incorporating pieces of its substratum. A slab of competent character can take advantage of the presence of an incompetent member and slide down along its surface.

All possible transitions between the two extremes can be found. The sedimentary series may possess several incompetent layers, so that the original slab is divided into several slabs moving independently. If these intermediate incompetent layers are relatively thick, the competent layers may be broken up, and distinct secondary folds may develop, separated by internal gliding planes. If the incompetent mass predominates, we may find large blocks or folded remnants of the competent layers distributed in an incoherent way throughout the mass. The parautochthonous flysch of the north flanks of the central massifs of the Alps is a good example of this mode of folding and gliding (Fig. 176). Some of the masses of the Argille Scagliose in the northern foothills of the northern Apennines give a very good idea of the chaotic structure of a large incompetent mass of rocks in which float fragments of the competent members of the original sequence. This so-called "Argille Scagliose" is a comprehensive series, ranging from the Malm at least to the Cretaceous, and is so incompetent that it is able to form glacierlike gliding masses originating from a simple outcrop between younger strata, as I had the occasion to observe in the Turinese foothills.

Many good examples of remnants of synclinal and anticlinal folds of older and competent strata embedded in highly incompetent flysch are described by Schneegans (1938) in his thesis on the Ubaye-

* (See also *Geologie en Mijnbouw*, vol. 12, pp. 329–365, 1950.)

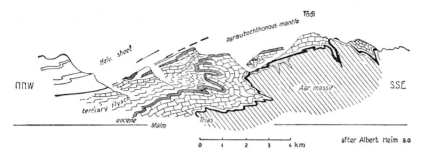

Fig. 176   The cascade folds of the sedimentary mantle of the autochthonous Aar massif, Switzerland, gliding down the northern slope of the massif under the influence of its own weight and that of the overriding Helvetian nappes, also gliding down. (*After Heim, 1921.*)

Embrunais gliding nappe (Fig. 183). The Helvetian nappes, which originally were successive overthrust anticlines, each having its own basal shearing plane at a different stratigraphical level in the series, illustrate nicely the case of a complicated gliding mass divided by incompetent layers into several independent units (Fig. 185).

The Liassic slabs on the southern border of the High Atlas, and some of the Cretaceous slabs on the southern border of the Pyrenees, are simple undivided masses of competent rocks gliding on a Triassic lubricating plane (Fig. 184).

The problem of reducing the friction on the gliding plane so as to allow gliding with a low angle of the slope was studied by Hubbert and Rubey (1959). They invoke what I have called the "quicksand" principle (pp. 35–37), where an increase of pressure by loading, taken over in the first place by the pore water when the impermeability prevents the escape of this water to the surface, causes the sedimentary column to float on its base. The loading can be due either to tectonic lateral loading or to sedimentary vertical loading.

The size of a gliding mass is probably dependent on several factors. If, as in the case of the Helvetian nappes, a preexisting thrust plane cuts through the whole series from the basal shearing plane upward to the surface, and the back portion is then uplifted and tilted, there will be very little or no resistance at the front. As soon as the slope of the thrust plane is sufficient, gliding will start, and it will accelerate as the tilting continues. If, on the other hand, no previous thrust plane has developed, the resistance at the front will in general prevent the gliding of larger masses. As Goguel (1950) has shown, the larger the mass, the smaller the slope of the gliding plane need be.

How far erosion at the bottom of the slope plays an active part in preparing the necessary room in front of the gliding mass by cutting through the competent top layers to the basal shearing plane is impossible to determine. I do not think erosion is a very important factor, but direct evidence either way is altogether lacking.

EXAMPLES OF GRAVITATIONAL GLIDING

The following examples of gravitational gliding quoted from the literature will give us the opportunity to discuss its particular character.

Bearpaw Mountains, Montana. The simplest case of gliding on a tectonic scale I know is that described by Frank Reeves (1946).

In the Bearpaw Mountains, a series of mostly Upper Cretaceous shale and sandstone 4,500 ft thick has been domed, and the top of the arched dome has been eroded. In Tertiary time a great mass of extrusive volcanic rocks, 5,000 ft in maximum thickness, accumulated on top of the dome. The accumulation of this localized mass caused a plainward sliding of volcanics and sedimentary strata, probably on one or two particularly incompetent bentonite beds in the lower part of the Upper Cretaceous shale. Still later the central portion of the dome caved in along normal faults. The accompanying map and section (Fig. 177) show the thrust-fault pattern and the curious arrangement of broad unfolded belts separated by narrow folded and thrust zones.

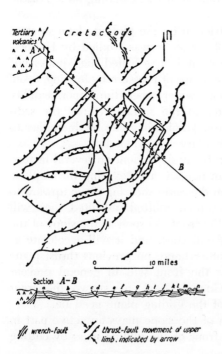

Fig. 177 Gravitational gliding in the Bearpaw Mountains, Montana. (*After Reeves, 1946. Published by permission of the Geological Society of America.*)

On the top of the dome there is a large gap in the volcanic cover, evidently because one half of the cover slid northward and the other southward, an example of what we may call "tectonic denudation." The slope never had an angle exceeding 3°, and each whole flank glided down this slope, producing thrusts and folding in the untilted horizontal strata of the plain.

The thrusts commonly merge laterally into asymmetric folds, the more deeply eroded structures showing thrusting. Probably no thrust plane ever reached the surface. The thrust planes may dip either toward the dome or away from it. Radial tear faults separate different blocks, with different intensity of thrusting; they have a pronounced tendency to cross the structures diagonally. These tear faults therefore illustrate the original stress condition, but subsequently they became limits to different "flows," one advancing farther than its neighbor.

The mass that slid on the 3° slope had an average thickness of 6,250 ft and a total mass of some 55 million tons.

Tangkuban Prahu and Karangkobar Volcanoes in Java. Very similar to the case described by Reeves are two examples of gliding described by van Bemmelen (1934; 1937; 1949, pp. 610, 641–644). North of the Bandung basin extends the Quaternary volcanic chain of the Tangkuban Prahu, in which we can distinguish an older and a younger volcanic series. At the foot of the volcanoes the volcanic series lie unconformably on folded Upper Miocene marine sediments. The youngest group of volcanoes, of which Tangkuban Prahu is the most western, lie on the axis of an elongated dome (Fig. 178). On the northern flank of the dome a series of arcuate faults were mapped, partly originating in the caldera subsidence of Tangkuban Prahu itself and, judging by their shape, clearly independent of any general tensional faulting. The northern half of the dome is surrounded by the Segalaherang depression, and that in turn by a row of hills, the Gunung Tembakan, or Damm Hills, consisting of the older Quaternary volcanic blanket. The flat dips in these foothills, surrounding the Segalaherang depression, are almost exclusively mountainward (to the south). It seems very probable that the arcuate faults in the volcano mantle and the abnormal dips in the foothills are due to sliding down of portions of the volcanic mantle. We can imagine that similar arcuate faults existed also in the volcanic mantle of the Bearpaw volcano, before erosion obliterated them.

A similar example is cited by van Bemmelen from the Quaternary Karangkobar volcanic region of central Java. In this volcanic mantle arcuate faults have developed, which apparently represent the upper limits of gliding blocks. These faults nowadays form precipitous fault scarps several hundred meters high. In order to check the possibility that these blocks were still moving, the topographical survey triangu-

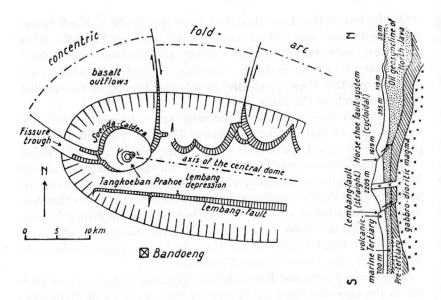

Fig. 178   Map and section of Tangkuban Prahu volcano, Java. (*After van Bemmelen*, 1937.)

lated the position of some of the blocks twice, with an interval of 5 years, and noticed a movement of 120, 200, and 200 cm. These displacements are supposed to be much larger than the possible errors of measurements and should indicate a movement of 24 to 40 cm a year.

Collapse Structures in Persia.   A very interesting phenomenon in which gravity certainly played a prominent role has been described by Harrison and Falcon (1934, 1936).

In the mountainous part of Iran, bordering the Euphrates-Tigris Valley, the structure of the folded strata is extremely well exposed because of the arid climate. The stratigraphic series consists of three thick limestone units, each 1,000 to 3,000 ft in thickness—the highest being the Asmari Limestone, famous for its oil-bearing capacity— separated by marls 1,000 to 2,000 ft thick and overlain by 10,000 ft of anhydrite-shale and sandstone, called the Fars Series. The incompetent marl series between the limestones have given rise, as is normal, to disharmonic folding, but some of the sections show undoubted gliding phenomena.

Harrison and Falcon distinguish several types of structures (Fig. 179): (1) *slip-sheet* structure, (2) *cascade folds*, where the limestone has crumpled up, as it glided downward, (3) *flap structure*, undoubtedly the most curious structural feature of the region, where a limestone wall has bent over gradually until a reversed position has been attained.

All these features are explained as purely gravitational structures, due to deep erosion in the soft synclinal material of the Fars Series and gradual collapse of the vertical limestone flank, which either broke off and glided down the slope in a normal position, or crumpled into cascade folds, or bent over into a recumbent fold. Because of the incompetency of the underlying marls, the structure of the Asmari Limestone first developed as a box fold, which later broke through in its flanks, starting the gliding movement.

West Africa. Gravity gliding and slumping (Chap. 25) are related phenomena, both being due to gravity. In the examples treated above, the slope that originated the gliding was caused by vertical tectonic movement. When the slope is due to subsidence during sedimentation, the resulting gravity gliding is synsedimentary, mostly of relatively small scale, and is called slumping. From West Africa a most astounding example of synsedimentary gliding has been described, on such a large scale that the term gravity tectonics seems warranted (Korn and Martin, 1959), although, strictly speaking, one ought perhaps to call it a slump. In this Naukluft area quick subsidence of a probably late Precambrian basin caused the gravity gliding in successive phases of two sedimentary series, each of several hundred meters thickness, separated by an unconformity marked by an unfolded flat-lying dolomite (Fig. 180). The exposures are so good and so complete, reaching from the center of the basin to its borders, that there can be no doubt that the interpretation of gravity gliding causing the highly contorted and imbricated beds must be right. The undisturbed posi-

Fig. 179 Examples of collapse structures in Persia. (*Simplified after Harrison and Falcon, 1936. Published by permission of the Geological Society of London.*)

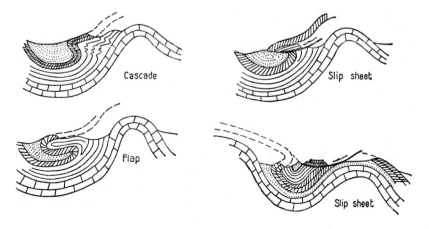

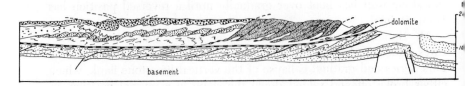

Fig. 180 Gliding structures in Naukluft Mountains, South-West Africa. (*After Korn and Martin, 1959. Published by permission of the Geological Society of America.*)

tion of the thin intervening dolomite proves that the strong folding of the beds below and above cannot be due to compression. The folding is often a typical 45° shear folding, its intensity increased toward the front where imbrication demonstrates the piling up of isoclinal folds. The front of the gliding mass forms a wide arc, and the fold axes are differently oriented in the lower and higher unit. Limestones and dolomites take part in the gliding process, the thicker dolomites being brecciated. At the base of the higher unit the detachment along a particular plastic pelite on top of the unfolded unconformable dolomite is clearly demonstrated.

Bergamasc and Luganese Alps. Gliding tectonics can frequently be found on the marginal slopes of the great Tertiary mountain chains. We often find there that the upper surface of the basement is lowered from its lofty position in the axial zone to its deeply buried position in the marginal trough by a series of steps separated by steep zones or faults. The difference of altitude between two steps commonly gives rise to a gravitational gliding of the sedimentary cover along an appropriate horizon on top of the stationary series of the same age belonging to a lower step. Numerous examples of these structures can be quoted from sections in the southern border of the Alps, of which two are reproduced in Fig. 181.

In the section east of Lake Lugano we see a whole mass of Triassic and Liassic limestones gliding down a slope and butting against a solid mass of Miocene Molasse. The cascade folds in front of the gliding mass are typical and illustrate the movement very clearly. The amount of gliding is relatively small, and gliding was probably set in motion by the steep synclinal folding in the Mount Boglia–Mount Bre region, which caused a horizontal push in the upper strata.

The Bergamasc section shows how the Triassic limestones, detached along the gypsiferous dolomites of the Lower Triassic, glided down from a higher step onto a lower one in front. In the frontal portion of the Camino thrust we find exposed the transition zone from a calcareous facies of the Middle Triassic to a marl facies. Evidently, the

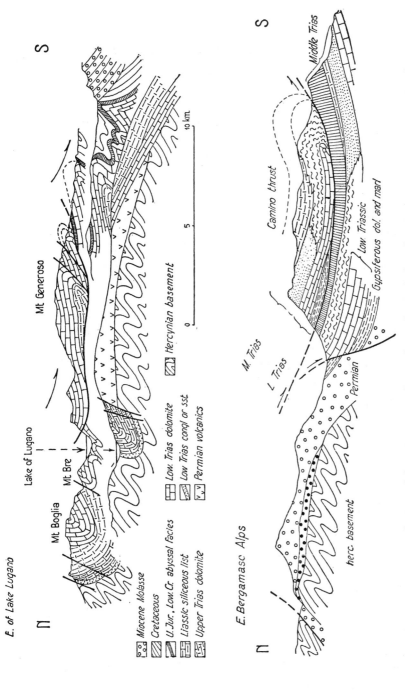

Fig. 181 Two sections showing gliding nappes on the southern slope of the Alps: Mount Generoso east of Lake Lugano and Pizzo Camino in the eastern Bergamasc Alps. (*After de Sitter, 1949.*)

243

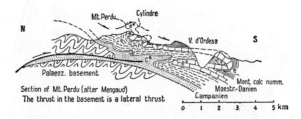

Fig. 182   Combination of thrust and cascade fold
on the southern slope of the Pyrenees. (*After Mengaud,*
1939.)

motion again originated in a fold cut by a thrust, located on the wedging edge of this limestone; the thrust plane cut through the Lower Triassic limestones to the incompetent gypsiferous layer. Once started, the structure glided down on the lower step. There can be little doubt that the general compression, which caused steep thrusts in the northern and highest region, and the doming of the basement in the central step were contributing factors, as well as the vertical upwarping of the successive steps, which originated the height differences and the resulting slopes.

Southern Border of the Pyrenees.   The southern border of the Pyrenees offers many similar gliding nappes, mostly of small dimensions. The best-known one is doubtless the cascade folds of Mount Perdu (Fig. 182). The sedimentary cover of the Paleozoic basement consists here of Senonian and Eocene. In this section we find, first of all, a subhorizontal thrust of the basement rock from north to south due to lateral thrust. Below the thrust mass a thin band of Upper Cretaceous has been preserved. The thrusting movement piled up the upper Senonian and Eocene blanket rocks in front of the nose of the basement thrust, and they started to glide down, forming a cascade of folds, the lowermost one being a large recumbent fold exposed in the Ordesa River. The lateral thrust and the gravitational gliding both operated at the same time, the first causing the second.

A recumbent fold with a complete reversed flank, as encountered in this section, can be considered typical for gliding tectonics under circumstances in which a considerable difference in altitude between the two blocks is most important. A reversed flank which has not been drawn out to the extreme or simply replaced by a thrust fault, or a combination of these two phenomena, is impossible in an ordinary overthrust anticline, because the result of lateral thrust is to produce a considerable shortening without accumulating too much mass in a vertical direction, gravity preventing a trebling of the load. When, on the other hand, the sedimentary rock series is gliding down a slope, the result is to fill up a marginal trough with rock masses from a higher altitude; thus gravity is not opposed to a multiplication of the original thickness of the sedimentary strata; on the contrary, gravity will favor it (Fig. 190). Hence, when the strata are sufficiently plastic, they may form a cascade of folds in which the larger ones are recumbent folds whose reversed flanks are not attenuated. The recumbent fold of the Grand Morgon (Fig. 183), mapped by Schneegans (1938), is a good example of this kind of structure. In that region we find two incompetent layers along which the higher beds have been detached, the Triassic at the bottom of the section and the Callovian-Oxfordian shales in the middle. In the Grand Morgon area both have been active.

All along the southern border of the Pyrenees we find gliding structures which have been mapped, however, without a view to gliding tectonics, and therefore are sometimes difficult to represent in a section. From Mount Perdu in the west to the "nappes" of Mount Grillera in the east, we find these isolated klippen of older formations on the Lower Eocene, sometimes doubled, always underlain by a thin slice of Triassic. In Mount Grillera (Fig. 184) we even have three superposed slices, and in the Montsech we find a slice of Paleozoic rocks on the Triassic.

All those gravitational gliding structures reflect two circumstances, namely, the presence of an extremely incompetent layer at the base of the Mesozoic mantle—the argillaceous Keuper—and very pronounced postfolding uplift along a narrow zone causing a rather steep slope, locally accompanied by thrusting as in Mount Perdu.

Helvetian Nappes of the Alps. The Helvetian nappes are without doubt the largest coherent gliding masses which have been described

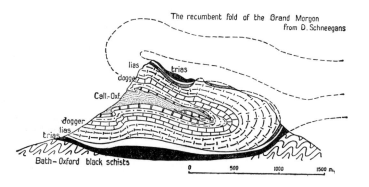

Fig 183 Inverted middle limb of recumbent syncline due to gliding, preserved in gliding nappe of Ubaye-Embrunais, French Alps. (*After Schneegans, 1938. Published by permission of Service de la Carte Géologique.*)

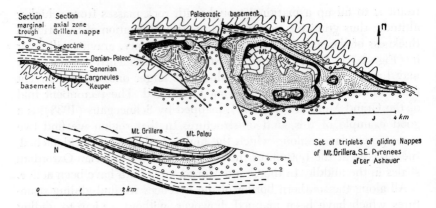

Fig. 184   Set of triplets of small gliding nappes of Mount Grillera, southern slope of Pyrenees; plan, stratigraphic section, and tectonic section. (*After Ashauer, 1934.*)

as such. In order to understand their mechanism I should like to recall the series of overthrusts exposed in the Charleroi coal basin of the Ardennes (Fig. 149). We may imagine that subsequent to this folding the rear could have been lifted up to a certain degree, tilting the thrust planes to a horizontal position and even farther to a northward slope, causing the thrust sheets to slip downward. With this example as a starting point, we can try to reconstruct the Helvetian nappes to their undisturbed position before folding. We find then that each of the three principal units, the Upper, Middle, and Lower Helvetian nappes, is characterized by its own stratigraphical sequence (Fig. 185). The Upper nappes show a Cretaceous sequence with a thick

Fig. 185   Reconstruction of the original sedimentary basin of Helvetian nappes between the Aar and Gotthard massifs. Incompetent layers (Valenginian marl, Dogger shale, Triassic shale, and evaporites) alternate with competent layers (Cretaceous limestone, Malm limestone, Liassic limestone, Permian conglomerate, and sandstone). Thinning out of competent layers against basement ridge of Aar massif has caused splitting up of mass by low-angle thrust planes into future Upper, Middle, and Lower Helvetian thrust sheets, which later, after uplift of the Gotthard massif, glided down the northern slope of the Aar massif.

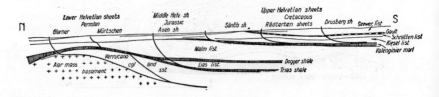

competent limestone wedging out toward its front; the Middle nappes are characterized by a Liassic limestone also wedging out in the same direction; and finally, the Lower nappes consist primarily of Permian and Triassic and are located on wedges of Malm limestone and Verrucano (Permian). The rears of the thrust planes are located respectively, in the incompetent Valenginian, Upper Triassic, and basal Permian; the fronts are located on the wedges of competent strata. Each thrust plane forced the next one in front of it down, with the result that, in the rear, all thrust planes converged on the same basal shearing plane below the Permian and above the crystalline basement. Wherever a rearward thrust plane cuts obliquely downward to the same shearing plane as that of the next thrust plane in front, it first forces the frontal one down to another, lower gliding plane, which, however, soon becomes inactive because it has been cut off from its own rear.

Strong compression narrowed the Helvetian basin between the Aar and Gotthard massifs, and the thrust anticlines were piled one above the other against the south flank of the Aar massif. Subsequent uplift in the rear started them gliding down the northern slope of the Aar massif, accompanied by more chaotic gliding and shearing of the sedimentary cover of this massif (Fig. 176).

We are obviously not able to trace the events in detail, but can point out only some general features of the mechanism, in which gliding down is probably continuously or rhythmically accompanied by compression.

When the trough into which the nappes came tumbling down was particularly deep, the frontal noses were partly overturned, as in the section along the Axen road on the Lake Lucerne (Fig. 186). Where thick masses of conglomerates had accumulated already in the Molasse trough, the frontal lobes were arrested sooner than where the late-tectonic Molasse sediment was less coarse and less massive.

It is impossible to evaluate the amount of erosion that preceded the gliding mechanism, but I do not think that erosion ever was an

Fig. 186 The piling up of the Upper and Middle Helvetian sheets in the marginal trough of the Alps, north of the Aar massif. (*After Heim*, 1921.)

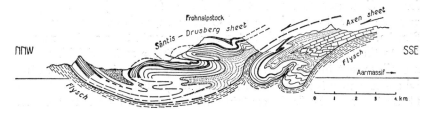

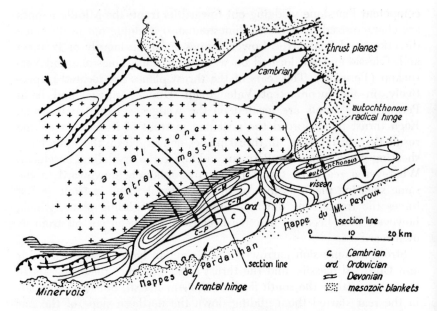

Fig. 187   Tectonic sketch map of Montagne Noire, southern France. (*After Gèze, de Sitter, and Trümpy, 1952.*)

important factor, because the nappes themselves were never carried away by denudation while at the top of the slope, nor was the autochthonous cover on the northern flank of the Aar massif, and the trough was a place of sedimentation and not of denudation.

Montagne Noire.   An instructive case for which gliding tectonics has been proposed is represented by the southern Paleozoic zone of the Montagne Noire, whose general geology is described by Gèze (1949) and gliding tectonics by Trümpy and de Sitter (Gèze, de Sitter, and Trümpy, 1952). The Paleozoic block of the Montagne Noire in southern France is the southwestern prolongation of the Massif Central and is separated only by the small gap of the Corbières from the Massif de Mouthoumet, which is considered a part of the Pyrenees.

The Montagne Noire consists of a central massif of gneiss and granite surrounded on all sides by Paleozoic sediments ranging from Lower Cambrian to Lower Carboniferous (Fig. 187). To the north and southeast the Cambrian and Ordovician, with occasionally some Silurian, is thrust in an imbricated structure against the ancient massif, but to the south of the central massif we find a series of folds which are all, except in the west, characterized by the curious fact that the whole sequence is reversed. In the core of synclines we find the Lower Cambrian, and the flanks contain Ordovician, and farther to the east the Devonian covers the Visean schists. The whole zone is some 20 km wide and thrice as long (Fig. 188).

The stratigraphic sequence consists of two competent zones, viz., the Devonian limestones and dolomites and the Lower and Middle Cambrian limestones and sandstones, separated, covered, and underlain by incompetent zones of great thickness, viz., the Visean shales above, the Ordovician slates and schists in between, and the Lower

Fig. 188 Development of Montagne Noire gliding nappes according to de Sitter and Trümpy. The three superposed units, Pardailhan nappe, Mount Peyroux nappe, and autochthonous Minervois folds, are, in fact, nowhere present in one section. Hence this section represents a combination of sections along the two lines indicated in Fig. 187.

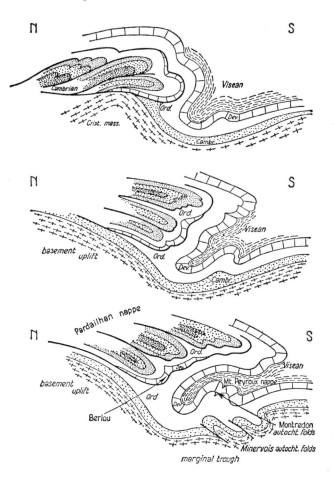

Cambrian and Precambrian schists below. All formations are well dated by a classical fauna.

Whatever the course of events, it is obvious that in order to over-turn completely a thick series of sediments, a considerable trough must have been formed south of the central mass before and during the folding process, which was subsequently filled by the overturned folds, of which we now see only the reversed flank.

As explained below, the development of a reversed flank is already strong evidence for gravity tectonics, and since we see exposed here the inclined gliding surface, I have little doubt that the reversed syn-clines and anticlines of the southern border of the Montagne Noire are indeed due to a southward gliding of the sedimentary blanket down the south flank of the central massif. To be sure, Gèze originally thought, and still thinks, that the folds have a southern origin; his view and the alternative here presented are contrasted in a joint paper by Gèze, de Sitter, and Trümpy (1952).

The southern border consists of three units. The western one, the Minervois, consists of normal steeply folded anticlines pressed against the buttress of the central massif; the central one, the Pardailhan nappe, is formed by three longitudinal reversed Cambrian synclines floating in a mass of Ordovician schists; and the eastern one has an autochthonous anticlinal core of Devonian, the Montredon anticline, covered by an arch of Visean shales overlain by Devonian and Ordo-vician, together called the Mount Peyroux nappe. There is a strong westward plunge, so that the Pardailhan nappe covers the Mount Peyroux nappe, the two being separated by a narrow squeezed-out band of Devonian limestone in Ordovician schists.

Evidently the two nappes, which are formed of totally different series of sediments, represent two portions of the same blanket, sheared off in turn from the crest of the central massif. The upper part of the blanket, consisting of Visean and Devonian with a basal shearing plane in the incompetent Ordovician, forms the Mount Peyroux nappe, and it is covered by the Cambrian core of what was originally the same blanket, now forming the Pardailhan nappe. Most probably the shear-ing off started as a series of thrust faults on top of the still submerged central mass, identical with the structures still preserved north and east of the central mass. The basal shearing plane of the upper nappe cut obliquely through the Devonian, with the result that the frontal lobe of the lower nappe still retained a broad wedge of this limestone on top, which now still forms the base of the Pardailhan nappe.

The three Cambrian synclines of the Pardailhan nappe were origi-nally three fronts of thrust-faulted anticlines which slid down one after the other, the originally southernmost one first, being nearest to the edge of the central mass. The frontal nose of the last one is still preserved, and the innermost contact of the whole nappe against the central mass shows all the characteristics of a squeezed-out, stretched, and broken middle limb.

The disharmony between the Devonian-Visean cover and the Cambrian core is emphasized by the fact that the former is now found as one undivided inverted sheet, whereas the latter is formed by three separate synclinal folds. It seems probable that this disharmony had already originated in the early phase of folding and thrusting, the Cambrian bed in three separate thrust anticlines penetrating into the Ordovician slates and schists, whereas the Devonian limestone with Visean shales on top sheared off in a single large blanket along the top of the Ordovician (Fig. 188). This kind of structure was called an intercutaneous thrust by Fallot (1949); (cf. Chap. 15, Fig. 144).

When the whole structure started gliding down along the newly formed south-facing slope, a large slab of Devonian limestones came into a vertical position, measuring from top to bottom the total height difference between trough and horst. It rested with its back against a Visean syncline and was pushed down and outward by the advancing Cambrian structures embedded in the Ordovician schists. In this way the mechanism of the nappes can be imagined without having to postulate an unrolling of the Devonian limestone, the width of the Mount Peyroux being about equal to the total subsidence of the marginal trough.

The whole structure resembled very much the plunging fronts of the Axen and Säntis-Drusberg nappes on Lake Lucerne (Fig. 186).

Northern Apennines. The most grandiose example of gliding tectonics that has ever been imagined is that of the northern Apennines. The geology is extremely difficult to unravel because of the lack of distinctive formations with distinctive fossils, but the effort of three Italian geologists, Trevisan (1950) from Pisa and Merla (1951) and Migliorini from Florence, have finally resulted in a comprehensible general picture, in which gliding tectonics and vertical movements play a dominant role. Long before these geologists formulated their point of view, it was known that great portions of both the calcareous core of the northern Apennines, the Apuane Alps, and its extensive northern flank, the northern Apennines, *s. str.*, were overthrusted in an abnormal position. The lubricating formation is the Argille Scagliose, or scaly shale, a chaotic shale-marl formation characterized by chunks of greenstones (ophiolites), red radiolarites, jaspers (diaspiri), and limestones. The cover consists of a series of beautifully graded sandstones, the Macigno, and a marl-sandstone sequence, which floats in large masses on the Argille Scagliose. As the Macigno-Argille Scagliose sequence occurs both west and east of the Apuane Alps, whereas this core itself is free of any ophiolitic intrusion, it has been suggested both by the older school of lateral thrusting and by the modern school of gliding tectonics that the origin of the Argille Scagliose sedimentary basin must be sought in the Tyrrhenian Sea between Corsica and Elba. The major objection to a lateral thrust mass of 200 km width is its extreme thinness and its general incompetent character, which by no stretch of imagination can be thought able to transmit the stress needed to transport the whole as one coherent mass. The new point of view therefore supposes that the original deep-sea basin in which the Argille Scagliose accumulated was situated between the islands of Elba and Corsica and that the shale was pressed out by an east-west lateral thrust, flowing over its borderland far to the east. Afterward a first zone of upwarping on the eastern border of the original basin, now covered by a thick mass of the Argille Scagliose that had been pressed out, made it slide down farther toward the east. This mechanism of upheaval of longitudinal anticlinal ridges was repeated five times, each successive ridge being situated farther to the east. Each time the plastic mass of Argille Scagliose glided down the eastern flank of the new ridge and was thus displaced farther eastward. During its repeated movements, its original content of clay, ophiolites, and radiolarites became diluted with strange elements of much younger date, of which the more coherent portions moved as great slabs and the softer formations like shales and marls simply became mixed up with the original shale content. In this way the relative decrease of the ophiolite content of the Argille Scagliose in an eastern direction finds a ready explanation.

Several objections against this rather sweeping theory of gliding can be made. First of all, if one abandons the theory of lateral thrust over 200 km and accepts gliding to explain the superposition of the Argille Scagliose on younger strata, it seems illogical still to postulate such enormous transportation. Second, the whole mechanism of the 200-km transportation would break down if one of the ridges rose before its turn, thus stopping all farther eastward transport. Third, the ridges are very different in tectonical style. The first ridge on western Elba is a Miocene granite intrusion; the second ridge is represented by the insufficiently exposed synclinal structure of Spezia containing Triassic and Liassic; the third ridge is the large arch of the Apuane Alps in which a thrust sheet of nonmetamorphic limestones of considerable size overlies highly metamorphic marbles of the same age (Lower Mesozoic) (Fig. 189); the fourth and fifth ridges consist of more or less simply compressed domes in Oligocene strata, locally with Liassic cores, much broken by steep thrusts of the kind called "composite wedges" by Migliorini (1948; cf. Chap. 15, Fig. 153). In my opinion, the Italian investigators have underrated to some extent the intrusive capacity of such an incompetent formation as the Argille

Fig. 189 Section through Apuane Alps and northern Apennines, showing third ridge—Apuane Alps in the core of the Apennines—and fourth ridge of quite different structure. (*After Merla*, 1952. *Published by permission of Società Geologica Italiana.*)

mg Oligocene, Macigno

c Cretaceous – Eocene, polychromous schists, scaglia

J Jurassic, Liàs – Malm, list. marble

t Trias, dolomite. breccia. "Grezzoni"

P Permo-carboniferous, sericite-mica schists

as Argille scagliose Malm

253

Scagliose under lateral compression, producing simple diapiric action. Much of the abnormal position of this formation must certainly be due to gliding down appropriate slopes, but much may be due also to lateral compression, squeezing out, and diapiric intrusions. This implies, of course, that originally more than one deep-sea basin with ophiolite intrusions existed, most probably both east and west of the central core, the Apuane Alps, the latter being free from these ophiolitic intrusions. The intensive mixing of younger and older strata, the gliding down of great slabs, the inserted position of some of these slabs and their frontal noses (which can be ascertained most convincingly by the graded facies of the Macigno sandstones) are facts which very strongly suggest gliding as the origin of many of the structures; on the other hand, the steep thrusts bounding the ridges suggest strong lateral compression through the whole width of the northern Apennines. The combination of the two structural theories evidently leads to the conception that the gliding followed the compression and is due to the upheaval of the longitudinal ridges.

The Tell in Algeria.   Numerous French geologists have worked out, in the last decenniums, the extremely complicated structures of the Tell geosynclinorium between the central Algerian autochthonous and the Berber coastal highlands. A good comprehensive review of the whole structure has been given by Kieken (1962).

What happened in this quickly subsiding trough is that, after a more or less continuous sedimentation up to the Miocene, due to a steepening of the northern flanks and quick subsidence of the basin, a whole series of gliding nappes filled up this trough, causing a manifold repetition of the same series. Finally, a nappe of flysch sediments, coming from even farther north, in many places covered the glided structures in the synclinorium.

CHARACTERISTICS OF GLIDING STRUCTURES

The main question that arises from our survey of gliding structures is, how can one distinguish between a lateral low-angle thrust and a gliding nappe? As always in geology, the answer cannot be conclusive. There is no structural feature that can be decisive in either direction, but the evidence must necessarily be of a circumstantial nature. To my mind the most important evidence is the following:

1. An appropriate slope must be recognizable in the field to account for any gliding. One may of course reason, in case such a slope is absent, that the original slope has been destroyed since the gliding by the sinking of its highest portion, and if such oscillation can be proved by inde-

pendent evidence, the reasoning may be sound, but in general it can hardly be accepted. For instance, a gravitational gliding of the Jura Mountains toward the north, as suggested by Lugeon and Gagnebin, against its present slope seems highly improbable. Marginal troughs of orogenic belts seem to be the most favorable recipients of gliding nappes.

2. A downward plunge of the basal thrust plane at the rear of the thrust sheet can be regarded as conclusive evidence of its thrust nature. The upward curve one would expect in a gliding nappe will seldom be conserved except in small-scale gliding like that of the volcanic mantles described in the foregoing pages. Since many gliding structures originated as thrust sheets, a downward curve may be present at the rear even in the case of gliding, but then it can no longer be directly connected with the frontal lobes.

3. An inverted position of a large mass, in particular when it is not laminated or squeezed or otherwise tectonically reduced in thickness, is strong evidence of the gliding nature of the transport mechanism (Fig. 190). A real thrust sheet has no inverted flank; it is the result of maximum lateral shortening with a minimum of piling up of strata, a compromise between the lateral stress and gravity. Whereas gravity prevents the development of an inverted flank in the case of the thrust sheet, it favors its formation in the case of a gliding nappe, because in the latter case the ultimate aim of gliding is the filling up of a preexisting trough. See the foregoing Figs. 176, 179, 181, 182, and 186 as compared with Figs. 146, 148, and 149 in Chap. 15.

4. In general, a chaotic, or even a geometrically obscure, structure may be an indication of gliding because each portion of the gliding nappe may move independently of the other, each being under the same gravitational stress as the other. However, in a thrust sheet the stress must necessarily be conveyed from one end of the sheet to the other by a coherent and competent mass, and any failure would result in the standstill of the portion beyond the failure. Therefore isolated slabs, often anticlinal or synclinal in shape, of competent rocks in an incompetent matrix, are valuable indications for later gliding following on former lateral-thrust folding.

5. In the smaller-scale gliding structures the lateral extension of the structure is ordinarily small and has no connection with its surroundings, whereas in lateral-thrust structures the opposite is true. This is so because

Fig. 190 Contrast between structures produced by gravitational gliding (*A, B*) and by lateral thrust (*C*). A middle limb is preserved unthinned in gliding but is absent in thrusting.

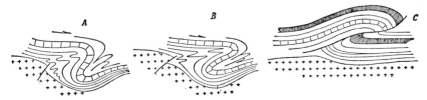

the gliding may be due to the hazards of erosion in the lower reaches of the slope or to other irregularities, whereas the thrust structures can move only when a large portion of the crust is in a stressed condition.

From the general outlook on gravitational gliding tectonics we have now gained, there is one fact that emerges clearly, namely, the close relation between gliding tectonics on a larger-scale, vertical uplift and lateral compression. In all instances which I cited, the southern Pyrenees and the southern Alps, the Montagne Noire, the Apennines, and the Helvetian nappes, we found that the structures started as thrust sheets, that the upheaval that caused the slope came later, and that the gliding tectonics are only an accompanying feature. In all the larger structures described it is very much a question of preference how much one believes should be accounted for by thrusting and how much by gliding. We find this transition not only between thrusting and gliding, but also between slumping and gliding.

In the case of gliding in a volcanic mantle, there is no longer even any real difference in origin from slumping, for both are due to accumulation of sedimentary materials; their distinguishing feature is only that in one case the process took place under water and in the other it did not.

Gravity is certainly not a force that plays a role in tectonics only occasionally; it is always present and always influences any structural shape, whether we think of folds, faults, or gliding.

The extent to which the conception of gliding tectonics changes our views on the structural characteristics of mountain chains is rather important in one aspect. Formerly, any klippe meant to us that large-scale horizontal thrusting had occurred and therefore that the particular mountain chain had been submitted to important lateral compression. Such a conclusion is no longer warranted. The supposition that the Helvetian nappes and the klippe nappes have gained their present position by gliding certainly means a considerable reduction of the formerly supposed total lateral shortening of the cross section of the Alps. The same is true for the Argille Scagliose gliding nappes of the Apennines and for many other less well known structures. A klippe is no longer a proof of strong compression.

Chapter 19

Cross-folding of the
Paratectonic Type

CROSS-FOLDING IN ONE
OROGENIC PERIOD

In many instances peculiarities of fold and fault patterns have been
ascribed to a preexisting system superposed by a younger system of
another direction. Sometimes the inference is purely hypothetical,
when the older system is not exposed independently in the same
region, for instance, but careful analysis can sometimes achieve reliable results.

The fact that in a folded belt one may be able to distinguish, apart
from the obvious anticlinal and synclinal axes, other oblique lines—
joining, for instance, culminations of successive anticlines—is no proof
of a separate folding phase with a deviating compressive direction.
When a compressive force is acting in a block of sedimentary strata
ABCD (Fig. 191), some irregularity in the sedimentary series will
localize the first fold at some particular point *P*. As we have seen,
the width of the fold *w* is soon established by the thickness of the

Fig. 191 Development of plunging and alternating folds.

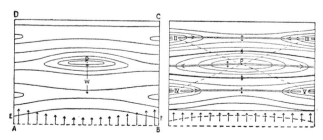

strata involved. From the point *P*, the future culmination, the anticline will develop to the right and left, and after some compression the straight line *AB* will be in the position *EF*, with a bulge in the center due to the culmination in the anticline at point *P*. The growing load on the first anticline due to its uplift will favor the birth of new anticlines. Their distance from the first (i.e., the wavelength) is roughly fixed at any one time by the amplitude of the first fold. As the compressive stress will be greater to the left and right of the bulge in the line *EF*, because the yield of the material has been greatest opposite this bulge, the starting points, and therefore the future culminations of the new anticlines, will be located at points II, III, IV, and V, either simultaneously or successively. The lines joining II, *P*, V and IV, *P*, III are not then due to a compressive stress perpendicular to these lines; the pattern is determined solely by the thickness of the section involved in the folding and by occasional irregularities in this section.

On the other hand, one can find several examples where two distinct directions of folding can be discerned and where particular irregularities in the folding pattern must be attributed to their interference. We find a good example in the High Atlas, where a post-Eocene and a post-Miocene folding interfere with one another (Fig. 192); this has been described in some detail (de Sitter, 1952). The most convincing element in this structural pattern is an anticline crossing a syncline. The anticline of Bou-Hamid plunges in a NE direction and is still discernible crossing obliquely the broad EW syncline of younger age (the J. Ograne–J. Tazigzaout). It emerges again at the other side in a sharply folded and slightly displaced anticlinal culmination (Fig. 192).

Fig. 192   Crossing of anticline with syncline in the High Atlas.

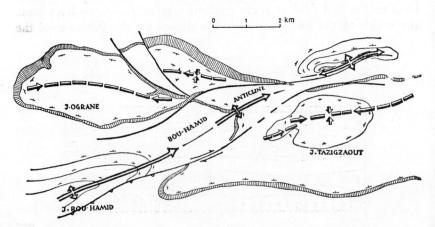

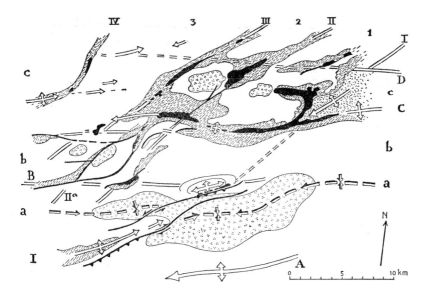

Fig. 193   Structural pattern of crossing folds in High Atlas.

The actual crossing of the anticline is accompanied by two wrench faults in its flank. The southwestern of these finds its origin in a thrust fault of the Bou-Hamid anticline, and the synclinal flank of the Bou-Kandill curves sharply against the fault. In the north flank of the syncline, the western fault probably disappears in the strike of the Dogger marls, and the northeastern one becomes a thrust fault along which the anticline north of the syncline is pushed into the synclinal flank in a southerly direction.

In accordance with the general situation in North Africa we may presume that the ENE-WSW trend is older than the EW trend, the first being Pyreneic (post-Eocene), the second post-Miocene, the Miocene syncline passing through a depression of a preexisting Eocene anticline.

On the evidence of this structural feature we can explain many other peculiarities of the adjoining folds. It appears that, in general, the more or less diapiric Triassic cores of the culminations of the anticlines are situated at the crossing of two sets of anticlines and that the basinlike synclines are situated in the center of the lozenges formed by the anticlinal axes with two different directions (Fig. 193). In this case we clearly have a superficial kind of folding where the Mesozoic (largely Lower and Middle Jurassic) cover has glided along the detachment plane of the Triassic on its Hercynian basement. In such a case we might be able to distinguish different kinds of adapta-

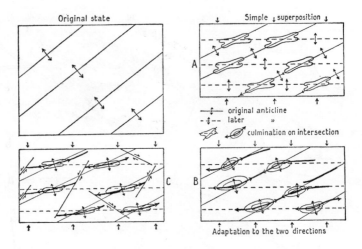

Fig. 194   Diagrams of interference of successive directions.

tion of the older parallel anticlines to the new compressive stress. In
Fig. 194 three possibilities have been sketched, and all the irregularities of the fold pattern of Fig. 193 can be attributed either to one or to
a combination of these possibilities.

Another particularly clear case of refolding has been mapped in
northern Spain (de Sitter, 1959) where an original flat thrust plane
now shows strong undulations (Fig. 195). The thrust remains over the
whole exposed surface, except the frontal part between almost the
same two stratigraphical horizons, a Cambrian dolomite resting

Fig. 195   Folded Esla nappe in the southern Cantabrian Mountains in Spain.
(*After de Sitter, 1959.*)

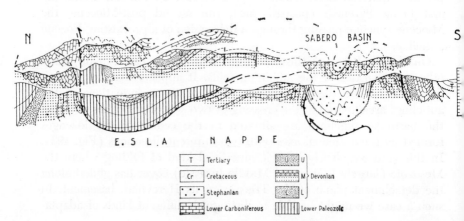

everywhere on an Upper Devonian limestone or quartzite or Lower Carboniferous. The original structure must have been something like the Cumberland thrust of the Appalachians, a very flat structure (Chap. 15, Fig. 148). Later movements originated the steep asymmetrical folds of Fig. 195, and in the surrounding autochthonous the two main folding trends, E-W and NNE-SSW, can also clearly be recognized. There are good reasons to suppose that the time interval between the two folding phases is somewhat less than the length of the Westphalian.

INFLUENCE OF BASIN STRUCTURE ON SUBSEQUENT FOLDING

In the last two examples the same stratigraphical section has been folded twice, but in many other instances it is supposed that the grain of the basement rock, due to an older folding phase, has influenced the folding direction of the younger sedimentary cover. In general, such interference remains highly hypothetical because the structural features of the basement can be inferred only from observations a long distance from the folded sedimentary cover. Nevertheless, there are some clear examples where older structures do influence the younger folds. One of the most striking examples is furnished by the influence of the shape of the basin on the alignment of the folds in the sedimentary rocks.

We have seen that the position of a fold is largely determined by the sedimentary structure, or in other words, that the location of a fold is related to a large sedimentary feature such as the sharp edge of a competent layer which is wedging out. We have studied this phenomenon in vertical section, but it will be equally true in the horizontal plane. There the anticlinal axis will have a tendency to follow the edge of the wedge, which will be parallel to the border of the basin. Although in general the folding force is directed perpendicular to the longer axis of the elongated basins, this need not be true everywhere in one basin nor for every basin. In some cases the folding direction will make an acute angle with the border of the basin, and therefore with the edges of the wedging competent layers. In such cases there are two factors which tend to determine the direction of the fold axis: the sedimentary structural feature and the direction of the force. The result is usually an arrangement of short folds en échelon, each of them perpendicular to the folding force, but together forming a string of beads parallel to the basin border. The famous three domes of the Kettleman Hills demonstrate this principle clearly (Fig. 196).

We find the same en échelon arrangement in the normal faults

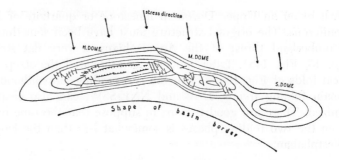

Fig. 196 Kettleman Hills en échelon structure.

which together constitute the Mexia fault zone, west of the Cretaceous basin of the Texas embayment (Chap. 10, Fig. 74). Their alignment is parallel to the basin border, but each of them makes an acute angle with this direction. I think it extremely probable that their general alignment is determined by the overall structure of the basin, but their individual directions by a tensional force perpendicular to the actual faults; but it may be true that a deep-seated shear-fault, parallel to the basin border, has originated the normal faults at the surface in the same way as has been proposed for the fault belt in Creek and Osage Counties in Oklahoma (cf. Chap. 11).

We have described, for instance, in Chap. 12, the compressional North Pyrenean fault which has an en échelon structure possibly due to the superposition of a Tertiary phase on a Hercynian phase (Fig. 104).

In many cases the location of folds in the blanket sediments on a known basement rock has been attributed to faults in the basement. There is, for instance, a controversy between Goguel (1952) and Glangeaud (1944, 1949), the first maintaining that the folds of the pre-Alpine western Alps are perfectly independent of the basement, the other advocating the contrary for the narrow folds of the table Jura, the external zone of the Jura Mountains. In the same way Buxtorf (1910) believes the Jura folds to have glided over a plane, unbroken basement surface, whereas Aubert (1945) draws thrust faults in the basement below the larger folds.

From a general point of view the gliding of the blanket rocks would be opposed or even prevented by strong fault scarps in the basement. When the fault scarps are small, however, it may be imagined that the irregularity at the bottom of the folding blanket localized the folds; but this is different from simultaneous faulting in the basement and folding in the blanket.

One can detect differences in level of the basement when the general level of the synclines in one zone of the folded chain is lower than in another, but even then I would prefer to suppose a bending of the basement rather than faulting, when positive information is lacking.

INFLUENCE OF THE STRUCTURAL GRAIN OF THE BASEMENT ON A YOUNGER FOLDING PHASE

In the last two examples the control of the folding direction by the general shape of the basin has been described, but the basin formation and the folding both more or less relate to one and the same structural cycle of one basin. However, when an inhomogeneity in the structural grain of the basement rock is supposed to influence the folding of its sedimentary cover, the two determining factors are even wider apart, and therefore still more difficult to prove. One can often notice that the original grain has no influence whatsoever on the later folding. In the western plunge of the High Atlas, for instance, the grain of the Paleozoic basement rock is N-S, whereas the Tertiary folding is E-W. But, on the other hand, the Middle Atlas chain is rigorously parallel to the NE-SW trend of the Paleozoic structure. Hence the supposition that the Hercynian trend of the Moroccan Meseta determined the folding (and faulting) directions of the Middle Atlas is considerably weakened by the evidence of the western High Atlas.

Similar arbitrary suppositions are frequent in geological literature, and it is rare that real evidence can be brought forward in their support.

In general, the evidence supports the view of Argand that an older major orogenic phase has consolidated the basement and that it will no longer move except in large blocks. I should like to add that, although the basement cannot be folded again in the ordinary sense of the word, it may still be compressed by metamorphic processes ranging from simple cleavage to gneissification, which will not necessarily be parallel to the original grain, but perpendicular to the younger compression.

Basin formation, the deformation phase preceding the compressional phase, may, on the other hand, be influenced by the older structure and therefore may have an indirect influence on the subsequent folding of the basin. It seems probable, for instance, that the strongly indurated migmatized arcs of the older Hercynian structures remain the positive areas in the new basin formation, but quite possibly different in arrangement from their original alignment—the Brabant mass between the North Sea and the Parisian basins, for example. Also, it is certainly true that the Caledonian and Hercynian belts envelop the

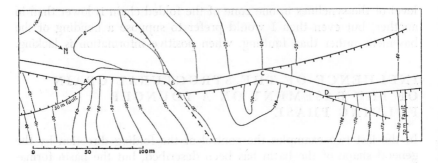

Fig. 197 A big N-S Tertiary fault deflected by older Carboniferous faults in southern Limburg. (*After Sax, 1946. Published by permission of Geologisch Bureau voor het Mijngebied, Heerlen.*)

Precambrian shields, extending the shield outward, as will be explained later. The Alpine folding, however, seems to be independent of the folded Paleozoic belts.

I can point out in detail some instances where older structural features have actually influenced later tectonic features to some degree.

The normal faults of southern Limburg in the Netherlands, step faults limiting the Roer Valley rift, have been mentioned before (Chap. 10, Fig. 71). They are particularly well known within the coal field, where the Hercynian structure of the Coal Measures is equally well known. In several instances it has been shown that post-Paleozoic normal faults have been deflected for some distance from their original trend by striking an older Hercynian fault. In Fig. 197 we notice that each time the younger normal fault encountered an older fault, as at the points *A, B, C,* and *D*, it followed the course of the older fault for a short distance, but then resumed its own course again. This example shows clearly the interaction of the younger and main fault directions and the older structure, but at the same time the dominating factor of the younger tensile stress.

A very instructive example of the influence of a structure in the basement on its blanket rocks, described by Reed and Hollister (1936), can be found in the Newport-Inglewood belt of the Los Angeles basin (Fig. 198). A long row of domes and diagonal faults is located on this belt; many of the structures are oil-bearing. The belt is flanked to the west by a straight syncline which separates it from the NW-striking anticlines of Playa del Rey, El Segundo, Torrance, and Wilmington.

Evidently, the main stress had a SW-NE direction and caused, besides the last-named anticlines, a dextral tear fault in the basement, parallel to the St. Andreas fault farther to the NE. The deep-seated tear fault sometimes reaches the surface, as in the Seal Beach anticline (Chap. 14, Fig. 129). Sometimes, however, domes such as those of the Dominguez oil field are formed, diagonal to the fault but parallel to the western anticlines; sometimes diagonal tear faults cross the domes, as in Inglewood; and sometimes normal faults are formed, as in the Baldwin Hills. All these structures comply with the single stress field mentioned above, although the parallelism is not very precise.

The relative independence of the Tertiary mountain chains from the grain of the Hercynian folding is, however, in general much more striking than are a few isolated instances where an interaction is discernible.

The moderately folded Hercynian belt of Europe extends from Cornwall to the Saharan border, whereas the Tertiary folded chains are perfectly individual units, with many different directions. We certainly cannot assume, therefore, any large-scale influence by the grain of the Hercynian on the Tertiary folding; on the contrary, the two are largely independent and often are at right angles to one another.

But even in this Hercynian belt, there are a few examples of large-scale conformity between the Hercynian and the Alpine directions. The most conspicuous instance is without doubt the Pyrenean orogeny, which is principally a Hercynian E-W mountain chain, rejuvenated in two phases, Late Cretaceous and Early Tertiary, with only a slight variation of deviating strike. It seems probable that in this and similar

Fig. 198 The Newport-Inglewood belt in southern California.

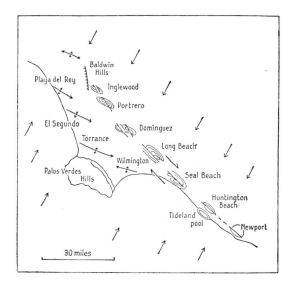

cases both the earlier and the later orogenies are influenced by a common invariable factor, in this case the border of a long-enduring cratonic block.

Chapter 22 will describe the very common feature of successive folding phases in schistose or cleavage deformation.

In conclusion, I may say that interference between successive phases of the same major orogenic period is common, but can be observed only when the two phases are not parallel. Interference of the shape of a basin on the folding of the subsequent folding phase can also be quite often observed, although it is often difficult to prove. The shape of the basin may in its turn have been influenced by an older folding phase, particularly by granitization or batholith intrusions. On the other hand, it is improbable, except in detailed minor structural features, that the grain impressed by an older major orogenic period on the basement influences to any great degree the alignment of younger structures, unless the same cause which originated the older strike is still active in the younger orogenic period.

Chapter 20

Cleavage and Shear Folding

INTRODUCTION

In Chapter 13 the fundamental difference between cleavage and concentric folding was explained; in the first group deformation is expressed by planar surfaces; in the second, by the bent bedding planes.
In cleavage folding two important deformation principles are involved,
flattening and shear, both along planar surfaces. They are extremely
difficult to separate, but there can be no doubt that both exist.
Roughly speaking, shear folding is more pronounced in distinct
regional metamorphic regions, the infrastructure, and flattening in nonmetamorphic or only slightly metamorphic rocks, the suprastructure.
Accordingly, ordinary slaty cleavage is generally only due to a flattening process, and schistosity more often to shearing, but flattening is
never absent in schistose structures and neither need shearing be
completely absent in cleavage folds.

The distinction between cleavage and schistosity is rather arbitrary;
most cleavage is characterized by a certain amount of new mineral
growth, mostly of mica, perpendicular to the stress direction, but
when these micas become macroscopically visible and the original
sedimentary structure becomes vague or invisible, the term schistosity
is applied, but no clear boundary between the two rock types can be
drawn.

In the following discussion we shall be concerned, in the first place,
with cleavage. Different kinds of cleavages can be discerned, considering their structural function or their different petrographic morphological aspects:

Structural	*Petrographic-morphologic*
Stress cleavage	Slaty cleavage
Slip, or shear cleavage	Fracture cleavage
	Crenulation cleavage
	Schistosity

Ordinary slaty, or true, or flow cleavage and schistosity, as it occurs in slates and schists, is due to the parallel arrangement of mica flakes, and the distance between the cleavage planes is microscopic, being limited only by the grain size of the rock. In fracture cleavage the interval is much larger, of the order of millimeters; the rock slivers between two cleavage planes called microlithons. It is the usual type that occurs in coarse-grained rocks, but is also common as a secondary cleavage formed in the refolding of all other rock types. Flow cleavage is more or less identical with true, or slaty, cleavage, but the term means that recrystallization of mica on the cleavage plane is plainly visible. It leads to a higher state of metamorphism and more extensive recrystallization affecting the whole rock, in which the cleavage is called the schistosity. False cleavage, or shear- or strain-slip cleavage, refers in general to a secondary cleavage cutting the cleavage plane or causing a wrinkling, or crenulation, of the original cleavage plane, and for this reason it will be called "crenulation cleavage" here.

In our structural subdivision we mentioned stress and slip, or shear, cleavage with the intention of making a clear distinction between cleavage due to flattening and cleavage due to slip. The purest stress cleavage is found in axial-plane cleavage folds in which the parallelism between the axial plane of the fold and the cleavage proves the perpendicular orientation of the cleavage plane to the stress direction. If this parallelism does not exist, the cleavage may be due to a shear oblique to the stress or it may be a superimposed stress cleavage on already existing folds with another orientation.

There are many and various transitional types of deformation between stress cleavage, concentric folding, and shear cleavage, and it is very difficult to unravel such relations, which are often complicated by the superimposition of one type of deformation on another.

For some reason or other it often happens that cleavage is much more pronounced in the hinges than in the flanks of certain folds. The flanks remain straight, and their slip is not along cleavage planes but along the bedding plane. It seems reasonable to suppose that this will

Fig. 199 Accordion folding.

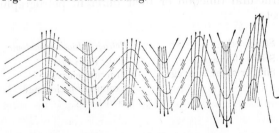

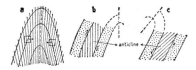

Fig. 200 Cleavage in relation to the axial plane.

happen when the bedding is well marked and the slip relatively easy. The result, then, is a series of straight-flanked folds which have been called accordion folds (Fig. 199), or chevron folds, in American usage (see next chapter). Accordion folds have the same characteristics as cleavage folds in that they are similar, with thickening in the hinges, but the straight flanks maintain their original thickness.

Other kinds of cleavages that are not due to axial-plane stress are oblique slip cleavage and "concentric" cleavage, both described more fully in the next chapter. The slip-cleavage process is very common in schistosity deformation, but less so in cleavage folds. It is called "Gleitschieferung" in German, and the original Belgian term for oblique-slip-cleavage folds is "chevron" folds.

The fact that, in axial-plane-cleavage folding, the cleavage is parallel to the axial plane gives the field geologist a valuable opportunity of deciding on which side a formation is "younging," and on which side the anticline is situated, even when the fold is overturned. In Fig. 200a a normal anticline is represented; the cleavage will always be steeper than the bedding unless the bedding is near 90° or the fold is recumbent. As the cleavage gives the approximate position in space of the anticline, an outcrop of the size of one of the small squares on the drawing allows one to determine the direction in which the axis of the anticline must be sought. Theoretically, it ought to be possible to locate all anticlines and synclines in a certain region by measuring the cleavage and bedding without seeing a single hinge. In practice, however, the outcrops are seldom sufficiently numerous to allow a trustworthy result.

In concentric-cleavage or slip-cleavage folds this method does not work, of course, so that the nature of the cleavage must be established before the method can be used. Even in stress-cleavage folds the cleavage planes are not always strictly parallel; they tend to fan out in a fold, converging toward the core (Fig. 204). Moreover, it can often be observed that the cleavage planes are parallel to the axial plane in the slates, but are refracted and become coarser where they enter a competent bed (Fig. 201).

A distinction has also been made between parallel and transverse cleavage, to indicate that parallel cleavage is parallel to the bedding, and transverse when it cuts obliquely through the bedding. When the folds are open, all the cleavage is transverse, and when the folds are

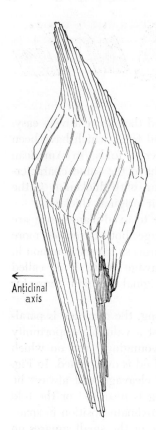

Anticlinal
axis

Fig. 201 Slaty cleavage in slate, deviated
in a fracture cleavage in sandstone.

isoclinal, transverse cleavage occurs only in the hinges. Therefore
such a distinction has no genetic sense. Even in metamorphic regions,
where the schistosity is mostly parallel to the bedding, if the latter
can still be discerned, a careful and detailed field analysis often reveals some of the hinges where the schistosity is obviously transverse.

Another peculiarity of cleavage folding is that recrystallization of
the whole or part of the rock material may occur along the cleavage
planes, often as a segregation recrystallization forming lighter bands
of quartz or quartz and feldspar, alternating with darker bands with
a concentration of dark minerals. This tectonic banding can obliterate
the original bedding completely and is the leading principle in highly
metamorphic rocks like migmatites. It is also frequent in slates and
phyllites in the form of parallel quartz veins.

LINEATIONS

A very important characteristic of cleavage folds is their lineation (E.
Cloos, 1946). Lineation has been defined as any striping on any rock

surface and can have numerous origins. Lineations may be grooves on the bottom of a sandstone bed, parallel oblong crystals in a metamorphic rock, and glacial grooving of a rock surface, so that some phenomena so named need not necessarily have any structural significance.

When we refer to lineations in cleavage folds or metamorphic rocks we think of various structural characteristics of these rocks. There are four kinds of significant tectonic lineations, caused by (1) an intersection of two planes, (2) a tectonic rippling of a plane or minor folds or microfolds, (3) oriented growth of minerals, and (4) elongated rock fragments such as stretched pebbles or oolites. The first two kinds are not very different, often grading into one another, frequently the rippling, or crenulation, being the expression of an intersection. The most common intersection is that of the bedding with the cleavage, often called δ lineation. And when the cleavage is parallel to the axial plane, the intersection is parallel to the axis of the associated fold. By measuring the direction and plunge of this lineation, we obtain the attitude of the axis. In an area of simple cleavage folding, field measurements of this kind of lineation and those of the axes of minor folds are rigorously parallel and generally designate the b-axis trend of the terrain.

In metamorphic rocks we may find oriented crystal growth, parallel biotite crystals in mica schists, aligned hornblende crystals in amphibolites, and streaked-out quartz or felspar crystals in augen gneisses. Their direction again is in general parallel to the b axis in simple and relatively undisturbed regionally metamorphosed areas. Deviations do occur and are significant; they often indicate a more complex folding and/or metamorphic history, which can sometimes be traced out by the geometric relationships.

TECTONIC SYMBOLS

The relation between bedding plane, cleavage, and lineation, as measured in the field, can best be represented on a stereographic projection in the way proposed by Sander for the petrofabric orientations. The symbols used are:

ss = bedding plane; sc = cleavage plane; s_1, s_2, s_3, etc. = successive cleavage or schistosity planes

π = pole of plane; π_{ss} = pole of bedding plane; π_{s1} = pole of cleavage plane

β = constructed intersection of planes; β_{ss} = that of bedding planes; β_{s1} = that of one set of cleavage planes

B = a measured fold axis

l = a measured lineation; δ_1 = intersection bedding/cleavage, or l_{cr} (crystal growth)

l_1, l_2, l_3, etc. = successive lineations (belonging to s_1, s_2, s_3, etc.)

Further, *a*, *b*, and *c* are Sander's perpendicular axes, in which *b* is taken as being the direction of the most prominent fold axis or crystal elongation, perpendicular to the symmetry plane of the fold; *a* as the direction perpendicular to *b* lying in the schistosity plane, often taken as giving the direction of expansion; and *c*, perpendicular to the *ab* schistosity or cleavage plane. These axes definitions give rise to numerous misunderstandings and controversies because the fold axes of minor folds need not be parallel to the main fold axis of the region; they can be perpendicular or oblique to it; neither is it true that crystal elongation is necessarily parallel to the minor-fold or microfold axes, so that it often is quite arbitrary which direction is defined as *b* and which as *a*. In a simple axial-plane stress-cleavage fold, the *c* axis is identical with the stress direction, but in an oblique-slip-cleavage fold it is not.

In a rhombic fold, of the two symmetry planes, one the axial plane, the other the plane perpendicular to the fold axis, the first is the *ab* plane, the second the *ac* plane (Fig. 202). In a monoclinic or asymmetric fold, a reversed fold, for instance, the axial plane would still be taken as the *ab* plane and the cross-section symmetry plane as the *ac* plane.

When successive phases of tectonization occur, the *ss* planes are folded several times, with possibly different fold axes; an *sc* plane becomes folded, sometimes more than once; original *l* and *B* directions can be deviated, and the analysis of their change in direction with the help of stereograms informs us about the cross-folding in its successive stages. Figure 203 gives two examples of an equal-area

Fig. 202   The conventional *a*, *b*, and *c* axes of folding in relation to an axial-plane cleavage fold.

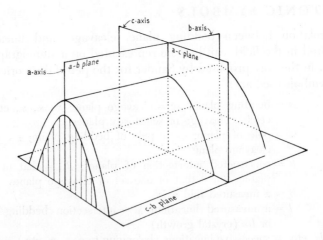

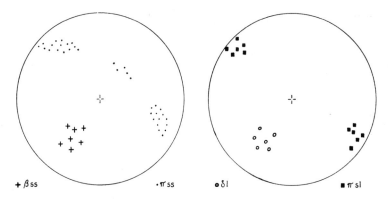

Fig. 203   To the left: bedding plane poles in a girdle around the fold axis. To the right: bedding-cleavage intersection lineation gives fold axis of axial-plane cleavage fold.

stereogram with maxima and girdles formed by such structural features in a simple axial-plane-cleavage fold. Such diagrams demonstrate the relation of cleavage to folding, lineations to cleavage, etc., and are irreplaceable for the analysis of successive stages of tectonization. In this analysis porphyroblasts may also play an important role.

AXIAL-PLANE STRESS-CLEAVAGE FOLDS

The simplest and most fundamental form of cleavage fold is that with an axial-plane cleavage. It has many associated phenomena which elucidate its origin as a stress-cleavage phenomenon. In principle it is a flattening process, proved by fossil deformation and other evidence; it must have been preceded by some concentric folding, since folds would not result from mere flattening. Differential movement along the cleavage planes is not essential and is hard to demonstrate. The existence of the cleavage planes, as in slates, is due to parallel orientation of mica flakes, which is the result of the gradual compression of the rock material, and to recrystallization under directed pressure.

The coarser the grain of the rock, the greater the distance between the cleavage plane: in sandstone they may be more than 1 cm apart (fracture cleavage), in slates they can be seen only under the microscope. Essentially, the cleavage planes do not cut one another; although they may meet and branch, they are always roughly parallel, independent of their frequency. In some cases the flattening is due to two obliquely cutting shear planes, especially in more competent rocks. In the most common and simplest case the cleavage fold is symmetrical

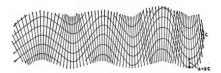

Fig. 204   Cleavage folding.

to the axial plane, and then it is obvious that the cleavage develops perpendicular to the main stress direction and therefore is not an oblique-slip cleavage but an axial-plane stress cleavage.

When the flattening is equally distributed through the whole mass of rock, having the necessary preliminary undulations, we get typical similar folds with thin limbs and thick hinges, as sketched in various stages of compressions in Fig. 204, in which the fanning of the cleavage is somewhat exaggerated. The amount of flattening can be calculated, as had been done by Sharpe in 1847, by measuring the deformation of fossils and reduction spots and, as Sorby demonstrated in 1853, by comparing the length of parasitic folds with the distance in the flattened rock. Both arrived at a 50 to 70% flattening.

When the folds are steep, the amount of flattening can be roughly evaluated by comparing the thickness of a particular bed in the hinge and in the flank (Fig. 209). This is only an approximation because the cleavage planes are never strictly parallel, but often fan out toward the convex side of the arc, and extension in the *b* direction can be a further source of error. E. Cloos (1947b) showed, in his survey of the oolite flattening in the South Mountain fold, that the flattening in limestone starts before the cleavage planes become visible megascopically. From a flattening of 20% onward the cleavage became increasingly clear. Pure compression without dilatation could possibly account for the observed 20% flattening. This kind of folding is a pure stress-cleavage process, called "Druckschieferung" in German.

The flattening of the rock is sometimes demonstrated by fossil deformation, and in other cases it can be detected under the micro-

Fig. 205   Deformation in microlithons of fracture cleavage. (A) folding; (B) knicking; (C) shear.

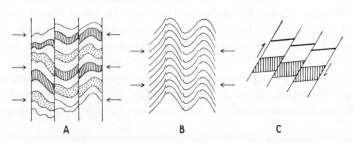

A   B   C

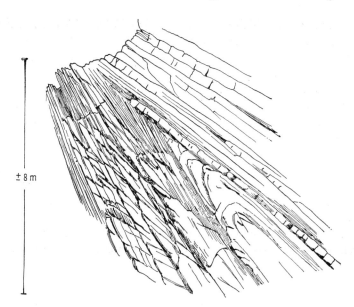

± 8 m

Fig. 206 Sharp stress cleavage fold in Devonian of North Devonshire.

scope in the microlithons. We see, then, either a folding, as in Fig. 205A, or a knicking, as in Fig. 205B, but in most cases it is impossible even to guess how much flattening has actually taken place.

Because we do not know how much of the final fold shape is due to the original concentric fold and how much to the later flattening,

Fig. 207 Flat stress cleavage fold in Devonian of North Devonshire. (The flatness of the structure is somewhat exaggerated because the outcrop is somewhat oblique to the cleavage.)

the question arises which of the two folds of Figs. 206 and 207 shows most flattening; and as we do not know the proportion of the total compression due to the initial concentric folding, the question remains unanswered.

In some rather exceptional cases we can find an answer. Figure 208 represents an outcrop in the Ordovician slates of New Jersey. It shows a slate with almost horizontal cleavage crossed vertically by a folded sandstone. The sandstone folds are more or less concentric because there is only a slight thinning in the flanks or thickening in the hinges, although they show a distinct, coarse fracture cleavage. The cleavage planes in the slates show also a distinct drag against the sandstone, thus demonstrating the slip on the sandstone/slate bedding plane.

Disregarding the slight thinning of the sandstone in the flanks, the shortening of this layer can easily be calculated. Its folds are almost

Fig. 208 Concentrically folded sandstone in slates. Ordovician; Delaware Water Gap, Pennsylvania.

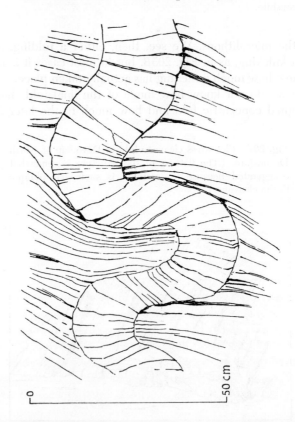

50 cm

0

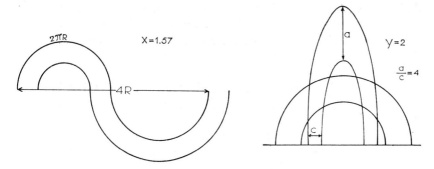

Fig. 209 Shortening of 36° in concentric fold and additional shortening of 50% by stress cleavage flattening. Total shortening 68%.

90° folds, and therefore the shortening

$$Y = \frac{2\pi R}{4R} = \frac{1}{2}\pi = 1.57, \text{ or } 36\%$$

and consequently the cleavage in the slates is also due to a flattening of 36%.

The problem of the total flattening can also be approached from a more theoretical point of view. An isoclinal fold showing an average ratio of 4:1 between the thickness of a layer in the hinge and the flank can be supposed to have been formed in two stages (Fig. 209), first a concentric fold of 90°, and then a flattening of $1: \sqrt{4} = 50\%$. The total flattening is then

$$36\% + 50\% \text{ of } 64\% = \pm 70\%$$

Since these proportions are fairly typical of folds in slightly metamorphosed slates, the total compression in general does not seem to have exceeded about 70%.

SHEAR FOLDS

Besides the folds which are described above, other structures accompanied by the development of a cleavage, or better, a schistosity, occur in many mountain chains. They differ from these cleavage folds in several respects. First, the schistosity is not a steeply dipping plane, but develops as a flat-lying, or even horizontal, plane. Second, when sedimentary bedding is present, the schistosity is usually parallel to the bedding. Folds do occur in these rocks although they are much scarcer, or at least much more difficult to detect. These folds show the following properties: they are isoclinal, recumbent, and asymmetric;

their size varies from a few centimeters to at least several hundreds of meters, and possibly much larger. Further, it is evident that such structures are characterized by their occurrence in higher-grade rocks than slates and phyllites; they are frequent in schists, gneisses, amphibolites, etc., although certain phyllite areas may show these characteristics as well. Lineations are abundant in such rocks, but because of the parallelism of bedding and schistosity, they are not intersecting lines, but are indicated by preferred orientation of prismatic minerals like amphiboles or by elongated mica or feldspar crystals. These lineations are in most cases parallel to the axes of the isoclinal folds.

The occurrence of such flat-lying structures has led to the concept of load metamorphism, where it is thought that mimetic crystallization parallel to the bedding planes, due to great depth, is responsible for this kind of schistosity. This hypothesis can be altogether discarded on the following grounds. Several basins are known where sediments have been buried under at least 10 km of sediments without showing any trace of recrystallization or the formation of a schistosity. Bedded rocks that are metamorphosed in the aureoles of intrusive granites often show an unoriented texture without any parallel development of minerals; in this case mimetic crystallization is certainly not operative. Therefore, neither loading nor a temperature rise in itself can cause a schistosity. Then the occurrence of folds in these schistose rocks is a clear indication of deformation; and finally, the existence of lineations due to oriented and elongated minerals can never be explained by mimetic crystallization, but must be due to growth in a stress field, accompanied by deformation.

Although these structures with flat-lying schistosity show many differences with normal cleavage folds, there are also similarities. For instance, flattening, an important process in cleavage folding, has also been active in the formation of these schistosities, as shown by the occurrence of boudinage, parasitic folds of earlier discordant veins, and the deflection of the schistosity around hard bodies such as porphyroblasts or small pebbles.

As far as the mechanism of the formation of this type of schistosity is concerned, a definite conclusion is difficult to reach. It seems, however, logical to assume that, besides being a plane of flattening, the schistosity is also a plane of slip, and as such can only represent an example of simple shear whereby the conjugate shear plane for some reason is not developed. The difficulty arises from the fact that most cases are hard to prove. The only way to demonstrate this kind of movement is by observing the result of the internal rotation of crystals. Rotated crystals have been described from several regions. In one example, however, the Bosot area in the central Pyrenees (Zwart, 1960a and b), the association of flat-lying schistosites, isoclinal recumbent folds, and thousands of porphyroblasts, all rotated in the same direction, the occurrence of this kind of flow deformation seems to be definitely established.

The present attitude of the schistosity does not give a clue to its original position, since vertical cleavages could have been flattened out and horizontal cleavages put in an upright position by later folding. Therefore detailed investigation is necessary to demonstrate whether the type of deformation is that of stress cleavage or shear folding or flow.

PARASITIC FOLDS, BOUDINS, MULLIONS, RODS, AND PTYGMATIC FOLDS

Cleavage folds are often accompanied by different kinds of distortion of competent layers imbedded in their slate surroundings. Among these, boudins, mullions, and so-called "drag folds"—I prefer the term "parasitic folds"—are significant.

The word "boudin" is French for a kind of sausage. The word "mullion" is derived from architecture, meaning an upright division in a window usually, when in conspicuous relief from the wall. In longitudinal section the three phenomena are somewhat similar, but in cross section (Fig. 210) they clearly show their different origins. The parasitic folds and mullions show a shortening of the competent bed in cross section; boudins, a lengthening.

In *parasitic folds* the axial planes of the minor folds are parallel to the cleavage plane of the surrounding slates, as in Figs. 211 and 212. They can be very much compressed, as in Fig. 211, or only slightly folded, as in Fig. 213, or even show overthrusts, as in Fig. 214. In the flanks of the fold they are asymmetric, with the steep flank toward the anticlinal axis of the major fold; in the hinge of the major fold

Fig. 210 Boudins, parasitic folds, and mullions.

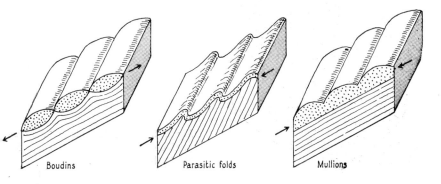

Boudins   Parasitic folds   Mullions

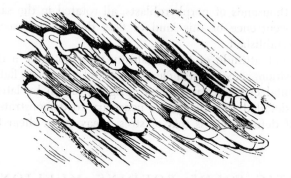

Fig. 211   Compressed parasitic folds of limestone in slates. Devonian of North Devonshire.

they become symmetrical (Fig. 212). They cannot be due to drag along the bedding plane because there is in principle no movement along the bedding plane in cleavage folding. In addition, parasitic folds occur on the hinges, as well as in the flanks (Fig. 212), although even in concentric folds there is no slip on the bedding plane in the hinges. Because the competent beds in such minor folds are deformed differently from the surrounding slate, there is always some slip along their bedding planes as a result of the folding and flattening process.

There is some apparent contradiction between the general dilatation in the plane of cleavage and shortening of the folded bed, almost in

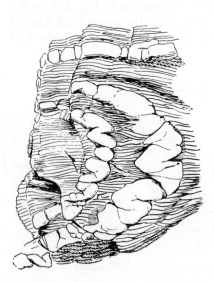

Fig. 212   Parasitic folds of limestone in slates in anticlinal crest. Devonian of North Devonshire.

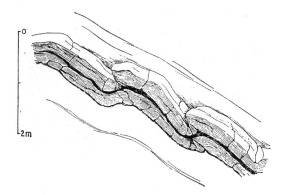

Fig. 213 Flat parasitic folds of limestone in slate. Devonian of North Devonshire.

the same plane, which will disappear, however, when the development of a cleavage fold is analyzed.

The diagram of Fig. 215 represents the gradual compression of a flat layer of rock, in 10% stages of increasing compression, to a narrow vertical slice.

The original flat horizontal slab gradually changes into a thin slice standing vertical. When we consider a thin layer in this slab representing a competent rock originally in a horizontal position, it will either be thickened or be folded into vertical folds. But when we consider a similar bed forming a diagonal in the undeformed slab, again representing a competent rock layer, but now in a slightly tilted position, we see that this layer is first shortened and stretched afterward. The changing length of the diagonal can easily be calculated

Fig. 214 Overthrusted parasitic fold of sandstone in slate. Lower Paleozoic of Columbia County, N.Y.

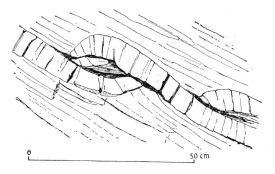

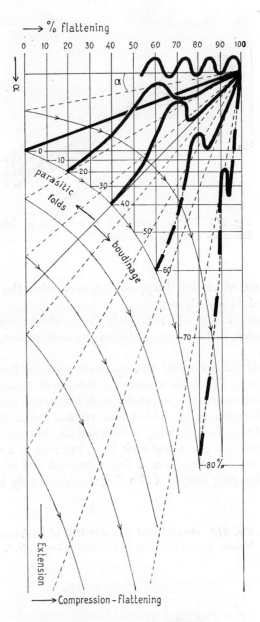

Fig. 215 Diagram illustrating the gradual
shortening of tilted layer through parasitic
folding up to 45° dip and stretching through
boudinage beyond 45°.

because the area of the rectangle is approximately constant. Therefore

$$x \sin \alpha \cdot x \cos \alpha = c$$

where x = length of diagonal
  α = angle of diagonal with horizontal
  c = area of rectangle
Then

$$x = \sqrt{\frac{c}{\frac{1}{2} \sin 2\alpha}}$$

and x reaches a minimum value for $\alpha = 45°$.

The result is that any bed which already had a slight dip at the start of the compressive process will gradually increase its dip and will be first shortened until it reaches a dip of 45° and afterward will be stretched again, as has been sketched in Fig. 215. The small folds of a competent layer will necessarily be asymmetric because its base is tilted whereas its axial plane remains constant. One may expect that these folds will be still more compressed after the tilt has exceeded the 45° limit, as illustrated, for example, by the folds of Fig. 211.

Thus, in Fig. 215, two fields can be discerned, a field of shortening above the 45° dipping line and a field of stretching below this line, representing, respectively, the field of parasitic folds and the field of boudinage.

It depends, of course, to a large degree on the dip the competent bed reached before flattening set in, whether it will reach the 45° limit or not. If this dip was zero, the bed will only be compressed and never be stretched; if only a few degrees, only asymmetric parasitic folds will be formed; and when the original dip was near 45°, only boudinage will occur.

Therefore *boudinage* is generally and rightly ascribed to a stretching of the rock in one or two directions lying in the bedding plane, or to a compression perpendicular to this plane, which is, mechanically speaking, the same process (E. Cloos, 1947a; Ramberg, 1955). The boudinaged bed is always composed of a more competent rock than its surroundings, a sandstone or limestone bed in shale, for instance, and the boudins have an oval shape in cross section and run like welts on the bedding plane. Not having the same capacity for stretching as the shale, it breaks up in small longitudinal sections which have rounded edges, where the competency of the two layers is not too dissimilar, a sandstone in shale, for instance; it remains sharp in other cases, where the two rock types are very different, a chert in limestone or a limestone in gypsum, for instance. These angular blocks are not called boudins, but are due to a similar stretching mechanism. As the relative competency of rock changes with temperature and con-

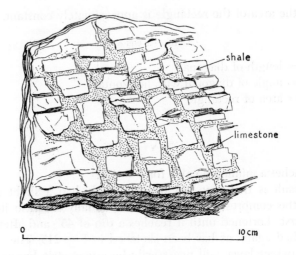

Fig. 216 Stretched thin shale layer on limestone forming regular pattern.

fining pressure, and even may be reversed, we may also find stretched shale layers in limestone, as shown in Fig. 216.

Under the microscope it can be seen that the cracks between the shale patches of Fig. 216 or the cracks in a chert bed between limestone are filled by recrystallized calcite derived from the surrounding limestone. Sometimes it is the boudinaged rock itself which furnishes the recrystallized material to fill up the tension fissures between the boudins.

In one instance I noticed that a boudinaged limestone with chert layers showed recrystallized calcite opposite the limestone and recrystallized quartz opposite the chert bands (Fig. 217). There can be no doubt, therefore, that the intersections represent zones of tension, and consequently that the whole phenomenon is attributable to stretch-

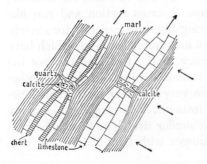

Fig. 217 Boudinage in limestone with chert beds. Opposite the chert beds the filling of the cracks between the boudins consists of quartz.

ing of the competent bed in the direction of the dip, or conversely, to compression of the bed perpendicular to the bedding. The fact that boudinage occurs only in strongly compressed areas of isoclinal folds supports this view.

Boudinage is not restricted to sedimentary beds, but also occurs in quartz veins (Lohest, 1909) and dikes (Holmquist, 1930).

The boudins themselves have also often been fractured by shear-planes oblique to the bedding. In an advanced stage of boudinage the elongated segments may be separated completely and linked only by thin streaks of their recrystallized components (see, for instance, E. Cloos, 1947a, with many illustrations and bibliography).

In the cliffs of Tintagel, on the west coast of Cornwall, many boudins of more competent siliceous rocks occur in slates. Both the beds and the cleavage are in a horizontal position, probably forming parts of recumbent folds. Near Ilfracombe, in North Devonshire, limestone boudins occur in slate (Fig. 218). An enlargement of the structure of the stretched ending of the Tintagel boudins gives an interesting detailed view of the tensional process (Fig. 219). Here the boudin-aged rock consists of several layers, of which the central ones broke off first. The outer ones in that stage curved inward in the same way as can now be seen in the surrounding slate. In a later stage these outer layers also broke off, but here they still envelop the inner ones.

Ramberg (1955) has studied boudinage experimentally and confirmed the relationships, as sketched above, between competent boudinaged beds and incompetent host rock.

Mullion structures are linear structures of competent beds related to compression parallel to the bedding, like parasitic folds, and are of

Fig. 218   Limestone boudin in slate. Devonian of Ilfracombe, Devonshire.

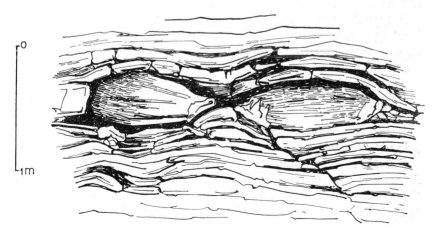

0

1m

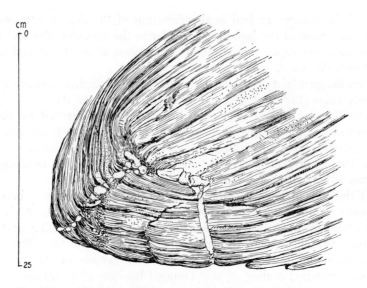

Fig. 219   Limestone boudins occurring in slate, showing two
stages of stretching. Tintagel area, Devonshire.

quite different origin than boudins. In typical mullions only one side
of a competent bed has been contorted in regular folds.

Wilson (1953) first distinguishes mullion structures from rodding,
mullions being formed from the normal country rock and rods from
quartz that has been introduced into, or has segregated in, the rocks.
Among these mullions he then distinguishes (1) bedding mullions, or
fold mullions, (2) cleavage mullions, and (3) irregular mullions. In
my opinion this subdivision of Wilson's is not necessary; real mullions
are Wilson's bedding mullions and are mostly related to a cleavage
in the surrounding schists (Fig. 220).

In typical cleavage mullions the intersection of cleavage planes and
bedding planes is more pronounced. Their cross section may be either
angular or rounded off like fold mullions, and once again they are
parallel to the *b* axis of the folds.

After very detailed research in the Eifel, Pilger and Schmidt (1957)
came to the conclusion that there the mullions are due to a secondary
cleavage phase, later than the original axial-plane cleavage.

In bedding mullions, the mullion structure is developed on only one
side of the competent bed.

Quartz rods are frequent in severely crumpled metamorphic rocks.
As soon as quartz veins have developed (mainly by segregation from
the phyllitic country rock in zones of minimum tension, but also by
recrystallization on cleavage planes), subsequent internal movement

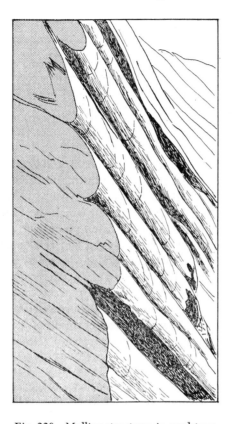

Fig. 220   Mullion structures in sandstone, Dedenborn, Eifel Gebirge, Germany. (*After Pilger and Schmidt, 1957. Published by permission of Hessische Landesamt Bodenforschung, Wiesbaden.*)

may crumple them and form cylindroidal quartz rods. They occur more frequently in the incompetent rocks between competent beds, since internal movement is concentrated in these more plastic intercalations. They are closely related to crystal-growth lineation.

PTYGMATIC STRUCTURES

This term, coined by Sederholm (1913), connotes contorted veins which show a meanderlike pattern. They occur most frequently as pegmatitic veins in either migmatites or in gneisses, but occasionally consist of other material. Their most distinctive feature is their apparent independence of the crystal texture of their host rock; in par-

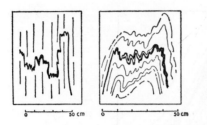

Fig. 221   Ptygmatic veins from Finland with deformation concordant with that of country rock. (*After Kuenen, 1938. Published by permission of the Geological Society of Finland.*)

ticular, the schistosity planes of the country rock do not cross the ptygmas. Nevertheless, the numerous illustrations given by Sederholm (1913), Milch (1900), Read (1928), Kuenen (1938), and Wilson (1952) contain quite a few examples in which the folding process of the ptygma is obviously due to the same process of deformation that prevails in the country rock, with limbs and thickened hinges (Fig. 221). Kuenen (1938) has illustrated by experiment the possibility of the development of this type of ptygma by deformation of a planar vein during deformation of the country rock around it. The lack of foliation in the vein is doubtless due to some difference in physical properties, such as a slightly greater rigidity. These concordant ptygmas are not, however, the most typical. Wilson quotes several

Fig. 222   Ptygmatic veins from Finland with deformation independent of that of country rock (migmatite). (*After Wilson, 1952, in Geological Magazine. Published by permission of the Editor.*)

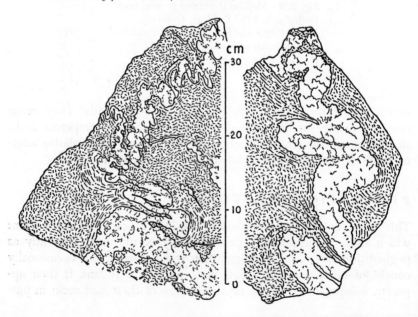

instances (his figures 1, 3, 7, 8, and 9; the last is reproduced here as Fig. 222) in which the country rock either shows no regular foliation at all or has foliation which is deflected along the margins of the ptygma. In the nonfoliated migmatites of the first type, a texture parallel to the ptygma is visible, as is shown in Fig. 222. Wilson concludes from this evidence that the vein material was injected in the fashion of putty injected into a jelly and that it attained its tortuous shape when an obstacle prevented its further forward advance; he illustrates his thesis with experiments.

Wilson's conclusion seems highly improbable, and Ramberg (1959, 1960) has convincingly demonstrated, both theoretically and experimentally, that true ptygmatic folding can be due to compressive strain acting parallel to the surface of an originally flat layer or vein, the material of the layer being more competent than the host rock. Many of the ptygmatic veins are probably segregation veins which originated during the migmatization or granitization process; they need not represent a faithful recording of the strain of the whole rock mass, because there is no reason to expect segregation to take place along planar surfaces only.

Chapter 21

Transitional Types of Folding

The differences in physical properties of layers of different thicknesses of variable rock types and the variations in the intensity of the stress field naturally give rise to tendencies for different types of deformation in the same fold or same set of folds. As stress cleavage, slip cleavage, and concentric folding may all be due to a simple compressive stress field and as concentric folding generally even precedes cleavages, we can expect that many kinds of transitions exist between them.

Such transitions are mainly of three different types:

Mixed folding. In a layered sequence of rocks certain lithological units, the most competent, show concentric folding, and the others, the incompetent layers, show cleavage, of either axial-plane or concentric type.

Accordion folding. Cleavage is restricted to the axial planes, and in the flanks the movement has been along the bedding.

Chevron shear-slip folding. One flank shows concentric movement; the other shows shear movement.

MIXED FOLDING

Mixed folding is common in numerous cleavage folds where slate and sandstone or limestone beds alternate, of which Fig. 223 is a typical example. If this tendency of different behavior of competent and incompetent rocks exists, all competent layers either show a different cleavage from the slates, coarser and making an acute angle with the axial-plane cleavage (Fig. 201), or do not show any cleavage at all. If their cleavage is coarser, it is often referred to as fracture cleavage, in contrast with the slaty cleavage of the incompetent beds. As in Fig. 201, the acute angle always dips downward toward the axial plane, and very often a flat S shape of the fracture planes has been formed by the slip on the bedding plane. The fact that the angle of the cleavage plane is related to the grain size of the rock is demonstrated

290

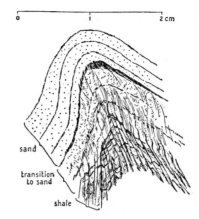

Fig. 223 Microfold with axial-plane fracture cleavage in slate and concentric folding in sandstone.

by layers with graded bedding in which the cleavage plane gradually turns (Fig. 224). In this kind of mixed folding the overall shape of the fold can be either concentric or similar.

Even the distortions described in the foregoing chapter, parasitic folds, boudins, etc., are a kind of mixed folding. They all have their origin in the fact that the type of deformation is mainly dependent on two important factors: the level of the main stress field and the resistance qualities of the different layers. Even when the overall shape of a large fold is completely governed by the general average resistance of the thick sequence of layered rocks, in detail the specific properties of particular layers may prevail. An extreme case is a pure fluid reaction of an incompetent layer like salt, allowing flow. In fact, the stress within the incompetent layers will show a great variety of orientations, although retaining a symmetry basic to the main stress field.

It is easy to see the immense variety of possibilities of orientation for the deformation structures within an incompetent bed. Even if all cleavage had the same role, one would expect variations; however, differences in time of development relative to degree of compression clearly complicate the situation enormously. What remains strikingly

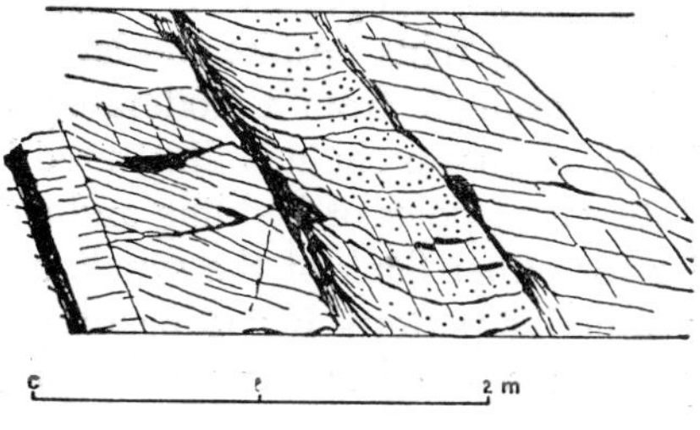

Fig. 224 Curved cleavage in graded sandstone. Devonian of Valle de Arán, Spanish Pyrenees.

clear, nevertheless, is the basic symmetry in relation to the major stress direction, which corresponds to the fact that all the planes of deformation contain a common perpendicular to the main stress. This fact is notably similar to that derived by structural petrologists from their studies on the internal effects of deformation.

CONCENTRIC CLEAVAGE

A special kind of mixture of concentric folding and cleavage is the concentric cleavage, in which the cleavage may have the remarkable tendency to be flatter than the bedding, just the opposite from axial-plane cleavage. It has the typical property of mixed folding of being completely restricted to the argillaceous beds and not penetrating into the more competent beds. It even curves into the bedding plane when approaching a competent bed, clearly showing that it is closely connected with concentric folding. The macroscopic partings may be quite widely separated, with somewhat irregular cleavage planes, but may be seen to be due to a parallel arrangement of mica flakes, and therefore can be distinguished from ordinary axial-plane slaty or fracture cleavage only when their relation to the macrofolds and bedding is well established (Savage, 1961).

Therefore the term concentric cleavage is intended to include cleavage that, generated contemporaneously with a fold, bears a relation to the fold axis similar to that of the folded bedding planes. It includes the true bedding schistosity, where both sets of planes are parallel, but in fact it more typically has a low angle to the bedding. As has been noted, axial-plane cleavage can be so defined only in a statistical manner, because deviations from exact parallelism with the axial plane are almost always to be seen. Consequently, there can be no precise delimitation between the two—axial-plane and concentric cleavage. In practice, however, the dominantly crosscutting nature of the axial-plane cleavage through the bedding is usually in contrast to the subparallel attitude of concentric cleavage. Naturally, this leads to ambiguity in isoclinally folded rocks, but it should be taken as an extra incentive to determine fully the nature of this kind of fold and its cleavage. It has too often been assumed that cleavage or schistosity subparallel to bedding or banding implies the existence of isoclinal folds despite the lack of evidence of hinges or repetition.

The example from a moderately folded large syncline of the Cantabrian mountain chain is illustrated by the stereograms (Fig. 225). The patterns of poles of bedding and cleavage planes are clearly very similar for either flank of the syncline, although each flank shows its own distinctive pattern. It will also be noted that while similar, the stereograms from either flank differ slightly in orientation. The shift is systematic, the cleavage dipping at a lower angle than the bedding in both. This symmetry implies the existence of the fold when the cleavage was being formed. However, the spread of bedding and cleavage planes has been caused by the development of numerous minor folds clearly identified as later by the crosscutting nature of their axial-plane cleavage, so that only a relatively short period could have divided the formation of the major fold and the concentric cleavage. It seems that this type of slaty cleavage changes in its character even within this fold. Along the strike it has been observed to form axial-plane cleavage to minor folds in one place and to major folds in another.

Fig. 225 NE–SW section Lechada syncline, stereographic projection of bedding plane and slaty cleavage poles, showing similar axial-plane symmetry for both. (*After Savage, 1961.*)

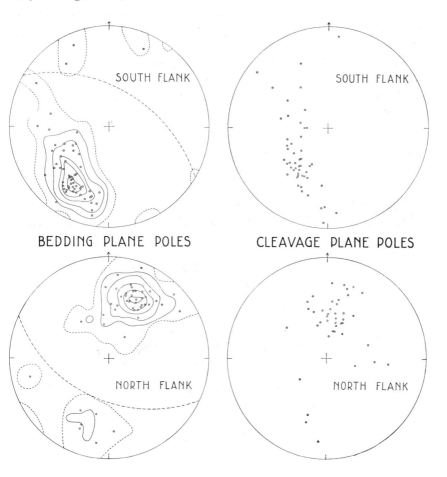

BEDDING PLANE POLES CLEAVAGE PLANE POLES

ACCORDION FOLDS

Synonyms are concertina folding and chevron folding, in American usage. This type of folding is characterized by straight flanks and sharp hinges (Fig. 226). It seems probable that the beginning of the fold was a knicking process and that the subsequent bending of the strata was restricted to the knick zones. They occur only in well-stratified rocks with relatively thin competent layers of sandstone or limestone and are common as microfold and minor folds in well-foliated rocks. The stretching along the axial plane is very obvious, and even a slight difference in dip in the two flanks will cause a different axial extension in the one flank compared with the other. This results in frequent axial faults (Fig. 232), often followed by dikes (Fig. 230). Their throw is very variable and can easily become contradictory along one axial plane with variations in dip of either flank.

In concentric folding the maximum possible compression without involving overthrusting occurs when both flanks are vertical, and is then about 36%.

In accordion folding there is no such definite limit, but when the dip of the flanks steepens, the slip along the bedding for each percentage of compression increases exponentially (a tangent function). In Fig. 227, the bedding slip

$$b = a \tan \alpha$$

where a is the thickness of a layer, and the shortening in percentages

$$x = (1 - \cos \alpha) \, 100$$

Because the slip increases with the thickness of the layers, it is obvious that a thin-bedded sequence will be easier to fold in accordion

Fig. 226 Accordion folds in Carboniferous of Hartland Quay, Devonshire.

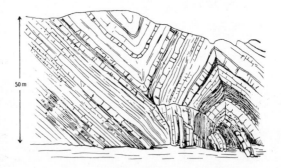

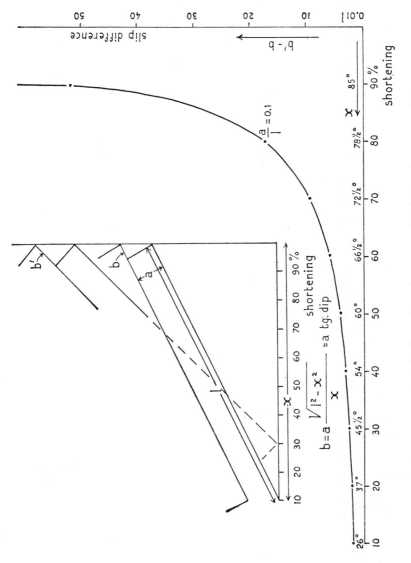

Fig. 227 Graph showing increase of bedding-plane slip in accordion fold with increase of dip.

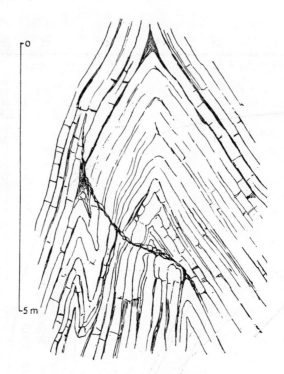

Fig. 228   Accordion fold with thrust fold. Jurassic
limestone, Sierra Madre Oriental, Mexico.

folds than a thick-bedded one. In the graph of Fig. 227 the shortening
is compared with the increase of slip $(b^1 - b)$, and it shows that
above a 65° dip in the flanks, the slip starts to increase very rapidly
and soon becomes prohibitive for further shortening along the same
principle. According to my experience, the dip in the flanks of accordion folds does not increase beyond 50 to 60°; after that, faulting
and thrusting set in. In the folds of Fig. 226 the flanks dip at 53°,
equivalent to some 40% compression, about the same as the compression
reached in a concentric fold with vertical flanks.

Other examples I have measured give roughly the same result.
Further compression of an accordion fold will cause either oblique
thrust faulting when the folds are near the surface, as in Figs. 228 and
229, where we can see how closely the thrusting is linked to the folding process, or further deformation by stress cleavage, as in Fig. 236.

In Fig. 228 we see that the thrust disappears in the bedding plane
of both flanks and a secondary fold has obviously formed below the
thrust, during the thrusting.

EXAMPLES

The Ballarat and Bendigo Gold Mine Districts, Victoria (Australia).
Particularly good and clear examples of cleavage folding of the
accordion type are known in three separate belts of the Ballarat
district, Ballarat West, Ballarat East, and Little Bendigo. A section
through the Bendigo gold field shows the general structure, consisting
of a synclinorium with numerous pinched folds and a few vertical
faults parallel to the axial planes and cleavage, combined with oblique
faults.

Detailed sections are available from a number of gold fields. In
Fig. 229 the folds are slightly overturned and the steep flank is cut by

Fig. 229 Thrust faults with ore bodies in flattened
accordion folds. Ballarat East gold field, Victoria,
Australia. [*After Baragwanath, 1923. In David, 1950.
Published by permission of Edward Arnold, Publishers, Ltd.*]

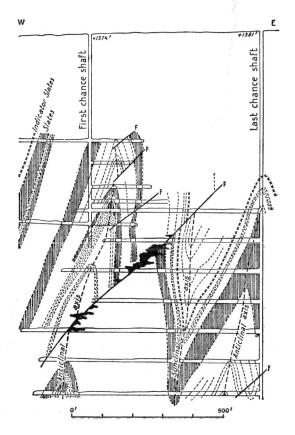

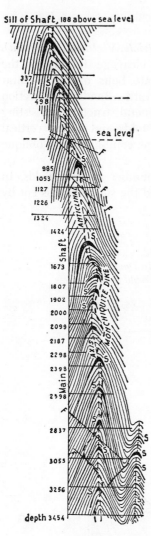

Sill of Shaft, 188 above sea level

sea level

ANTICLINAL

Shaft

MORCHIQUITE DIKE

Main

depth 3454

Fig. 230 Bendigo, Victoria. Hustles Shaft showing saddle reefs and dike in axial plane. (*After Herman, 1923. In David, 1950. Published by permission of Messrs. Edward Arnold, Publisher, Ltd.*)

a series of oblique faults, which make an angle of 40 to 50° with the axial plane, and as such suggest an extension in the vertical axis or a lateral compression. This is confirmed by the shape of the ore bodies, which show a clear horizontal extension starting from the inclined fault line. The whole structure seems, therefore, to have resulted from a single deformational episode with a uniform orientation of the stress field, with the minimum principal stress in the vertical direction and the largest principal stress in a horizontal position.

The saddle reefs of Bendigo (Fig. 230) give a similar picture. As has been explained above, it is the anticlinal axial plane which is the main zone of extension in this kind of structure. The monchiquite dike along the axial plane also demonstrates an axial-plane fault, with very little displacement. A few fault lines, with the same inclination and character as in the former section, demonstrate the close resemblance of the two structures.

In Fig. 231 a combination of saddle reefs (both of the anticlinal and synclinal type), fault reefs, and axial dikes demonstrates the close relationship between these features. Any discussion of the origin of the ore should start in this case from the clearly demonstrated fact that structural control is absolute. Both the saddle reefs, anticlinal or synclinal, and the fault reefs occur on planes or zones of minimum stress or, in other words, are associated with structural features due to extension in a vertical direction and lateral compression. I should like to suggest that all the reefs are due to recrystallization of the country rock itself, with concentration of its most mobile elements, the metals, in the reefs themselves.

Ruhr Coal District.   In the Westphalian Ruhr coal field the folding has a remarkable character—half concentric folding, half cleavage folding. The two styles of folding are not equally distributed through the whole field; similar folding is best seen in the older beds in the

Fig. 231.   Wattle Gully gold mine, Chewton, Victoria, with axial-plane dike, thrusts in flank, and saddle reefs. (*After Thomas, 1939–1941. In David, 1950. Published by permission of Messrs. Edward Arnold, Publishers, Ltd.*)

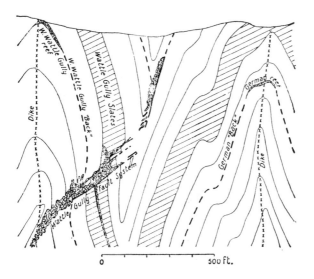

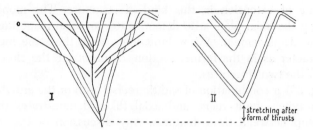

Fig. 232 Ruhr coal district section of Fröhliche Morgen-
sonne, with axial-plane fault and thrust faults in flank.
(*After Nehm, 1930. In Kukuk, 1938. Published by permission of Springer-Verlag, Berlin.*)

south, while the concentric habit is better represented by higher beds,
and in the north, a "stock werk" structure.

In the section in Fig. 232 we recognize the typical features of accordion folding—straight flanks and narrow and sharp anticlinal hinge.
Even the axial fault with very small displacement is present, and in
the flanks we find the same kind of thrust faults that we noticed
before and which emphasize the vertical dilatation. By reconstructing
the fold before the thrust planes came into action, one gets an idea of
how much they contributed to the dilatation in the vertical direction.

CHEVRON FOLDS

The Belgian-Dutch Coal District.   From this coal district many
good examples of concentric, accordion, and chevron folding can be
collected. I will mention here two series of chevron folds. The first is
a section from the Domaniale colliery (Fig. 233). The section shows
two thrust planes with a 30 and 35° dip, which seem to be of post-

Fig. 233 Section in Domaniale colliery with
thrusts and chevron folding. (*After Sax, 1946.
Published by permission of Geologisch Bureau
voor het Mijngebied, Heerlen.*)

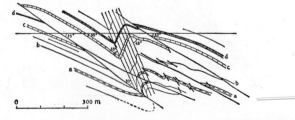

folding origin on first sight because they are independent of the fold shape and cut from flank into crest. The folds themselves are clearly of chevron type. When we draw in the anticlinal and synclinal axial planes, both straight lines in this section, they enclose the steep flank of the fold. The shear makes an angle of 35 or 45° with the bedding, depending on which flank one measures, and is apparently shear oblique to the lateral stress. When we consider the thrust planes in greater detail, it becomes clear that they cannot be altogether post-folding because their throw is too variable. Along the lowest thrust, for instance, the slip for bed c is some 300 m, whereas for beds a and b the thrust is only some 50 m on both branches of the thrust combined. Apparently some of the folding is taken over by the thrust movement. As both the thrusts and the oblique shear folding are thus due to the same stress field, one wonders why they have a different orientation. The next section gives us some insight into this problem.

The section from the nearby Liège coal field (Fig. 234), after Humblet (1941), also shows chevron folds and thrusts. A reconstruction of the folds before thrusting is given in Fig. 234II. When we draw a line tangential to the foot of the synclines, we get a gently flattening curve, starting from a very flat thrust in the upper left-hand corner. We find then, to our satisfaction, that the oblique shear folding consistently makes a 45° angle with this lower curve, with the result that the axial shear of the folds becomes steeper toward the left. Apparently

Fig. 234   Section through Liège coal basin: (I) present section, (II) thrust movement reconstituted, showing chevron shearing making 45° angle with curved basal thrust plane. (*After Humblet, 1941; in Revue Universelle des Mines. Published by permission of the Editor.*)

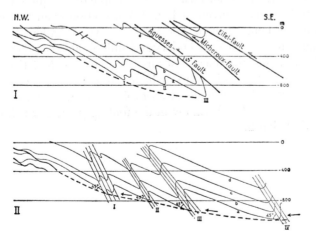

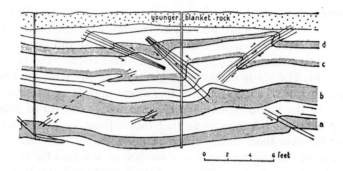

Fig. 235 Section through Kingston colliery, anthracite basin, Pennsylvania, with lines indicating direction of oblique-shear movement. (*After Darton, 1940. Published by permission of the United States Geological Survey.*)

a detachment plane, somewhere below the folds and showing itself as a flat overthrust in the upper left-hand corner, locally reorientated the lateral stress, to a position parallel to this plane. This local stress field caused the shear folds. At a later moment during the folding the shear folding stopped, the detachment plane over which it moved stopped functioning, and the temporarily reorientated stress field returned to its original horizontal position; the thrust steeper than the shear folding developed again, making a 45° angle with the deformative stress. This example shows very clearly the local variation in the orientation of the stress field caused by the development of the deformation. In such a simple case, where the relation between slip direction and stress orientation in the course of the deformation process can be reconstructed, we get a clear picture of the successive phases.

The Pennsylvania Coal Basin. An example of oblique shear folding of a peculiar kind is given in Fig. 235, a section from the anthracite coal basin of Pennsylvania. The steep but very shallow folds in the coal seams are not easy to understand unless one sees them as shear folds. By drawing the lines of shear it becomes evident that we have here a conjugate set of shears, which intersect in the center of the section. They make an angle of 25 to 45° with the lateral stress and cause a pronounced disharmony in the folding picture which is typical for the whole basin.

Chapter 22

Cross-folding and
Superimposed Folding

In Chap. 20 cross-folding of the paratectonic type was described. The same phenomenon is much more frequently encountered in regions of cleavage folding and particularly frequent in metamorphic regions.

In the last decade the study of cross-folding and superimposed folding has assumed large proportions, principally in England, Germany, and Scandinavia. A few general works may be quoted here: Bhattacharji, 1958; Clifford et al., 1957; Engels, 1959, Hoeppener, 1956; Lindström, 1961; Ramsay, 1960; Sutton, 1960; Whitten, 1959; Voll, 1960; Weiss, 1959; Zwart, 1960a and b, 1963. All refer to the Scottish and Scandinavian Caledonides, the Rheinische Schiefergebirge, and the Pyrenees.

By the term cross-folding is generally meant two fold systems in the same area having a different strike. The term superimposed folding indicates that one phase is later than another, a time relation which cannot always be proved.

In general, superimposed folding can be studied from folded cleavage planes, intersection of cleavages, reoriented lineations, and similar phenomena. Superimposed folding can be of two kinds: either two differently oriented structures have developed simultaneously or one orientation is definitively later than the other. Its most typical occurrence is manifested by folding of an axial plane. When a later deformation has exactly the same orientation as the earlier, the succession can often not be established from evidence of the final structure. A superimposed axial-plane cleavage succeeding a parallel concentric fold, the normal case, is not evident from the structure itself. The orientation of the second folding can differ from the first folding by its strike and by the dip of its axial plane or axis. The first case is most easily detected, but when the strike is parallel, the difference in dip must be rather pronounced in order to establish the successive stages. The growth of new minerals in metamorphic regions, often after the first folding but before or simultaneous with later deformation, can often be a great help in unraveling the complicated tectonic history.

The question whether successive deformations belong to one and the same stress field or really are separated by intervening periods of quiescence or stress relaxation is often impossible to solve. A careful analysis reveals that, in general, the whole sequence of events can be seen as derived from one overall stress field with locally varying directions and intensities. In the Rheinische Schiefergebirge the stress direction remains the same; in the Pyrenees the different stress directions form a regular and symmetric set, separated by periods of relative quiescence.

Apart from the variation in axial-plane strike and dip, successive stages of folding can vary by the difference in type of folding; e.g., concentric folding can be followed by cleavage folding or the other way around; simple fracture cleavage can be superimposed on cleavage folding; temperature rise may cause porphyroblasts to grow between two phases; etc. The many factors involved cause the great variety observed and described in superimposed-folding styles, of which only the main ones will be treated in the following discussion.

CLEAVAGE FOLDING SUPERIMPOSED ON CONCENTRIC FOLDING

In Chap. 20 we showed that all stress cleavage folding must have been preceded by concentric folding; otherwise a simple thickening of the

Fig. 236 Superimposed slaty cleavage not parallel to fold axis. Slate with sandstone from flysch sequence in Helvetides of Switzerland. (*After Hoeppener, 1956. Published by permission of Ferd. Enke Verlag, Stuttgart.*)

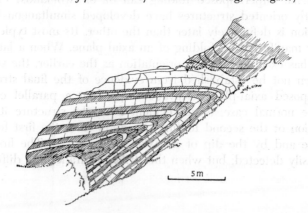

5 m

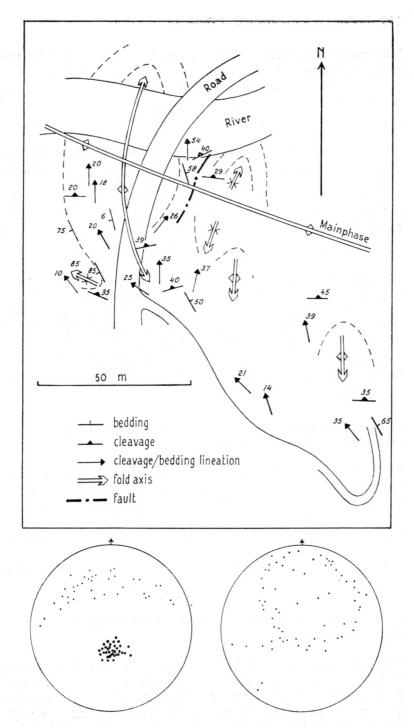

Fig. 237 Superimposed cleavage of main-phase E-W folding on N-S fold in Devonian of Ribagorzana Valley, Pyrenees. To the left, stereogram with center of cleavage poles and girdle of cleavage-bedding lineations; to the right, poles of bedding planes. (*After Boschma, 1962.*)

beds would occur without any folds. It often happens that the concentric fold becomes tilted for some reason or other before the flattening process sets in. Thus, when the stress field remains horizontal, the
plane perpendicular to the stress is no longer parallel to the original
axial plane and the cleavage is no longer an axial-plane cleavage
(Fig. 236).

In such a case the difference in angle between cleavage and axial
plane is never large. When the tilting has a strike other than the
original fold, the result becomes more complicated.

A more characteristic result is achieved when the cleavage folding
is independent of the concentric folding and has a completely different strike. Typical examples have been mapped in the Pyrenees.
In one structure the NE-SW concentric fold and the later E-W striking
cleavage are well exposed (Fig. 237; Boschma, 1962). Fold axes are
spread in various directions, but folds belonging to the cleavage and
δ lineations have a girdle distribution in the cleavage plane (Fig.
237). Folds not lying in this girdle belong to the first-generation concentric folds and have been shifted by the second set. Folds and
lineations lying in the cleavage plane belong to the second phase, and
their girdle distribution can easily be explained by the fact that the
bedding was already folded in oblique direction before the cleavage
developed.

CONCENTRIC FOLDING SUPERIMPOSED ON CLEAVAGE FOLDING

This is very frequently encountered in minor folds, but occurs always
in relation to fracture cleavage superimposed on slaty cleavage (see
the next section). Because of their extreme foliation the cleavage
planes can easily slip over one another. Such minor folds related to
the second fracture cleavage give important data on the strike of this
second phase.

A common occurrence is found also in metamorphic rocks where
large-sized recumbent structures have been gently refolded.

CLEAVAGE FOLDING SUPERIMPOSED ON CLEAVAGE FOLDING

This is the most common kind of cross-folding and shows a great
variability in its aspects. Different kinds of cleavages can be mixed:
shear cleavage, stress cleavage, axial-plane cleavage, crenulation
cleavage, etc. In general, we can distinguish two different groups: (1)
cross-folding in slates and phyllites where recrystallization takes place
only during the first phase and crenulation cleavages are formed

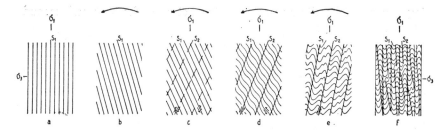

Fig. 238 Development of crenulation cleavage. (*After Hoeppener, 1956. Published by permission of Ferd. Enke Verlag, Stuttgart.*)

during later phases; and (2) cross-folding in higher-grade rocks where later phases are accompanied by active recrystallization and new slaty cleavage or schistosity is produced. Needless to say, transitions between both groups exist.

A good example of the first group cross-folding has been described by Hoeppener (1956) from the Rheinische Schiefergebirge. There the process was continuous without intervening periods of quiescence. After the formation of the first, slaty cleavage (s_1), rotation of this surface with regard to the stress field took place, roughly about the same b axis. Continued compression then produced two sets of shear planes, the existing slaty cleavage and a new cleavage (s_2). The slaty cleavage was deformed in S-shaped folds between the s_2 planes (Fig. 238). In that stage movement along the slaty cleavage ceased, and by internal rotation the s_2 planes became more and more perpendicular to the maximum stress. The microlithons between the s_2 planes became more and more compressed, and a typical crenulation cleavage was the result (Fig. 239). By this mechanism a further flattening after the development of the slaty cleavage was made possible. The fold axes of the first and second phases are roughly parallel, but sometimes tilt-

Fig. 239 Crenulation cleavage. (*After Hoeppener, 1956. Published by permission of Ferd. Enke Verlag, Stuttgart.*)

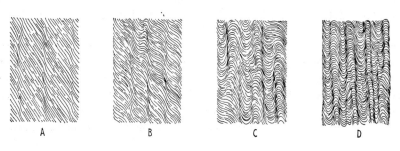

ing causes slight divergence in strike between the first and second phases.

In the Garonne dome of the central Pyrenees (Zwart, 1962) super-imposed folding occurs in phyllites and mica schists belonging to two distinct successive phases which apparently are separated by a period of other folding phases. The first, or main, folding phase caused a horizontal schistosity, in recumbent folds, isoclinal and often asymmetric. Their b axis has an E-W direction. Later a new compression with the same E-W strike was superimposed on these structures, but with vertical axial planes. This later folding caused minor folds and folds of several hundreds of meters cross section, with asymmetric minor parasitic folds on its flanks, all accompanied by crenulation cleavage. The effect of this refolding is of course very similar to a first-phase folding of horizontal bedding, and only careful analysis of the outcrops reveals that the originally horizontal schistosity really is the first recumbent folding accompanied by a parallel schistosity.

In other regions of the suprastructure of the Pyrenees this second E-W refolding phase has been superimposed on tilted cleavage of the first phase, very similar to the German examples.

Between the first and the later E-W phases at least two more deformation phases occur, with diverging directions. After the first phase a second set of structures occurs with N-S-directed axes. This set is almost exclusively restricted to metamorphic areas, but has been recognized at several localities. A third deformation consists of two conjugate sets with NW-SE and subordinate NE-SW directions. Both occur in regional metamorphic as well as low-grade slaty rocks. From the asymmetry of the folds, as well as the direction of rotation of porphyroblasts, the direction of movement of both sets can be established. Both indicate compression in an E-W direction. For the second N-S phase also an E-W directed stress field must be assumed. Therefore, the stress field has shifted considerably at least twice; first, it was N-S directed (main phase), then E-W (second and third phases), and finally again E-W (fourth phase).

The second group of superimposed folds in high-grade metamorphic rocks is perhaps best exemplified by the structures described from the Scottish Highlands. In three adjacent regions Ramsay (1958), P. Clifford (1960), and Fleuty (1961) described details of these structures, which, together with other surveys of the same larger region, are reviewed by Sutton (1960). In the Loch Monar area (Ramsay, 1958) two sets of folds have been ascertained: a first E-W-striking synform plunging westward and with an axial plane overturned to the north; the second set, with NE-striking vertical axial planes, causes vertical fold axes on the steep limb of the first fold and gently plunging folds on the gentle north limb (Fig. 240). Both phases caused

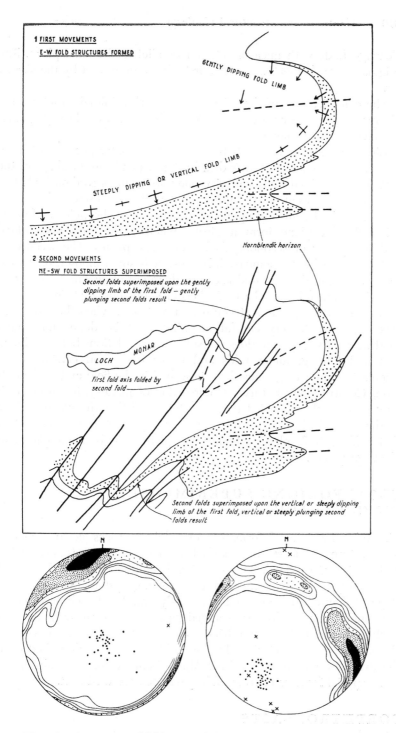

Fig. 240 Superimposed folding, Loch Monar, Scotland, with two
stereograms of first (crosses) and second (dots) lineations and
foliation plane girdles. (*After Ramsay, 1958. Published by permission
of the Geological Society of London.*)

cleavage folds with mica orientation parallel to the axial plane. The original parallel lineations of the first set are deformed by the second set.

The complications of the orientation of such refolded structures are always of the same nature. The poles of the last set of cleavage planes form a distinct maximum.

Lineations and minor folds belonging to this later phase must lie in that cleavage plane, and their distribution depends on the shape of the first folds: isoclinal folds will give one maximum, accordion folds two maxima and a weak partial girdle, and ordinary closed folds a complete girdle without any appreciable maximum. The poles of folded, originally flat plane form a girdle, whether they are once-folded bedding planes or secondary-folded cleavage planes. The second set of folds is no longer homoaxial, because it is superimposed on folded planes. Steeply dipping fold axes are therefore often due to a second superimposed folding phase. It becomes obvious that in order to unravel such complicated structures, in particular when three or more sets are present, very careful mapping must be done and simple plotting on a stereogram does not suffice. The relations between lineation and folding, minor folds and major folds, and crystal-growth orientation to cleavage must be established in the field and in the outcrop. Construction of β axes (intersection of planes), for instance, is only permissible when it has been established that the planes belong to the same fold or set of folds and were parallel and planar before that folding took place, whether the planes are bedding planes or cleavage planes.

FLOW FOLDING SUPERIMPOSED ON CLEAVAGE

The most intensive deformation of schistose rocks occurs when a temperature rise leads to a marked decrease of the resistance of the rock to the stress field. This granitization phase seems to be linked consistently to a superimposed cross-folding system. The incipient stage of flow can be observed in a partly granitized rock mass where the xenoliths are no longer arranged parallel to the surrounding non-granitized rocks, but have been randomly turned. Such effects of rheomorphism, characterized by flow folds, have been described from the Pyrenees, Greenland, and the Alpine Pennine core (Wenk, 1956). Some special features of cross-folding will be described next.

PORPHYROBLASTS

As the rise of temperature is mostly later than the start of the folding process, the deformation of the porphyroblasts gives us an admirable guide to the successive phases of the deformation process. Because the original schistosity has been preserved in the porphyroblasts as a relict texture (*si*), the movement of the crystals in later stages can be followed; they have been rolled sometimes as much as 180° along an axis which can be measured. Zwart (1960a and 1962) has given a description of how we can follow the development of the tectonization with the help of such porphyroblasts of andalusite, staurolite, or garnet (Fig. 241). At the left side of Fig. 241 the porphyroblasts have grown in a prekinematic stage, farther to the right in a synkinematic stage, and in the last column in a postkinematic stage. In the upper row the relation to a second shearing of the main-phase schistosity is represented; in the second row, in relation to a later flattening of this main phase; and in the lower row, in relation to a cross-folding crenulation cleavage.

In A_1 the rolling of the porphyroblast happened after it had grown completely and the original schistosity is preserved as an undisturbed *si* inside the new mineral.

In B_1 the new mineral has grown during a shearing of the schistosity, accompanied by a rolling of the porphyroblast, resulting in an S-shaped *si*.

In C_1 the new mineral has grown after all movement and does not give us any information about successive phases.

In A_2 the flattening perpendicular to the schistosity happened after the growth of the new mineral; in B_2, during this flattening process; and C_2 is identical with C_1 and gives no information.

In A_3 the growth of the porphyroblast happened, obviously, before the crenulation of the main-phase schistosity, because its *si* is undisturbed; in B_3 it happened during the second phase, and in C_3 after the crenulation.

Fig. 241 Porphyroblasts in relation to schistosity. For explanation see text. (*After Zwart, 1962.*)

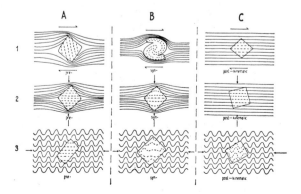

Zwart found in a certain area in the Pyrenees that secondary slip movement proved by rolling of the porphyroblasts often occurred on an axis perpendicular to the original first-cleavage B axis. Such structural development has often been called a $B \wedge B^1$ structure.

The rolling of the porphyroblasts is the only definitive proof we have of a shearing motion along the schistosity planes. But even here we most often find that the shearing is accompanied by a further flattening perpendicular to the schistosity.

KNICKING

A very common feature of cross-folding is the phenomenon of knicking of the cleavage. Cleavage planes have been knicked between two parallel planes ½ to 10 cm apart (Fig. 242). The knicking is always a late process, occurring after the refolding phases but still belonging to the same orogenic process. The knick planes are long planes and parallel; they occur in pairs; and their dip is uniformly opposite to that of the cleavage planes. The knicking itself is undoubtedly related to the preexisting foliation when the latter is less well expressed, as, for instance, in slaty limestone; the knicking is also less well developed and disappears in the noncleaved rocks of the same sequence. These *sk* planes are sometimes somewhat wavy, and when the two planes of a pair approach one another and merge, some slip may be observed on the remaining single plane. In general, the strike of the knick zones is parallel to that of the cleavage. The *sk* planes roughly bisect the angle between the dip of cleavage on both sides.

The movement is invariably the same over large areas, in the

Fig. 242   Simple knicking in phyllites.

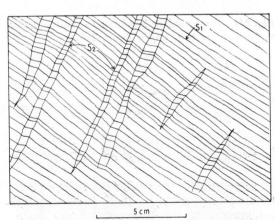

5 cm

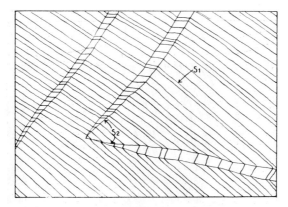

Fig. 243 Two sets of knick zones.

southern Pyrenees, for instance, always showing a subsidence of the southern limb (Zandvliet, 1961). Rarely, but still consistently, a conjugate set of knick planes has been observed, always with the opposite movement (Hoeppener, 1956). When the two sets meet they do not cross, but both movements die out at the intersection. Together they make a box fold (Fig. 243).

The effect of the knicking is a shortening in the plane of schistosity and a dilatation in the horizontal plane. These effects in some ways resemble accordion folds and can be compared with the effects of parasitic folds and of superimposed fracture cleavage accompanied by knicking, as described in the foregoing section. Recrystallization does occasionally occur in the microlithons.

TECTONIC BANDING

When a secondary fracture cleavage with distinct microlithons occurs in tilted first cleavage, as in the Rhineland (Fig. 238), which eventually develops into a compressive stage of deformation, there is often knicking within the new cleavage, one microlithon showing steepening of the first cleavage planes and the next flattening and crumpling (Fig. 244). With sufficient temperature, there can be a small-scale recrystallization of the white crystals (quartz and feldspar) in the crumpled microlithons and of dark minerals (biotite) in the steepened ones. Only in incipient cases can this process be followed. When the process has advanced far enough, only a banding of thin quartz-feldspar beds alternating with dark biotite beds remains, which could easily be mistaken for original bedding. Many migmatites have been formed by refolding of tectonic banding.

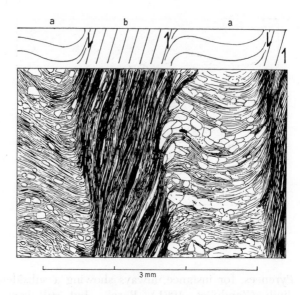

Fig. 244   Tectonic banding resulting from knicking.

The foregoing brief review of the effects of superimposed folding phases does not do justice to the great variation of the effects on the rocks, but presents only the essentials. The great problem, whether such refolding phases of the metamorphic core of a mountain chain can be correlated with stratigraphically determined folding phases of an orogenic period, remains doubtful. It is certainly true that the superimposed folding of the metamorphic core is more or less a continuous process and the different orientations of the local stress fields can all be derived from one main stress invariable in its direction but variable in its intensity, as summed up, for instance, by Harland and Bayly (1958). When these effects are followed, upward from the high-grade metamorphic zones to the slate and phyllite zone, they become less well expressed and they disappear in the highest concentric zones. Excepting such cases as a cleavage folding superimposed on distinctly nonparallel concentric folding, as described in an earlier section, or the latest knicking, there does not seem to be much of a direct correlation between the stratigraphic phases and the succession of phases as described in this chapter.

Chapter 23

Syntectonic and Posttectonic Sediments

SYNTECTONIC AND POSTTECTONIC SEDIMENTS

Whereas structural geology is concerned with the forms and history of the deformation of the earth's crust, sedimentology studies the consequences of these deformations. Every disturbance of a completely flat earth surface has its repercussion on sedimentation, by the creation, on the one hand, of the source of the detritus and, on the other, of the depositional environment. Seen from this point of view, every sediment is wholly determined by structural events. But in general, we accept the environmental circumstances which determine the facies of a sediment as being static and determine its structural control as the variations imposed on it by the ever-changing structural conditions. Thus we arrive at a classification of static environmental conditions based on facies characteristics and try to interpret the variations of the facies in structural terms. The classification of environment is primarily the distinction of continental, littoral, epineritic, infraneritic, bathyal, and abyssal environments, whereas structural control is expressed in terms of stable and unstable shelves, intercratonic basins, and geosynclinal conditions. From a structural point of view this procedure is not quite satisfactory, because it does not take into consideration the fact that environment is not conditioned only by the negative and positive movements imposed on it by its own structural history, but also by the structural history of the adjoining or surrounding regions. This is true in particular for the orogenic belts, where it makes a great difference whether the sediment is deposited in the early geosynclinal stage, in the late geosynclinal or early orogenic stage, or in the post-orogenic stage. The classification above is valid for the geosynclinal

315

stages of an orthogeosyncline and for intercratonic basins, but does not bring into sufficient relief the orogenic and postorogenic stages of sedimentation, which are of primary importance from a structural point of view.

The main divisions of a structural classification of sediments should read:

1. Orogenic facies
   a. Synorogenic, or graywacke, flysch facies
   b. Postorogenic, or molasse facies
2. Epeirogenic facies
   a. Epicontinental facies
   b. Geosynclinal facies

OROGENIC FACIES

The Synorogenic Facies Type (or flysch facies, partly due to turbidity currents). Originally, the term Flysch indicated only a stratigraphical stage from the Alpine chain, but since it has been proved that the stratigraphical limits of the Flysch as a lithologic unit vary considerably, and that the facies is bound to a certain phase of the Alpine orogeny, it has become increasingly used as a term in the sequence: "Schistes lustrés" (geosynclinal bathyal facies)—flysch (orogenic facies)—molasse (postorogenic facies) (Marcel Bertrand, 1897; Arbenz, 1919). These terms express the close relation between sedimentation and orogenic processes. This has become such a widespread usage that Scandinavian geologists, for instance, discussing Precambrian geology, tried until recently to outline their undated orogenic periods by establishing the chronological sequence of the flysch and molasse facies. It is therefore of the utmost importance to understand the flysch facies type and its orogenic significance, which has been described by Tercier (1948, p. 166) as "the facies which just precedes the main paroxysmal phase of a mountain chain," in contrast with the molasse facies which "is bound to the terminal phase of mountain building." Because the type locality of flysch facies is the Alps, a Tertiary orogeny of the Mediterranean type, it has all the local characteristics of this kind of orogeny, and therefore a considerable divergence of this flysch facies can be expected in other kinds of orogenies. This is particularly true for older orogenies (Hercynian and Precambrian) and for circum-Pacific orogenies, both having much stronger volcanic phases.

The main characteristic of the flysch facies is its detrital contents, which largely predominate over organogenic deposits, resulting in an alternation of micaceous sandstones and shales with much rarer marls and limestones. It is essentially a thick formation of purely marine origin, with a facies ranging from neritic to bathyal. The alternation of sandstones and shales, mostly very regular and monotonous, is its most prominent characteristic. The sandstones are micaceous, often arkosic and graded. Cross-bedding and ripple marks are rare. Thick sequences are often almost barren of fossils, and when these are found, they are often derived from other formations. Glauconite is frequently found. Conglomerates are scarce, but when they occur they replace sandstone zones. They are not restricted to the base of the formation, and are always polygenic. Breccias are sometimes frequent in certain zones, and their rock fragments may attain unusually large dimensions. They are derived from cliff erosion and do not originate in wave disturbance of a bottom sediment; nor have they the characteristics of transgression breccias. The shaly rocks are often mudstones and always occur in alternation with the sandstones. Although the rocks are in general well bedded, they are badly sorted, because they are derived directly from erosion of a rising cordillera and are not reworked and redeposited by wave disturbance. Their depth of deposition was below wave- or surface-current influence except near the steep coastal slope. (For more details the reader is referred to the article by Tercier, 1948.)

The structural environment is perhaps best defined as the paroxysmal phase of the geosynclinal prelude to the orogeny, which at the same time is the incipient phase of the orogenic paroxysm. The orthogeosyncline has been narrowed and split into several geosynclinal basins, between which island arcs are warped up. Erosion of the quickly rising cordilleras is violent; the basins are rapidly subsiding; the littoral facies is deposited next to the bathyal facies without the intervention of a shelf facies. The strikingly regular alternation of micaceous sandstones and shales is at first rather an unexpected feature of a relatively unstable process of sedimentation. The explanation of this feature, when combined with grading of the sandstones, has been given by Kuenen and Migliorini (1950) in their work on turbidity currents. Kuenen arrived at his conclusion from experiments with mud flows in the laboratory; Migliorini, from observation of the typical flysch facies of the Macigno in the northern Apennines. The principle of the origin of turbidity currents is that the rapid accumulation of detrital matter on a continental slope is again and again interrupted by gravitational sliding. Once the labile equilibrium of the thick, water-saturated, and loosely packed sediment is broken, a catastrophic reaction sets in by the sudden decrease of the grain pressure (as explained in Chap. 2), and immense masses become involved in a mud stream flowing downward toward the basin center. In this flowing and dense mass, sand and clay are mixed by turbulence until the mass reaches the bottom of the basin. Sedimentation then begins with the deposition of the larger and heavier grains which have accumulated at the nose of the flow, followed by finer material behind the nose, on account of decrease in the velocity of the current. Thus a lateral grading in the turbidity current which develops during its motion downhill results in a vertical grading in the deposited bed. The sorting in the graded bed is poor at every level because of the relatively high percentage of mud which forms an essential constituent of every turbidity current. One of these turbidity currents can cover a large area with a uniformly graded bed several meters thick. The normal sedimentation of clay in the basin center continues until the next turbidity current caused by further marginal-slope accumulation sets in. The absence of large-scale current bedding, the graywacke facies, the absence of ripple marks, and above all the grading, are adequately explained by this process.

The typical graded beds are called turbidites, suggesting that all grading is due to turbidity currents, which is certainly not the case. Neither is it a fact that true turbidites occur only in geosynclinal basins and are a proof of deep-sea sedimentation. Nederlof (1960) describes them from an intramontane basin of small dimensions, relatively shallow, but probably with steep slopes. Bersier (1958) describes graded sandstones from the Swiss Molasse basin, which are of fluviatile origin and certainly are not turbidites.

The concept of turbidites has revolutionized our ideas about bathyal and neritic facies. According to Haug (1900), the typical bathyal facies was the limestone-marl alternation, and the typical neritic facies, the sandstone-shale alternation. It was later realized that limestones are formed primarily on the shelf and indicate an epicontinental neritic facies; the bathyal facies was thus robbed of its most typical constituent. It has now been replaced by the flysch facies; the filling up of rapidly subsiding basins has become intelligible, and the sequence of sedimentation has become much clearer.

The Postorogenic, or Molasse, Facies. An analogue to the development of the term flysch can be found in the term molasse, which first meant a definite stratigraphical stage, then a facies of the northern marginal trough of the Alps, and then gradually became used for a general facies type related to the orogenic history of a mountain chain.

In most of its characteristics it is in complete contrast to the flysch. Irregular bedding, predominance of conglomerates and sandstones, continental or fresh-water environment, and frequent cross-bedding and ripple marks are its most prominent properties.

Nevertheless, the Alpine molasse is so closely associated with the flysch that its lowest member, the Rupelian (Lower Oligocene), shows an almost imperceptible transition into the Rupelian of the top layers of the flysch. It definitely belongs to the last phase of the orogeny, characterized by the upheaval of the central geosynclinal basin and accompanied by formation of a marginal trough. Gradually, the area of sedimentation was shifted from the center to the margin, a process which continued to act throughout the sedimentary phase of the marginal trough. The last sediment of the central basin is therefore the same as the first sediment of the marginal trough.

A marginal trough is a decidedly asymmetric basin during its whole history. The *internal* margin, i.e., *facing* the original central portion of the geosyncline, is always sinking more rapidly than the external margin, which merges with the continental platform (Fig. 281). Hence its external margin has many characteristics in common with the margins of intercratonic or geosynclinal basins, but its opposite border, the *internal* margin, is quite different and typical of the molasse facies.

A prominent property of the molasse facies is therefore its rapid facies change in a direction perpendicular to the basin axis. On the *internal* margin we find enormous accumulations of conglomerates, often interstratified with sands, sometimes with lignites and fresh-water deposits of small dimensions. They rapidly change, however, into thick, often red-colored sands and shales with evaporites (gypsum, anhydrite, salt, etc.), becoming more fine grained farther away from the central chain. The conglomerates contain a considerable proportion of crystalline rocks furnished by the erosion of the deeper migmatic horizons of the central chain.

The facies change parallel to the basin axis is also very marked. In the Alps the internal margin of the Molasse basin is characterized by a string of conglomeratic deltas, each marking a depression, or saddle, in the axial-chain structure. In the same way the red-colored Devonian delta representing the post-Caledonian molasse of the Appalachian mountain chain marks the axial depression between the maritime provinces and the Appalachians proper. As most of these sediments are transported and deposited by rapidly flowing streams, they show strong current bedding and frequent ripple marking. The molasse, in contrast to the flysch, shows massive sedimentation of particular types of rock, conglomerates on the internal margin, sandstones in the center. The molasse and the flysch have in common the fact that enormous thicknesses have been deposited in a restricted time interval, in contrast to the preorogenic facies, which is equally thick or thicker but needs a much longer time for its accumulation.

The molasse facies of the Hercynian orogenies, the Permian, is characterized by a strongly developed volcanic component. The same is true for the circum-Pacific chains; there also the flysch facies has a pronounced volcanic aspect. In Part Three this fundamental difference in the character of the orogenies of the Mediterranean and the circum-Pacific belt will be further worked out. In the Precambrian orogenies the dominance of magmatic and volcanic phases during the whole history of their structural development tends to obliterate the facies differences between the geosynclinal—flysch—and molasse phases; there is continuous preponderance of arkosic rocks in all three phases.

EPEIROGENIC AND GEOSYNCLINAL FACIES

The two types of structural basin, on the one hand geosynclines and on the other intercratonic basins, have much in common. As I shall explain later, in Chap. 31, the real orthogeosyncline differs from the "basin" principally in the fact that the first has been submitted to a later orogenic deformation and the second has not. Obviously, this does not a priori make any difference in their sedimentary history. We shall see also that basins, geosynclinal or not, may either be asymmetric, formed on the margin of a continent, or symmetric, i.e., on the continent. The second kind is the intercratonic basin. This makes a great difference in their sedimentary history. The asymmetric basin receives its sedimentary material from one side only. Its thickest accumulation will be on the continental slope, and when it becomes a geosyncline, it may develop volcanic arcs on its ocean-bounded side. Furthermore, the incipient stage may be marine, just as its final stage, though this is not necessarily the case. In contrast to the circum-continental basins, the intercratonic basin always starts and finishes with a continental facies. Transgressions and regressions play an important role on the continental margins of both types of basin.

Their most typical characteristic is the epicontinental calcareous facies, and in particular its epineritic subdivision (i.e., from 10 to 40 m depth of water). Biohermal limestones on the littoral side or on ridges and biostromal limestones on the shallow shelf are the most typical members of the epineritic facies, witnessing the quiescence of its environment. Slow sedimentation with no strong relief nearby are the predominant conditions. The long time interval during which this sedimentation continues and the slow but unbroken subsidence of the basin make it possible for very large thicknesses of sediments to accumulate. The stratification is usually well marked, the beds being well sorted by wave and current action. Quartzites, marls, and mudstones predominate. The prevailing shallow depth of the sea means that slight changes in coastlines or depth are immediately expressed in their fossil content by faunal breaks. The lithology of the limestone is also very sensitive to any depth change. These conditions, continuous sedimentation, and sharp faunal and lithological changes mean that the epicontinental facies is the "dorado" of the stratigrapher. The epineritic facies is also the domain of cyclic sedimentation, either in facies of coal-bearing sequences or in marine cycles of limestone-marl-shale and sandstone.

A characteristic of major importance for oil accumulation is the facies changes which take place from the margin of the basin to its center. In the center the finer-grained clay accumulations are the source rock of oil; and the sand tongues that enter the center from the margins are the natural conduits of the oil, liberated from the shales by compaction through the ever-increasing load of new sediments. The reef limestones on the margins of the basin offer the same possibilities in slightly different circumstances. Their detritus accumulates in front of the reefs and stretches out far into the basin center, where the oil is generated, thus giving it its access to its later reservoir. Toward the border of the basin the formations wedge out, either by regressional or by transgressional processes, bearing witness to the rhythm of the advancing and retreating shore line and building up reservoir rocks for oil in the form of beach-sand ridges and similar sedimentary traps.

The epineritic facies is not only the domain of carbon and hydrocarbon accumulation; it is also the environment of accumulation of sedimentary iron, manganese, and phosphorus. Ferruginous sandstones, either in the form of iron oxide coating quartz grains or of pisolitic iron oxide concretions, are typical of the stable shelf. Its manganese counterpart is more restricted to the continental margin of the shelf. The large thick phosphate accumulations of North Africa and elsewhere, on the contrary, are related to somewhat deeper water conditions than the iron-bearing sandstones. The curious fact that only one particular element—carbon, iron, manganese, or phosphorus—is predominant in one particular kind of neritic facies of stable conditions due to its immediate environment is understandable. But why it should be bound to one particular stratigraphical stage, as often happens, is less intelligible.

As we have seen, the neritic facies occurs in two types, the sand-claystone type and the limestone-marl type, which correspond in the first place not to the immediate environment but to that of its continental surrounding. When erosion is active, the supply of detrital matter prevents the development of the limestone type, which needs clear water. The two types are therefore in principle mutually exclusive, but numerous transitions of course exist.

Whereas pure quartzites and sandstones are typical of the stable shelf, subgraywackes, graywackes, and arkoses, characterized by a certain content of felspars and micas, indicate less stable conditions. The reworking of the newly deposited sediments is less thorough, the sorting less complete. Intraformational irregularities such as unconformities and disconformities will become more frequent. Unstable shelf conditions grade into real geosynclinal environment, where graywackes predominate and limestones are entirely restricted to the margins. There is no fundamental difference between ordinary basin accumulations and shelf accumulations because the sea bottom itself remained more or less stable, the subsidence being matched by the accumulation of sediment. Only gradational differences exist, chiefly due to the instability of the surrounding land and the consequent variation of detrital supply, but also to variation in subsidence. The extreme type of instability is reached in the flysch facies.

One more facies of a distinctly geosynclinal character ought to be mentioned here, i.e., the bathyal clay facies represented in the Pennine Alps by the "schistes lustrés" (phyllites); in the northern Apennines by the "Argille Scagliose," or scaly shales; and in the Californian coastal geosyncline by parts of the Franciscan Sequence. The clays, shales, or phyllites are characterized by the absence of bedding, by their uniform character, dark color, and high plasticity, and above all by their remarkable association with, on the one hand, ultrabasic rocks and, on the other, very fine-grained limestones and radiolarites.

The facies is typical of the first geosynclinal stage and indicates a considerable deepening of the basin, before the border regions were elevated. Its association with basic rocks of the initial magmatic stage points in the same direction, since it suggests a direct connection between the crust substratum and the basin bottom (Chap. 30). In exceptional cases the basic rocks can predominate over the sediments, as is the case in some trenches of the Near East (Kündig, 1956; Dubertret, 1953).

Another peculiarity of this type of facies, but also occurring in other environments, like the flysch facies, where steep slopes of the sedimentary basin have been realized, is the occurrence of slumps and great slabs of foreign rocks. The latter phenomenon has been called olistostromes by Beneo (1956) and is explained as a sliding down of great blocks from the wall of the trench into the mud-filled basin, distorting the original layering. It is closely related to what Swiss geologists call "wildflysch," and often has been called "melange" by English geologists. The "chaos" of American geologists is probably of the same origin.

Chapter 24

Contortion of Nontectonic Origin

CAUSE OF CONTORTION

Contorted beds, which may be regarded as microstructures restricted to particular layers, have been described from various environments. They have been attributed to widely different causes, of which the following are the main types:

1. Slumping and loading
2. Action of ice flows
3. Movement in thawed beds above a permafrost floor, so-called "cryoturbate contortion"
4. Gravitational gliding
5. Thrusting
6. Intraformational tectonic contortion

One is nearly always justified in assuming that the quicksand principle, which is due to a decrease of the grain pressure, has (in consequence of a relative increase of the hydrostatic portion of the rock pressure) played an important role in all these disturbances (Chap. 2). The nonlithified rock then becomes a suspension of grains in water and can flow under almost any stress gradient. In arctic climates, for instance, near the surface, when the permafrost has been forced down a few feet or more by thaw of the surface layers, the latter may start flowing or may allow upper portions of sand to sink down into an underlying clay because the water has not yet had time to escape to the surface, and cryoturbate phenomena are the result. Folding stress may create an extra stress above the rock pressure (thus diminishing by an equal amount the grain pressure), and in unconsolidated sediments, covered by an impermeable clay layer, the same effect may give rise to complete contortion of sands and clays with but little tectonic movement. Afterward, when the surplus water

323

has escaped by slow filtration, the sediment regains its solid phase but preserves its thoroughly contorted aspect.

When one compares, for instance, the photographs accompanying the papers by Arkell, Barrington Brown, and Baldry (1938 volume of the *Quarterly Journal of the Geological Society of London*), it becomes clear that the present aspect of a contorted rock can hardly be expected to give us a clear understanding of the cause of disturbance. The structures illustrated by the first author, which are ascribed to internal movements due to Tertiary folding, show a marked similarity to those described by the latter two authors, which are convincingly attributed to the gravitational sliding of great masses of sedimentary rocks. The complete similarity of all these contortions convinces us that they have a similar origin, controlled by different factors.

Because the circumstances in which the flow takes place are almost identical, it seems unnecessary to look within the contorted beds themselves for distinguishing features indicating the stress origin, as Kuenen (1949) and Rich (1950) have done.

Nevertheless, there are some general considerations which have to be taken into account:

1. Cryoturbate contortion is necessarily limited to glacial deposits, of Quaternary or of the older ice ages.
2. When the contorted bed is also a break in the stratigraphical sequence, e.g., forms the lower boundary of a thrust mass, its contortion is obviously due to tectonic movement, either gliding or thrusting.
3. When the contorted bed is in direct connection with sandstone or silt "dikes," its structure cannot be due to slumping and must be due either to gliding or to folding.
4. When the contorted beds are horizontal and belong to a nontectonized region, the contortion is obviously either slumping or loading.

LOAD STRUCTURES AND SLUMPING

Load casts, one of the most common basal characteristics of sandstone beds overlying shales or marls, are due to the loading of a mud deposit with a sand bed. The mud, having a lower permeability than the sand, keeps its pore water longer than the sand, has a looser packing than the sand, and has, therefore, a lower specific gravity. As a consequence, the sand is able to sink into it, forming basin-shaped hollows. This can happen only directly after the deposition of the lower sandbeds, because otherwise the mud would lose its surplus water

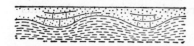

Fig. 245   Load cast of sand in shale.

Fig. 246 Load casts deformed by gliding of upper sand bed.

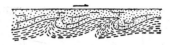

content to the sand. Hence the upper part of the sand bed is not concerned in the sinking mechanism, as is shown by the fact that its surface is often perfectly plane (Fig. 245). As the mud is still oversaturated with water when the load castings are made, it still has a very low viscosity and a great fluidity. One might expect, therefore, that any stress gradient, the slightest slope, for instance, would result in an internal movement of the mud. That is exactly what has often been observed. The more compact sand has often moved a little as a solid sheet over its fluid substratum, deforming the load casts, which then show a singular asymmetry, as in Fig. 246. The horn-shaped mud intrusions between the sand pockets, called "candle flames," are all curved in the same direction, i.e., the direction of movement of the overlying bed. When the movement of the upper sand sheet is somewhat greater, the sand protuberances in the mud may be entirely severed from the overlying sand bed and form sand balls in the mud (Fig. 247).

Eventually, the gliding movement of the sand sheet may be so great that the flat sand balls themselves are turned over and even contorted. All these phenomena can be observed on the cliffs of the Millstone Grit and higher Carboniferous exposures along the coasts of Pembrokeshire, from Amroth to Tenby and near Broadhaven.

The internal motion mentioned in the last paragraph is itself a kind of slumping, and further flow leads to completely slumped beds, sometimes including both the sand bed and its underlying mud deposit. Slumping is the mechanism which causes the most common type of local contortion, and is explained by the movement inside a water-saturated mud due to sliding down a slope, which need not be more than a few degrees. Real slumping must take place before the deposition of the next bed and is therefore a purely superficial phenomenon. However, there can be little doubt that slumping can happen after—and is probably even stimulated by—the deposition of an overlying sand bed, as explained above. On the Pembrokeshire coast one can even observe violent slumping in which the whole overlying sand bed of some 5- to 8-ft thickness becomes eventually involved in the slumping of the mud bed.

Fig. 247 Sand balls in contorted shale formed by severance of load casts due to gliding of upper sand bed.

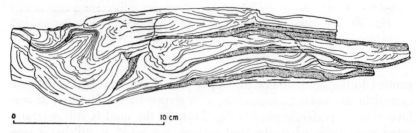

0   10 cm

Fig. 248   Slumping in Ordovician silstone from the Western High Atlas, Morocco.

A particularly instructive example of intraformational slumping is given by Fig. 248, a drawing representing a polished slab of rock from the Ordovician of the western High Atlas in Morocco. We observe in these slices, which truncate one another, a thinning at their origin and a considerable thickening, accompanied by crumpling at the end of the flow. In this microexample the principle of slumping is admirably expressed by recurrent flows, truncating one another, each successive one gathering in speed and volume by incorporating material from its substratum and finally arriving at its end in a great turbulent whirl.

It seems unreasonable to draw a distinctive line between purely superficial slumping and the same phenomenon after the deposition of another bed; on the contrary, it is probable that in certain circumstances the gliding will take place only after a considerable sequence of layers has been deposited.

The introduction of the concept of slumping processes into geological thought is mainly due to O. T. Jones (1937), and the definitions are due to him. Jones is anxious to avoid ascribing any contortion whatsoever to slumping and advances as his most important criterion for real slumping that the next sand bed deposited on the slumped bed should truncate the slumped structures of the mud bed, as in Fig. 249. In cases where the gliding started only after the deposition of the next sand bed this condition cannot of course be fulfilled, and structures like those described by Rich (1950) can result, in which the types described as "anticlinal" contortions show considerable thinning of the constituting layers, but no truncation.

In such a case of slumping without truncation the contortion of the

Fig. 249   Slump structure. (*After Kuenen. Published by permission of the American Association of Petroleum Geologists.*)

mudflow could just as well be due to origins other than superficial sliding down a slope. Much later folding, for instance, could have originated the same kind of internal structures.

Slumps can be subdivided into channel slumps and sheet slumps. In a sheet slump only the particular bed or succession of beds shows the synsedimentary contortions. They are often remarkably regular and give us sometimes most perfect examples of folds, overthrusted folds, and even refolded folds. Such contortions of a regular character in silts and fine sands have been called "convolute bedding," but there is no fundamental difference between sheet slumps and convolute bedding. It occurs often in turbidites and is also due to the still liquefied state of the sediment just after its deposition and therefore is very closely related to slumping in general and the quicksand principle (ten Haaf, 1956; Emyr Williams, 1960). The laminar flow in the sediment does not noticeably influence the thickness of the bed; neither is the disturbance so great that it has led to real slumping.

Beautiful examples of sheet slumps can be seen in the otherwise completely undisturbed Pleistocene of the Dead Sea Valley between the Sdom salt dome and the western fault escarpment (Fig. 250). The gravity gliding structures from West Africa described in Chap. 18 could be regarded as large-sized sheet slumps.

In a channel slump a whole set of beds limited on both sides by noncontorted beds has slumped. In such a channel we can find recumbent slump folds on the flanks and in the center a complete chaotic slump. Both sheet and channel slumps are admirably exposed on the west coast of Ireland, in County Clare.

The most peculiar feature of "sand volcanoes," described by Gill and Kuenen (1958), proves the important role of pore water in the slumping process. When, after the slump occurred, a sandstone was deposited on top of it, the original pore water of the slumped clay,

Fig. 250 Slump structure in Pleistocene Lissan Marl of Dead Sea.

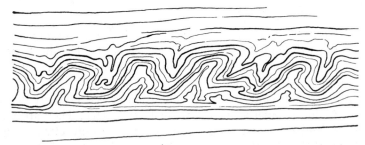

1 m

forced upward by the loading of the sand bed, pierced its way through the sand and built up a "volcano" shaped by sand flows. Many contortions are not of synsedimentary origin, but are purely tectonic.

Limestone mylonites on thrust planes, as they have been described, for instance, from the base of the Helvetian thrust sheets, represent typical tectonic contortions. Such thrust-sheet contortions might also be expected in the tail end of all thrust planes of thrust anticlines, where the thrust plane runs over long distances in the same incompetent bed, as has been described in Chap. 15. There are, however, much simpler structures in which we might expect tectonic contortion in incompetent beds. In young clay sediments, where compaction has not yet got rid of much water because of the low permeability of clays, any source of additional pressure will create a great fluidity, as explained in Chap. 2. When this additional pressure is due to a lateral folding stress, the unconsolidated clay with very low viscosity will absorb most of the internal movement necessitated by the folding, and contortion will be the result. A proof that this actually occurs in many young structures is given by mud volcanoes and by silt and sandstone dikes, described from many parts of the world. The "heaving shales" encountered in boreholes, where the sudden decrease of pressure in the hole originates a mudflow toward the drill hole, often stopping all drilling operations, are another proof of the existence of extremely fluid muds at considerable depth. As long as the superfluous water cannot escape, this state of fluidity remains.

In particular basin conditions, the pore pressure can be increased by gas pressure due to the generation of gas. Laubscher (1961) and Kugler (1933) attribute great importance to this gas-generation process in the sandstone-dike origin found in Trinidad. Laubscher describes many examples of strongly folded sedimentary dikes, proving the direct relation between their intrusion and tectonization. Certainly the quicksand principle, whether increased by gas pressure or not, is at the origin of these curious phenomena.

GLACIAL LOADING AND
GLIDING STRUCTURES

A special case of nontectonic disturbances is that of certain glacial structures, partly due to the loading effect of the ice sheet, partly to the ice movement, partly to the thrust in front of the ice sheet on its unconsolidated sediments.

A rather special kind of glacial contortion, called cryoturbate contortions, is due to melting of the permafrost surface. They are really a kind of load cast, and there are consequently only circumstantial criteria to distinguish them as a special group. The fact that they are

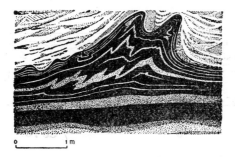

Fig. 251 Folded lignite bed in strip mine near Borna-Gnandorf.

due to a shallow melting of a permafrost surface gives the load casts of this type a rather extreme development, because the contrasts in fluidity are exceptionally great.

Many examples of contortion in strip-mined lignite beds have been described from Germany. The beds have apparently been shorn off from their basal beds by the advancing glacier and crumpled up in front of it (Fig. 251). This example gives an exceptionally good instance of oblique shear folding.

Another section (Fig. 252) shows more rounded forms, and its basal shear is not exposed. Slater (1927) gives many examples of extremely disturbed sections in which the bulging up of the Eocene London Clay on the floor of the glacier and the deposition of slices of London Clay, Pleistocene boulder clay, and Pleistocene sands form a very intricate pattern (Fig. 253). Slater explains the slices as being mainly due to very slow melting of the glacier, which leaves behind its own laminated structure in the form of englacial material. Thus the structure as observed now represents a fossilized remanent of a glacier.

Sharp faults are also often observed in fluvioglacial and glacial

Fig. 252 Folded lignite bed from the Merkur mine near Drebkau.

W   E

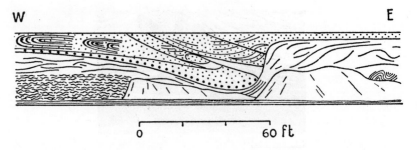

Fig. 253   Disturbed glacial drift and London Clay in clay pit near Ipswich.
(*After Slater, 1927. Published by permission of the Geologists' Association.*)

sands. Sometimes they are ascribed to thrusting of an ice lobe, sometimes to drag of an ice blanket, sometimes to loading by a local ice
lobe. They could also be caused by differential sagging due to
unequally distributed melting.

The whole gamut of glacial disturbances is very ably treated by
Fairbridge (1947), who advances many examples from various parts
of the world. He agrees with the modern view that many contortions
formerly ascribed to glacial activity may be due to slumping.

Viete (1960) describes the glacial distortions in Germany and
arrives at a classification of the various phenomena in groups due
either to a stationary ice cover or to a gliding ice sheet. Köster (1957–
1958) has experimentally demonstrated the shear folding and thrusting one can expect under those circumstances. In all these examples
the most striking fact is the great similarity between such superficial
contortions on a relatively small scale in unconsolidated sediments and
the real tectonic deformation on much larger scale in hard rocks, proving that it is only the relation between stress and yield values of the
material that matters, and not their absolute value.

PART THREE

Geotectonics

Chapter 25

Introduction to Fundamental Concepts of Geotectonics

EPEIROGENESIS—OROGENESIS

When we study in any detail in any part of the world the succession of the sedimentary strata and their relationships, we are struck by the fact that there are apparently long periods of quiescence and continuous sedimentation and shorter periods of deformation, indicated by unconformities, transgressions, and other irregularities. From observation on the sedimentary sequence we conclude that, during the quiet periods also, there has certainly been some vertical motion in the earth's crust in that particular region, either downward or upward; this is suggested either by nondeposition during certain periods or by the excessive thickness of some stratigraphic units. But these motions appear to have been very slow and did not result in folded or faulted structures and angular unconformities. The conclusion has been expressed in the terms "orogenesis" and "epeirogenesis." The first term designates the quick deformation of a belt of sedimentary rocks, the other the slow motion of basin formation and upheaval of large blocks. In recent years, a tendency to connect the two phenomena has developed, and the hypothesis of isostasy, combined with other concepts of the origin of tectonic forces, has been used to a large extent in order to establish a theoretical basis for this connection.

Haarmann (1930) has pointed out that the term "orogeny," meaning "mountain building," is, as a matter of fact, a misnomer when we use it to designate the actual folding, because the mountain chains have as a rule been formed by the upheaval of a previously folded belt. He therefore proposed the term "tectogenesis" for the folding and faulting action and the term "orogenesis" for the later upheaval of the folded belt. Orogeny would then mean only a kind of epeirogenesis. The term "tectogenesis" has, however, never succeeded in replacing "orogenesis," but has been used mainly to indicate the folding processes as distinct from other processes inherent in an orogenesis. This is rather fortunate, because the horizontal compression of an orogenic belt is often compensated by a contemporaneous rise of the surface, proved by the coarse posttectonic sediments in the flanking basins. Nevertheless, we can recognize a more or less independent posttectonic phase of upheaval, which we might call the "morphogenic phase." A causal connection between the folding and a later upheaval has never been quite satisfactorily established. *Orogeny*, then, is a general term for all relatively swift and severe deformations of different kinds which have more than a local extension. An "orogenic phase" embraces the deformation that happened in a distinct time interval, and an "orogenic period" is comprised of successive phases. A "mountain chain," or "orogene," is a comparatively narrow deformed zone, and an "orogenic belt" consists of several related orogenes, which have been deformed in one orogenic period. The definition of the term "epeirogenesis" is much more difficult. In general, one may say that both the sinking of a basin and the slow lifting of a part of the earth's crust may be called epeirogenic. But when one talks about the sinking of a rift-valley block, opinion is divided. There is, moreover, in modern thought, a tendency to blot out the limits between epeirogenesis and orogenesis, the former being regarded as a slow-motion process of the same origin and function as the latter.

Stille is a fervent supporter of the view that orogenesis and epeirogenesis are two quite different processes and advocates the theory that all folding and accompanying faulting activity are short-lived and more or less of a world-wide nature in distinct short periods separated by long periods of quiescence. He gave every recognized unconformity a distinct name and thought that future knowledge would increase the evidence that each of them had been active over large parts of the world. The original idea is much older of course; since Haug (1900) published his famous book we have known that we can distinguish four major orogenic periods, the *Huronian* at the end of the Precambrian, the *Caledonian*, in the Lower Paleozoic, the *Hercynian* (or Variscan) period at the end of the Paleozoic, and the *Alpine* period, starting at the end of the Cretaceous. Stille subdivided each of the major periods into many phases and subphases, all of which were assigned to well-defined, distinct short periods of the earth's history. He originally named three Caledonian, five Hercynian, and eleven Alpine phases. The names of his principal phases have won wide acceptance, but the principle of their world-wide simultaneity has lately been under severe attack.

In the first place, the growth of our precise stratigraphic knowledge has shown that there are innumerable small discontinuities in any sedimentary series. Gilluly (1949) found that there were 43 in the Miocene of California alone and that any of them might locally be of importance. Furthermore, the dating of the Stille phases is often so inexact, as Rutten (1949) and Gilluly pointed out, that it is very doubtful whether certain unconformities really are due to the same folding phase or not. In many instances an observed unconformity representing a wide stratigraphical gap has been placed at a convenient place in the time scale simply because that place had a Stille phase name. More and more the conviction has grown that although the Stille phases are very convenient to indicate the general situation of a folding movement in the stratigraphical scale, we must not have too many phase names nor attach too much theoretical value to them. A certain phase may easily vary a little in time from one end of a mountain chain to the other or from one border of a basin to the opposite one.

I am also convinced that much confusion has arisen from the fact that once a certain well-dated unconformity has been locally observed, whatever its size, it has been apt to receive a phase name, and forthwith regarded as an equal to all other phases. After all, one can and ought to distinguish major phases such as the pre-Oligocene "Pyrenean" phase in Europe, which marks major paroxysms in the Alps, Pyrenees, and elsewhere, from a small tilting causing a local unconformity between some substages in the Pliocene. There is, furthermore, always a tendency to place unconformities in between two stratigraphic stages, for instance, between the Eocene and the Oligocene, notwithstanding the fact that the paleontological evidence allows only a broader dating, perhaps between post-Middle Eocene and pre-Late Oligocene.

An orogenic process is determined by so many factors—the rate of stress increase, the resistance of the rock masses, and migmatizing agents, for instance—which may vary independently of each other even from one end of a mountain chain to the other, that one can expect its initiation to vary considerably in time and place. Therefore we must accept the notion that a stress condition acts at one place in the earth's crust for a long time, long in the geological sense of the word, and that the actual intensity of folding or faulting may vary somewhat erratically over the whole period and over the whole stressed region, so that we can discern only certain maxima, i.e., the orogenic phases and subphases.

Moreover, the fact that gravity-gliding tectonics have been recognized means that spectacular tectonic movements may be the result of a slow epeirogenic rising of a part of a folded belt, and need not coincide with any known orogenic phase. The same is true for the rising of salt domes, which are often initiated by folding stress but then continue independently of any lateral stress condition and are controlled by the gravity field only.

From this point of view we can distinguish, in both hemispheres, at least three major orogenic periods: a Precambrian period, a Hercynian period at the end of the Paleozoic, and an Alpine period beginning at the middle of the Cretaceous. Between the Precambrian and the Hercynian near the end of the Silurian occurred the Caledonian period, whose effects were restricted to a zone of the earth, but between the Hercynian and Alpine periods, there was an extremely quiet interval corresponding to the Mesozoic Era.

But even these major events are not fully equivalent in America and in Europe. The major phase along the Pacific Coast, for instance, is the Nevadan phase, which occurred later in the Jurassic, and not at the end of the Paleozoic. On the Atlantic Coast of America we find a Taconic period (Caledonian), an Acadian phase (Late Devonian), and an Appalachian period (Hercynian). All three periods are known in Europe, too, but it is a question of opinion whether one reckons the Acadian phase as a Late Caledonian manifestation or as an Early Hercynian one.

This brings us to another question, concerning the supposed cyclic development of the earth's crust and its world-wide synchronism. In sweeping simplification, it has been suggested that fixed periods of some 200 million years of epeirogenic character are separated by equally fixed periods of some 50 million years of orogenic phases, forming together an orogenic period, a cycle which is furthermore emphasized by glaciations (Precambrian, Hercynian, and Quaternary), volcanic activity, and evolutionary steps of plant and animal life (cf. Umbgrove, 1947). Such a schematization is perhaps valid for glaciations, but it is not valid for mountain building, for between the Precambrian orogenies of 600 million years ago and the Hercynian orogenies about 300 million years ago, we find the Caledonian phases, about 400 million years ago. Between the Tertiary phases beginning with the Pyrenean phase (50 million years ago) and the Hercynian (300 million years ago) we find the Laramide phase (about 70 million years ago) and the Nevadan phase at 120 million years ago, of which the first is of world-wide significance. The schematization is not always true either for one large mountain chain or one orogenic belt. Nevertheless, it is true for the Mediterranean area that a Late Paleozoic orogenic period is followed by a Mesozoic period of quiescence and then disturbed again in the Late Cretaceous or Early Tertiary; and that in the Appalachians, *s.str.*, a Precambrian orogeny was followed by a Paleozoic period of quiescence, and subsequently by a very late Hercynian folding phase.

The very detailed stratigraphic work of oil geologists in particular has shown that there is never a really tranquil lapse of time; the forces are always working, but show accelerations, of which the important groups—the orogenic phases—are more or less simultaneous in one mountain chain or over a whole continent.

The orogenic period and phase names of Stille have won such uni-

Table 11

European Orogenic Periods	Age in m.y.	European Orogenic Phases	Stratigraphic Epochs		American Orogenic Periods
	1	Wallachian		Pleistocene	
			Cenozoic Era	Pliocene	
Alpine	13	Attic			
				Miocene	
	25	Savic			
				Oligocene	
	50	Pyrenean			
				Eocene	
				Paleocene	
					Laramide
				Upper Cretaceous	
	110	Austrian			
			Mesozoic Era	Lower Cretaceous	
	135	Young Kimmerian			Nevadan
				Upper Jurassic	
				Lower Jurassic	
	180	Old Kimmerian		Triassic	
				Upper Permian	
	260	Saalic			Appalachian ± 250 m.y.
				Lower Permian	
Hercynian (Variscan)	280	Uralic			
	290	Asturian		Upper Carboniferous	
	310	Sudetic	Paleozoic Era		
				Lower Carboniferous	
	345	Bretonnic			
				Upper Devonian	Acadian ± 365 m.y.
				Lower Devonian	
	410	Eric Ardennic			Taconic
Caledonian				Silurian	
				Ordovician	
	500	Sardic			
				Cambrian	
	600	Assyntic			
				Precambrian	

versal acceptance and are so useful that it would be foolish to try to substitute something else or to change their definition. The custom of using more or less local phase names should be encouraged, unless strict simultaneity can be proved.

Moreover, it would be advisable to use these names only for major tectogenes and to avoid coining new terms for each minor unconformity. Table 11 lists the European and American phase names of major importance.

When we attempt to extend our list of orogenic periods and phases into the Precambrian, we are at present confronted with great difficulties. In the Canadian and Baltic shields we find (Gastil, 1960; Magnusson, 1960; Polkanov and Gerling, 1960) the cycles shown in Table 12.

Table 12

Canadian Shield	Baltic Shield	
950–1,100 Laurentian (Grenville)	900–1,150	Riphean
1,250–1,450 Labrador	1,260–1,420	Gothian
1,650–1,850	1,640–1,870	Karelian (Sveccofennian)
	1,950–2,100	Belmonian
2,400–2,700	2,500–2,870	Saamian
	3,200–3,500(?)	Katarchean(?)

The definition of an orogenic period in the Precambrian rocks has to be based on mineral dating of various kinds on different minerals and on many types of rocks, which can at present give only a very broad outline and cannot be compared with the much more precisely determined stratigraphic events known from the beginning of the Cambrian onward.

CRUST OF THE EARTH

Constituents of the Crust. We have been concerned up till now principally with the structural features on continents, but as only 35% of the earth's surface is occupied by continents and their surrounding shelves, 13% by the continental slope, and 51% by oceans, the last merits our attention perhaps more than the first. Until a short time ago little was known of this inaccessible part of the earth's crust, but since geophysical techniques have developed so much in the last decades, our fundamental knowledge has increased immensely.

The crust of the earth is nowadays defined as the layers above the Moho discontinuity. Originally, it was thought that an outer solid shell rested on a fluid or vitreous layer, but since we know that both transverse (*S*) and longitudinal (*P*) seismic waves can penetrate deep in the mantle, the fluidity of the mantle has been put seriously in doubt. Admittedly, the Moho-discontinuity surface is not always clearly defined in the seismic sections.

It has been definitively established by seismic evidence that all oceans have a completely different crustal layering than the continents. Roughly speaking, a true ocean basin consists of 4 to 5 km of water and a thin cover of unconsolidated sediments and below that 5 to 6 km of rock with a 6.2 km/sec velocity for *P* waves, probably basalt, separated from the upper mantle layer with a *P* velocity of 8.2 km/sec by the Mohorovicic discontinuity. Below the continents, on the other hand, there is an average thickness of 35-km rock layers above the Moho discontinuity, consisting of an upper sialic layer of some 20 to 25 km in thickness and a lower, supposedly basaltic layer some 10 to 15 km in thickness. The oceanic crust dips below the continental sialic layer, which thins out rapidly near the continental slope. The boundary between the sialic and basaltic layer in the continental crust is called the Conrad discontinuity; its position is still only poorly known and seems to be rather variable; it is of course missing below the oceans.

Isostasy. The fact that the thicker and lighter continental crust rises above sea level and the thin and heavy oceanic crust lies far below it is attributed to the principle of isostasy. Isostasy is not a hypothesis but a fact established by gravity measurements. It means that the larger units of the earth's crust, continents and oceans, mountain chains and plains, are not just irregularities carved in the upper layers of a rigid crust and wholly supported by them, but each of them is compensated by a relative mass defect or mass surplus underground. The simplest way of imagining isostasy is by comparing the continents to icebergs floating in the sea, where the mass surplus above sea level is compensated by an equal mass defect (difference of weight of the ice and the replaced water) below.

In order to compare gravity measurements, they have to be reduced to sea level; the shape of the earth has to be taken into account, and the densities of different kinds of rocks as well as of sea water have also to be accounted for. The differences that remain after these reductions are referred to as the Bouguer anomalies.

It has been generally assumed that isostatic compensation is restricted to differences in weight of the crust, but in recent years it has become clear that variations in the constitution of the upper-mantle layers may also influence the elevation of the crustal surface. The image of light masses floating on a heavier substratum is not the only solution to the problem. Different geophysicists have offered different solutions, not necessarily as actual physical conditions of the earth's

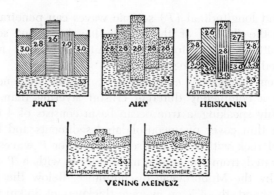

Fig. 254 Physical interpretation of isostasy by
different authors.

crust, but more as a method of putting the hypothesis of isostasy into
calculable form (Fig. 254).

Pratt (Fig. 254) imagined that above the equilibrium surface each
volume of material had its own specific weight, the higher the lighter.
The bottom of his columns rested on the substratum on one plane
surface.

Airy followed another method, and imagined all columns of equal
density, floating in a heavier substratum. Airy's columns therefore
reach different depths, like icebergs.

Heiskanen admitted an increase of density in Airy's floating columns; hence his columns penetrated less deeply into the substratum
than Airy's.

Vening Meinesz imagined that an extra load on the surface caused
an elastic bending of a much larger surface than the diameter of the
actual load, and hence a diffusion or a regionality of the compensating
mass below. The radius of the regionality around the disturbing mass
can then be chosen, so that, with the measured values of gravity, the
best result of isostatic compensation is reached.

The upheaval of mountain chains, or subsidence of basins, is accordingly thought to be accompanied by respective thickening or
thinning of the sialic blanket. Such vertical movements are apparently
slow. An instance most frequently quoted as an example of recent
isostatic adjustment is the rising of the Scandinavian block following
the melting of the Pleistocene icecap. This is considered to be demonstrated by the elevated beaches along the Scandinavian coast, but it
remains doubtful whether the removal of the ice load was the sole
cause of the uplift.

It is reasonable to presume that on the same principle the erosion of the elevated mountain chain must activate the upward motion and that the deposition of sediments must maintain the sinking of the basins. But the original uplift of a mountain chain cannot be due to erosion, nor can the sinking of the basin be due to accumulation of sediments. Both the elevation and the sinking must have had an independent origin. Because all the great Tertiary mountain chains of the world are more or less folded structures, bearing witness to compression, it is obvious that the thickening of the crust beneath them could be directly related to the folding.

In the following discussion the principal crustal features will be briefly outlined. A more detailed description is contained in the next chapters.

Oceans. The most typical feature of a large ocean is the "abyssal plains," or basins of some 5,000 m depth, which occupy, for instance in the North Atlantic, some 500,000 km². The floors of these basins are remarkably flat, although they do carry ridges and seamounts. Toward the adjoining continent either they become slightly shallower in the continental rise, until the much steeper continental slope is reached, or the ocean bottom is separated from the continental slope by a deep trough. The continental slope is the real boundary between continent and ocean.

In the Atlantic, Pacific, and Indian oceans, ridges and rises occur, separating the deep basins. Besides these ridges four remarkable fracture zones have been mapped in the North Pacific which divide the ocean floor into blocks (Fig. 261) (Menard, 1955).

The basins have a loose sediment blanket of variable thickness, mostly derived from turbidity current supply.

Trenches or deep-sea furrows are found on both sides of the Pacific and south of the Sumatra-Java island arc.

Volcanism and seismic activity are very prominent on the rises and ridges in the oceans, as well as along the island arcs.

The Mid-Atlantic Ridge is a broad swell forming a continuous feature through the North and South Atlantic from Iceland to Tristan da Cunha. It is 1,500 km wide and never more than 1 km below the surface of the ocean, apparently consisting of an accumulation of volcanic rocks, which may occasionally be seen at the surface in islands. The crest of this ridge is followed by a rift valley which has a high frequency of shallow earthquakes in addition to the volcanic activity.

A very striking property of this ridge, and also of ridges in the Pacific, is the fact that they coincide closely with a median line between the continents (Fig. 255) (Menard, 1958).

The Pacific Ocean is bordered on both sides by deep-sea troughs, which in the west are closely connected with island arcs. These troughs and arcs are characterized by deep-focus earthquakes, which are

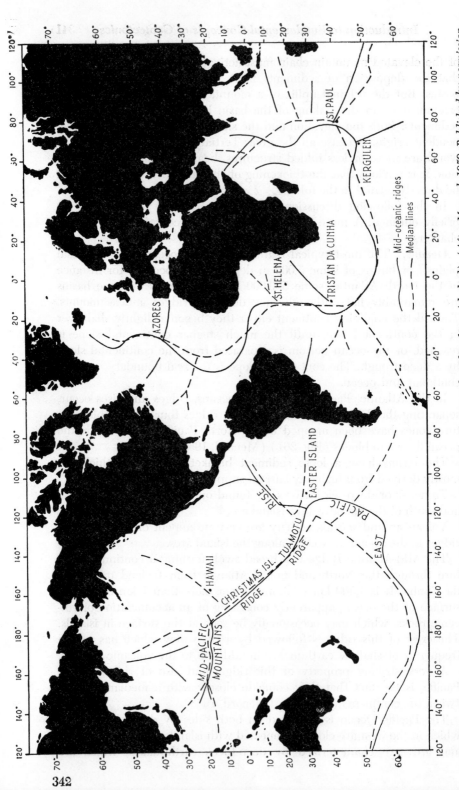

Fig. 255 Comparison of the oceanic ridges (solid line) with the geometrical median lines (dashed). (*After Menard, 1959. Published by permission*

arranged roughly on planes dipping away from the ocean below the continents (Fig. 261).

Continents. The continental crust of 35 km thickness is considered to be built up of two layers, the basaltic layer at the bottom and the granitic layer on top, separated by the Conrad second-order discontinuity surface (Fig. 256). The discontinuity is difficult to find in refraction or reflection seismograms, but has nevertheless been detected in many surveys, in particular in Germany (Dohr, 1959). It is not strictly parallel to the surface nor to the Moho discontinuity. "Granitic" for the upper layer below the sediments is certainly a misnomer; it is denser than granite and consists mostly of metamorphosed sediments, gneisses, and mica schists. Both oceans and continents are approximately isostatically compensated, and therefore the lighter continents stick up above sea level. The isostatic compensation cannot be solely due to thickness of the crust, because we know many instances where crustal thickness is not compatible with elevation.

In mountain chains the crust is thicker than in the plains, but in many cases a mountain chain is cut off by the sea, the eastern extension of the Pyrenees and the Caledonian chain of Norway and Scotland, for instance, or longitudinally, as the coastal chain of northern Algeria. The elevated Colorado block ($\pm$2,000 m) is underlain by a particularly thin crust, 30 km only (Tatel and Tuve, 1955), whereas, for instance, below the Alberta plain (+800 m) in Canada, we find a crust of 43 km (Richards and Walter, 1959).

There is, moreover, no correlation between the total shortening of the crust in a cross section through a mountain chain and its elevation (de Sitter, 1953), and even in one mountain chain there are remarkable deviations. In a cross section through the eastern Alps, for instance, the extremely strongly compressed northern part, north of the Insubric line, is not elevated much higher than the Dolomites south of it, which have hardly been folded at all. Apparently the compensation is often found below the crust in the upper mantle, as also must be the case in ocean ridges like the Mid-Atlantic Ridge.

Transitional Territories. There can be no doubt that we find territories near the ocean coasts which have some oceanic properties and some continental characteristics in varying proportions. Menard's (1955) "Ridge and Trough province" in the northeast Pacific, for instance, has apparently a fault structure running parallel to the west coast, which is certainly structurally connected with the San Andreas and similar NNW-striking faults. Its longitudinal valleys are being filled up by turbidity currents (Menard, 1955). The Bay of California, with its islands, deep basins, and submarine canyons, is another example of continental structure invading the oceanic territory. On the Atlantic side of America we find the relatively small Interior Basin east of Florida described by Hersey et al. (1959), with a filling of loose sediments on a basaltic floor and separated by ridges from the North American basin. These ridges have the same physical properties as the Mid-Atlantic Ridge: a narrow volcanic-rock accumulation on top of the oceanic layer and below it a bulge of rock having 7.5 km/sec velocity. In both examples the floor is still purely oceanic, but above it the sediments accumulate, continental structures penetrate into it, and the mantle structure below the oceanic layer has changed.

Of more importance than these coastal invasions of continent on ocean are the two principal island-arc provinces, those of the Caribbean and the western Pacific. One is situated between two continents, North and South America, the other between the Asiatic continent and the Pacific Ocean. The southern continuation of the latter, the Indonesian island arc, runs again between the continental blocks of Asia and Australia. The island arcs either are volcanic arcs, with a considerable thickening of light crustal material by accumulations of volcanic rocks, or have characteristics of a continental structure, e.g., Puerto Rico. Deep basins, such as the Venezuelan basin, are different from both the typical oceanic and continental sections. The sediments are thicker, of course, because most of the detritus coming from the continents has been trapped and retained. Besides, there is some 2 km thickness of hard rock, volcanic or sedimentary, and a normal oceanic (basaltic) crust 5 km thick, and below the Moho discontinuity, the rocks of the mantle have P-wave velocities lower than the usual 8.2 km/sec, some 7.4 km/sec, often extending deeper than the range of investigation (Officer et al., 1957).

The Gulf of Mexico has a purely oceanic crust (Ewing and Heezen, 1955). The troughs, like the Cayman Trough or the Puerto Rico Trough, are still oceanic in character, but the arches and the basins show this same property of having a different rock mass below the Moho discontinuity from that found below ridges in the ocean. Whether this rock is a contamination of the subcrustal material by other rocks or a phase change or something else will be discussed later.

THE INTERIOR OF THE EARTH

We are not concerned in this book with the physics of our globe in general, but we have to consider what is generally regarded as the most probable constitution of the earth's interior and to what extent hypotheses form a solid basis for theories dealing with the deformation of the crust.

There are a strictly limited number of independent sources of information about the substratum which is hidden beneath the crust. In the first place, the nature of the volcanic and intrusive rocks gives us valuable indications about some zones of the crust, and perhaps of the mantle, but these rocks rarely afford direct evidence of the actual depths from which they originate. Second, isostasy proves that there must be some more or less plastic layer, the so-called "asthenosphere," at some relatively shallow depth. In the third place, the velocity of seismic waves in different zones is different. And finally, theoretical deductions about temperature and hydrostatic pressure at depth may give us some purely hypothetical information.

It must be borne in mind that discontinuity planes for different physical properties need not coincide at depth, even when they are apt to coincide at the surface of the earth. For instance, the depth of melting points and the base of the zone capable of carrying transversal shock waves need not be identical. The great hydrostatic pressure and high temperature at depth create circumstances which are difficult to imagine or to extrapolate from experimental data.

All the views formulated about the earth's interior before good seismic information became available were influenced by one of two preconceived ideas: either that the earth was once hot, fluid, or even gaseous, and then cooled down to its present state, or that the earth was once cold and became heated by radioactivity and gravity. The proponents of an originally hot earth thought it to have been derived from the sun by a cataclysm caused by near collision with another star and favored the formation of the core and mantle by a process of segregation by gravity and chemical selection, which permits the simple assumption that the mantle may still be fluid. Those in favor of a cold origin seen as the result of slow selective accretion and gravitational differentiation of galactic matter preferred to think of a solid mantle.

There is of course a strong interaction between the conclusions and premises in every geophysicist's mind. A seismologist does not like a fluid mantle because it transmits transversal seismic waves. Hence he prefers a cool earth and will be careful to draw his temperature depth curve in such a way that it does not cross the melting point of silicates before reaching the core. But someone who believes in contraction due to cooling as the mechanism responsible for orogenies does not hesitate to admit higher temperatures; neither does a convection-current enthusiast. The present trend is certainly toward a viscous mantle, a fluid outer core, and a solid inner core.

Our knowledge about the constitution of the deeper layers of the earth is almost wholly derived from measurements of seismic-wave velocities, because they are practically the only geophysical data giving direct measurements below the immediate crustal layers. Beneath the Moho discontinuity the velocity of all seismic waves increases until about half the distance to the center. At this distance of about 2,900 km another first-order discontinuity leads to the core, which cannot be penetrated by transverse waves and where the velocity of the longitudinal waves start to rise again from a much lower value (Fig. 256). At about 5,000 km depth there is again a sudden change, also a first-order discontinuity, which leads to the inner core. There is good evidence that the outer core consists of liquid material and that the inner core is solid again.

The Mantle. The increase of seismic-wave velocity from 8.2 km/sec at the top to 13.6 km/sec at the bottom of the mantle is not a simple linear function of depth. The first 100 km shows a decrease of velocity from the top of the mantle from 8.2 to 7.8 for P (longitudinal) waves and of 4.6 to 4.4 for S (transverse) waves (Gutenberg, 1959); this is underlain by a low-velocity zone between depths of 100 to 200 km below the continents (140 to 220 km depth in Europe according to Lehmann, 1961). Deeper, the velocities start to rise again, and between depths of 300 and 1,000 km the increase is particularly rapid, from 8.6 to 11.5 km/sec for P waves in this 700 km. Below, the increase from 11.5 to 13.6 km/sec for P waves is much slower and probably rather regular (Fig. 256).

The existence of a low-velocity layer in the upper part of the mantle has been established independently by "shadow zones" of seismic refraction waves (Gutenberg, 1959) and by the observed dispersion of mantle Rayleigh waves (Aki and Press, 1961; Dorman et al., 1960). It has been attributed to a near melting of the material at this depth and could represent the asthenosphere, the weak layer long ago proposed as the layer above which the compensations of isostatic nature took place and which formed the boundary between the shrinking interior

Fig. 256   The constitution of the interior and crust of the earth.

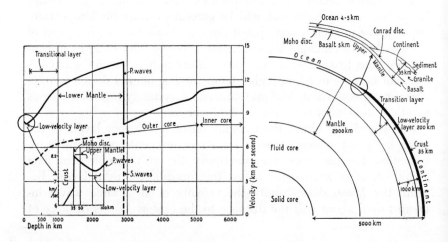

and the crumpling crust. This view has been recently corroborated by the observations from different sources that the origin of the molten basalt of Pacific volcanoes comes from depths ranging from 60 to 100 km.

There are many indications that the part of the mantle above the low-velocity layer is not homogeneous, as is often supposed. We have already seen that the *P*-wave velocity of 8.1 km/sec just below the Moho surface is often replaced by velocities ranging from 7.2 to 7.8 km/sec, in particular below the Mid-Atlantic Ridge and other swells like the Bermuda Swell (but not the Hawaiian Ridge). Moreover, there is an increasing amount of evidence that gravitational isostatic compensation is not restricted to variations in the thickness of the crust, or rather to bulges and depressions of the Moho surface, but changes in the density of the upper mantle itself also contribute. Woollard (1959) gave an account of the relation between crustal thickness, as determined by seismic evidence, and topographic elevation (Fig. 257), which showed that under the continents the depth of

Fig. 257   Relation between thickness of crust and elevation. (*After Woollard, 1959. Published by permission of the Journal of Geophysical Research.*)

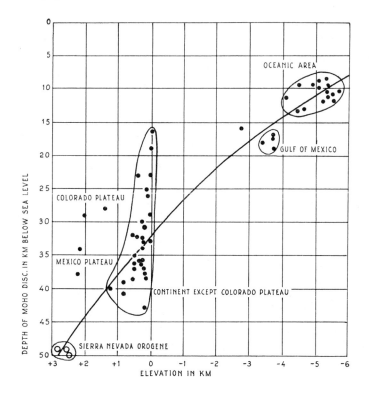

the Moho discontinuity varies from 15 to 43 km, where the topographic elevation is only 0 to 1 km. Apparently, there is not a very good correlation. He came to the conclusion that isostasy is best explained by a crust of constant mean density floating on a substratum having a systematic decrease of mean density below areas of thickened crust.

The low-velocity layer does not seem to be at exactly the same depth below continents and oceans; it is probably shallowest below the Pacific at a depth of only 60 km (Dorman et al., 1960). This depth of 60 km is in agreement with the depth of the magma chamber below the Hawaiian volcanoes and can explain the unexpected large heat flow found in the ocean floors, which equals that found in the continental crust. All this evidence points in the direction of crustal disturbances reaching down to the low-velocity layer at 100 to 140 km in depth.

The second important layer in the mantle is the transition layer reaching to 1,000 km depth, with a sudden acceleration in the rate of increase of velocity of seismic waves. In general, the increase of velocity can be attributed to an increase of compaction, which may be due to simple contraction, to phase changes or mineral conversions, or to changes in composition, mainly an increase of iron content. Simple contraction alone is certainly inadequate. Much work has lately been done on mineral conversions, which in most cases has been more relevant to regional metamorphism in the continental crust than to conversions in the mantle. However, Ringwood's work (1958–1959) on the olivine-spinel transition and other solid-solution effects on the mineral composition is particularly important for considerations of compression of the mantle. This process of polymorphism allows a much closer packing of the element atoms than is usually encountered in rocks exposed at the surface, although we know it from the rather rare eclogites. A very useful general review of different polymorphic transitions has been given by Holser and Schneer (1957).

In the lower mantle, from 1,000 to 2,900 km in depth, the rate of increase of wave velocity is much smaller. It is supposed that mineral conversions determine the rapid increase in the transition layer and that below 1,000 km the increase of velocity is due merely to a further slow increase of density with the increase of pressure. Near the core boundary the velocity curves flatten, which might be due to an increase of iron content.

The Core. The core boundary itself is a very marked first-order discontinuity surface. Transverse waves fall out altogether, and P-wave velocities drop suddenly. The mean density of the core is 11.03; near the outer boundary it is 9.96, and in the center, about 13. At a depth of 5,000 km there is another sudden jump in P-wave velocity, from 10.2 to 11.2 km/sec. This boundary of the inner core is most probably again a transition from the molten material of the outer core to solid matter of the inner core (Bullen, 1958; Gutenberg, 1958). The outer-core boundary is due to a change from the solid to the molten state and to a change in composition, whereas the inner core differs only in the return to the solid state again of the same iron-rich material as the outer core. The molten iron-rich outer core is the site of the origin of the earth's magnetic field caused by a self-acting dynamo process probably due to thermal or other convection currents.

Chemical Composition of the Earth. Knowledge of the chemical composition of the entire earth is derived from two main sources, the igneous rocks and the meteorites. The latter are supposed to have originated from the explosion of a solidified planet, a hypothesis supported by considerable evidence (Rankama and Sahama, 1949).

The meteorites are generally recognized to be divided into two types: the stony and the iron meteorites. The stony meteorites consist mainly of olivines and pyroxenes, and are subdivided into chondrites, containing an appreciable iron-nickel content, and achondrites, where the content of these elements is small. The iron meteorites, or siderites, on the other hand, consist almost entirely of nickel-iron. The average chemical composition of igneous rocks and the various types of meteorites are compared in Table 13.

Table 13

	Average Igneous Rocks (after Daly)	Meteorites		
		Iron Meteorites, Siderites	Stony Meteorites	
			Chondrites	Achondrites
O	46.59	. . . .	37.10	42.05
Si	27.72	. . . .	18.34	23.00
Al	8.13	. . . .	1.55	3.26
Fe (metallic)	. . . .	90.67	11.46	1.18
Fe (silicate)	5.01	. . . .	12.88	12.33
Ca	3.63	. . . .	1.65	5.09
Na	2.85	. . . .	0.59	0.5
K	2.60	. . . .	0.11	0.22
Mg	2.09	. . . .	13.54	10.91
Ti	0.63	. . . .	0.01	
Ni	0.02	8.5	1.31	0.33
Co	0.001	0.6	0.07	0.04
P	0.13	0.17	0.06	0.06
S	0.05	0.04	1.98	0.54
Cr	0.04	. . . .	0.28	0.31

The stony meteorites are presumably of igneous origin, and they differ mostly from basic volcanic rocks on the earth by their iron-nickel content.

From these data it has been concluded that the interior of the earth has to some extent the constitution of the meteorites, the core resembling the siderites and the mantle the stony meteorites. From this general consideration Goldschmidt (1924–1926) developed the idea that the composition of the earth resembles that of a blast furnace, with iron and nickel in the core, elements with a strong affinity to sulfur in the mantle, and the oxidized slag in the crust. The partition of the elements with depth is admirably demonstrated when their atomic numbers are plotted against their atomic volumes as in Goldschmidt (Fig. 258). The resulting curve shows at the tops the elements having a complete electronsphere, the lithophile elements, and at the minima those with free electrons; the siderophile elements and the chalcophile elements are in between. The concentration of the elements in the different spheres is a result of many factors—their chemical properties, along the lines explained above, but also gravity and pressure. Gravity will favor a concentration of the heavier elements in the core, but will drive the lighter chemical compositions upward according to their affinities; pressure will favor heavy and compact compositions downward. Near the center gravity is low, and we might perhaps expect there a center of the original undifferentiated matter in a compact form.

Goldschmidt's considerations have often been challenged, in particular for the composition of the core, but it seems that in general outline they still offer the most acceptable solution.

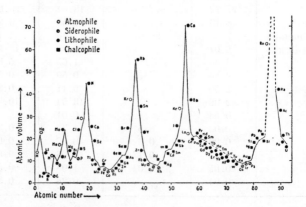

Fig. 258 Atomic volume of elements as function of atomic number. (*From Gutenberg, 1951. Reprinted by permission of Dover Publications Inc., New York.*)

There is still much discussion about the chemical constitution of the upper layer of the mantle directly below the Moho discontinuity. The original hypothesis that it is of ultramafic composition, a dunite, has been seriously challenged, and it has been proposed that a rock of basaltic composition, but changed to eclogite by mineral conversions, forms the top of the mantle (Lovering, 1958, with discussion by Kuno, 1958). Until the Mohole drill has reached the upper mantle this problem will not be solved, and even then the chemical composition of the deeper mantle will still remain unknown. Birch (1961) has offered an approach which liberates us to some extent from these discussions about chemical composition by introducing the relation between P-wave velocities and the mean atomic weight of rocks and minerals at high pressure as measured in the laboratory.

The mean atomic weight m, that is, the molecular weight divided by the number of element particles of a mineral or rock, is independent of mineral conversions, and for most rocks the mean atomic weights average close to $m = 21$. An increase of m can be caused only by an increase of heavy metals, principally iron. There is a simple linear relationship between P-wave velocity and density for a constant mean atomic weight of about 21, and the variations of the velocities observed in the mantle can be attributed to variations in density.

Temperature. The increase of temperature below the surface, i.e., the temperature gradient, is known from such sources as drill holes, obviously not very deep in comparison with the thickness of the crust. This temperature gradient varies widely from some 20 m to about 100 m per degree centigrade. It is generally higher in sediments than in crystalline rocks. This variation is easily understandable when we think of the variation of thermal conductivity in rocks of different kinds and of differences caused by varying geologic history, such as upheavals and subsidence, intrusions, circulation of mineralizing solutions, compaction, flow of water, and so on.

Van Orstrand (1951, in Gutenberg, 1951) concludes from all the available data that in basins the isogeotherms tend to reflect the depths of the basement and are therefore elevated over domes and anticlines. As a rough estimate of an average gradient in sedimentary areas he gives 33 to 60 m per degree centigrade.

Obviously, these data cannot be used for extrapolation for the great depths of the basaltic layer and for the mantle or core, except in a general way.

The temperature of the earth's surface depends on the incoming solar radiation, of which some 70% is absorbed, and on the radiation from the earth itself. Deeper down, however, the temperature is regulated by the conductivity of the rocks, by the original temperature, and by the heat produced inside the earth by the disintegration of radioactive matter. The rates of heat flow in the upper layers can be calculated from the numerous temperature-gradient measurements and the properties of the rocks. It has been found that, despite the wide variation in the latter, almost all flow values tend to be very similar, e.g., approximately 1.2×10^{-6} cal/cm² sec, even for both the oceanic and continental regions.

The discovery that the rate of heat flow through the floors of the oceans is equal to that of the continents (Bullard, Maxwell, and Revelle, 1956) invalidates the supposition that all the heat produced by the earth is due to the radioactive elements concentrated in the granitic crust of the continents; on the contrary, we have to presume that some part of this flow is due to an internal source of heat.

The steady increase of temperature and density downward causes the near approach of the temperature and melting-point curves in the low-velocity layer and their intersection at the outer- and inner-core boundaries.

Exceptionally large rates of heat flow have been found in the top of the Mid-Atlantic and South Pacific ridges. On the Mid-Atlantic Ridge this heat flow is directly connected with the rift and its volcanic activity.

Magnetic Field of the Earth. The magnetic field of the earth is a dipole field oriented with its north pole some 10° away from the earth's rotational axis. We know that the magnetic pole shows a secular irregular movement completely around the rotation axis of the earth about every 1,000 years. There are strong reasons for believing that the origin of the earth's magnetic field lies in the fluid part of the core, perhaps generated by a complicated system of convection currents.

In the last decades extensive surveys on the orientation of the remanent magnetism of volcanic and sedimentary rocks have been made. The temperature of fluid lavas is well above the Curie point of ferromagnetic minerals, principally magnetite, which becomes magnetized by the earth's field when the lava solidifies. Therefore a measurement of the orientation of their remanent magnetic field will show the orientation of the earth's field at the time of solidification.

In sedimentary rocks, deposited in quiet water, one can assume that the earth's field influenced the deposition of the ferromagnetic grains in such a way that their remanent magnetic field was aligned parallel to it.

Thus a measurement of the remanent magnetism of little disturbed rocks of different ages will show the position of the magnetic pole at the moment of their solidification or deposition and, assuming that the variation from the geographic pole was never greater than in historic times, the position of the earth's rotational axis also.

The results of extensive surveys which are still going on are extremely interesting from several points of view. First of all, it has been proved in many surveys extending over a thick vertical section —the Islandic basalts, for instance (Hospers, 1953–1954)—that complete 180° reversals occur regularly, the north pole becoming the south pole and back again at intervals of some 20 basalt flows. Whether these reversals really mean a reversal of the earth's field or are due to some kind of self-reversal of only local significance is still undecided, but the first hypothesis looks much more probable.

Second, it has been proved without reasonable doubt that since the Eocene, the magnetic pole has only wandered around its present position, but that during the Mesozoic and Paleozoic, a considerable shift of the pole can be surmised almost over 90°, from the present equator to the present pole. Moreover, the American and Euro-Asiatic-African measurements on rocks of this age seem to give a significant difference in result, which perhaps may be interpreted as a shift of these continental blocks in relation to each other (Fig. 259).

The question arises what these results imply in terms of global tectogenesis, and we want to emphasize from the beginning that the analysis of these shifts depends on the assumption that the orientation of the remanent magnetism of a rock is not altered in time and is of the same origin as the rock itself. There are indications that this may not always be true.

There is a process, for instance, depending on crystallization of hematite from solutions, forming the coating of the sand grains of a red sandstone, which at that moment became magnetized by the earth's field. This is called "chemical magnetization." In that case the remanent magnetism of the rock need not be of the same age as the rock itself. It has been shown also that mechanical stress can affect the remanent magnetization, either by a sedimentary overburden or by tectonical stress (Graham et al., 1957).

It has also become clear that in many cases even fresh surface samples show more scattering and change in orientation than samples from underground works due to weathering. This has been ascribed in some cases in South Africa to the effect of lightning hitting the rock.

The magnetization of schistose rocks is generally oriented in the schistosity plane because the magnetic field of the elongated minerals is influenced by their shape. The same is probably true in some dikes where the orientation is parallel to the dike boundaries.

Nevertheless, where the north poles, derived from the orientation of the remanent magnetic fields of rocks on the same continent of successive ages, are plotted on a world map, a more or less smooth curve of pole shifts of 90° since the beginning of the Paleozoic is revealed. For Europe we refer the reader to Nairn (1960a); for America, to

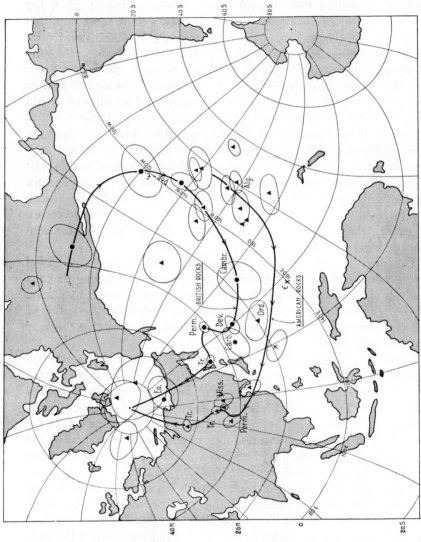

Fig. 259 Pole positions and paths based on British and American rocks. (*After Runcorn, 1960. Pub-*

Collinson and Runcorn (1960); for Africa, to Nairn (1960b); and for a general review, to Cox and Doell (1960) and van Hilten (1962).

Assuming that the present rough coincidence of the magnetic and geographic poles is not fortuitous, a polar shift would have the consequence of considerable stress fields in the crust due to the change of position of the equatorial flattening in the shape of the earth.

Vening Meinesz (1947) considered this stress problem and fitted the lines of maximum stress to the structural lines of the crust. The result is not very convincing; nevertheless, we can note that consistent leverage of shields like that of the Canadian and Baltic shields toward the Mediterranean zone might have something to do with this pole shift.

The fact that the paths of the pole shifts indicated by different

Fig. 260   Drift of Australia relative to pole. (*After Runcorn, 1959. Published by permission of the American Association for the Advancement of Washington.*)

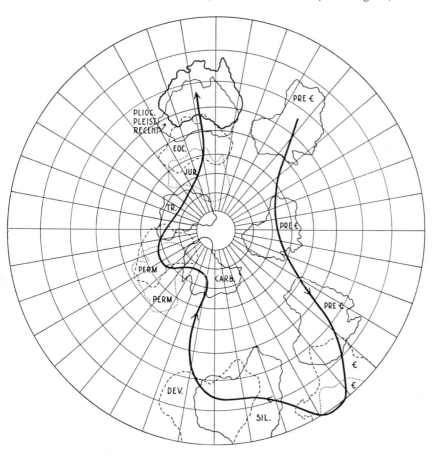

continents do not coincide is much more important (Fig. 259), and this fact has been used as a strong argument in favor of continental drift. But it is not only drift of the continent, but also very strong rotations —up to 90°—which must be assumed (Nairn, 1960b). In general, paleomagnetic data give, by the declination, the orientation of the continent relative to its contemporary pole and, by the inclination, its distance from this pole, but it does not give the longitude of the continent. Further, we have two different methods at our disposal to fit the continents in their right position at a given time, polar wandering and independent continental drift. Where the pole-shift lines for Europe and America are of similar shape, Australia seems to have wandered and rotated in quite a different manner (Runcorn, 1959) even when the Precambrian movements, which are of doubtful value, are disregarded (Fig. 260). Serious objections can be raised against the continental-drift hypothesis, but if these prevail, another explanation of the consistent drift of the magnetic field has still to be found.

Chapter 26

Oceans

The structural knowledge of the great ocean basins is still inadequate for a thorough tectonic analysis of their features, although extensive research programs have extended our information enormously in the last decade. The Atlantic Ocean and the eastern Pacific have been explored by extensive sounding and seismic, magnetic, and gravity measurements.

The basic fact has been established that in all oceanic basins the earth's crust consists exclusively of a relatively thin basaltic layer, averaging 5 km in thickness. All structural features concern this basaltic crust; some of them penetrate deeper.

The main structural features that have been established are the Atlantic and East Pacific rises, smaller swells or ridges, and fracture zones with the abyssal plains between them. There can be no doubt that the great longitudinal rises and the smaller ridges are closely related to volcanic activity, but volcanoes also occurred commonly outside these swells. Moreover, we must keep in mind that submarine volcanoes, seamounts, and guyots have not been eroded away in the course of time as on the continents, so that their great number is possibly due in part to their great range in age.

Besides the structural features mentioned above, there are deep-sea troughs and island arcs restricted to the ocean borders.

SEAMOUNTS IN THE PACIFIC OCEAN

The boundary of the eastern Pacific is taken roughly as the edge of the continental slope, which is very near the present coastline, but the andesite line is adopted for the western boundary, thus excluding the Asiatic island arcs and the South Pacific island clusters. To the south the Pacific extends to Antarctica (Fig. 261).

In this ocean about 400 volcanic islands and 1,000 seamounts with a relief of more than 1 km have been found, mostly in clusters of 10

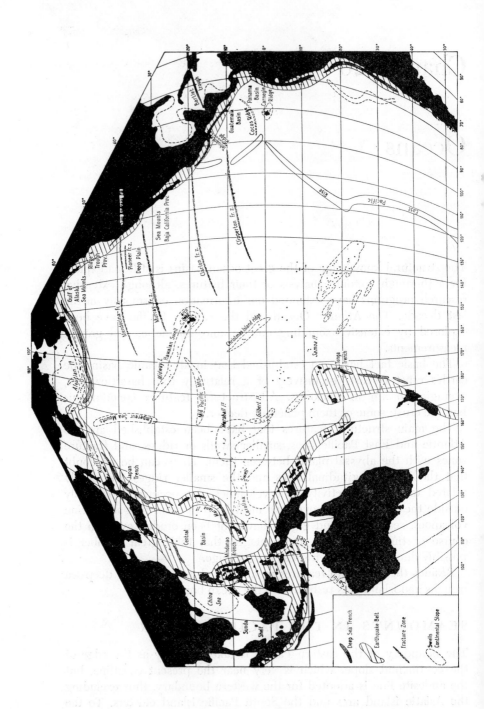

358

to 100, and it seems probable that about 10,000 are actually present on this ocean floor (Menard, 1959).

No age greater than Late Cretaceous has been established, but information is very scarce and difficult to obtain. Oceanic islands characterize Melanesia in the southwest Pacific; guyots (flat-topped sunken seamounts) occur in a strip just north of these island groups and in the Gulf of Alaska. Seamounts are scattered over the whole northern and eastern Pacific; some are definitely grouped on a line, like the Emperor Seamounts, the Hawaiian group, and others, and are therefore thought to be related to deep faults. The fracture zones which have been mapped in the northeastern Pacific are also accompanied by submarine volcanoes.

The guyots of the Mid-Pacific mountain range have been studied in particular by Hamilton (1956). There is no doubt that they are sunken Cretaceous atolls formed on volcanic peaks and ridges truncated by wave action.

Elevations on the sea floor that do not rise higher than 1 km are called abyssal hills; some of them may be volcanic, others tilted crustal blocks. The thickness of the crust in the Pacific basin is very uniform, some 6.5 km, of which 4 to 5 km belongs to the basaltic crust; in Melanesia the crust may be thicker, 11 to 13 km (Raitt, 1956).

EAST PACIFIC RISE

The East Pacific Rise forms a very prominent feature in the eastern Pacific (Menard, 1960). Recently, it has been surveyed by the Scripps expedition "Downward." It is similar in structure to the Mid-Atlantic Ridge, being a bulge 2,000 to 4,000 km in width, 2 to 3 km in height, except that it does not carry a central rift on its crest. It is marked by an exceptionally high heat flow, some two to seven times greater than normal, and the seismic survey proved that the oceanic crust is thinner on the crest of the rise. In the eastern Pacific it occupies roughly the median line between South America and New Zealand, but northward it approaches the coastline of the Lower California Peninsula. Toward the south it curves westward on the median line between Australia and Antarctica and may join the Indian Ocean Ridge near St. Paul Island, and thus be connected to the Mid-Atlantic Ridge.

The broad belt of the East Pacific Rise seems to be offset by a fracture zone at latitude 22°S, by the continuation of the Carnegie Ridge near the equator, and by the Clipperton fracture zone at latitude 10°N. It butts against the South American Trough along the Mexican coastline, where the eastern extension of the Clarion fracture zone also reaches the coast.

THE FRACTURE ZONES

From north to south these are the Mendocino (with the Pioneer fracture zone?), Murray, Clarion, Clipperton, and Carnegie fracture zones, narrow ridges a few hundred kilometers wide and a few kilometers high, very straight, and several thousands of kilometers long. They separate gently westward-sloping blocks of the ocean floor of different height (Menard and Fisher, 1958; Menard, 1955; Menard and Dietz, 1952). The eastern ends of these ridges are more like escarpments, the western ends, more like longitudinal intersected ridges. They cannot really be followed as fracture zones on the continent from the points where they abut against the coastline, but some of them can be connected to peculiar structural features. The Mendocino fracture intersects with the San Andreas fault just where the latter reaches the continental slope. The Murray fracture finds its continuation in the transverse ranges of southern California. The Clarion fracture is aligned with an active volcanic zone in Mexico. The Clipperton fracture abuts against the Mid-American Oceanic Trough. These widely divergent features suggest that the oceanic fractures are older than the Miocene-to-Recent structural deformations of the continental border. Their function as fault zone has been proved by magnetic surveys of the ocean floor (Mason, 1958; Raff, 1961) for the Mendocino, Pioneer, and Murray fracture zones, of which the Pioneer fracture is characterized only by the magnetic pattern, and not in the topography. The magnetic surveys revealed a remarkable pattern of anomalies parallel to the coastline, again and again interrupted by straight lines, sometimes perpendicular, sometimes oblique to the coast. A few of these coincide with the topographical expression of the fracture zones; most of them, the Pioneer interruption, for instance, do not. Supposing these interruptions to be wrench faults and matching the magnetic patterns on both sides by shifting them, one gets extremely improbable values of 80 miles of shift along the Murray fracture, 130 miles for the Pioneer fault, and 600 miles for the Mendocino fracture. Both the Mendocino and the Murray zones, as expressed by the magnetic pattern, stop before they reach the coast, but their topographic feature sometimes continues and really cuts into the continental shelf. The precise nature of the structures causing the magnetic anomaly pattern is unknown; lava flows and intrusions have been suggested. One could suggest, for instance, that they express a layering of the crust, dipping westward at a slightly greater angle than the slope of ocean bottom. Possibly there is an alternation of lava flows and sediments, each lava-sheet outcrop giving a positive magnetic anomaly. The fracture zones could then be normal faults with increasing throw toward the west, dying out near the coast and giving the impression of enormous horizontal apparent slip of the outcrop pattern.

SWELLS AND RISES

In the central and northern Pacific many *swells* of the ocean bottom are revealed by island clusters like the Hawaiian and Christmas Island ridges or by submarine ridges like the Emperor Seamount Ridge and Mid-Pacific Mountain Ridge. They are also characterized by volcanic activity (Dietz and Menard, 1953; Hamilton, 1957). The best known is the *Hawaiian Swell,* a flat swell 600 miles broad on which the volcanic Hawaiian Ridge proper is superimposed as peaks in the center. The swell is flanked in the south first by a semicircular deep and beyond that by an arch. The arch and deep are thought to be regional gravity compensations due to the loading of the swell by the ridge (Vening Meinesz type; see Fig. 254), but this conclusion is contradicted by the fact that the arch is faulted.

Fig. 262   The Atlantic Ocean with the Mid-Atlantic Ridge.

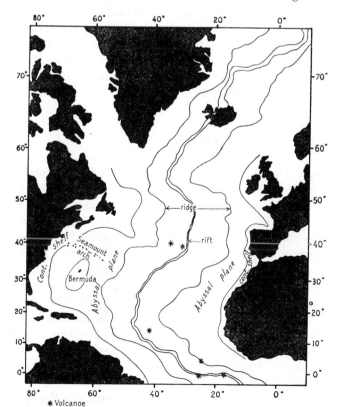

It is of considerable interest that the Hawaiian Volcano Observatory (Eaton and Murata, 1960) has concluded that the Moho discontinuity is at a depth of about 14 km, with a very slight depression beneath the volcano, and that the magma chamber is at a depth of about 45 to 60 km, deep in the mantle. This depth coincides roughly with the well-known low-velocity layer.

In the Atlantic Ocean (Fig. 262) the *Bermuda Rise*, or swell, has been explored in detail (Heezen et al., 1959; Officer et al., 1952). The eastern edge of this northeast-oriented arch is marked by steep scarps, 500 to 1,500 m high. On this gentle arch rises a flat-topped pedestal, carrying the Bermuda Islands on its southeast rim. Round the pedestal is a smooth sloping apron of detrital material, but deep borings have proved that the pedestal itself consists of basaltic material covered by a calcareous sediment layer 100 m thick. The seismic surveys of the Atlantic around Bermuda showed that the rise is surrounded by real abyssal plains, with the Moho discontinuity at usual depth, but below the Bermuda Rise this discontinuity disappears and a mass having a P-wave velocity of 7.2 km/sec replaces the normal 8.2 km/sec velocity of mantle material. In this respect the Bermuda resembles the Mid-Atlantic Ridge and differs from the Hawaiian Rise. North of the Bermuda Rise, in the flat abyssal plane, a seamount arc has been discovered (Northrop et al., 1962). Each seamount rises abruptly to a height of as much as 4 km with very steep slopes (15 to 20°), increasing upward, from the flat plane. No doubt here again the seamounts represent submarine volcanoes.

MID-ATLANTIC RIDGE

The Atlantic Ocean (Heezen et al., 1959) is longitudinally divided into two roughly equal areas by the *Mid-Atlantic Ridge,* which coincides substantially with the median line between the two continents on either side. This ridge is a swell, some 1,500 km broad, the top generally not more than 1 km below the water surface, supporting in places volcanic islands (e.g., Iceland and Tristan da Cunha), generally of basaltic character (Fig. 263). A median valley with steep slopes from 25 to 50 km in width and from 1 to 3 km in depth runs consistently on its crest (Tolstoy, 1951; Hill, 1960). The rift is characterized further by shallow earthquakes, and basaltic rocks have been dredged from its sides, of which one sample has given a Tertiary age (−30 million years, Carr and Kulp, 1953). Sometimes the valley splits into two adjacent trenches. In Iceland the volcanic rocks range from Tertiary to Recent.

The ridge with its rift valley has been traced into the Arctic basin to the north (Heezen and Ewing, 1961) and into the Indian Ocean around South Africa in the south (Ewing and Heezen, 1960). Eventually, it seems to run into the Dead Sea rift.

The median valley is generally accepted as a rift valley and is often compared with the African rifts. The structure of crust below the ridge (Fig. 263) shows that the ridge itself is probably built up by volcanic rocks and that below the whole width of the swell, the layer having a *P*-wave velocity of 8.2 km/sec below the Moho discontinuity is replaced by a mass having a lower velocity of approximately 7.4 km/sec. This structure is very similar to that of the Bermuda Ridge described above, which is typical of other local swells and quite distinct from that of the Hawaiian Rise.

A continuation of the Atlantic Ridge can be traced into the Arctic Ocean; it runs first through Iceland, then west of Spitsbergen and then turns to the east, finally abutting against the Asiatic continent (Heezen and Ewing, 1961). It is much narrower in the Arctic Ocean and runs parallel to a much higher feature, the Lomonosov Ridge, also associated with earthquake epicenters (Fig. 264).

The continuation from the South Atlantic around the Cape of Good Hope into the Indian Ocean has been verified by a "Vema" cruise; the ridge is still provided with a central rift valley and apparently finally runs through the Aden Gulf into the Red Sea. Here the ridge as such has disappeared, of course, but the central rift with a narrow and northwestward pinching-out zone of a high-gravity anomaly and a high-magnetic anomaly certainly indicates a basic or ultrabasic rock upwelling in a rift valley (Girdler, 1958). A direct connection with the African rifts through Ethiopia looks probable.

The independence of the oceanic structures from the continental structures has been demonstrated in many instances. The East Pacific Rise disappears as a structural feature before it reaches the continental slope, and the Mid-Atlantic Rise butts against the Siberian continent. The same independence is demonstrated by the abrupt disappearance of the East Pacific fracture zones against the continent or against the Middle-America Oceanic Trough. In some cases we find some kind of structural connection, in the doubtful cases, of the East Pacific Rise with the San Andreas wrench fault and of the Indian Ocean Rise and

Fig. 263   Seismic cross section across the Mid-Atlantic Ridge.

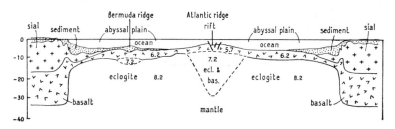

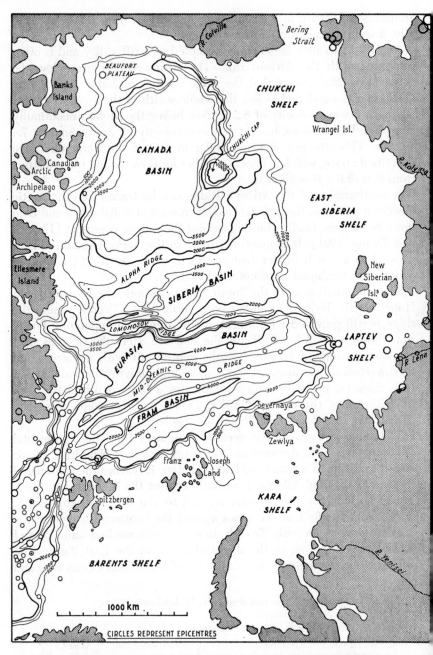

Fig. 264 The Arctic Ocean (*After Heezen and Ewing, 1961. Published by permission of the University of Toronto Press.*)

rift with the Red Sea and South African rifts, both fault relations. The Mid-Oceanic Rise in the Arctic might continue in the Mesozoic Verkhoyansk fold belt in Siberia. We shall take up this problem again further on.

THE CONTINENTAL SLOPE

The continental slope has been studied closely on the east coast of North America between Newfoundland and Florida, both by seismic

Fig. 265   The continental margin of the east coast of North America (*After Worzel and Shurbet, 1955. Published by permission of the National Academy of Science, Washington.*)

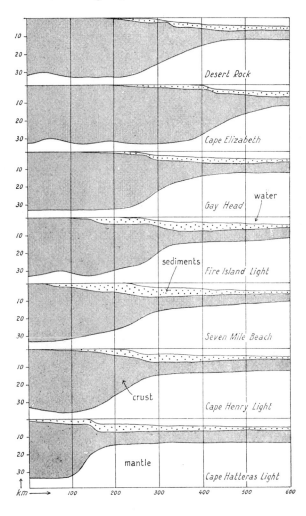

and gravity methods. Worzel & Shurbet (1955) gave a survey of the results in seven sections (Fig. 265). In each section we see a rapid thinning of the crust from continent to ocean, the transition taking place over 50 to 200 km. On the eastern side of the Atlantic we should presumably get the same kind of section, although the great embayment of the Gulf of Biscay may reveal some complications. The sedimentary layer is thicker near the coast, thinning out toward the abyssal plains, and the steep continental slope is certainly related to the wedging out of the continental crust.

One of the most interesting features of the continental slopes is the submarine canyons, or gorges, sometimes 600 m deep and 5.5 km wide, cut in the steepest part of the slopes. They have probably been scoured out by submarine turbidity currents.

Chapter 27

Island Arcs and Deep-sea Troughs

Among the most striking and conspicuous phenomena in the structural pattern of the earth's crust are undoubtedly the island arcs, which bound the Pacific Ocean to the west and reach from Alaska to Australia (Fig. 266). Their southern extension in the Indonesian island arcs is very similar in shape to the Antillean island arc. The discussion of island arcs starts from a mass of general data of a type rarely realized in any other typical feature of crustal disturbance. Nowhere do we know so much of the general character and, I am tempted to say, so little of the geological detail. This is due to the fact that the island festoons which decorate the western border of the Pacific are morphologically conspicuous features; deep-sea troughs and lines of volcanic activity draw a remarkably consistent pattern, regular in many details, which are emphasized and brought into a three-dimensional perspective by the arrangement of earthquake foci and the zones of negative and positive gravity anomalies discovered by Vening Meinesz. The deep-sea troughs bound to island arcs reach enormous depths; one of the deepest in the Pacific is the Mariana Trough, where a bathyscape descended to the bottom and reached 10.9 km depth. Still deeper is the southern part of the Mindanao Trench, which runs N-S for 15 miles and, with a width of only 2 to 6 km, reaches a depth of 11,516 m. The Puerto Rico Trough reaches a 8.4 km depth.

The scarcity of geological information relevant to these structures is due to the facts that most of the territory is covered by sea and that our knowledge of these remote islands, often covered by dense tropical forest or by thick recent volcanic products or coral-reef terraces, is naturally scanty.

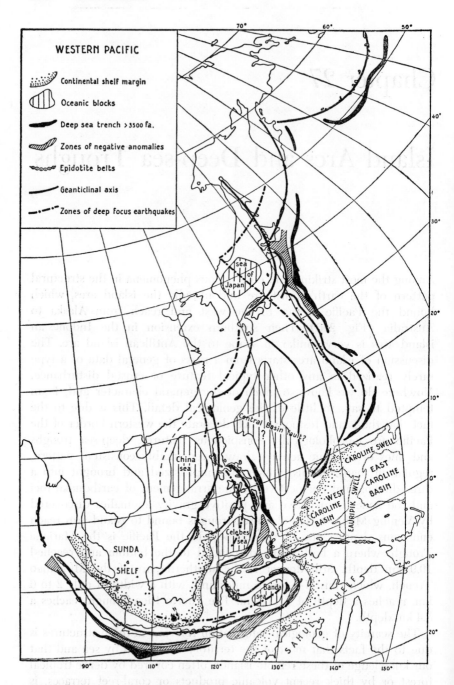

Fig. 266 Island arcs of the western Pacific coast. (*After Hess, 1948. Published by permission of the Geological Society of America.*)

GENERAL PROPERTIES OF THE WEST PACIFIC ISLAND ARCS

As mentioned above, the festoon of arcs possesses a series of remarkable, unique, and constant features which give us the opportunity of gaining an insight into the connection between superficial shape and deep subsurface structure.

1. Their *location* is very significant; they lie exactly on the border of the sialic crust of the Asiatic continent and the oceanic crust of the Pacific Ocean, just inside the "andesite line," a line separating the basaltic volcanics of the Pacific from the andesitic volcanics of the island arcs.
2. Their *shape*, intersecting arcs en échelon with their convex sides facing the ocean, gives a strong impression of ocean waves with a directed movement. Complications of the pattern arise only in the eastern portion of the Indonesian Archipelago, which is squeezed between the Australian continent and the Sunda Shelf.
3. Deep-sea troughs invariably accompany them on their convex side.
4. A zone of large negative gravity anomalies is equally constant in its presence on the convex side of the arcs.
5. A zone of volcanism is present, but not always active, on the inner side of the arc or on the arc itself.
6. Seismic activity is very great in this zone and has the peculiarity of possessing foci descending landward to a depth of 700 km.

The first three properties are superficial features; the last three are manifestations of the infracrustal structure. Let us start with the zones of large gravity anomalies, which Vening Meinesz discovered by his famous pendulum measurements during several trips aboard a submarine. His field of observation is principally concerned with the Indonesian Archipelago (Fig. 267), but two crossings were made farther north across the Nero and the Yap troughs. The sections from Java to the Indian Ocean all show negative anomalies, coinciding with the row of islands which lies on the oceanic border of the isle of Sumatra and is continued south of Java by a submarine ridge; the latter emerges again in the arc formed by the row of islands from Timor to the Tanimbar Islands to Ceram and Buru. The deep furrow lies to the south and west of this line. Between the two outer main arcs we find ocean depths ranging from 1,500 to 3,500 m, and on the main island arc we find rows of active volcanoes.

The Pacific sections are somewhat simpler because they contain only a single row of islands, accompanied by a deep-sea trough. The gravity-anomaly sections show exactly the same kind of narrow zone of negative anomalies, but coinciding roughly with the furrow and asymmetric. Because of the narrowness of the zone of negative

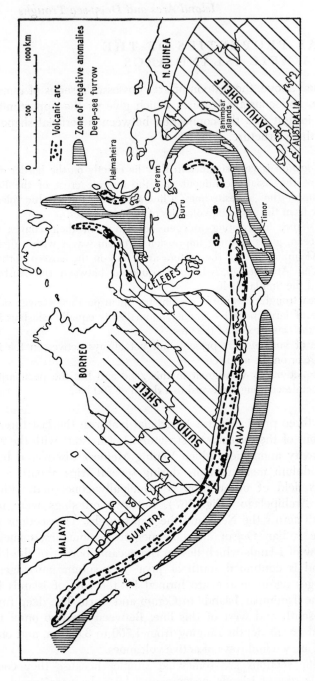

Fig. **267** Negative gravity anomalies in the Indonesian Archipelago. (*After Vening Meinesz, 1934.*)

anomaly, the crustal disturbance cannot extend deeper than about 100 km.

The cross sections of gravity anomalies are not always symmetric, as, for instance, in the Guam section, which might indicate an asymmetry in the structural shape. Many kinds of structures can be postulated which will satisfy the gravimetric curves, and only with the help of seismic information can we select the most probable solution.

Fortunately, we have a very illuminating accumulation of seismic evidence to guide us in our choice. All the island festoons are characterized by great seismic activity with shallow foci on the island arcs next to the deep marine troughs, by foci of intermediate depth (200 to 500 km) farther away from the Pacific, and by deep foci (500 to 700 km) in a zone still farther inward, below the sialic crust. When we presume that the shocks originated on shear zones, as the primary shocks indicate, the shear planes have a dip of some 50° away from the ocean. Consequently, we may assume that the suggestion of a thrust of the continental shelf over the Pacific Ocean floor has much in its favor—the thrust plane cutting through the rapidly thinning sialic crust and forming simultaneously the root of the zone of negative gravity anomalies and the deep furrow bordering the ocean basins.

The relations of the geological and geophysical features are best represented in a section (Fig. 268) slightly modified after Gutenberg (1951) across Japan.

The superficial features, a deep-sea trough in front of a geanticlinal volcanic arc, with a basin behind separating the geanticline from the continent, are seen in relation to the geophysical data. The island arc

Fig. 268   Earthquake hypocenters, relief, and gravity anomalies along a profile in the northern Japanese region. (*After Gutenberg and Richter, 1949. Published by permission of the Geological Society of America.*)

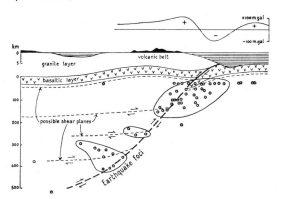

is a zone of positive gravity anomalies; the trough, or its slope toward the geanticline, is the site of a zone of negative anomalies. The epicenters of the deeper earthquakes are situated in clusters on a plane sloping with a dip of about 50° toward the continent. The cluster of shallow earthquake centers reaches to about 200 km depth, suggesting that the thrust plane slips here into the low-velocity layer, where the movement no longer causes earthquakes in this almost fluid material.

All these facts are consistent with a thrust movement of a marginal geanticline of the continent over the Pacific Ocean floor. The gravity minimum on the convex side of the belt marks the line where the low part of the buckle was formed, here drawn as an overthrust. The geanticline behind the volcanic ridge then corresponds to the overriding mass above the thrust. The volcanic belt can be understood as the result of tension in the upper arch, which is sometimes clearly demonstrated by a longitudinal rift valley on top of the anticline, as in southern Sumatra (the Semanko rift described by van Bemmelen, 1949), but we can hardly expect such fissures to reach very deep down into the crust.

A section across the Malayan geosyncline, in the island of Sumatra, for instance, has a slightly different pattern. The zone of negative anomalies coincides with a secondary nonvolcanic outer ridge, separated by a shallower longitudinal trough from the volcanic arc. It is supposed that this is due to a greater age of the orogeny in this region, adjustments either below or in the crust having taken place in the meantime.

Hess took up the subject of the Pacific island arcs in 1948, armed with much more detailed knowledge acquired during World War II, and Gutenberg and Richter (1949) commented upon it. The old concept of the relation between deep-sea troughs, island arcs, volcanic zones, and earthquake zones was confirmed everywhere, but extremely interesting details throw much light on the mechanical problem.

First of all, it became established that the south Pacific must be regarded as a separate unit, different from the North Pacific and much more like the South Atlantic, and characterized by swells and basins (map, Fig. 266). The shapes of the West and East Mariana arcs and the Palau arc strongly suggest that the Caroline-Pacific acted as a block, against which the westward movements of the crustal layers abutted, and could only develop fully to the north of it, with the great swing of the East Mariana arc.

Second, Hess made it clear that in the Japanese islands the earthquake foci of moderate depth follow the geanticlinal axes of the Bonin, Honshu, and Kurile arcs, but that the deep-focus earthquake lines have a simpler pattern, clearly indicating that there is a difference in the structural pattern above and below a depth of 300 km.

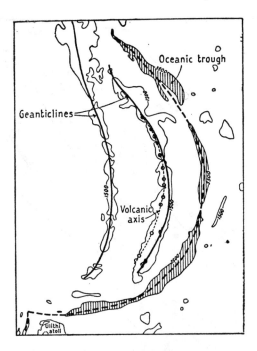

Fig. 269 Slight shift of volcanic axis from geanticlinal axis in Marianas arc. (*After Hess, 1948. Published by permission of the Geological Society of America.*)

Third, Hess showed that the line of volcanoes is not always coincident with the geanticlinal axis, but tends to diverge slightly (Fig. 269), again indicating that at a much slighter depth we may also expect a detachment and shifting of one layer over another.

Another feature of great interest is the arrangement of the deep-focus earthquakes in clusters of greatest activity separated by zones of much lower frequency, which together still show the 50° landward slope mentioned before (Fig. 268). Again we might conclude that there are horizontal layers of different character possibly slipping one over the other. Moreover, Hess succeeded in distinguishing two sets of arcs differing in age. The older one runs in larger festoons, the first festoon from Sakhalin to Hokkaido and along Honshu, the second festoon from the Ryukyu arc to Taiwan, the third festoon from Taiwan through Luzon to Borneo; together they form a more or less straight line, or in other words, require a single direction of compression, NW-SE.

The younger set is different in having one northern set of festoons, first the Aleutian arc and next the Kurilean arc, with a NNW-SSE

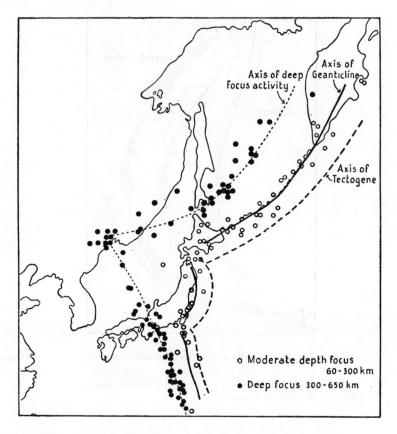

Fig. 270 Divergence of the arcs of deep-focus seismic activity from arcs at moderate depths and island arcs. (*After Hess, 1948. Published by permission of the Geological Society of America.*)

direction of movement; and a southern set, formed by the Mariana and Bonin festoons supplemented in the background by the Iwo Jima geanticline, the West Caroline and Palau-Kyushu geanticlines, and the Philippine geanticline, all with an EW direction of movement.

The two younger directions meet in Japan, where they form the well-known cross-structure of the Fossa Magna in Honshu. At depth, they meet just below the edge of the mainland of Asia, north of Korea (Fig. 270), where the intersection is characterized by a concentration of deep-focus epicenters. It is obvious that the geanticlinal arc of Honshu and its present trench in front are partly the old geanticline and partly a result of the interference of the two younger directions in the higher (less than 300 km in depth) reaches of the mantle and the crust.

When we turn our attention to the Indonesian Archipelago, we find the third direction, approximately N-S, which originated the Malayan, or Sunda, geanticline with its trench, its volcanic arc, and its deep-focus earthquake zone. As we shall see further on, the older intercontinental Banda geosyncline has been reshaped in this last N-S compression, causing its exaggerated S-shaped curve.

All these ideas about the origin of the pattern of the western Pacific island arcs are of course highly speculative. Still, they are of some interest because, in particular, they do make us realize that, first of all, we have to consider the necessity of separating older from younger structural features and their mutual interference. Moreover, we get the strong impression that the crustal deformations are entirely dependent on much deeper seated and wholly unknown factors. The recurrent conclusion that the crustal layer is detached from its substratum by orogenic stress can be observed only in this particular instance, where the absence of sialic crust on the North Pacific floor allowed the upper crust to glide forward.

Furthermore, the section of Fig. 268 shows that the medium and deep foci occur in clusters, sometimes two, sometimes three, each having a slightly greater extension in a horizontal direction than in a vertical one. A further separation of horizontal layers, and differential gliding of these layers, one over the other, accompanying the general eastward (or southward) thrust, could explain this localization of earthquake foci.

Very little is known about the deep basins between the arcs of different age and the Asiatic continent, the Sea of Japan, the central basin, the China Sea, Celebes Sea, and Banda Sea. They can at least be compared in size and depth with the deep oceanic basins in the Caribbean region, which are much better known.

THE INDONESIAN ARCHIPELAGO

Although the Indonesian Archipelago is perhaps not a typical example of island festoons, it cannot be omitted from our discussion of island arcs, for it has become a much discussed and controversial object which has unfortunately been taken, because of its spectacular features, as an example for other regions. Our knowledge of the region as a whole is relatively extensive and certainly very diverse, but in detail and precision, it is woefully inadequate.

The Indonesian Archipelago is situated on the point of intersection of two large and long orogenic belts, the western circum-Pacific belt ending in the Philippines and entering by the northern arm of Celebes and the northeastern Indian Ocean belt running from Malaya into the arc of the Greater Sunda Islands (Sumatra and Java).

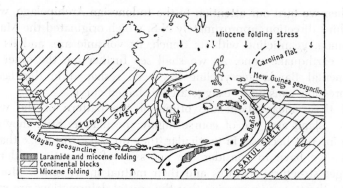

Fig. 271 Banda geosyncline with strong Mesozoic sedimentation and Laramide orogeny. (*After Umbgrove, 1938. Published by permission of the American Association of Petroleum Geologists.*)

On the other hand, the archipelago is also an intracontinental zone between the Asiatic and Australian continents.

This dual character has perhaps not been sufficiently realized by the various authors who have analyzed its geological history; the present configuration, with the separate units welded in one continuous pattern, is often misleading.

The boundary between the Australian and Asiatic continents is formed by the intercontinental Banda geosyncline (Fig. 271) described by Umbgrove (1938 and 1949) as having had almost continuous, although very variable, sedimentation during the whole of the Mesozoic and a strong Laramide and subsequent Miocene folding. Its extremely curved shape is probably due partly to the shape of the edges of the continental plateau, partly to differential movement in these continents, and partly to the Miocene orogenic phase. At its southern extremity it is met and joined by the Malayan geosyncline, and at its northern extremity by the circum-Pacific belt. No wonder that the regular pattern of the Malayan belt, with its double arc, negative-gravity-anomaly zone on the outer arc, volcanism on the inner arc, and longitudinal basins at the concave side, becomes deranged and unrecognizable when it merges into the older intercontinental Banda geosyncline. The same is true for the less well known Philippine arc. There can be little doubt, for instance, that a considerable amount of shearing took place between the island of Timor of the Banda geosyncline and the island of Sumba of the Malayan outer arc.

Kuenen (1935) gave a good summary of the existing "explanations" of the structural features. At that time he had four so-called "geotectonic" maps, by H. A. Brouwer, van Es, Staub, and Smit Sibinga, at his disposal. Since then many others have been added to the list, most of them engendered by the negative-gravity-anomaly zones of Vening Meinesz. All of them consist of a curve pattern joining islands and ridges. Some draw tear faults; some prefer curves when the lines do not join up very well; and in doubtful cases they differ in linking up the different islands. It is the same game as that which has been going on in southern Europe for a long time. Do these lines inform us about the unity (in time or in space) of an orogenic system or of the unity (again in time or in space) of basin formation? It is impossible to represent the ever-changing pattern of geosynclinal basins, fold directions, and their interference through geological history by a single set of lines. And worse, it is misleading. The set of paleographic maps by Umbgrove (1949) give a much better picture, and from them the dual character of the Malayan geosyncline running from Sumatra through the Banda arc to the Philippines becomes evident.

There is a distinct omission, however, in all the more theoretical sections of Umbgrove—the fact that the limit of the Sunda continental shelf lies not somewhere on the south coast of Java or Sumatra, but just on the border of their north coasts. We have there a very rapid decrease, within some tens of kilometers, of the whole Tertiary geosynclinal series, from several kilometers in thickness to a few hundred meters on the shelf. The real continental border is therefore on the north coast of Java and Sumatra, and farther south we probably have a thinner sialic crust, which perhaps extends into the outer arc. This limit of the shelf border is also expressed in the difference between the volcanic rocks on the shelf and on the volcanic arc. The volcanic arc is andesitic; on the shelf we find typical alkaline rocks.

THE ANTILLEAN ARC AND ITS BASINS

An entirely new approach to the problem of the relation of the deep-sea furrow to the negative-gravity-anomaly zone has been opened by Ewing (1952, 1954). This worker, with his collaborators, first made a seismic investigation of the ocean floor over the deep-sea furrow of Puerto Rico and later extended surveys over much of the Caribbean region. Their work has defined deep oceanic basins surrounded and traversed by island arc ridges and the Puerto Rico Trough as a typical deep oceanic furrow in front of an island arc.

There are four deep basins: the Gulf of Mexico, the Yucatan basin, the Columbian basin, and the Venezuelan basin, separated by the Cayman Ridge and Trough, the Nicaraguan Rise, and the Beata Ridge, respectively (Fig. 272).

The Antillean island arc commences as an eastward continuation of

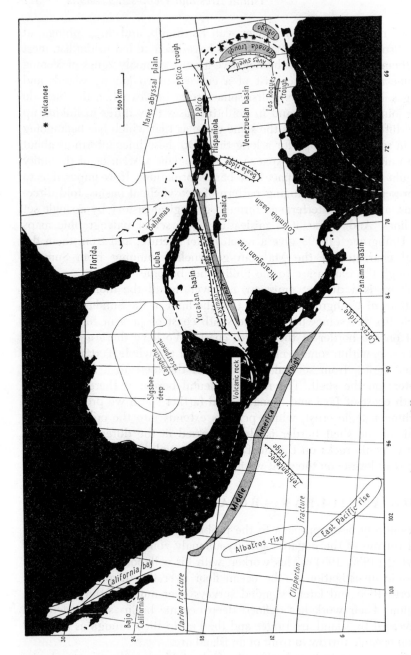

Fig. 272   The Antillean Arc in relation to Middle America.

the coastal structures of Venezuela. Swinging north, the arc defines the eastern limit of the Venezuelan basin, and a farther anticlockwise swing in trend connects it with the structures of Hispaniola, Cuba, and Yucatan.

Instead of this western connection with the mainland, there are good reasons to draw the connecting line from Hispaniola over the Bartlett Ridge and Jamaica to Guatemala.

This latter arcuate line connects the eugeosynclinal facies of thick Mesozoic and Tertiary rocks and ultrabasic-rock intrusions of the Greater Antilles with those of the Cordilleran system of North America (King, 1959). The Cuban arc and the Central American young volcanic arc (Weyl, 1961) are later additions to these arcuate structures.

All four deep basins go down to 4 km below sea level, despite the fact that the crust has been found to be between two and three times thicker than below parts of the Atlantic and Pacific oceans of the same depth. This is not wholly due to increased sediments, since they are only up to 1 km thicker than in the open oceans. The extra crust seems to be due to the existence of a layer having a P-wave velocity of 5 to 7 km/sec, the basal part of which approaches the properties of the oceanic basaltic layer and the top those of the continental sial.

Beneath the ridges, swells, and island arcs the crust becomes much thicker, both the continental and the oceanic layers taking part in the increase; the oceanic layer often has velocities of more than 7 km/sec near its base.

Of particular interest is the Cayman Ridge and Trough, a high ridge with a thick crust, in the base of which a velocity of 7.2 km/sec has been measured, and a true deep trough, some 100 km wide and more than 6 km deep, where there is only 5 km of crust above the mantle. This trough therefore affords the only example of typical oceanic crust within the Caribbean.

Another particularly interesting feature is the Puerto Rico Trough, situated between the oceanic crust of the Atlantic and the continental crust of Puerto Rico. The basaltic layer with a P-wave velocity of 6.2 km/sec plunges steeply down below the trench and the island.

The Antillean island arc is largely volcanic, and like Pacific island arcs, it is not basaltic, but andesitic, in character. The velocities of 5.8 to 6.1 below the Greater Antilles are in agreement with this, but the real thickening of the crust in this section is due to a layer with 7.0 to 7.6 km/sec velocity.

The negative gravity anomaly over the Puerto Rico Trench is partly due to the infilling of loose sediments and partly to the great difference in density between the crustal material and the water plus sediment, and not to a downbuckle of sialic matter in the heavy mantle material (Fig. 273) (Ewing and Heezen, 1955).

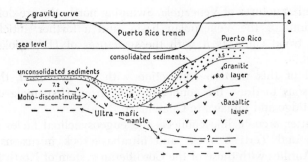

Fig. 273 Puerto Rico trench, gravity curve, and constitution of crust after seismic evidence. (*After Ewing and Heezen, 1955. Published by permission of the Geological Society of America.*)

The Middle American Trough. The Middle American Trough was extremely accurately surveyed between 1952 and 1959 by the Scripps Institution (Fisher, 1961) and seems to form an example of a simple deep-sea furrow (Fig. 272). It runs with a depth greater than 5,500 m for 600 km off the west coast of Central America reaching a maximum depth of 6,400 m opposite Guatemala, the landward flank being generally steeper than the offshore flank. It starts just south of the intersection of the Clarion fault line and the continental margin. The Tehuantepec Ridge, an offshoot from the Clipperton fracture zone, runs straight to the trough, but does not cross it nor influence its development, except in that the trough becomes deeper south of this intersection. The trough dies out just before reaching the intersection of the Cocos Ridge with the continental shelf.

This trough shows great seismic activity, with the typical arrangement of shallow earthquakes in the trough and deep focus earthquakes (70 to 300 km in depth) toward the continent.

Fig. 274 Schematic crustal structure across Middle America Trough off western Guatemala. (*After Fisher, 1961. Published by permission of the Geological Society of America.*)

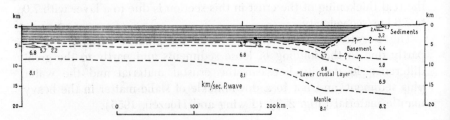

The crustal layering determined by seismic methods is shown in Fig. 274; the oceanic crust starts to bend downward some 150 km from the coast, and its lower boundary, the Moho discontinuity, flattens out just below the center of the partly sediment-filled trough, leaving space for the continental sialic rock layer to wedge out in the continental slope.

THE BANDA ARC

The most conspicuous arc of the whole western Pacific is the Banda arc, and since it has been used extensively as a prototype of other arcuate structures, we shall examine it in further detail (Fig. 267). We have seen that we can regard the Banda arc as the deformed intercontinental geosyncline between the southeast point of the Asian continent and the Australian continent, which originally must have been considerably straighter than the present exaggerated S shape. The Banda arc is limited to the north by a long straight structural feature, the E-W geanticline passing from the Sula Islands through Obimajor and Misool into the western extremity of New Guinea. In the south, the Banda arc is bounded by the Australian continent, which does not show any Tertiary deformation, although it may have moved as a block, and the arc merges topographically into the Malayan folded geosyncline, which also has an E-W strike. There can be little doubt that in the Miocene folding phase there was a considerable shortening, in a N-S direction, of the whole region occupied by the present Banda arc. A shortening by compression in one direction is always accompanied by an extension in either one or two directions at right angles; the vertical direction is usually preferred by the surface layers, but we may presume that the horizontal direction is preferred by the substratum. The vertical extension of the superficial layers is shown by their numerous folds and thrusts. The horizontal extension perpendicular to the main stress can be perceived at the surface only by the general shape of larger structural units or by dilatation features like oblique wrench faults. The E-W stretching which inevitably took place in the Banda arc, combined with the strong compression in a N-S direction, deformed the original slightly curved geosyncline into an extreme S shape (Figs. 267 and 271). One could compare this mechanism with the formation of ptygmatic folds of aplite veins in a gneiss. In the same way that the aplite is somewhat more rigid than the gneiss, and therefore follows another mode of deformation, the geosyncline is, as a result of its cylindrical cross section, somewhat stronger than the surrounding part of the crust.

The peculiar deep-sea trench behind the Banda arc, the Weber Deep, and the adjoining inner Banda arc on which the island of Banda is situated are also readily explained by the proposition of narrowing and compression of the outer Banda arc.

The folded geanticline of the Sula Islands–New Guinea apparently became stretched, so much so that its nose pressed into the southern extension of the Philippine arc, causing the opposed arc of west Celebes.

The interference of the E-W direction with the slight S-shaped Laramide geosyncline of the Banda arc is also clearly demonstrated by the surface features of their southern junction. The Malayan arc penetrates into the Banda arc west of Timor. The arrangement of the island ridges en échelon, probably accompanied by vertical shearing, is typical of such interferences, as I pointed out in Chap. 2.

ARCUATE STRUCTURES

Sollas (1903) and Lawson (1932) explained the arcuate shape of the festoons by pointing out that a gently dipping planar surface would intersect the sphere of the earth along a curved line. An overthrust plane, however, must then dip at 15°, whereas the seismic evidence points to a 50° dip. It is possible, of course, that the thrust plane flattens out near the surface as a result of difference in altitude between the sialic crust and the Pacific or Indian Ocean bottom. But there may be other reasons, and when one considers the very long curve from the Tanimbar Islands Deep into Burma and the strong curvature of the Aleutians and Mariana arc, the suggestion of Sollas and Lawson seems difficult to accept.

I think it much more probable that the thrust plane itself has a curved surface, varying from almost flat to a strong curvature. In this respect we might recall that, in general, a deformation sets in at one particular point and then spreads to the right and left, upward and downward. But the fact that the central point gives way first alters the stress conditions on both sides of that point. First of all, we shall find in the center a stress much smaller than at the initial stage, but still capable of thrusting the broken block forward, and much larger stresses toward both extremities, which diminish again outward to the degree of the initial stress (Fig. 275). The unequal stress yield will also change the stress directions, which will become divergent outward. Seen from this point of view, the curvature of the island arc has the same nature and origin as the curvature of an asymmetric anticline. But having established a strong N-S stress in the southern area of the Indonesian Archipelago, we might also expect this stress field to have extended much farther north. It would then certainly have contributed to the arcuate shape of the Japanese group of arcs by adding a N-S compression to the eastern advance.

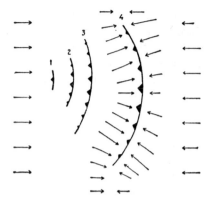

Fig. 275 Origin of arcuate structures.

Without doubt the island arcs of the western Pacific border are the most instructive examples of orogenic deformation. We have seen that the detachment of one horizontal zone from the next is one of the principal features of the folding, which can develop particularly well here because the upper continental layer can actually be shoved over the Pacific floor. It is the same principle that prompted us always to distinguish the distortion typical of the upper sedimentary layer as opposed to that of the basement, a principle we already deduced at an earlier stage of investigation, when we had an opportunity to point out that every incompetent layer between competent series is apt to become a detachment horizon originating disharmonic folds. I should like to suggest that these incompetent layers, or at any rate the upper ones, are the layers that furnish the magma of the extrusive lavas and the intrusive basic rocks.

We deduced from the development of island arcs that two perpendicular directions of stress can act either at the same time or alternately, but that in either case both stresses contribute to the final shape. Moreover, we inferred that the cylindrical cross section of a preexisting geosyncline constitutes an exceptionally strong element in the structure of the basement, which may be bent if it has been arched beforehand, but will withstand great stress if originally straight.

Furthermore, we learned that the stress condition is certainly not limited to the upper 60 or 100 km of the crust, but reaches at least to 700-km depth, and that it is very probable that discontinuity surfaces split this section up into two or three concentric zones.

Whether or not the double arc of the Lesser Antilles is a replica of the Banda arc, with a similar later compression of a Laramide geosyncline of simpler shape, seems undecided. But from a general point of view we need not expect any great analogy because the Banda arc is an intercontinental structure and the Antillean arc more of a circumcontinental one. According to the gravity map of de Bruyn (1951), the zone of negative gravity anomalies does not curve round to the north into the Leeward Trench as Hess (1938) drew it, but enters the mainland of South America in the Orinoco delta in close accordance with purely geological considerations (Bucher, 1952).

A comparison of the Banda arc with the Gibraltar arc is certainly not warranted. The Gibraltar arc (Chap. 28, Fig. 276) is *not* a true arc because the structural lines do not curve round from their E-W position in southeast Spain to a N-S direction west of Gibraltar and an E-W direction in North Africa. On the contrary, the two units, the Riff in North Africa and the Betic Cordillera in southern Spain, are two orogenic units, which are perhaps associated in one two-sided orogenic system, or more probably separated by a block, but are not connected by an arc around the Strait of Gibraltar.

On the other hand, the S-shaped curve of the western Alps has an origin which is similar, but not exactly analogous, to that of the Banda arc, because part of its curved shape seems to be due to a compression of an already existing curved geosyncline.

Whether the western Pacific arcs and their rows of volcanoes are an analogue of the volcanic activity of the eastern Pacific is an open question. The latest (Pliocene to Recent) volcanoes of the Cordilleran system are probably to be regarded either as a posttectonic volcanic phase or as a continental phase and can hardly be compared with the volcanic island arcs. The volcanic activity in the Jurassic and Miocene may have had an origin similar to that of the island arcs, as advocated by Kay (1951), but the geology is still so obscure that a well-considered opinion is impossible. Personally, I would hesitate to take the island arcs of the western Pacific, with their unique assembly of geotectonical and geophysical features, as a prototype of any other structural feature of the earth's crust except the Antillean arc, and perhaps the Falkland Island arc, although some of their separate characteristics may certainly be present elsewhere.

Chapter 28

Mountain Chains and Geosynclines

In our short review of the fundamental characteristics of the earth's surface and interior we have still left the continents, the main concern of the geologist, out of consideration.

Returning, then, to our principal subject, we observe, first of all, that the constitution of the continents is far from uniform. Precambrian shields form bigger and smaller blocks, alternating as units with mountain chains, together with geosynclines and basins filled with thick marine sedimentary sequences, all pointing to very variable conditions in the course of geological time.

A glance at the globe tells us that the Tertiary mountain chains are distributed according to a very definite pattern. We find one circum-Pacific belt and another equatorial belt—the Tethys or Mediterranean belt—meeting in the West and East Indian archipelagoes. We might expect characteristic differences between these two belts since the latter is situated between two continental blocks of sialic crust, Eurasia and Gondwana, whereas the former rises on one side of a continental sialic bloc with the great sial-free area of the Pacific Ocean on the other flank.

Looking further back in history we find a different pattern for the Hercynian orogenic belts, and again another for the Caledonian orogenies. We find that some orogenic belts surround a stable shield, the circumcontinental type; others are situated between such shields, the intercontinental type; and finally, we may perhaps consider the circum-Pacific belt a distinctive unit. We must investigate each of these on its own merits, although in many instances it will be difficult to decide to which group a particular belt belongs.

The following list may provide a preliminary base for our survey:

Caledonian orogenes. Circumcontinental mostly, around the Angara, Canadian, and Australian shields.

Hercynian orogenes. Circumcontinental, around the Angara, Baltic, Brazilian, Australian, and Canadian shields; intercontinental, between the

Gondwana and Eurasian shields (Paleozoic Tethys) and between the Llanorian, Appalachian, and Canadian shields.

Alpine orogenes. Intercontinental Alpine Tethys and circum-Pacific belt.

It would be premature to suppose that all mountain chains belonging to one particular type of orogeny have the same characteristics. A brief survey of some mountain chains of the European Tethys orogene and of their mutual relations would convince us of the wide variety presented by such a small group.

THE ALPINE STRUCTURAL HISTORY OF THE WEST MEDITERRANEAN

The western Mediterranean belt is enclosed between two stable blocks, the Sahara shield in the south and the Hercynian shield in the north. The Sahara shield is an old cratonic shield covered by subhorizontal Paleozoic; the European shield has had a long and complicated Paleozoic history with many Hercynian orogenes which extend far into the Alpine mobile belt.

In the Alpine belt we can distinguish a northern belt bordering the European shield—the Pyrenees, Alps, and Carpathians, and a southern belt, the High Atlas in Morocco and Sahara chains in Algeria (Fig. 276).

Right in the center of the belt we find the Betic Cordillera extending into the Balearic Islands and the Moroccan Riff trending farther along the coastal region of Algeria. Both are roughly parallel to the main E-W trend.

Besides these longitudinal belts there are some diagonal mountain chains, the Apennines and the Dinarides, the Middle Atlas and the Tunisian chains.

In between these Tertiary mountain chains we find numerous blocks relatively undisturbed by the folding going on around them. They include the Moroccan Meseta, the Castillian block, the Hauts-Plateaux in Algeria, some undefined blocks in the western Mediterranean, perhaps one in the Tyrrhenian Sea, the Hungarian Pannonian block, and perhaps many more of smaller size. We can sometimes trace the events of their Paleozoic history from one block to the next across the Tertiary mountain chain when the latter contains sufficient exposures of older rocks in a not too metamorphosed state.

The orogenic belts never became clearly defined until they had been deformed practically to the extent we see today. It would certainly be erroneous, for instance, to suppose that one could have predicted the present configuration of orogenes with any accuracy from the geological map in the middle of the Upper Cretaceous.

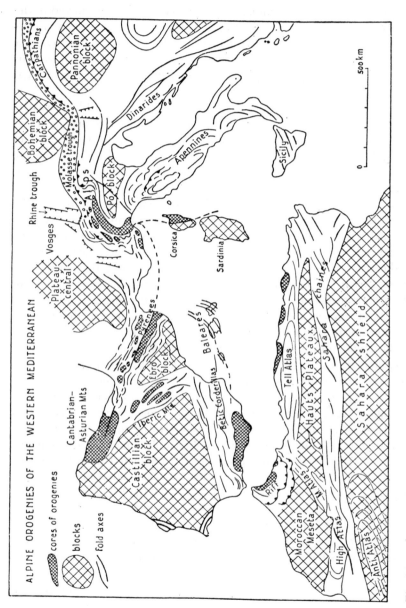

Fig. 276 Alpine orogenies of the western Mediterranean.

387

When, after some preliminary movements, real folding started in the Upper Cretaceous, the borders of the African and European shields moved toward one another, squeezing up the border zones, whether geosynclinal or not. The intervening blocks were pushed in various directions, sometimes being broken, and their connecting links folded in various degrees of compression.

In this sequence of events it is clear that the Sahara block was by far the most solid and stable (none but the Upper Cretaceous transgressions ever covered it, for instance) and that, as we go farther north, the geosynclinal subsidence was deeper and larger and the folding more intense. The northern boundary of the orogenic belt is, in accordance with this fact, much less clearly defined, and one could easily defend the thesis that the Betic Cordillera in the south of Spain, which has a great pile of nappes on its northern flank, like the Alps, is the real northern boundary, and not the Pyrenees, which have been folded only moderately in the Alpine Period. On the other hand, one might assign the Wealden dome in southern England, the Paris basin, or the North German basin, all of them lightly folded by Tertiary or Mesozoic movements, to the orogenic belt of the Tethys.

A brief review of three major mountain chains of the western Mediterranean belt will show us how different they are.

The *High Atlas,* bordering the Sahara shield to the north and partly separated from it by a marginal trough filled by younger Cretaceous and Tertiary sediments which are partly of continental facies, was part of a Lower and Middle Jurassic basin folded in post-Eocene time, and again, to a lesser degree, in Miocene time. A peculiarity is that the Tertiary chain extends much farther west than the Jurassic basin did. In the central High Atlas the Precambrian and Paleozoic was never covered by the Jurassic nor by the regional Upper Cretaceous transgressions; nevertheless its upheaval surpasses that of the calcareous High Atlas farther east. Farther east along the border of the Sahara shield the geosyncline is mainly of a Lower and Upper Cretaceous age, and the folding is quite different from that of the High Atlas. Toward the Atlantic the High Atlas chain disappears with a sharp plunge; toward the east it flattens out. Apparently, both the geosyncline and folding are bound to the Sahara shield border, but are independent of each other. The folding is very superficial and of the type encountered in the Jura Mountains. There is no central crystalline mass, and the marginal troughs are only slightly developed. A very interesting feature is the longitudinal zoning by faults, separating blocks of relative intense folding and blocks with hardly any folding. There was some post-Liassic igneous activity of a basic (anorthosite-trondhjemite) nature which was certainly later than the geosynclinal phase and earlier than the folding.

The present altitude of the High Atlas chain is due to a Pliocene uplift.

The *Pyrenees* represent a real orthotectonic Hercynian orogeny, simply rejuvenated by uplift; paratectonic folding took place in its marginal troughs during the Alpine orogenic period (an Upper Cretaceous and a Late Eocene phase). A large longitudinal fault (Chap. 12) reached down below the crust into the basic layer and permitted the ascension of small masses of basic rocks and metasomatizing solutions. The marginal troughs remained free of any magmatic activity. Toward the west the southern marginal trough develops into an independent Cretaceous geosyncline with the same kind of folding as farther east. Toward the east the axial zone plunges a little and is then cut off by the Mediterranean. Its northern marginal trough flattens out to some extent toward the east and can be followed along the coast into the western Alpine front zone. Long after the last folding a general uplift, in the Miocene or Pliocene or both, gave the Pyrenees their present level. Thus the Pyrenees are essentially a symmetric structure with a bilateral development, encroaching on its continental margins both to the north and south.

The *Alps* are characterized by a whole series of geosynclines separated by geanticlinal ridges. The southern geosyncline is Triassic, the middle is Jurassic, and the northern is of Cretaceous age. The central geosyncline developed into the Pennine Alps, and is characterized by an initial basic magmatic phase and by extreme folding accompanied by strong metamorphism (Chap. 30, Fig. 277).

The northern geosyncline, the Helvetides, had no magmatic phase, was very strongly folded and thrusted, and finally glided down the northern slope of its originally northern geanticlinal ridge into the marginal trough.

The southern Triassic geosynclinal region, the Lombardy Alps, was strongly disturbed by longitudinal faults and subsequent folding. It had no proper magmatic phase, but on the very deep reaching fault line which now separates it from the Pennine Alps, we find several posttectonic granitic intrusions and one pre- or syntectonic basic intrusion, the Ivrea zone. The folding was very intense over the whole breadth of the structure and occurred in many phases, the oldest in the center, the younger ones in the marginal parts. To the west, the structure curves round southward and becomes simpler and less intensely folded. Finally, it plunges toward the Mediterranean and is cut off by the sea. Toward the east its northern units merge into the Carpathians and its southern units flatten out and are replaced by other structures.

The final uplift occurred in the Pliocene, not long after the strong Miocene orogenic phase.

The southern marginal trough merges into the independent Po basin, the sediments of which cover, in the west, all the original southern Alpine unit.

The northern marginal trough is well developed in the center and to the east, but disappears in the west, where the Jura Mountains join with the Alpine structures. Thus the Alps are a typical asymmetric structure, slowly encroaching their northern foreland. It is even doubtful whether one can regard them as of the intercontinental type because the Triassic and Jurassic of the southern Alps continue in the same marine facies far into the northern Apennines, so that there never was a real continental hinterland.

To detect fundamental characteristics of mountain chains of the intercontinental type, one should inquire if there are any properties which these three chains have in common. There are very few indeed. A Pliocene uplift, after largely varying intervals of quiescence following the last folding phase, is perhaps the most obvious common trait.

In addition, the thickness of sediments in the marginal troughs is perhaps roughly in accordance with the intensity of folding, and finally, the pattern of longitudinal zoning is common property to all of them. But all their most prominent features are totally different, and hence it would be a fallacy to look a priori for a common origin.

When we direct our attention to circumcontinental mountain chains we need not wonder that we again find great differences and little in common in the Appalachians and in the Cordilleran belt. It is somewhat doubtful whether these last mountain chains can really be regarded as a separate group, for in both cases, and perhaps in all circumcontinental chains, there is good reason to suppose that these chains were originally flanked by some emergent land beyond their present limits, land that has disappeared since then, warped down into the adjoining ocean.

But more recently these hypothetical outer land regions have been imagined more as hypothetical island arcs, often volcanic, and themselves a portion of the orogenic belt.

Finally, in reviewing the typical island arcs of the Pacific (Chap. 27), we again found other and different characteristics.

GEOSYNCLINES AND BASINS

I have already remarked that there is a close connection between a mountain chain and a geosyncline, the geosyncline being the forerunner of a mountain chain. But this relation has proved to be only approximative. We find many deep basins which were never folded, and we also find portions of mountain chains which have never been geosynclines. The unfolded basins are numerous; the folded mountain chains not preceded by a geosynclinal phase are perhaps exceptions.

The conception of the relation between a mountain chain and a geosyncline is due to James Hall, who published in 1859 the third volume of his "Palaeontology of New York," containing his conclusions that mountain chains are apt to occupy elongated belts with exceptionally thick sediments, the sinking and the folding being due to the loading of sediments on a relatively narrow strip. Since then the causal connection between sinking and sedimentation and between sinking and compression has been continually discussed, but no generally accepted conclusion has been reached, although the necessity of a causal connection has been recognized as valid.

There are two problems. The first is simple: Is the sinking the cause of sedimentation, or is the sedimentation the cause of the sinking? The answer is definite: to start more intensive sedimentation in one place rather than in another, there must be a basin in the first place; to sustain the basin as a place of extra sedimentation the sinking must at least keep up with the rate of sedimentation, and this result can never be reached without active sinking. The load of sediment helps, but isostatic adjustment is always only a fraction of the load, and the sinking must therefore be primary in order to keep up with the filling.

The second problem is the causal relation between mountain building and the geosyncline. If the compression were the result of basin forming, all ordinary longitudinal basins ought to have been folded, which is certainly not the case. The original concept of James Hall that the loading caused the folding cannot be sustained. If, on the other hand, the basins were due to compression, one could expect that the arrest of compression could occur either before or after actual folding took place, resulting either in an unfolded basin or in a mountain chain. This point of view is all the more attractive because we have already concluded that subsidence is the cause of sedimentary infilling. Our final result, then, is that compression causes the sinking of the basin and the mountain building and therefore that the connection between geosynclines and mountain building must be sought in a common cause and not in a direct interaction.

The result of our reasoning is not new in any way, but was reached by Dana as long ago as 1873. Dana recognized the division of the crust into continental and oceanic areas—a division inherited from the time when the crust was first formed—and thought that lateral stress first caused basins to form on the margins of continents by a downbending of the crust, and then threw up the mountain chains, simply because these margins were the weaker portions of the crust. It is to be regretted that the basic truth and soundness of Dana's reasoning have so often been neglected and that so much new but irrelevant evidence has been used to challenge his views. Most of the confusion has arisen from the fact that the definition of a geosyncline had from the beginning a dual character, because both Hall and Dana saw it as a combination of thick sediments and folding. The question therefore arises as to whether a geosyncline is mainly characterized by its sedimentary rocks or by its folding. Haug (1900), for instance, defined a geosyncline as sedimentation in his bathyal zone (800 m) and therefore considered deep-sea troughs typical geosynclines, though admitting the existence of shallow-water geosynclines. For others, e.g., von Bubnoff (1931) and Stille (1936), the main characteristic of a geosyncline is its intensity of folding. An excellent discussion of the development of thought in this respect has been given by Glaessner and Teichert (1947), to which the reader is referred for details. A complicated nomenclature has sprung up in recent times, culminating with Kay (1947), which has been discussed and reduced to a reasonable size again by Aubouin (1959).

We shall use the term *geosyncline* for those elongated basins filled with a relatively thick series of sediments which either have been folded themselves or run parallel to a mountain chain, but shall avoid its use when no direct connection with folding can be established. The term *basin* can then be used for thick sediment accumulations which have not been folded, or, in a historical sense, which have not yet been folded or are not connected with folding. A deep-sea furrow, or trough, which has not been filled with sediments can be referred to as a *trough*. A *rift* is a strip depressed between faults.

A basin, as defined above, conforms to general usage and is a synonym for the "parageosyncline" of Schuchert and Stille, as well as for some of the nuclear and discordant basins of Umbgrove (1947). However, some of Umbgrove's nuclear basins I should call "blocks." Umbgrove made a subdivision of basins in our sense and distinguished "isochronous" nuclear ones, concordant within a territory with a single trend; "anisochronous" ones, enclosed between different trends; and finally, discordant basins, superimposed upon any kind of trends in the basement. A close study of basins reveals, however, that one can always detect some kind of connection between the elongation or axis of the basin and the trend of the basement, and, in my opinion, the subdivision is therefore superfluous. A typical discordant basin like the Michigan basin, for instance, is enclosed between broad arches in the Precambrian basement of the Canadian shield; and the Paris basin shows trends, particularly in the older formations paralleling the Hercynian trend of the Brabant massif. Some of Umbgrove's nuclear basins are blocks between mountain chains which have sometimes been submerged and received sediments, the Pannonian block, for instance (the Hungarian plain); others, such as the Castillian block in Spain, have been mainly elevated. In general, the thickness of their sediments is less than in the surrounding geosynclines, and their facies is apt to be continental.

Other basins are situated on the margin of a continent, e.g., the Gulf Coast basin, which is a "paralia-geosyncline" in Kay's nomenclature. But here also the older sedimentary series show distinct parallelism with the continental border, and their transgression on the continent is not fundamentally different from any other circumcontinental geosyncline. In our terminology it is a basin because it has not been folded—yet.

The "rift" in our terminology becomes a "taphro-geosyncline" with Kay. I prefer the shorter word which every geologist knows.

A deep-sea furrow becomes a "geotectocline" in Hess's nomenclature because this author suspects that a deep-sea furrow will become the axis of a major orogeny; I feel safer with the purely descriptive term.

The proper geosyncline certainly merits a closer examination. According to our definition it is an elongated basin with a thick series of sediments which has been strongly folded, in contrast with the mild folding that many basins show.

But this definition leaves a very wide range of epeirogenic and orogenic structures of different character under one heading. We have already seen, in the preceding discussion, how totally different mountain chains of the same period and the same elevation may be, and their original basins were at least as different. In my opinion, however, the current subdivisions are not satisfactory, for they are mostly genetic and not descriptive and therefore tend far too much to generalize special features of particular orogenies.

As in mountain chains, I should like to distinguish three groups: *intercontinental geosynclines,* like the Urals (mesogeosyncline = Mediterranean geosyncline of Schuchert); *circumcontinental geosynclines,* like the Appalachian geosyncline; and *circumoceanic geosynclines.* We have to admit that in many cases one is in doubt whether at the time of formation the basin was of circum-Pacific or circumcontinental character. Perhaps the types are not so very different. But the subdivision is clear in its purpose, and their characteristics may emerge later. Besides this orographical distinction, one can distinguish clearly two types, those that precede the main folding and those that come after. The latter type of basin is called a *marginal trough* ("Saumtiefe" of Stille; idiogeosyncline of Umbgrove), and it may be folded or not. The Molasse basin of the Alps is a very gently folded marginal trough; those of the Pyrenees have been more strongly folded. The marginal trough is short-lived and filled with syntectonic and posttectonic sediments; it is the effect of the folding, and it is marginal to the folding. The geosynclines which preceded the folding may be called *orthogeosynclines* when they are large. They are long-lived and show several stages during their development and end in an orogeny. Sometimes they show an initial magmatic phase in the beginning of their history (eugeosyncline, Stille and Kay); sometimes this is absent (miogeosyncline, Stille); and they are apt to split up into separate basins (epieugeosynclines, Kay) toward the end. Trümpy (1955) pointed out that the thickness of some of the Mesozoic series in the central Alpine geosyncline is not at all large and coined the term "leptogeosyncline" for those with a thin sedimentary filling. But I think that many more subdivisions would have to be created to do justice to the great variety of geosynclinal development. Since we are not yet far enough advanced in our knowledge about the genesis of a mountain chain, I prefer to restrict the term orthogeosyncline to large, severely compressed geosynclines; the smaller ones like that of the High Atlas we may call minor geosynclines (the monogeosyncline of Schuchert, 1925).

When we want to emphasize the fact that a particular orogenic zone is characterized by an initial basic magmatic phase we can use Kay's term eugeosyncline.

An orthogeosyncline has a special characteristic, a shifting center; when it is an intercontinental geosyncline we can generally recognize an epicontinental facies on both margins; and on only one margin of the circumcontinental type. The center may be filled with graywacke facies, which for some people is the typical geosynclinal facies (O. T. Jones, 1938, for instance) and which is called flysch facies in Switzerland. There they regard the flysch facies of alternating sands and clays not only as typical of the central zone of the geosyncline, but in particular of its later phases when intergeosynclinal ridges have emerged and have increased the slopes. Others, like Haug, think of the epicontinental facies of well-stratified limestones and marls as the typical geosynclinal and bathyal facies (cf. Chap. 23). The shift of the geosyncline may be either toward the continent or away from it, but one can state in general terms that a shift toward the continent occurs during the development of one single geosynclinal period, as in the Alps, for instance, and a shift away from the continent takes place when different geosynclines separated by orogenic periods are peripheral around the same continent, as in northeast America, where the Laurentian, Taconic, and Acadian orogenies are concentric around the Canadian shield (Grabau, 1940). In the Paleozoic Cordilleran geosyncline, the original orthogeosyncline of very large width was eventually split up in two by a central geanticline (the sequentgeosyncline of Schuchert). This is, however, a distinction in geosynclines which may be of some importance in their later development but which is not made in the current systems of subdivision.

A basin like that of the present Gulf Coast is decidedly asymmetric in the sense that it is bordered by land on one side and by sea on the other. This results in the thickest sedimentary series accumulating on the continental slope, wedging out landward by transgressive and regressive series and seaward by simple thinning of each member, i.e., by facies change. The same situation can be found for the end of the Lower Cretaceous of the central Alpine geosyncline, where the Upper Cretaceous has a deep-sea facies, in the southern Alps, which continues southward in the Apennines. Subsequently, a ridge, separating the center of the geosyncline from its seaward extension, was warped up in the Upper Cretaceous, during the first Alpine folding phase in the center of the geosyncline, but in its early phase the geosyncline had only one shelf margin and one deep-sea margin.

This asymmetrical shape stands in contrast with the symmetrical geosyncline, for which we may take the Welsh Caledonian geosyncline described by O. T. Jones (1938) as the prototype. Such a symmetric geosyncline has shelves on both sides, and its sediments have the typical graywacke facies of graded sandstones in its center, a facies which is not present in the asymmetric open geosyncline.

Whether the symmetric type and the asymmetric type have a different orogenic history cannot be ascertained at present with our incomplete knowledge of too few mountain chains. One would suppose that the asymmetric geosyncline would develop into an asymmetric structure like the Alps or Appalachians, and the symmetric type into a more or less symmetric structure like the Pyrenees or High Atlas; but whether this is a rule or just a coincidence is difficult to decide.

In summarizing the subject of the nomenclature of sedimentation areas, we can formulate our point of view as follows. As a first subdivision we recognize:

Blocks: stable units within an orogenic system, either submerged (ocean blocks) or emerged (continental blocks) or outside the orogenic systems (shield blocks).

Basins: subsided, sediment-filled, only slightly folded or unfolded areas on the shield or on their margin.

Rifts: elongated, subsided strips between faults.

Troughs (trench or furrow): subsided elongated strips on the margins of ocean, not filled or only partly filled with sediments. A *marginal trough* is a basin, folded or not, which is marginal to a mountain chain and is due to the folding.

Geosynclines: elongated, subsided, strongly folded basins, containing thick sedimentary series. They may be asymmetric or symmetric. They may be large and continuous, i.e., *orthogeosynclines*, or smaller, and then called minor, or *monogeosynclines*. On the other hand, they may be *intercontinental, circumcontinental,* or *circum-Pacific*. They may have an initial magmatic phase (eugeosynclines) or may be of the epicontinental type (miogeosynclines).

I think that we have to be content for the moment with this subdivision because our knowledge of geosynclines in general and their orogenic history in particular is too scanty to warrant any genetic system.

Chapter 29

Magmatic Phases in Orogenesis

Orogenic belts and rift valleys are both accompanied by magmatic phenomena which are clearly connected with their formation. On the other hand, there are magmatic manifestations which are outside the rupture zones of the earth's crust and are typical of the shields. An interesting symposium on this question can be found in "Tectonic Control of Igneous Activity," published in 1954 by the Department of Geology of the University of Leeds.

The orogenic belts, being without doubt the most profoundly disturbed of the earth's crust, have also the most complex magmatic history, with migmatization and batholiths, basic intrusions and volcanic zones, whereas the rifts and shields are characterized only by volcanism.

The distribution of types of igneous activity warrants a subdivision of magmatic phenomena into those related to mountain chains and those related to stable shields and is therefore of fundamental importance.

THE OROGENIC MAGMATIC CYCLES

The most simplified picture of the magmatic cycle of an orogenic belt contains four distinct phases:

First, or initial, phase: extrusion and intrusion of basic magma in geosynclinal stage

Second, or metamorphic, phase: synkinematic regional metamorphism followed by granitization and migmatization accompanied by pegmatites

Third, or intrusive, phase: late-tectonic intrusion of granodiorite-granite plutons

Fourth, or volcanic, phase: posttectonic volcanism

The magmatic cycle in four phases is often not complete, or cannot be ascertained to be complete, because the region has not been suffi-

ciently denuded. It is very doubtful whether there is any direct connection between the first and second phases; they seem to be independent since one may be lacking, with the other attaining full development. The second and third phases are often closely connected,
but erosion may not have penetrated deeply enough to expose the
second phase at the surface. A connection between the third and fourth
phases is also often evident; sometimes the volcanoes seem to be
almost contemporaneous with the batholiths, but sometimes the volcanic action is very much retarded, and it then becomes doubtful
whether it may still be regarded as belonging to the preceding
orogenic phase. Nevertheless, large mountain chains frequently show
all four magmatic phases, and the less intense the orogenesis, the less
complete the phases. Moreover, the older chains have a much stronger
magmatic character than the younger ones, and the Mediterranean
belt less than the circum-Pacific belt.

The Initial Phase.   The initial magmatic phase is either a volcanic
phase of basic rocks of which pillow lavas are the most typical components, or equally typically, a basic intrusive phase, or both. The
volcanic rocks alternate with the sedimentary rocks; the olivine-bearing
ultramafic rock with transitions to gabbro and diorite is intrusive in
these sediments. As these ultramafic olivine-bearing rocks, peridotites
or dunites, are often very much serpentinized, they are frequently
referred to as the serpentine belt of a mountain chain; a better term
would be "peridotite belt" (Hess, 1955). They are always accompanied
by rocks of basaltic composition, as described, for instance, by Burri
and Niggli (1945), who give an exhaustive survey of all these rocks
of the Alps, Apennines, and Dinarides. These basic rocks seldom cause
any thermal metamorphism in the surrounding rocks, although in some
cases, as in the Pyrenees, the enclosing limestones are highly metamorphosed and altered into scapolite and hornblende-bearing car-
bonate rocks. In this case the field evidence shows, however, that the
metamorphism cannot be due to the intrusion of the basic rocks, but
is an independent phenomenon, although probably related to the same
compression which caused the peridotite (and gabbroic) intrusions.
The temperature of the intruded rock must therefore have been low,
probably lower than 500°C (Turner and Verhoogen, 1960). As a
result it is supposed that the rock consisted largely of olivine crystals,
with small quantities of magmatic water or other liquid lubricating
the whole mass (Bowen, 1928). The association with spilitic lava or
other basic volcanic rocks would suggest that the peridotites represent
the gravitative basic differentiate of a spilitic magma. The widespread
and often very deep-reaching serpentinization of the peridotites can in
most cases be attributed in some part to the action of this water-rich
lubricating intergranular liquid, but in the main to the water content

of the invaded sediments, and not to weathering, which would attack only the surface of the rock. In the case of the North Pyrenean fault, it is more probable that the connection between the surface (or the near surface) and the great depth at which the peridotite accumulation must have originated is not a result of the subsidence of a deep geosynclinal basin, but due to a fundamental fault reaching down to this great depth. All peridotite belts need not, therefore, be in the axis of a geosyncline. The peridotites are often associated with radiolarites and very fine grained limestones in a pelitic sediment, indicating a large basin of deep water far from the emerged land.

This association of serpentine, radiolarite, and spilite has been called the "Steinmann trinity" because Steinmann (1926) was the first to call attention to this rock association, and recently Bailey and McCallien (1960) discussed the petrological implications of the serpentine-spilite association.

A good account of the peculiarities of the initial basic magmatic phase in its purest form has been given by Kündig (1956), based mainly on examples from the Mediterranean belt, Cyprus, Syria, Turkey, etc. It is from this eastern Mediterranean region that the most detailed descriptions have been published. We refer the reader to the *International Geological Congress*, Algiers, 1952, Vol. 17 and to Hiessleitner (1951) for the Balkans, to Borchert (1957 and 1958) for Turkey, and to Dubertret (1953) for Lebanon and Syria. They are exceptionally interesting because the admixture of sediments is rather limited in amount, and accumulations of thousands of meters thickness of basic igneous rocks of varying character, together with sedimentary rocks, which can be dated, occur in zones where later compression has not been very active.

The chaotic character of these occurrences is explained by two separate but often simultaneous actions, in the first place, the plowing action of the thick extrusive flows of peridotite and spilite on the bottom sediments of a deep-sea furrow, and in the second place, the gliding down of slabs of older sedimentary rocks from the walls of the trench, deposited in the moving flows and carried forward by them. The trench is thought to have been formed either by strong thrust faulting or by normal faulting, and the flows to have originated from the walls of the trench where the faults have formed a connection between the surface and the basaltic layer.

The intrusive bodies are often small in comparison with granite stocks and batholiths, and their distribution in the invaded rock is mostly very chaotic, at any rate as regards smaller bodies. Their very smallness contributed to their susceptibility to serpentinization by the activity of connate water. Later orogenic deformation of a peridotite belt often has the character of extreme imbrication in which the original structure has been completely destroyed, but sometimes, as in the Near East belt, a "root" zone of vertical structure can be distinguished from a zone of horizontal layering.

The volcanic rocks belonging to the initial magmatic phase are usually of the spilite-keratophyre class, although rhyolites occur also. Many of the spilitic lava flows form pillow lavas, assumed to indicate a subaqueous effusion. The sodic nature of the spilite rocks is assumed by Turner and Verhoogen to be due to a contamination of a basaltic intrusive, deep down in the geosyncline, by the sodic environment of arkosic graywackes typical of the eugeosyncline and by their connate water, but the relation graywackes-spilites is not always present. On the other hand, there are numerous examples of the relation of arkosic graywackes with spilites, of which one of the simplest is that formed by the Algonkian Dal Formation of southwest Sweden. Both below and above the spilite-bearing middle Dal Formation occur thick arkosic graywackes, and there is every reason to believe the spilite flows to be subaqueous (Overeem, 1948), but there is no field evidence whatsoever of contamination. In the Appalachian belt of the eastern United States the Cambrian and Ordovician rocks include large quantities of basaltic and rhyolitic lava flows, but as in many other cases, it is difficult to decide whether the volcanic phase should be regarded as posterior to a Precambrian orogeny or anterior to a Caledonian orogeny; both orogenic periods saw activity in this region. The classic spilites of the Devonian of the Variscan chain stretching from Cornwall into Germany are a much better example, because they occur outside a Caledonian orogenic belt. In general, one has to admit that in the older orogenies the volcanics of the initial magmatic phase do not consistently show the typical spilite association. Often they are of the basalt-andesite rock association. Nevertheless, the spilites are more or less confined to the initial magmatic phase when they do occur. The Alpine orogenies of the Mediterranean belt seldom have an initial volcanic phase, but only of intrusive basic rocks, whereas the American geosynclines, both eastern and western, have very large initial volcanic phases (Marshall Kay, 1951).

In the better-known mountain chains the peridotite belt is often restricted to one longitudinal zone, in the Piedmont province of the Appalachians and the Pennine zone of the Alps, for example. This is not always true; Anatolia, for instance, forms a notable exception. Hess (1939–1955) made a fairly complete analysis of all the known peridotite belts, and I refer the reader to his work for more details.

The origin of the basic melt is difficult to ascertain, but its restriction to the most central and deepest part of the largest geosynclines, in the younger orogenies at least, proves that it is formed only in special circumstances of the eugeosyncline and that it is derived from a

deeply buried level which can usually only be tapped by a geosyncline which has subsided deeply.

This conclusion is confirmed by the occurrence of the same association of basic and ultrabasic rocks along the fundamental fault in the
northern Pyrenees.

Whether we accept the sodic character of spilites as a secondary
feature acquired during the ascension of the magma or see it as a
special differentiation trend of basaltic magma, there is in neither case
any objection to the supposition that the origin of the basic magma
must be sought somewhere in the basaltic substratum, which also
furnishes the volcanic rocks of the shields, the flood basalts.

How this magma reserve is tapped, how it is formed, and why it is
different from the later phases of the orogenic magmatic cycles will be
shown in the next section and discussed further in the final chapter.

Syntectonic Regional Metamorphism.   The core of many orogenes
is characterized by metamorphic rocks, which are neither related to
narrow zones of movements nor to aureoles around intrusive rocks,
but are regional in extent.

This regional metamorphism is certainly closely related to tectonic
activity, but it is of a very complex nature. Its study is partially a
petrological problem because the movement is largely expressed by
recrystallization of new minerals, but the movement itself is of para-
mount structural importance.

In the recrystallization processes three factors are of major importance, namely, depth, temperature, and chemical exchange, loss of
water being a major factor in the last.

The metamorphic depth-temperature zoning, in epi-, meso-, and
catazones (Grubemann), or greenschist, amphibolite, granulite facies
(Eskola), expresses roughly the experience that the same process of
tectonization takes on different mineral-facies aspects with increasing
depth and temperature. Above the greenschist facies we find the
transition from schistose rocks to cleaved rocks and from cleavage
folds to concentric folds, or in other words, from phyllites to slates
and from slates to shales. As long as the original bedding has not
been completely destroyed, the characteristics of cleavage folding
can be traced down into the phyllites and mica schists, but in general,
when feldspars appear, the complete recrystallization obliterates all
vestiges of bedding. Nevertheless, the direct and complete connection
between the cleavage folding of the upper layers and the deformation
of gneisses and other completely recrystallized rocks at depth can be
ascertained with the help of lineations which are evident as bedding-
cleavage intersections and microfold axes in the higher levels and
which can be followed downward by the occurrence of crystal-growth
lineation far down into the linear gneisses. It is the parallelism of these

lineations which convinces us that the different deformation processes near the surface and at depth are contemporaneous.

The regional metamorphism is a complex process, and in general terms two succeeding phases can be distinguished: first, a synkinematic phase and later a static postkinematic phase (Misch, 1949) or a late-kinematic phase related to a new stress field. The first synkinematic phase can be correlated from surface to depth, but the late kinematic phase is much more difficult to trace upward. The latter is characterized by recrystallization of new minerals, most often nonoriented, andalusites, for instance, and by a coarser fracture cleavage cutting the first schistosity. This secondary fracture cleavage may develop into a secondary axial-plane folding, a cross-folding. Traced downward into the gneisses, the same secondary movement has been proved to be connected with the granitization process and with rock flowage (Zwart, 1960a and b). In a more advanced stage these secondary folds may become visible in the outcrop as microfolds. Stronger cross-folds of the same size as the primary ones have been described from Scotland (Sutton, 1960; Sutton and Watson, 1959). In other cases this secondary folding becomes so strong that it dominates the whole structure. Examples have been described from Finland, Greenland, and Canada, mostly in the shape of large migmatite domes (a good summary of these structures is given in Kranck, 1957, with literature; see also Haller, 1956). In these structures the migmatites have become mobile and have influenced the structure to a large degree. Wegmann (1935) has described their action as a kind of diapirism, a notion which has won wide acceptance.

This most intensive stage of tectonization proves that granitization and migmatization are connected with the secondary folding, a fact which has also been convincingly demonstrated in a much less advanced stage in the Pyrenees by Guitard (1955) and Zwart (1960a and b). There it has been observed that wherever nonoriented recrystallization of feldspar and mica occurred in the linear or planar gneisses of the first stage, it was always accompanied by a new disturbance on a small scale. In some of these pockets of recrystallized nonoriented rock the random orientation of gneissic or schistose inclusions or xenoliths proves that this disturbance can develop into flow. This phenomenon has been called "rheomorphism." Whereas in the upper sheets of gneisses the micro cross-folding shows a distinct orientation, the cross-folding in the lower reaches tends to be non-oriented and the rock looks more like a stirred porridge. Such transition from oriented structures to flow with increasing temperature is in perfect accordance with theoretical considerations.

The principal argument in favor of the close relation between the regional metamorphism and the nonoriented quartz-felspar (granitic) rocks with their pegmatites is the fact that the pegmatites and these granites are entirely restricted to the zone of high metamorphic grade; they do not occur in the zones of lower grade. Murawski (1957) reaches exactly the same conclusion on the evidence of the regional metamorphism of the Spessart, which is also characterized by a late phase of metamorphism with nonoriented recrystallization. In complete accordance with Zwart's result in the Pyrenees, Murawski also concludes that succeeding phases of tectonization bear a relation to the succeeding metamorphic events, the later tectonization having a cross-cutting character in relation to the synkinematic schistosity.

From a chemical point of view the synkinematic phase has a mainly isochemical character, although considerable water must have been expelled during mineral changes, such as the sequence of clay mineral-chlorite-biotite-pyroxene. The granitization phase, on the other hand, means an increase of water accompanied by an increase of SiO_2 and alkalies and a loss of Al, Fe, Mg, and Ca (see also Mehnert, 1959). Some experiments under high pressure and temperature performed by Winkler (1957 to 1961) and Wyart and Sabatier (1959) throw much light on this granitization process. Using the same kind of apparatus as Griggs and Kennedy (1956), with shale and graywacke samples, sometimes adding sodium and/or calcium, Winkler succeeded in demonstrating that in each case a portion of the rock was melted at between 685 and 780°C, sometimes as much as two-thirds of the mass, the melt having a chemical composition different from that of the original rock. The melts varied from aplitic to granitic, granodioritic and tonalitic, and thus had a higher Si + Alk and a lower Al-Fe-Mg content. The variation of the melt depends principally on the original sodium/potash relation in the original rock. Another interesting result of these experiments is that the temperature at which a melt was formed differed for different kinds of rock, so that at a given temperature half the bulk of a certain kind of graywacke had been melted whereas another kind was still completely solid. These experiments demonstrate in an admirable way the external features of reomorphism and of migmatitic layering and the origin of palingenetic magmas.

Nevertheless, it is still somewhat difficult to see whence the silica and alkalies needed for granitization are derived.

Both Michot (1956 and 1957) and Mehnert (1959) point out that, in the deepest catazone, we find a process of degranitization resulting in rocks of charnockite, anorthosite, and basic granulite character which can have produced during their recrystallization the elements needed for granitization in higher levels, in the upper catazone and lower mesozone. Mehnert supposes that the high sodium content of these deep-seated rocks is due to their origin as graywacke of Archean age; Michot explains it as a property of the crustal layer below the Conrad discontinuity.

One of the most important conclusions derived from these facts is without doubt that the origin of granitic rocks is located within the sialic crust itself, and not deeper down.

In the Pyrenean Paleozoic it could be proved that the metamorphic zones rise much higher than it was thought possible; the mesozonal rocks are found there at a stratigraphic depth of probably less than 2,000 m, but increased to some 4,000 m by tectonical compression in contrast with the generally accepted 8 to 10 km depth.

This important conclusion about the depth of metamorphic zoning has been confirmed by Mehnert (1959) and proves that regional metamorphism is due to a rising temperature front and not to sinking of a geosyncline. It has been suggested that the pressure needed for certain mineral conversions is due to the tectonic stress field, and not only to the depth of burial.

The structural type also changes with depth in the metamorphic zones. The epizone and top of mesozone have a subvertical schistosity, in which the microstructure and intersection lineation are complemented by mineral-growth lineation, first of biotite and later of feldspars. Deeper down the subvertical schistosity is replaced by a subhorizontal one, with strong mineral-growth lineation (augen gneisses) and new layering of the rocks by a migmatization process.

The relation between the synkinematic and the late- or postkinematic phase and the rise of temperature is variable. In many cases we find cross-folding without any rise in temperature; in others, the second phase had little or no stress but high temperatures, and often the late phase had both high compressive stress and temperature. Whether successive orogenic phases in nonmetamorphic rocks determined by stratigraphical evidence are comparable with the succession of phases revealed by microtectonic evidence in metamorphic rocks still remains doubtful.

The Late-tectonic Intrusive Phase. From the succession of events sketched in the foregoing paragraph it is clear that the development of regional metamorphism leads, by the process of reomorphism, to the formation of palingenetic magmatic rocks, which have a tendency to move upward, to form migmatic domes acting diapirically in relation to their original surrounding and cover.

The intrusive batholiths distinguish themselves from these granitization products in the first instance by their different relation to the surrounding rocks. They are not bound to a distinct level of metamorphic grade, and they are distinctly discordant. Their boundaries truncate older structures, and they are surrounded by a relatively thin thermal metamorphic aureole. The chemical composition of the intrusive granites is also somewhat different; they tend to be less leucocratic and more of a granodioritic character. Both Read (1957) and Raguin (1957) describe this difference in character, and Buddington (1959) has assembled many examples of the mode of occurrence of granite bodies. The earliest ones, those most closely related to the palingenetic process, are without doubt the phacoliths, concordant sheets mostly occurring in anticlinal hinges. Hence they are syntectonic to that folding and sometimes really are replacements and not intrusions. They form the transitional type, belonging to the catazone, or core, of the mesozone and may be regarded as the first, pressed-out products of rheomorphic palingenetic granites. The folds they follow are late-tectonic folds, and they have been emplaced in the zones of least pressure.

The true batholiths may occur in any metamorphic zone, but are most typical of the epizone and higher, where their contrast with surrounding rocks is most striking. They form large or small bodies, stocks and dikes. Careful mapping of the boundary zones generally reveals that they have been actively injected as indicated by small or larger extra folds, deviational structures, and similar phenomena. These cannot, however, explain their total emplacement; their volume is often far too great. As far down as they can be mapped, their sides are steep, going more or less straight down. The principle of overhead stoping, postulating the sinking and absorption of the overlying rocks in the magmatic body, has never been proved for large masses, and in many cases it looks more probable that the cover has simply been pressed upward and has since been carried away by denudation.

A particularly interesting feature has been described by Pitcher (1953) from the intrusive Ross Granite in Donegal, Ireland. The granite is built up of concentric sheets the boundaries of which can be traced on the surface by the slightly different structure and composition of the sheets and occasional thin pegmatitic bands on their boundaries. Evidently, the intrusion did not happen as one event but in successive stages. Similar results have been reported from elsewhere, but in most well-surveyed granite bodies nothing of the kind can be traced. Still, Cloos (1936) has shown that by measuring the orientation of felspars, one can map a concentric flow structure in a seemingly homogeneous granite body, showing it as having steep flow lines on the sides and being flat on the top.

More direct observation can be made on those intrusive stocks which are directly connected with ring dikes and volcanic-cauldron subsidence. These form the transitional type between the late-tectonic intrusive rocks and the posttectonic volcanic phase and are actually later in relation to the orogeny than the normal batholiths, often even intrusive in the posttectonic molasse formation. Intrusions of Scotland (Glen Coe) and the Oslo rift are typical examples. Their intrusion is apparently directly due to stoping and block subsidence.

In the discussions about the intrusive or palingenetic character of granite bodies the "ghost structures" play an important role. In replacement granites, those sedimentary rocks of which the chemical composition is very different from granite simply recrystallize and retain their divergent character; they are the "resisters." Limestones, quartzites, and basic rocks are typical examples. When they still have maintained their original orientation, the granitization has not passed in the reomorphic stage. Nevertheless, typical intrusive granites also carry xenoliths, in particular in their outer shell, and even they can maintain their original orientation.

Posttectonic Volcanic Phase.   The posttectonic volcanic phase either follows the second intrusive phase almost directly or, as often happens, is separated from it by a long period of denudation. The most striking examples of a long retardation of the posttectonic phase are the Permian volcanics of Europe, which are certainly closely related with the Late Carboniferous folding and granite batholiths, as is shown both by the field evidence and by the close resemblance of their differentiation diagrams (de Sitter, 1949). The retardation is here represented by a long denudation period, and the volcanic rocks are deposited on a new peneplain. There are other examples, however, where postvolcanic rocks are directly connected with their own synchronous granites, which then have a more alkaline character, as, for instance, in the late Precambrian of the Anti-Atlas (Choubert, 1952).

These volcanic rocks are very often accompanied by an intricate system of dikes showing all kinds of differentiation tendencies in the magma and are themselves equally variable, but all of them have a calc-alkaline character in contrast with the alkaline character of the nonorogenic type. The volcanic vents are sometimes aligned along a fault, suggesting that late movements tapped magma reservoirs below.

In other instances they are distributed without any appreciable relation to tectonic lines. The difficulty of explaining their emplacement does not lie in their origin or in their location, but only in their high temperature.

When one accepts the view of Turner and Verhoogen (1960) that the batholiths and palingenetic granites never reached temperatures higher than 500 to 600°C, which is certainly strongly corroborated by the structural features of their intrusion, it is difficult to understand how the high temperatures of the volcanic rocks, which reach 1100 to 1200°C, are generated. As has been mentioned, Turner and Verhoogen call it an unsolved problem.

Plutonic and Volcanic Rocks of Continents and Oceans. The occurrence of plutonic and volcanic rocks on the continents, outside the orogenic belts, is much less a structural than a petrological problem, and a short summary will accordingly suffice.

They may be subdivided into three groups:

1. Basaltic rocks of the oceans
2. Flood basalts of the continents
3. Volcanic rocks of rifts

In these three groups the basaltic rocks predominate. Each of the first two groups is far greater in volume than the third. From this world-wide predominance of basalts stems the belief that the primary magma is basaltic and that from such a magma all other plutonic associations are derived.

Basaltic Rocks of the Oceans. In the Pacific, all the noncoral islands consist of volcanic rocks, and olivine basalt is by far the most predominant type. The line that separates the basaltic rocks of this type from the volcanoes associated with the island arcs along its western and eastern margins is called the andesite line, since andesites predominate in this circum-Pacific belt. The line is thought to separate the ocean floor, characterized by the absence of a sialic cover, from the continental border formed by a sheet of sial. The basalts are of the olivine basalt type and show a differentiation to trachytes and phonolites which is generally thought to be due to fractional crystallization of the parent magma. It is noteworthy that the Indian and Atlantic Ocean volcanoes do not differ in any respect from those of the Pacific. Oceanic volcanoes can often be proved to be related to a fracture zone, like those connected with the Mid-Atlantic rift, but in most cases their locations do not show any relation to known tectonic lineaments.

Flood Basalts of the Continents. The flood, or plateau, basalts cover very large regions of the stable part of the continents of today, but definitely belong to a rather late period of their history. They range from the Jurassic to Recent in age. Their chemical and mineralogical composition is slightly different from the oceanic basalts; olivine is much scarcer because the magma is slightly oversaturated with silica, and its rare differentiation products are different from those of the olivine basalts of the oceans. The parent magma is called the tholeiitic basalt magma (Kennedy, 1938). The volume of perfectly fluid basalt expelled from the interior is enormous, far greater than that of any other kind of rock ever produced by volcanism. Through all these thousands of lava streams very little variation in composition occurs, and the conclusion is warranted that they all tapped the same layer, which must be somewhat different from that which produced the olivine basalts of oceanic regions. Because the vents are always covered by the lavas themselves, it is doubtful whether the mode of extrusion is of the fissure type. Nevertheless, their horizontal attitude and their occurrence in undisturbed regions only prove that their upwelling is in principle not a tectonic process; they seem to be strictly bound, nevertheless, to orogenic phases. It is thought that their ascent is induced by gravity because the lava, with a density of 2.7, is less dense than the overlying rock. The flood basalts are thus simply pressed out by hydrostatic pressure. The supply of molten rock at depth must be limited to a certain extent, for after each lava flow, which is often not thicker than 5 m, there follows a long interval during which even lateritic weathering can develop before the next flow covers the weathered ground. The great and unsolved problem is that of the local heat supply, which must repeatedly heat up this particular layer of the substratum to a temperature at which the basalt is fluid enough to be expelled. But this problem is a general problem, equally true for all volcanic activity, whether of oceanic, orogenic, or of continental origin.

Volcanic Rocks of Rifts.   Many volcanic rocks outside the orogenic belts have definite associations with tectonic trends, mostly rift valleys. They are either of the olivine basalt type and its differentiates or of the tholeiitic basalt type, with strong alkaline differentiates (Shackleton, 1954). Apparently the olivine basalt type is not exclusively oceanic in the same way that the tholeiitic basalt is definitely continental. Typical of the continental type of volcanic rocks are the leucite-bearing rocks, but their distribution, often haphazard, shows that their alkaline character must be due to local circumstances. The rocks of the eastern rift in Africa, for instance, are of the olivine basalt type, whereas the western rift shows some highly alkaline rocks, with carbonatites at the extreme end of their differentiation curve.

There can be little doubt that the great rifts provided opportunity for magma to rise to the surface. All along the European-African rift system, volcanoes have arisen, from its southern extremity in Africa to the Oslo region in Norway. The different ages of the volcanics, ranging from Permian to Recent, show the fundamental function of these rifts. It is to be noticed that their time range is about the same as that of the flood basalts.

In the case of the rifts there is some reason to ascribe a special function of magma differentiation to tectonic factors. The rifts are without doubt regions of tension and dilatation, and there is every reason to suppose that at the bottom of the rift valley a region of minimum pressure was created; we can even advance further and suppose that the thinning of the crust at the bottom of the stretched layer caused a flow of rock to this strip of the crust. In this magma chamber considerable reduction of hydrostatic pressure favored melting, and when renewed activity along the faults opened a vent, the magma, which had had time for the operation of fractional differentiation, would yield many different kinds of derivates. Most of the rifts are broad enough to allow their normal faults, even with a dip of only 45°, to reach below the sialic crust into the basaltic layers. Stress periods which occurred occasionally could also add to the upward surge of magma.

The problems connected with magmatic evolution are largely of a petrological nature, but as we have seen, they enter also into the province of structural geology. This, in particular, is the case in orogenic belts, which have received much more attention in this chapter than have the quiet regions of the earth's crust, but even there structural considerations are of importance.

MAGMATIC CYCLES IN THE COURSE OF THE EARTH'S HISTORY

In this chapter we shall learn that the magmatic cycles of an orogenesis have a somewhat different aspect in the older Precambrian orogenic phases from the younger systems. In Scandinavia, where the sequence of igneous events has been followed up most closely, Backlund (1936) and Magnusson (1937) propose the following phase sequence:

1. Primorogenic granites, granitization, and extensive basic and ultramafic volcanic action
2. Serorogenic granites, migmatization, and granitization, with special emphasis on pegmatitic igneous action
3. Postorogenic granite

This compares extraordinarily well with the schematic picture drawn above, principally from evidence from Paleozoic mountain chains. The difference lies in the intensity. Whereas our younger orogenies generally include in their initial phase only a phase of intrusive, and less frequently extrusive, basic and ultramafic rocks, the Precambrian, and especially the Archean, orogenies have extensive developments of volcanics in the geosynclinal stage, including pyroclastics and notably pillow lavas, which may form the predominant rock.

In the more central parts of the orogenies these supracrustal rocks are granitized or are in relation with so-called primeval granites. In the second half of the geosynclinal period the igneous activity diminishes, both in Canada and in Scandinavia. The descriptions of the second phase, with their widespread migmatization, granitization, and gneissification, are only more severe versions, intensifications, of the synkinematic phase of the Paleozoic orogenies already described. Pegmatites are typical of both.

The postorogenic phase embraces mainly granite intrusion and is the same as our postkinematic phase.

The posttectonic volcanic phase has probably been washed away by denudation in the Archean regions—or is represented only in the postorogenic conglomerates, which are also typical of the postvolcanic phase of the Paleozoic orogenies.

I have already drawn attention to the fact that in the youngest Alpine orogenies of the Mediterranean the magmatic cycle appears much reduced. The initial phase is sometimes present, sometimes absent; the synkinematic phase is sometimes absent; the late-kinematic batholiths are much less frequent; and a posttectonic volcanic phase is also very much reduced.

This is true only for the Mediterranean region, and not for its continuation in the Near East—Iran, Caucasus, and Turkey—where the initial phases are very important. Nor is it true for the circum-Pacific region; initial and posttectonic volcanism is very prominent there. The Californian coastal region, for instance, starts with almost as active an initial volcanism in the Jurassic (post-Nevadan) as in the Archean of Canada and Scandinavia, and is even repeated in the Miocene, perhaps as a posttectonic phase of the Cretaceous folding, but more probably as an initial phase of the Pliocene folding. The Nevadan (Late Jurassic) folding is characterized by large syntectonic intrusions and migmatization and immense late-tectonic batholiths. The posttectonic volcanic phase is present in profusion (Yellowstone Park blanket, for instance), but is not easily distinguished from flood basalts of the continental type (e.g., the Columbia Plateau).

The intensity of the magmatic action in orogenies is dependent on the position on the earth's crust, the intensity of the orogenic forces, and the relative age of the orogeny.

Looking back on the evidence we have deduced about the relation between magmatic activity and orogenesis, one fact stands out very clearly, that is, that the early basic-rock intrusion and extrusion is to a large degree independent of the later acid magmatic activity. There is much evidence for the sialic origin of the latter rocks and for the simatic origin of the former. The granitic and associated rocks seem to belong to the continental sialic crust; their origin is probably palingenetic; their distribution is closely tied to the orogenes. The basaltic and associated ultrabasic rocks have their origin much deeper, probably from the low-velocity layer at 60 to 100 km below the oceanic crust and 100 to 200 km below the continental crust. Both in the oceanic and continental regions the rise of basalt to the surface is bound to cracks in the crust, and it seems probable that the longitudinal high-temperature zones which characterize the orogenes have the same origin.

Intrusive granites are of relatively low temperature, and rising into levels of lower pressure, they solidify before reaching the surface. Basaltic rocks have a much higher temperature, and rising into the lower-pressure region, they become even more fluid.

The presumed depth of high metamorphic zones based on laboratory experiments is not confirmed by geologic evidence. It seems probable that, instead of the crust subsiding, the high-temperature front rose in the crust, and that the required high pressure is due not only to great depth, but to tectonical stress as well.

Chapter 30

Characteristics of Orogenes

There are no two mountain chains that are characteristically alike, but many characteristic features occur repeatedly in different mountain chains.

The genesis of an orthotectonic mountain chain consists of a very complex succession of events. In a complete and well-developed orogene the following phases are discernible:

1. Geosynclinal phase, which is not really of orogenic character until in its last stages; nevertheless, the initial magmatic phase belongs to its start. In its last stage the basin narrows and deepens and is characterized by flysch sedimentation.
2. Precursory folding phase(s), accompanied by regression of the sea.
3. Main folding phase, intensive compression, eventually accompanied by regional metamorphism in two stages, synkinematic and late kinematic.
4. Late-tectonic phases, eventually accompanied by pluton intrusion.
5. Posttectonic faulting phase, accompanied by volcanic activities and followed or preceded by aplanation.
6. Posttectonic morphogenetic phase characterized by high upheaval of aplanation surfaces.

Any of these stages can be absent or weakly developed or incomplete, but their succession is never reversed. In many orogenes the metamorphic stages are completely missing; sometimes even one relatively mild folding is followed only by a posttectonic morphogenetic phase, and still an imposing mountain chain with snow-covered peaks presents itself to our admiring eyes.

Besides the variation in style due to the varying intensities of the successive phases, there is the difference in localization of the orogene in relation to continent and ocean, intracontinental or circumcontinental. In a complete orthotectonic orogene four main units can in general be recognized: (1) an axial zone in the center, (2) marginal

412

or external zones on the outsides, (3) the intervening internal zone of complex nature, and (4) the marginal posttectonic molasse basin.

When regional metamorphism accompanies the orogenesis, it is found, certainly in the axial zone, possibly also in the external zones, but not in the marginal zones. It is certainly true that to some extent this subdivision in axial, internal, external, and marginal zones will already have developed in the later stages of the geosynclinal process. The axial zone can be identified with the eugeosyncline, the external zone with the flanking miogeosyncline, the marginal zone with the posttectonic molasse basin. The late geosynclinal flysch deposits can transgress from the axial zone into the external zone, but the great difference is between the earlier axial-zone facies with deep-sea sediments and basic intrusive rocks and the epicontinental facies of the external zone.

The marginal basin, or trough, is decidedly later, and is sometimes missing altogether. I want to emphasize that this general conception of the development of an orogene is very schematic, and in many cases cannot, or can only partially, be applied.

THE AXIAL ZONE

The best-known axial zone is without doubt the *Pennine zone* of the central Alps. It consists primarily of a set of piled-up recumbent folds with their front toward the north and their axis parallel to the main E-W trend of the Alpine structure (Fig. 277). Each nappe consists of a completely recrystallized core of basement rock (pre-Permian, in this case), contained in an also recrystallized Mesozoic envelope. Its recumbent-fold character is established without any doubt by the presence of the enveloping Mesozoic mantle as reentrants between the frontal lobes and the central bodies of the nappes, dividing them into three large units, the upper, middle, and lower Pennine nappes.

Fig. 277 Section through the Pennine nappes in central Ticino. (*After Nabholz, 1953.*)

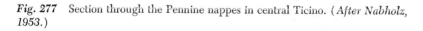

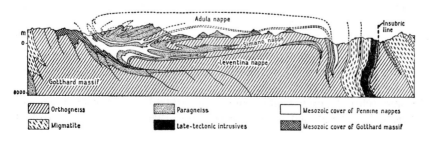

Each unit is built up in its turn by a core of granitic gneiss, locally developed as augen gneiss, and a mantle of paragneiss, within another mantle of Mesozoic phyllites, often accompanied by basic igneous rocks. The paragneiss zone comprises mica schists and migmatites (Fig. 277).

The crystalline core consists largely of the original Hercynian basement, which certainly had already been metamorphosed by the Hercynian orogeny, but had become completely recrystallized again during its Alpine history, possibly also intruded by Alpine palingenetic magmas.

The central core of the Pennine nappes, the Lepontine nappes, as Wenk has called them, undoubtedly shows successive compression phases, particularly well expressed by Wenk's structural map (1955; Fig. 278), which gives us a clear picture of the three-dimensional structure of this Pennine core.

The Lepontine core plunges down, eastward and westward below the higher Pennine nappes (Bearth, 1956), and the structural difference between the two units is emphasized by a 1-km-wide mylonitic zone. The isogrades of metamorphism are not parallel to the present structure, because a late-kinematic and metamorphic phase was superposed on the original flow structure, a phenomenon which can be ascertained by following these isogrades through the Mesozoic cover involved in the flow structures. This nonparallelism of isogrades and structure is a general phenomenon; it has been observed in the Scottish recumbent folds of the Dalradian and in the Pyrenees.

The root zone of the Pennine nappes, this peculiar vertical, very much compressed zone, which in the conception of Staub and Argand was originally a zone of flat-lying thrust planes that only later, in a Late Alpine ("Insubric") phase, were put in their present vertical position, has quite another aspect when we regard it—as does Wenk (1953)—as principally the vertical part of the syntectonic granites. Argand's Insubric phase of steepening is in direct contradiction to all the evidence of the Lombardy Alps, where parallel steep thrusts, often even with a flattening southerly dip, occur very frequently and can certainly not be regarded as tilted, older low-angle thrusts. In Wenk's conception the steepness of the so-called "root-zone" is, then, partially due to the steep ascent of the granite gneiss and only partially to lateral compression.

Because we can follow the Mesozoic, probably Triassic, dolomites right from the frontal lobes along the horizontal bottom of a nappe to the "root" zone, where it often appears as a lime-silicate rock, we can be assured that each nappe represents an originally individual dome with its own syntectonic magmatic phase. During its growth the nappe developed as a flow structure. The flow-structure style is

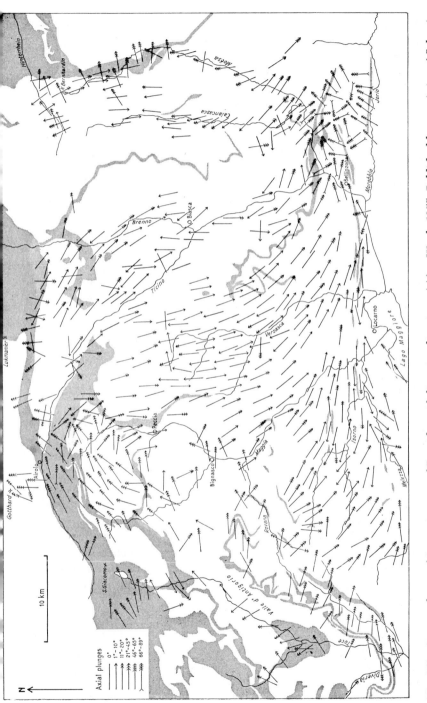

Fig. 278 Structural map of Lepontine core of Pennides with lineation directions. (*After Wenk, 1955. Published by permission of Schweiz. Min. Petr. Mitt.*)

415

emphasized by peculiar steep and highly metamorphosed zones, starting from the "root" but penetrating deeply in between the horizontal
nappes in a N-S direction.

The fact that the supposed Alpine laccolithic intrusions of the
Pennine sheets never intruded the Mesozoic cover need not surprise
us when we recall that syntectonic palingenesis is always restricted to
the appropriate metamorphic zone. This syntectonic magmatic phase
is a typical infrastructure phenomenon, closely connected with the
infrastructural tectonic style of large-scale doming beneath a cover of
tightly compressed superstructure.

Another example worth mentioning is the axial zone of the *East
Greenland Caledonides,* described by Haller (1955–1956). The perfect
and deep vertical exposures on the steep walls of the fjords, penetrating deeply into this continent, afford an exceptionally good insight
into the development of this orogene, which is characterized by a
relatively weak folding of its border zones and a strong, complicated
disturbance of its metamorphic core. There are many conformities between the Lepontine structures of the Alps and the core of this
Caledonide orogene, as Wenk (1956) pointed out.

The main orogenic cycle of post-Ordovician age caused intensive
regional metamorphism, migmatization, and granitization in the core
of the orogene, where the migmatite front reached far up into the
sedimentary filling of the geosyncline from Upper Precambrian to
Ordovician, and the basement became strongly involved in this process. This infrastructure has all the characteristics of flow structure, a
pronounced three-dimensional structure of migmatite sheets, bulges,
and mushrooms pressed out and expanding in different directions (Fig.
279). The isogrades of metamorphism are independent of the original
sedimentary boundaries; they cut across supracrustal folds.

North and south of the central core the migmatite front sinks lower,
and there both the basement and the sedimentary cover acted as
competent thrust sheets.

The boundary between the mobile migmatite infrastructure and the
competent, but still highly metamorphic, superstructure is a detachment plane with strong mylonitization, the same phenomenon as
Bearth found between the Lepontine core and the higher Pennine
nappes in the Alps.

In the two examples of axial zones cited above, there was no great
difficulty in distinguishing the axial zone from the external, or border,
zones. When several orogenic cycles have attacked roughly the same
zone, as, for instance, in the Appalachians, where Taconic, Acadian,
and sometimes Appalachian orogenies occurred, the identification of
the axial zone of any of these tectonic movements becomes difficult.

In the Pyrenees the axial zone of the Alpine orogeny is not quite parallel and certainly shifted to the south in relation to that of the Hercynian orogeny. The Hercynian axial zone is distinctly less intensely deformed than that of the two foregoing examples, although the metamorphic grade goes down to the catazone. Migmatization and late-kinematic granitization (Zwart, 1959) are important phenomena here, but mobilization was very restricted compared with that of the Alps or East Greenland, or perhaps it lies deeper down. Still, there are many resemblances. First of all, the structures are distinctly domelike, and second, there is a definite disharmonic detachment zone between the infrastructure of metamorphic domes with a subhorizontal schistosity and the supracrustal subvertical cleavage of the suprastructure (de Sitter and Zwart, 1960). The metamorphic isogrades, imposed in late-kinematic time, cut across the stratigraphic boundaries. Whether the basement is involved in the exposed structure seems doubtful. Refolding after the synkinematic phase is slight, as can be expected in a region of slight mobilization, but is distinctly bound to the late-kinematic phase.

The same is true in the Scottish Caledonides where the metamorphic zoning is not parallel to the large-scale flat recumbent folding of the mesozonal rocks. Here again we find flat structures in the axial zone, but the refolding is much stronger than in the Pyrenees and the basement was also involved in this structural development (Sutton, 1960).

The same characteristics of refolded regional metamorphic rocks, often originally in recumbent folds, have been reported from axial

Fig. 279   The plastic and diapiric structure of the metamorphic infrastructural core of the Greenland Caledonides. (*After Haller, 1956. Published by permission of Ferd. Enke Verlag, Stuttgart.*)

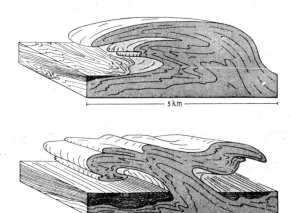

zones of many orogenes. The Appalachians have admirable examples in New York (Pound Ridge area, Scotford, 1956) and in New Hampshire, but as mentioned before, the superposition of three orogenic cycles makes the total picture less clear.

The center of the Scandinavian Caledonides again has the same character of refolded recumbent structures of highly metamorphic rocks (Hernes, 1956a and b; Rutland, 1959; Hollingworth et al., 1960).

A very well described example is the granulite core of the Variscan orogene of central Germany, the granulite mountains of Sachsen (Behr, 1961). Again we find a core of catazonal character with basic and ultrabasic rocks (Rost, 1961) and several succeeding deformation phases separated from its schist cover by a mylonitic zone.

Many more examples could be cited, although the study of the structural deformation of the highly metamorphic rocks is still in its infancy, but some characteristics of these infrastructures emerge clearly.

Very typical is the high mobilization which can accompany the late-kinematic granitization resulting in diapiric action of migmatites leading to three-dimensional structures. With less mobilization there still remains strong or weak refolding of the synkinematic gneisses and schists. This mobilization often leads to domelike structures, which are typical of the basement rock. Kranck (1957) assembled some very good examples from Finland and Canada.

Often a distinct mylonitic detachment zone develops between the mobilized core and its more competent cover or between the typical recumbent folds with subhorizontal schistosity of the core and the subvertical cleavage or simple vertical folding on the suprastructure (de Sitter and Zwart, 1960; Brace, 1958).

The late-kinematic metamorphic zoning is independent of the stratigraphical succession, and the basement, as well as the geosynclinal sediments, is often involved in the structure, both in the metamorphism and in the deformation.

THE EXTERNAL ZONE

In the classic conception of the geosynclinal development the eugeosyncline is flanked at least at one side by a miogeosyncline filled with sediments of a shelf facies of limestones and shales. The eugeosyncline and the miogeosyncline are separated by a ridge. During the structural development of the orogene the miogeosyncline, lying on the continental side, develops as a folded and overthrusted supracrustal fold belt, the internal zone; the ridge as a narrow upthrusted zone. The kind of structures formed in the miogeosyncline or external zone depends on the intensity of the compression, but the most typical ones are asymmetric folds developing into the helvetic type of nappes and, in their simpler form, the flat overthrusted anticline. They are well developed in the Valley and Ridge province of the Appalachians, in the Caledonide front in Scandinavia, in the Alps, and also in the southern slope of the Cantabrian Mountains.

The Valley and Ridge Province. This province is characterized by a complete series of Paleozoic rocks, some 10,000 to 13,000 ft in total thickness, of which the lower half up to the Lower Ordovician is of the carbonate-shelf type and the upper half of clastic rocks. Its western front, a distinct tectonic line, separates it from the Appalachian Plateau, the unfolded continuation of the geosynclinal shelf of the Appalachian geosyncline, of which the Valley and Ridge province is the folded part. All Paleozoic formations thin out westward (cf. Chap. 1, Fig. 1). There is no distinct break in facies or thickness of the sediments in the Appalachian front line. The eastern limit of the Valley and Ridge province is again a tectonic line only; the original miogeosyncline was separated from the eugeosyncline by a ridge, the later Blue Ridge, but the absence of younger Paleozoic in the Blue Ridge province prevents a closer comparison. An account of the Valley and Ridge province by J. Rodgers (1953a and b) gives an excellent description of the Tennessee section. Along the whole length of this section of the Appalachians we find a number of parallel thrust anticlines which remain constant over vast lengths, for hundreds of miles. Their consistency is due to the absence of axial plunging and of any cross-folding or faulting, and this phenomenon is itself due to the unchanging facies and thickness of the sedimentary sequence in a direction parallel to the basin axis. In the northern part of the province, where the Ordovician-Devonian sequence is thick, folding predominates; in the southern part, with a much thinner section, the flat overthrusts prevail. Although some disconformities can be discerned, as a whole the sedimentation was remarkably uniform between two major unconformities—at the top of the Precambrian and at the top of the Pennsylvanian or within the Permian Period. The Taconian and Acadian orogenic periods are represented by only slight disconformities or local slight nonconformities, increasing in importance toward the NE, and by the break in the sedimentary succession above the Lower Ordovician.

The parallel thrust folds are all characterized by low-angle thrusts, always following some incompetent bed in the Middle Cambrian, and by the total absence of any trace of an inverted flank. Consequently, the Precambrian and Lower Cambrian up to the Rome Formation (Middle Cambrian) are seldom exposed. As King (1950) and Rodgers (1950 and 1963a and b) point out, these significant facts lead to the same conclusion as Buxtorf (1916) drew for the Jura Mountains: that the folds are superficial folds, disharmonically folded on the basement. This conception is all the more probable when we take into consideration that in the Blue Ridge province and in the windows beneath the marginal thrusts of this province over the Appalachian folds, this same basement, including the Precambrian and Lower Cambrian, comes to the surface. Evidently the superficial sequence is stripped of its basement in the Blue Ridge too.

The low-angle thrusts reach great width, particularly in the frontal northwestern area. The Pine Mountain thrust (Fig. 243) and the Sesquatchie anticline are the most spectacular examples of the mechanism of these thrusts, and it seems quite natural that the thrusts of the center of the basin had similar horizontal extension in cross section before the top of the folds was eroded away. A peculiar character of these thrusts is that the width of thrust is very large, perhaps up to 20 miles, whereas the actual slip is not more than 4 or 5 miles.

The Helvetides. In the Alps we also find a miogeosynclinal development of the Mesozoic in a zone north of the eugeosyncline, separated from it by a ridge, the present Gotthardt massif. The basin deepened asymmetrically, and therefore a thicker sedimentary sequence was deposited in the south, very much like the Appalachian miogeosyncline. During the first folding, flat thrust sheets developed from asymmetric anticlines, where each thrust plane found its own basal detachment horizon. In the frontal ones the thrust sheet went down to the base of the Permian; in the central one it stayed below a Jurassic limestone; in the back it found its place below Cretaceous limestones (Chap. 18, Fig. 185).

The thrusting was quite strong, and the sheets were probably piled upon one another. In a later stage compression became associated with an upheaval of the back part, and the whole series of nappes glided down and over its original front, the Aar massif (Fig. 186).

The Eastern Front of the Caledonides. On the eastern border zone of the Caledonides a complicated set of very flat thrust sheets have developed in the Eocambrian-to-Ordovician sequence. The northern part has been described by Kulling (1955), the part in Jämtland by Asklund (1938), and the whole region in the description of the general map by Magnusson et al. (1960).

The structure is certainly very much comparable to the ones discussed above: the stratigraphic sequence is thickening westward toward the center of the orogene, and the thrusts are directed outward, advancing over the Fennoscandian shield. The uppermost western nappe, the Seve nappe, consists of metamorphic rocks, possibly indicating that axial-zone rocks have taken part here in the frontal-zone thrusting. Numerous quartzite klippes in the most frontal zone in Jämtland are witness, perhaps, of gravitational gliding in the last stage of emergence of the axial zone. The thrusting itself seems to have developed in several stages. The lowermost easterly nappes are found in the Cambro-Ordovician and are little thrusted; the middle and higher ones come from a greater distance.

Many other examples of external zones could be mentioned, some with nappe structures, some with simple thrusts, e.g., in the Ionian zone of the Hellenides (Aubouin, 1959), some with relatively simple folding, e.g., the Rheinische Schiefergebirge (Hoeppener, 1955). Nearly always one can follow a sequence of tectonic movements, either by an analysis of subsequent cleavage phases or by refolding of nappe structures, as, for instance, in the Cantabrian Mountains (de Sitter, 1962b) or by later gravitational gliding. The movement is always directed outward toward the continental platform or adjoining block, oceanic or continental.

THE INTERNAL ZONE

The internal zone represents the original ridge between the eugeosyncline and the miogeosyncline. It has been well defined in several instances—the Alps, the Appalachians, the Hellenides—but often it cannot be identified, for instance, in the Caledonides or Pyrenees.

The Blue Ridge Province. The rocks of the Blue Ridge province belong to the older section of the Paleozoic sequence from Lower Cambrian downward, are nonfossiliferous, often volcanic, and have consistently a slaty cleavage or marked schistosity. The great difference in altitude of the stratigraphic sequence between the Blue Ridge province and the Appalachian folds is often, though not always, marked by high- or low-angle faults on their boundary. At many places the younger Paleozoic rocks of the Blue Ridge have overridden their foreland, the Appalachian folds, with small nappes which invariably show some of the typical characteristics of gliding structures. The thrust plane plunges down from the high altitude of the Blue Ridge uplift and emerges again farther to the west (Fig. 280). Further, the thrust sheets have no great lateral extension, but each has its own individuality, and many consist of several superposed slices. Apparently the thrust planes have been bent again after the emplacement of the nappes.

In the northeast, the Blue Ridge has the appearance of an imbricated geanticline with a core of migmatites and flanks of Precambrian volcanics and clastic rocks. In the southwest, the Upper Precambrian becomes much thicker and is of sedimentary origin.

The character of the Blue Ridge deformation is everywhere of the schistosity-cleavage type, accompanied by migmatization in the lower reaches of Precambrian. Its great difference from the structural type

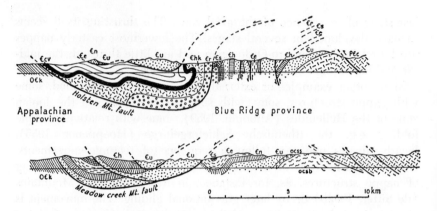

Fig. 280 Thrusts, perhaps gliding nappes, in Tennessee in front of the Blue Ridge. (*After Rodgers, 1953a. Published by permission of the Department of Conservation, Tennessee.*)

of the Appalachian folds may be due to several influences, of which the fact that it was affected by both the Taconian and Acadian orogenies is the principal. Its boundary with the Valley and Ridge province has been called the "tectonic front" by Cloos (1953) and is characterized by strong lineation in a direction perpendicular to the general fold axis. South of this front Cloos distinguishes the South Mountain fold (Cloos, 1947b; Chap. 6, Fig. 43). The structure of the Blue Ridge zone is much simpler in the north than in the south (Fig. 280).

In the central Alps the internal zone is represented by the strongly tectonized Gotthardt massif, originally forming the ridge between the eugeosyncline of the Pennines and the miogeosyncline of the Helvetides. Aubouin (1959) distinguishes in a much simpler form a ridge between two similar basins in the Hellenic orogene. In many cases a similar internal zone cannot be recognized, either because it never existed as a submarine ridge or because the later tectonization did not develop it as a structurally distinctive unit

When the orogene is subjected to several orogenic periods like the Appalachians or the Pyrenees, its significance also is changed. The older orogeny in the Pyrenees affected only the core of the mountain chain, and the Mesozoic basin developed outside this core as a miogeosynclinal basin. The boundary zone between this basin and the Hercynian core has the character of an imbricated internal zone (called the Nogueras zone in the southern Pyrenees), but here its character is not determined by its function as a ridge between a miogeosyncline and an eugeosyncline, but by the structure of the superimposed Alpine deformation.

THE MARGINAL ZONE

The prototype of marginal zone is no doubt the Molasse basin of the northern Alps. It is a post–main-orogenic-phase basin, filled up with the erosion products of the emerging folded orogene (Chap. 23). Its structure is very simple (Fig. 281) because it is posttectonic. It is a curious fact that apparently the formation of a posttectonic marginal trough is not essential at all to the development of an orogene. It is missing altogether, for instance, on the front of the Scandinavian Caledonides, and even the Alpine Molasse basin wedges out westward where the Jura Mountains merge with the Helvetides. In other cases, as, for instance, in the southern Pyrenees, a Mesozoic miogeosynclinal basin (Tremp basin) has the function of a marginal basin in relation to the Hercynian orogene, but is certainly not comparable with the Molasse basin. The Oligocene molasse of the Alpine Pyrenees lies directly and unconformably on top of the inner margin of this basin. One could postulate that the Californian coastal basins and ranges are a folded marginal trough in relation to the Nevadan orogeny, but here also it is not correct to stamp them with the name of molasse basin. They have the same relation that the marginal Tremp basin has to the Pyrenees, and the Appalachian miogeosyncline has to the Taconic Piedmont province.

Fig. 281 Section through Molasse basin of the Alps. (*After Schuppli, 1957. Published by permission of Schweizerische Geotechnische Kommission, Zürich.*)

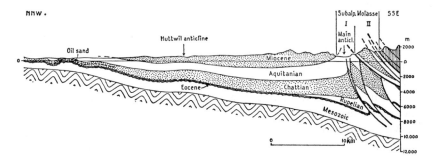

Chapter 31

Some Orogenes with Divergent Character

In order to show how completely high mountain chains can deviate from the pattern as it has been described in the foregoing chapter, I propose to present here a brief description of a few mountain chains with which I am personally familiar, the Pyrenees, the High Atlas, and the Cantabrian Mountains. The first two are of the intercontinental type, but this fact is not the only determining factor in the divergence of their character, because other intercontinental orogenes, like the Urals, are in much closer conformity with the general concept.

THE PYRENEES

The Pyrenees are essentially a Hercynian orogene reactivated in the Alpine Period. Its present configuration has been determined by the Alpine folding and uplift.

In the Pyrenees the Hercynian structure is exposed over large areas and can be studied in detail because the degree of camouflage by metamorphism is low.

We can distinguish (1) a central, or axial, zone consisting almost exclusively of Paleozoic rocks, (2) a northern and southern external zone separated from the axial zone by an important fault zone, the North and South Pyrenean fault zones, and characterized by folded Mesozoic rocks surrounding domes of Paleozoic series, the so-called satellite massives, and (3) sub-Pyrenean zones, marginal basins in relation to the Hercynian core, but representing true Mesozoic basins and not posttectonical marginal molasse basins. They are filled with Mesozoic to Eocene sediments and are strongly folded by the Late Eocene (Pyrenean) folding phase along their contact with the exter-
424

nal zones, a folding dying quickly outward toward the continental blocks north and south of the orogene.

Thus the Pyrenees present themselves as a more or less symmetrical structure with a Hercynian core and a Mesozoic mantle passing into Mesozoic marginal basins (Fig. 282).

The Hercynian structure of the Pyrenees needs some elaboration if we are to obtain a clear picture of this mountain chain.

The Paleozoic rock sequence can be divided into two portions, a lower sequence of Cambro-Ordovician age and psammitic character and an upper sequence reaching into the Upper Carboniferous, mostly of a shale-limestone character. The top of the Ordovician carries locally thick conglomerates and thick limestones of limited extension, indicating epeirogenic Caledonian movements. A magmatic phase of volcanic rocks has been found in the Cambro-Ordovician only in the east (Guitard, 1958) and is elsewhere perhaps present in highly metamorphic rocks. The whole of the Cambro-Ordovician of perhaps 3,000 m thickness has a neritic character. The Silurian, with its widespread thin black graptolite schists, represents a very quiet period, deposited over a much larger region than the Pyrenees themselves. In the Devonian the approaching Hercynian orogeny is already proclaimed by greater facies differentiation in a horizontal direction, indicating the splitting up into a whole set of longitudinal basins. In the Lower Carboniferous the center of the chain had probably already partly emerged.

The orogeny started after the Upper Devonian and reached its maximum somewhere in the middle or toward the end of the Carboniferous.

A synkinematic magmatic phase is very well represented by domes of regional metamorphism, which are much more widespread in the east and north than in the west and south. The metamorphism goes down into the top of the granulite zone and is characterized by a synkinematic phase of augen gneisses, mica schists, and phyllites, followed by a late-kinematic phase with migmatization and granitization in leucogranites. The first phase is isochemic with loss of water; the second phase shows addition of Si and certainly of water. By reomorphic processes it leads finally to the late tectonic phase of plutonic intrusion of large and small granodiorite stocks.

The synkinematic regional metamorphism nowhere goes higher than the top of the Ordovician, but this has the consequence that the deeper mesozone was formed beneath a cover of not more than 2 km of younger rocks.

The late-kinematic phase penetrates locally into the Devonian, proving that the whole process is Hercynian; the granodiorites penetrate into the Carboniferous. The late-kinematic phase is accompanied

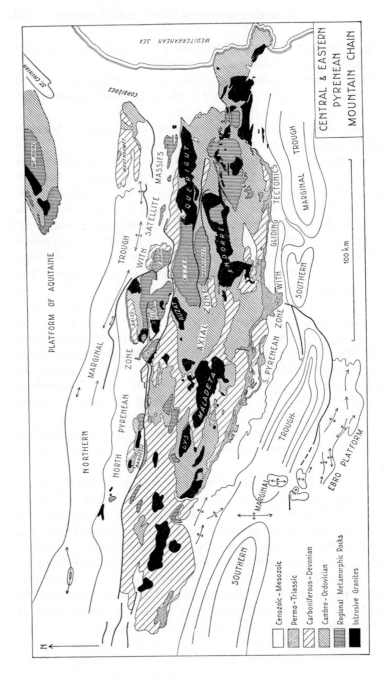

Fig. 282 Map of the central and eastern Pyrenees.

426

by rock flowage in the deeper parts and cross-folding in the higher parts; the intrusive phase, by flexuring and faulting in the phyllites and nonmetamorphic rocks.

The posttectonic volcanism is known to exist in the uppermost Carboniferous discordant cover, in particular on the south flank.

The synkinematic magmatic phase is particularly suited to our study here because it is restricted to a previously undisturbed formation, the Cambro-Ordovician, which was also not seriously disturbed by any later Alpine diastrophism. In the central axial zone we find several large domes of metamorphosed Ordovician, forming large flat bodies of granite gneiss, in its thickest part developed as an augen gneiss with large porphyroblasts of felspar, in between migmatite or mica schists. The original structure is sometimes rather disturbed by refolding on its margins by Alpine compression, but this latter deformation is mostly restricted to two large fault zones, the North and South Pyrenean faults, and confined to a steepening of the flanks of the axial zone. Two somewhat schematic cross sections (Fig. 283) show the main structural features.

The schistosity of the augen gneiss is often very pronounced and always parallel to its roof and therefore subhorizontal over large distances. The origin of this lamination must be sought in the combined action of flow and folding along concentric arched planes.

Small bodies of the late-kinematic white granite are almost invariably concordant in the host rock; their pegmatites are mostly concordant sills, but sometimes discordant dikes. Somewhat later intrusions of small bodies of the same white granite in a fine-grained facies are discordant; these, too, often grade into pegmatites.

The white granites never rise above the upper limit of the Ordovician.

The folding of both the Ordovician and the younger Paleozoic rocks up to the Devonian is of cleavage type, sharp and with very numerous small folds, steeply plunging anticlinal and synclinal axes, all combined in synclinoria and anticlinoria and cut by many longitudinal faults, of which some are late tectonic, even subsequent to the late-tectonic granites, and some have been rejuvenated in the Alpine cycle. The Silurian slates act as a detachment and lubricating horizon, so that folds of the Devonian are apt to be independent of the Ordovician structure, particularly where the latter formation occurs in its metamorphosed state.

The North Pyrenean fault cuts obliquely through the E-W trend of the Paleozoic structure. It had perhaps an important horizontal movement from east to west, which is suggested by the displacement of the cutoff parts of some of the late-tectonic batholiths. At the same time the northern block was folded in broad waves which accentuated

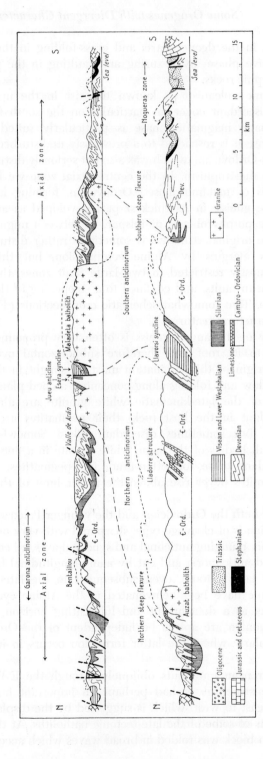

Fig. 283 Two sections across the central Pyrenees.

the uplifts of the migmatized domes, and the domes were separated by other tear faults. Thus basins were prepared for the later Triassic sedimentation, and there were uplifts which were only gradually covered by transgressing younger Mesozoic sediments.

The Alpine orogenic period comprises two major phases in the north, an older phase between the Lower and Upper Cretaceous and a Pyrenean phase (post-Lutetian).

It is doubtful whether the axial zone was ever covered to a large extent by Jurassic or Cretaceous sediments; the only Mesozoic remnants we find belong to the Triassic.

The Triassic has everywhere a continental facies; the Jurassic is incomplete but marine; the marine Lower Cretaceous is thicker and of some importance in the northern and southern zones. The axial zone was never a geosyncline in the Mesozoic; on the contrary, it maintained the geanticlinal character it acquired from the Hercynian folding.

Its emergence, which started before the Cretaceous folding, caused marginal troughs to be formed at both its flanks; these remained narrow, however, and had more of a shelf character than a typical geosynclinal sedimentation. The Cretaceous folding, which was not strictly parallel to the Hercynian structure, accentuated the North Pyrenean fault zone and the emergence of the axial zone. It shoved the marginal basins farther outward. The Pyrenean folding affected the marginal basins of both flanks, principally near the central zone, but had no influence or very little on the axial zone.

The Hercynian orogeny had an E-W strike, but both Alpine phases show a WNW-ESE trend, roughly parallel to the Late Hercynian North Pyrenean fault (Fig. 104, p. 162).

The North Pyrenean zone, with its domes and their migmatized cores, was severely compressed in the Cretaceous phase, a compression which was localized mainly along the front of the axial zone. The lower Mesozoic series became pressed in a narrow and vertical syncline between the axial and northern Pyrenean zone. This rejuvenated fault zone also became the site of ultrabasic to gabbroic intrusions and of large-scale intensive metasomatism of the scapolitization type in the Lower Cretaceous limestones.

The Pyrenean phase principally affected the marginal basins of the Cretaceous phase. It threw up the southern margin of the North Pyrenean trough in very long and rather sharp folds, often accompanied by thrusting, and threw down the center of the trough. The southern Mesozoic zone was strongly compressed, and numerous small gliding nappes slipped down from the uplifted axial zone; some of these have been described in Chap. 18.

After this last orogenic phase came a long period of denudation, creating enormous fans of conglomerates and sandstones at both sides of the central chain. The present lofty position of the central zone is due to discontinuous emergence in the Miocene and Pliocene.

The Alpine structure of the North Pyrenean zone is very much like that of the southern Alps. Large domes of the Hercynian basement, separated by steeply compressed strips of Mesozoic rocks leading down in steps to the Aquitanian plain to the north, are characteristic. On the other hand, neither large thrusts nor large gliding nappes have been mapped. The southern Mesozoic zone has several small gliding nappes and has the peculiarity that the thick subhorizontal Oligocene conglomerate blanket dips a few degrees toward the center of the mountain chain. Evidently, a collapse of the axial zone preceded the youngest upheaval.

There are some salient features which should be emphasized. First, an individual Pyrenean basin did not develop until after the Silurian and shows a graywacke-turbidite facies only in the Upper Devonian of the central axial zone and of only some 50 to 200 m in thickness. There never was a real Hercynian eugeosyncline. Immediately after this short-lived deepening of the basin, the first emergencies and foldings occurred. Nevertheless, the succeeding metamorphism is of the classic kind, complete with syntectonic, late-tectonic, and post-tectonic magmatic phases. Second, in the Hercynian structure we can distinguish between an axial metamorphic zone and nonmetamorphic external zones, but their tectonical style is not so different. It is true that in the center the cleavage is vertical and flattens outward, but the flattening is late tectonic. Third, refolding and cross-folding are common in the whole Hercynian structure, but a simple NE-SW or N-S striking concentric folding preceded the main-cleavage folding phase, so that the whole Pyrenean chain probably looked like a paratectonic folded basin before this principal compression set in.

Finally, it is very striking that the successive stage of basin development and folding phases all moved from the center outward after the Devonian and up to the Miocene. In this case the Hercynian and Alpine orogenic periods are connected logically and in space. In other instances the younger period seems to be to a large degree independent of the older one, as in the Cantabrian Mountains, for example.

THE HIGH ATLAS

The High Atlas (Fig. 284) is situated on the border of the Old Sahara shield, which, except for the mild arching of the Anti-Atlas, its marginal zone, has been extremely quiet since the Precambrian. The High Atlas zone has a Hercynian history of some magnitude, not parallel

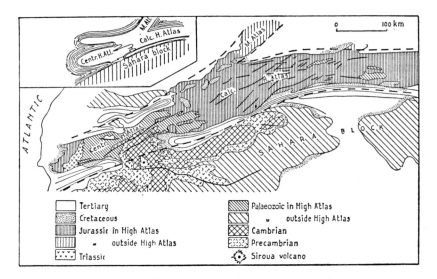

Fig. 284 Structural sketch of High Atlas Mountains.

to its present structure, but its Mesozoic history is extremely simple. During the Lias and the Dogger a broad strip along part of the Sahara shield border sank and a thick series of limestones and marls accumulated upon a blanket of continental Trias. A slight marginal trough was formed between this geosyncline and the Sahara shield after a mild Pyrenean folding phase. Figure 110 shows the kind of Jurassic folding it caused in these well-stratified limestones. A very mild post-Miocene folding, with here and there a slightly different direction, gave rise to some interesting features of cross-folding (cf. Figs. 192 and 193). In the strike of the folded basin the Jurassic strata wedge out toward the west, but not the uplift, with the result that, at the meridian of Marrakech, the chain becomes nothing other than upwarped Hercynian structure of the type of the axial zone of the Pyrenees, with the big difference that here the Hercynian structure is almost perpendicular to the axis of the chain.

Longitudinal faults limit the whole structure to the north and the south (cf. Fig. 88), and other longitudinal faults can be found in the structure, separating subhorizontal, or arched, blocks from folded blocks by a very sharp line. Both its shallow marginal troughs were filled with younger Tertiary sediments, mostly continental. Those of post-Miocene age are unfolded.

A Pliocene unheaval lifted the mountain chain to its present altitude; a similar uplift affected the unfolded Anti-Atlas chain.

Toward the Atlantic Ocean the whole mountain chain plunges

sharply, with the result that along the coast very little of the specific High Atlas structure is left. Its Jurassic and Cretaceous strata are simply a part of the coastal sedimentation area, striking SE-NW, and unconnected with the Mesozoic High Atlas basin. To the east the folds of the High Atlas flatten and the chain merges into the central platform of Algeria, an elevated continental block separated from the Sahara shield in the Early Mesozoic. Between this block and the Sahara shield a Cretaceous basin has developed; this, in the direction of the marginal basin of the Sahara shield, is the continuation of the High Atlas geosyncline.

Thus we find here a real mountain chain which has never been preceded by a geosyncline, warped up independently of the Hercynian structure, exclusively determined by its position as a marginal zone to the Sahara shield. Its emergence is due to a large arching accompanied by faulting.

THE CANTABRIAN MOUNTAINS

South of the deep Bay of Biscay a mighty mountain chain, the Cantabrian-Asturian Mountains, rises up to 2,800 m in the Picos de Europa, consisting of thick Carboniferous limestones. Like the Pyrenees, this mountain chain is a, in Tertiary time, rejuvenated Hercynian structure, where the older and younger orogenic trends are roughly parallel.

The central part of the mountain chain is occupied by a Carboniferous sequence many kilometers thick, partly containing coal measures, partly an enormous limestone development. It is flanked in the north and in the south by structures in older strata, from the Cambrian up to the Carboniferous; even Precambrian is locally present.

The southern zone has been called the Leonides, the central zone the Asturides (de Sitter, 1962). The line separating the two zones, the León line, is very sharp and has acted throughout the Devonian and Carboniferous as a facies boundary and in the Hercynian orogeny as a structural line. It is a curious fact that the present central zone, the Asturides, is a marginal trough, filled with thick Carboniferous sediments in relation to the southern zone, the Leonides. The latter has the character of an external zone with flat, but refolded, overthrusts, thrusted toward the north, toward the marginal trough. The axial zone of the Hercynian orogene can be expected to lie south of this external zone, but if it exists, it is covered now by Tertiary strata of the Castillian meseta.

The present configuration of the mountain chain is then due to a purely fortuitous Alpine deformation of a Hercynian orogeny, exposing the external and marginal zones and concealing the axial zone. Its Hercynian structure does not seem to be a direct continuation of the Pyrenees, and its Alpine folding is separated from that of the Pyrenees by the set of oblique Tertiary folds of the Basco-Cantabrian region.

The three examples of Mediterranean structures described very summarily in this chapter prove that an Alpine deformation can vary from complete independence to narrow conformity with the preceding Hercynian structure; also, that the latest upheaval and arching can be independent of any preceding folding, or even of any geosynclinal development (High Atlas).

Chapter 32

Shields

The structural study of the Precambrian shields is one of the most difficult tasks of geology, because the relative age of their rocks cannot be determined by fossils, but only by comparisons, analogies, and finally by physicochemical age determinations.

A shield is a relatively large part of the earth's crust which manifestly has not been seriously disturbed since the Precambrian. As we shall see, the Precambrian history bears witness to very severe and profound disturbances, and the rigid nature of a shield is therefore only a relative property. The Hercynian blocks of Europe, for instance, which have been severely folded in the middle or final stage of the Paleozoic but have withstood deformation during later Mesozoic or Cenozoic periods, could also be considered as shields. There is a special reason, however, for drawing the line at the end or near the end of the Precambrian and not at a later period, namely, the highly metamorphic state of most of the Precambrian shields; they show phenomena of migmatization and granitization over larger areas and to a higher degree than any Paleozoic orogenic belt.

There is a general notion that the Precambrian shields form the nuclei around which first the Paleozoic and later the Alpine chains came into existence, in concentric zones. We shall have occasion to refer to this again in Chap. 35. This notion, however, needs an important reservation, because the Paleozoic geosynclines certainly had a bottom, often consisting of a Precambrian basement and not of an oceanic crust; and undoubtedly, therefore, a part of the Precambrian shield did *not* resist deformation. As a matter of fact, one might as well postulate the thesis that the present shields are those portions of a much larger Precambrian continent which were not affected by later geosynclines and orogenic belts. And as the Caledonian and Hercynian belts in their original geosynclinal stage were nothing but basins on the Precambrian shield, their folding did not add anything to the shield.

434

Very clear evidence of this reworking of the basement in younger geosynclines is furnished by the Appalachian orogene. In Canada isolated spots, completely surrounded by Paleozoic rocks, have an age, determined by isotope methods, indicating that they belong to the Precambrian basement (Neale et al., 1961). A similar phenomenon occurs on the western border of the Appalachians much farther south, where a transition zone between the 1,100-million-year-old basement and the 350-million-year-old Appalachians has been ascertained (Long, Kulp, and Eckelmann, 1959). Both observations prove that the basement was involved in the younger folding (Gastil, 1960).

The evidence of the true relations between older and younger orogenes has become available through the modern mineral-dating procedures. The principle that a determination of the relative abundance of two isotopes of one element or two elements, one evolving into the other, in a mineral gives us its date of origin allows us to fix the event of the crystallization of the minerals and the rock they make up.

Starting from the hypothesis that a mica or a feldspar from a pegmatite dates the pegmatite, that the pegmatite dates the granite to which it apparently belongs, and that the granite dates the orogene in which it has been intruded, the mineral would date the orogene. The same reasoning applies to a metamorphic rock if that particular analyzed mineral was recrystallized during the metamorphic process of that orogene. Obviously, such assumptions are not always warranted, and one mineral can give a different date from that of another in the same rock. Besides this, there are many pitfalls in the method of analysis, in the stability of the isotopic relations, etc., so that mineral dating is still far from being absolutely reliable. Nevertheless, the results are often so consistent within certain rather wide limits that reliable information has become available for many Precambrian units.

THE CANADIAN SHIELD

In the Canadian shield the age relations have been established by extensive mineral dating, which started in 1932 with Pb/U ratio determinations. At present the results show that the Precambrian shield lying between the Tertiary Canadian Rocky Mountains (60 to 180 m.y.) and the Paleozoic Appalachians (250 to 550 m.y.) consists of several broad belts (Fig. 285), with the oldest in the center (2,400 to 2,700). This central core is flanked by zones of 1,650 to 1,850, 1,250 to 1,450, and 950 to 1,100 m.y. of age, respectively, the last being the Grenville province.

In the center of the shield we find the great depression of the Hudson Bay, whose subsidence started in the Ordovician and con-

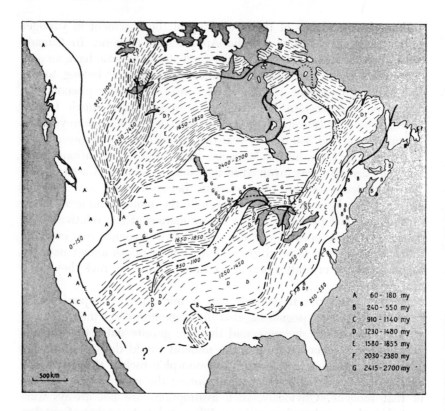

Fig. 285 Mineral province dates of the Canadian shield. (*After Gastil, 1960.*
Published by permission of Berlingske Bogtrykkeri, Copenhagen.)

tinued in the Devonian. On the shield we find large and small patches
of undeformed late Precambrian rocks (Proterozoic), as on the Baltic
shield. They are located south and west of Hudson Bay. As in the
Baltic shield, the provinces in the Canadian shield can be distinguished by the prevailing strike and general nature of the rocks.

By far the greater part of the rocks of the Canadian shield consists
of granites and gneisses, of which little is known. But enclosed in
these igneous and highly metamorphic rocks, there frequently occur
long stretches of slightly metamorphosed, but highly disturbed, sediments and volcanic rocks. Although the strike varies, they can be
grouped by similarity of strike into three large areas. In the southeast,
there occurs a special province with a SW-NE strike, the Grenville
province (1,000 m.y.), which is a true orogenic belt. Toward the
south, the shield is limited by the Huronian orogenic belt (1,250 to
1,480 m.y.), with an E-W trend.

The supracrustal formations of the shield outside the Grenville province fall into two groups, an older Archean group, typified by conglomerates, arkose, graywacke, and slate, and a younger Proterozoic group of quartzite, dolomite and limestone, slate, graywacke, arkose, conglomerate, and iron-bearing formations. Lavas make up a large part of both groups, and they are dominantly of a basic type. They are more prominent in the Archean rocks than in the Proterozoic sequence.

The trend of the folding is given by the stringers of folded Archean rocks in the granite-gneiss basement. At present the pattern of the less deformed Archean supracrustal formations suggests a multitude of oblong, relatively shallow basins, filled with lavas, pyroclastics, and coarse sediments, strongly compressed, highly metamorphosed, and invaded by granite intrusions.

The relations between the three great provinces are in no way clear, and we must not forget that the time intervals of each of these belts is between 200 and 300 m.y., as large as the whole of the Palaeozoic, and could easily include more than one orogenic period.

The detailed structure of the supracrustal rocks is known at many places from underground mining works and is almost invariably of the type in which the internal movement has been concentrated on parallel-plane schistosity-planes. Figure 286 gives an excellent picture of this kind of folding. The anticlinal axis dips here at 70° from the surface to the 3,500-ft level, and below that at nearly 90°.

The fold axes are far from straight, as shown by Fig. 287; the granite intrusions are more or less localized on the anticlinal axes and are bent together with the anticlinal axes of the invaded rocks, indicating several succeeding folding phases.

Taking account of the relatively short distance between the synclinoria of supracrustal rocks, some 40 to 60 miles, Gill (1952) concludes that the crust at the time of the thick lava flows was thin and relatively weak and subject to frequent and rapid deformations in swells and troughs. The resulting narrow mountain chains were less lofty than present ones and more numerous.

The period 1,650 to 1,850 m.y. was particularly favorable for gold mineralizations, and the famous iron deposits belong to the sediments of the Huronian Epoch, also in the Labrador geosyncline, which had its orogenic period 1,800 m.y. ago. Apparently, we are here in the presence of one of the oldest recorded histories of the earth's crust, and it may well be, as Gill supposes, that the nature of earth-crust distortion was fundamentally different then from what it has been since the Laurentian (−1,000 m.y.) Grenville province. The Grenville province, some 200 miles wide, represents a mountain chain trending northeast, and can be followed into the Adirondacks in New York

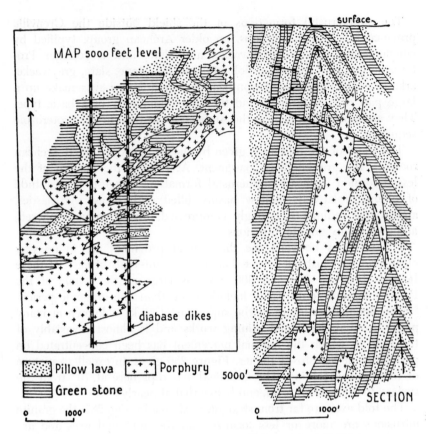

MAP 5000 feet level

N

diabase dikes

Pillow lava   Porphyry   5000'

Green stone

0   1000'

0   1000'

Fig. 286   Map and section of Coniaurum mine. (*After Caster, 1948.*)

State with its particular alkaline rocks. Its pegmatites indicate an age of −1,100 m.y., and its orogeny is named the Laurentian orogeny.

The Grenville orogene, with its broad orthogeosynclinal phase, is in many respects more like a Paleozoic orogene than the older ones.

In the south of the Canadian shield, in the district of the Great Lakes, we find the Huronian chain (1,800 m.y.) unconformably overlain by the Keweenawan Formation. This occurs in a very little disturbed longitudinal basin, with a very thick accumulation of basalts at the base and continental deposits on top. The Keweenawan is roughly contemporaneous with the Greenville, possibly a marginal trough of that orogene. Gabbros and norites occur in lopoliths at its base, and the Keweenawan is famous for its native copper and nickel deposits, related to these basic rocks.

The Canadian shield thus consists of an immense central mass which has been consolidated by a series of orogenic periods older than 1,100

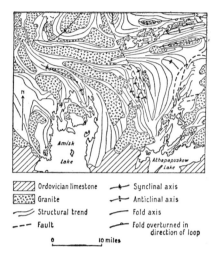

Fig. 287 Geological map of area
round Flin Flon mine. (*After
Stockwell and Harrison, Jubilee
Volume of the Canadian Institute of
Mining and Metallurgy, 1948.*)

Ordovician limestone Synclinal axis
Granite Anticlinal axis
Structural trend Fold axis
Fault Fold overturned in
  direction of loop

0   10 miles

m.y. In each period basins were filled with pillow lavas and other
basic lavas, pyroclastics, and coarse sediments. The sediments were
intruded by porphyries and later by granites and severely compressed
between large granite batholiths. The stress fields of the succeeding
compression periods vary in orientation; and the general character
of the cycles as a whole differs from that of later periods of geological
time, not only in the nature of the sediments, which are dominated
by volcanic rocks and include no limestones, but perhaps also in the
width and distribution of the geosynclinal zones.

THE STABLE INTERIOR OF THE
NORTH AMERICAN CONTINENT

South of the Canadian shield the basement rocks become covered by
younger, mostly Paleozoic sediments. To the southwest these Interior
Lowlands are bordered still by the Appalachian orogene and to the
west by the Rocky Mountains. The transition of the interior shield to
the Appalachians is effected by a gradual thickening of the Paleozoic
strata toward the Appalachian geosyncline (Chap. 1, Fig. 1), and the
same is true when we approach the Rocky Mountains.

The Paleozoic sediments of this stable part of the American continent were deposited in extremely quiet conditions. Individual beds
of only a meter in thickness can often be correlated over hundreds of
kilometers in boreholes. They have never been folded, and the only
movements which took place were of an epeirogenic character, either
positive or negative. In general, the younger layers overlap the older.
The most conspicuous feature is the NE-SW-trending transcontinental

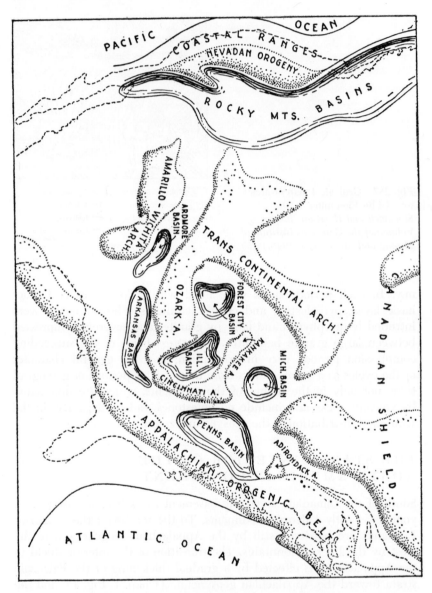

Fig. 288   Tectonic features of the Mid-continent region. (*After Eardley, 1962.*)

arch (Fig. 288), with later cross-arches trending NW-SE. Some of those cross-arches developed into more sharply expressed features, such as the Arbuckle-Wichita belt, and later the strongly compressed Ouachita-Marathon mountain chain. In between these arches, basins have developed, of which the Michigan basin will be mentioned in

Chap. 33. Even after the Late Paleozoic interruptions, the stable character of the shield persisted far to the south, subsiding, it is true, with variations in its subsidence imposed during Paleozoic times, but still essentially stable as far south as the continental slope of the Mexican Gulf in the Caribbean region. Thus we find here essentially the same picture that the Baltic shield presents, a northern region of Precambrian rocks, which are covered by Paleozoic rocks toward the south, showing epeirogenic deformation and remaining stable as far south as the Caucasus and the Balkan region of the Mediterranean.

THE BALTIC SHIELD

In northern Europe, just as in northern America, we find a large tract of land where Precambrian rocks form the surface, and it is only occasionally, in rift valleys, that their cover of younger sediments has been preserved. Since it extends both west (in Sweden) and east (in Finland) of the Baltic Sea, we can call it the Baltic shield.

The Baltic shield consists largely of gneisses and granites, with some less metamorphosed supracrustal formations. The age relations were established by long and patient field work before the advent of mineral-dating methods. When these dates became available considerable difficulties arose in bringing the well-established relations in agreement with the new data. First of all, everything became much older than was thought before, but that in itself is not a major problem. A much greater difficulty arose because the Karelian orogene, which had been established to be younger than the Sveccofennide orogene by an unconformable Karelian basal conglomerate, now became of the same age as its supposed basement, viz., —1,700 to 1,850 m.y. This problem has not yet been solved.

The available age determinations give a picture of the zonal arrangement of the orogenes somewhat similar to that of the Canadian shield (Magnusson, 1960; Polkonov and Gerling, 1960; Kulp, 1961). In the center is the broad Sveccofennian and Karelian orogeny of an approximate age of 1,700 to 1,800 m.y., flanked in the south by a Gothian zone 1,420 to 1,660 m.y. old, and farther west in west Sweden and south Norway a Svecconorwegian zone of 860 to 1,090 m.y. It seems probable that this latter group of age determinations can be split up into two main events, one at 1,100 and a younger at 900 m.y. It is interesting to observe that the great iron deposits of the Sveccofennides are roughly of the same age as those of Canada (—1,800 m.y.) (Fig. 289).

In northern Finland (north of the Karelides) an older basement occurs, with rocks yielding ages of —1,950 to —2,050 m.y. (Belmorides) and even 3,100 to 3,500 m.y. (Katarchean).

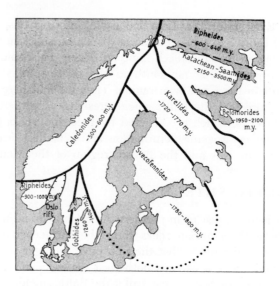

Fig. 289 Mineral province dates of the Baltic
shield. (*After Magnusson, 1960. Published by
permission of Geol. Föreningen, Stockholm.*)

Rocks younger than this strongly tectonized and metamorphosed
basement are preserved, consisting of lavas, graywackes, etc., partly
of Jotnian age, partly still younger, Eocambrian (Visingsö Formation).
Granites and diabases have been intruded frequently in this postorogenic episode.

The probable Jotnian Dal Formation (von Bubnoff, 1952; Magnusson, 1960) west of Lake Vänern is a geosynclinal development with
graywackes, spilites, quartzites, and slates. Even this basin has been
strongly folded, with large overthrusts (Fig. 290).

The Karelides (−1,700 to 1,800, m.y.). The principal part is
located in northeast Finland. The Karelides have a NW-SE strike.
They consist of numerous complex synclinal zones, pressed between
domes and elongated masses of older rocks. The base of supracrustal
rocks, according to Väyrynen (1933), is found in the eastern part of
the Karelian region, where a coarse conglomerate lies on the eroded
surface of older Sveccofennide rocks; the rocks above the conglomerate
consist mainly of arkoses, thick quartzites (700 to 800 m), followed
by dolomites, and then by a thick volcanic series of a basic nature. In
the center of this zone we find a different facies above the thick basal
quartzites, called the Kalevian facies, which is more metamorphosed
and has been intruded by granites. It consists chiefly of phyllites with
ophiolites and serpentines, a typical eugeosynclinal facies. The orogenesis of the system comprises, besides the ophiolitic initial phase,

acid granites, accompanied by strong migmatization and metamorphism, and late-tectonic porphyric granites. Wegmann's (1928) sections show the complicated Alpine type with important overthrusted structures.

The Gothides. In western Sweden we find a region of gneisses with a N-S trend, sharply separated from the younger posttectonic granites, with a series of ultrabasic intrusions along the contact. There seem to be transitions through a form of granite gneiss between the west Swedish gneisses and the Småland granites, and it is supposed that the gneisses are a tectonized facies of the granites. They have their own supracrustal formations of lavas and tuffs of the Åmål Formation, and these are regarded as the equivalent of the Småland porphyries. The line separating the eastern granite region from the western gneiss region is characterized by a strongly developed zone of schistosity (Fig. 291).

With this general picture in mind, it seems probable that the western gneisses, together with their supracrustal volcanic rocks, are an orogenic belt younger than the Sveccofennides and more or less synchronous with the posttectonic granites of the eastern region, which were originally thought to belong to the same orogenic period as the Karelides but have proved to be much younger ($-1,420$ to $1,660$ m.y.). The Gothide orogenesis ended with posttectonic granites (Bohus- and Karlshamm granite (900 to $1,000$ m.y.).

The Dal Formation, mentioned above as a Jotnian basin, is certainly discordant on the Åmål Formation and represents one of the few remnants of the youngest Precambrian geosynclines surrounding the Baltic shield. The Ural Mountains contain a cycle of the same age.

The sequence of events in the pre-Jotnian orogenesis is characterized by a profusion of granites. The supracrustal formations of the geosynclinal stage are largely volcanic, and are connected with their own granites; the syntectonic phase is again characterized by granites, strongly migmatizing the older supracrustal formations; and the posttectonic phase again consists of granites and volcanics, which at the same time forms the initial phase in a peripheral region of the first

Fig. 290   Overthrust over the Jotnian geosyncline of Dalsland, Sweden. (*After Heybroek and Zwart, 1949.*)

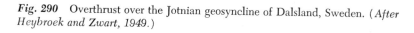

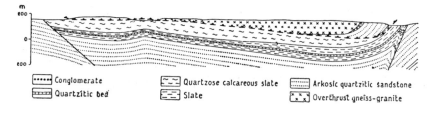

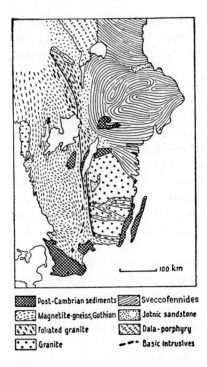

Post-Cambrian sediments Sveccofennides
Magnetite-gneiss,Gothian Jotnic sandstone
Foliated granite Dala-porphyry
Granite Basic intrusives

Fig. 291 The boundary line, marked by hyperite (ultrabasic) intrusions, between the western gneiss region and eastern granite region in middle and southern Sweden.

orogenesis, thus linking the great cycles together in one continuous series of granitization and volcanic activity.

The Sveccofennides (—1,700 to 1,800 m.y.).   The most important Sveccofennian structure is an orogenic W-E belt reaching from central Sweden to southern Finland. It has been thoroughly explored in the central Swedish iron ore belt by Magnusson and Geyer (1944), in Finland by the classic work of Sederholm (1932), and by Wegmann and Kranck (1931).

In the coastal regions of central Sweden the axis plunges sharply eastward into the Baltic Sea and emerges again in Finland. The rock types on both sides are closely comparable.

The Sveccofennide sediments, or Svionic cycle, as Magnusson et al. (1960) call them, start with the leptite formation, mainly pyroclastic rocks and lavas, which can be divided in a lower group with volcanic rocks and limestones and an upper group with graywackes and schists. The iron ores of central Sweden are restricted to this leptite formation. The leptite formation has been strongly granitized and migmatized by the oldest syntectonic granites, mostly forming laccoliths and sills. These granites range from basic to acid types. The folding and granitization were followed by the intrusion of numerous diabase dikes (now amphibolite), along fault systems, and by a new granite phase, of the Fellingsbro-Stockholm potash-granite type, rich in pegmatites. This granite phase has again migmatized and penetrated the surrounding rocks with pegmatites and in Finland forms large batholiths (Hängo granites). This is the serorogenic phase of the Scandinavian geologists, comparable with what we call the syntectonic type of granitization. The more solid and uniform Finnish granites represent the deeper palingenetic state, the Swedish granites being the higher pegmatitic migmatizing state, resulting in streaked gneisses. Still younger are the Philipstad and Småland granites, on the western margin of the Sveccofennides; they are clearly posttectonic and are accompanied by porphyries and pyroclastic rocks.

THE STABLE INTERIOR OF EURASIA
(von Bubnoff, 1952; Schatski and Bogdanow, 1958)

The extension of the Baltic shield toward the south is found in the Russian and North German plains, as far as the Alpine belts of the Alps, Carpathians, and Caucasus. This part of the shield is covered by Paleozoic and younger sediments and has been transformed in the west and southwest and south by many Paleozoic orogenic belts. It really forms a much larger unit with the Siberian shield, which in its turn links up with the Canadian shield. The Russian and Siberian shields are separated by the Hercynian Ural Mountains, which continue northward in the Novaya Zemlya Island.

Between the Scandinavian Caledonides, the Hercynian Urals, the Alpine Caucasus, and the Carpathians, we find a gently undulating plain, partly covered by younger sediments as in the North German plain or still open to surface study as in the Russian plain. These two parts of the plain are separated by a N-S welt, arch, or "anteklise," the Scythian arch, consisting of the Ukraine shield and the Belorussian anteklise, comparable with the transcontinental arch of North America. East of this arch great basins have developed, the Moscow basin, deepening eastward, and the Prikaspi basin (syneklise) in the south. These two large basins are separated by the Volga-Ural anteklise and are connected by a narrow and faulted trough, the Patschelma trough. Westward a broad arch, the Voronesk anteklise, and a long basin, the Ukraine syneklise, containing in the east the Carboniferous Donetz basin, separate these Moscow and Prikaspi basins from the Ukraine Plateau.

In Poland a deep Hercynian trough striking NW separates the Russian shield from the German plain (Sokolowski and Znosko, 1960). It consists of two flexures, or faults, each with a throw of 2 to 5 km. These faults continue toward the NW near the Bornholm Island toward Skåne, the southern county of Sweden. This important line is crossed,

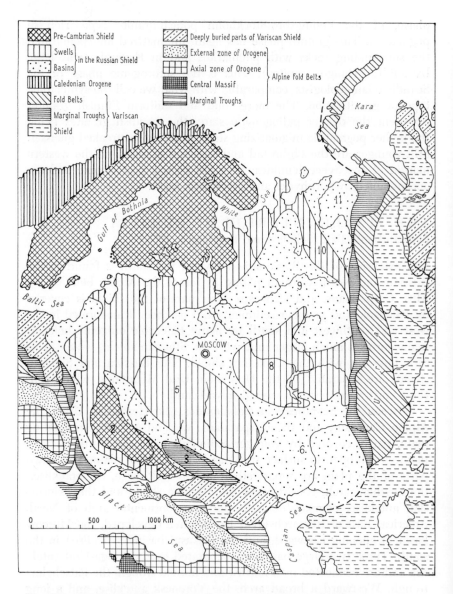

Fig. 292 The Russian Plateau. (1) Caucasus, (2) Ukraine shield, (3) Donetz basin, (4) Ukraine syneklise, (5) Voronesk anteklise, (6) Prikaspi basin, (7) Patschelma trough, (8) Volga-Ural anteklise, (9) Moscow basin, (10) Timan structure, (11) Petschora basin. (*After Schatski and Bogdanow, 1958. Published by permission of Akademie Verlag, Berlin.*)

of course, in the south, by the Alpine structures of the Carpathian Mountains.

Eastward the whole shield is flanked by the marginal trough of the Ural Mountains, but in the north an older structure, striking northeast, the Timan structure, separates the Moscow basin from the Petschora basin (Fig. 292).

The basins have developed more or less continuously during the Paleozoic and Mesozoic, and their depth to the Precambrian basement can become enormous, 10 km in the Prikaspi basin, the thickest series belonging to the Permian-Triassic. The Moscow basin is considerably shallower, only 2.5 km, but has a very complete stratigraphic succession from Cambrian to Cretaceous.

The boundaries between the syneklises and anteklises, basins and arches, are often flexures, or faults, of cratonic type, and the epeirogenic sinking of the basins can be proved to be related to the orogenic movements of the surrounding chains by the stratigraphic development of their sediments. The arches are often believed to be inherited and reactivated Precambrian structures. Although the pattern of the Sarmatian (Russian) shield is different from that of the North American shield, we find the same kind of epeirogenic movements in relation to its surrounding orogenic belts.

THE CENTRAL AFRICAN SHIELD

It is of considerable importance to compare the structural features of two of the great shields of the Northern Hemisphere with those of the Southern Hemisphere; the latter differ from their northern counterparts in that they have remained more stable since the Precambrian. The African shield is in parts better known than either the Australian or the Brazilian shields (Fig. 293).

The characteristics of the older rocks of the Central African shield have been described by Macgregor (1951). "The basement complex of Southern Rhodesia," he writes, "is composed of granites of different ages, enclosing masses of mainly older rocks which were formed at the earth's surface as lavas or sediments. These masses are widely scattered in the granite areas, but they are in the main very similar in their constitution."

The supracrustal rocks of the oldest epoch, the Bulawayan, consist of basic lavas, often pillow lavas, andesitic breccias, and interbedded coarse sediments. They overlie unconformably the older Sebakwian System, which contains ultrabasic rocks intrusive in coarse sediments, migmatized and granitized sediments, gneisses and granites. The Bulawayan System itself is overlain unconformably by the Shamvaian System, consisting of arkoses, graywackes, and conglomerates.

Fig. 293   The African orogenies. (*After Holmes,*
1951.)

The sedimentary rocks of these formations differ from our ordinary
sediments in that they consist predominantly of undifferentiated
arkoses and graywackes and, with a few exceptions, do not contain
clay or limestone. The exceptions are some quartzites and banded
ironstones. This is what one may expect in the oldest Archean sediments, where the decomposition of igneous minerals like felspar,
pyroxenes, and micas, which in more modern rocks has resulted in
abundant clay minerals, produced during a long sequence of periods
of deposition and erosion, has not yet had time to develop. The
granites and gneisses are partly older than the Bulawayan System and
partly younger. The larger batholiths are round or ovaloid bodies, and
the sedimentary systems fill up the "pore space" between them (Fig.
294). The typical triangular synclines of the sedimentary rocks (Fig.
295) suggest that their formation is not so much due to lateral compression as to the vertical rise of the granite masses. Inside the
triangles we find numerous small granite cupolas, often on the synclinal axes, suggesting that the axial planes are potential fault lines,
perhaps of the kind we often find in similar folds. The granite cupolas
could represent either recrystallization of the sediments in zones of
vertical tension on the axial planes or intrusions from below.

The oldest granites have a gneissic character caused by the segregation of biotite in parallel seams between wider lenticles of felspar

and quartz. The banding is parallel with the margins of the larger batholiths. The younger granites are clearly intrusive. The migmatites are very much contorted and do not show preferred directional texture. The logical conclusion from the facts is that we still find the same cycle as we found in Paleozoic mountain chains—early syntectonic migmatization and gneissification and late-tectonic intrusion. The abundance of ultramafic rocks in the oldest sedimentary system, the abundance of pillow lavas and serpentine intrusions in the Bulawayan rocks, and the coarse undifferentiated sediments of the youngest system also suggest one single cycle.

The age determinations of the Shamvaian pegmatites give an average of −2,650 m.y. (Holmes and Cahen, 1955). The Rhodesian region of great age described above is only a tiny patch in the great African shield. In Tanganyika the E-W striking belt of Dodoma is another representative of this oldest group of rocks of more than 2,000 m.y. ago. Much of that shield is covered by the Upper Paleozoic Karroo Formation, subhorizontal everywhere and disturbed only by the faults of the African rift systems. The Bukoban System forms an older, also undisturbed cover, of the older rocks. It stretches from Lake Victoria to Lake Tanganyika and Lake Rukwa. Its age is Late Precambrian, and it has been correlated with the Upper Katangan System. Around the enormous basin of the Congo, a series of apparently Cambrian or Eocambrian rocks comes to the surface, how-

Fig. 294 The structure of the oldest orogenies in Rhodesia. (*After Macgregor, 1951. Published by permission of the Geological Society of South Africa.*)

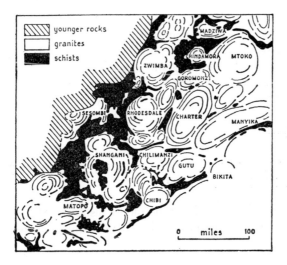

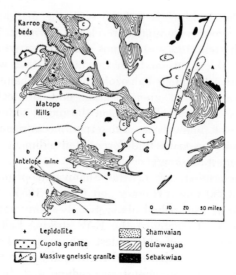

Fig. 295   Distribution of triangular geosynclines between granite masses in the
Bulawayo district. (*After Macgregor,
1951. Published by permission of the
Geological Society of South Africa.*)

ever, and extends into South-West Africa; these rocks have been
studied in some detail by Belgian geologists, mostly in connection with
exploration of the copper, gold, and radioactive minerals of Katanga
and the gold belt of the Great Lakes, east of the Congo basin.

The Katanga System, famous for its rich copper mines in the Rhodesian copper belt and in Katanga, is well dated by the Shinkolobwe
pegmatites. It has an age of $-630 \pm$ m.y., and has been taken as the
limit between the Cambrian and the Precambrian in Central Africa.
The belt to which these pegmatites belong has a roughly east-west
direction and is almost perpendicular to a much larger system, the
Kibara-Urundi belt, the orogenic age of which has been determined
as $-1,200$ to $1,400$ m.y. The Katanga sedimentary series, subdivided
with the use of many local names, ends with well-established tillites,
again showing that an ice age may be expected at the end of an
orogenic period.

PRECAMBRIAN AND YOUNGER OROGENIC
SYSTEMS COMPARED

What we have learned about the oldest history of the earth differs in
many ways, in its structural and its stratigraphical aspects, from our

experience of Paleozoic and Cenozoic mountain chains. The sediments differ in several respects: they tend to be less assorted, graywackes and arkoses are much more important, and limestones become definitely rare and often are altogether absent. This is understandable when we realize that the chemical separation of calcium from the silicates, as with the formation of clay minerals from felspars, is a very slow process. The mechanical separation of quartz from felspar and mica will also become more and more complete when the sediments are reworked by erosion and sedimentation.

The most striking difference from the younger rocks is without doubt the great bulk of volcanic rocks, which are often predominant in any supracrustal rock series.

The magmatic phases, which we got to know as initial, syntectonic, and late-tectonic and posttectonic phases, and of which only the middle ones were characterized by granites, are here all accompanied by granitic intrusion, migmatization, granitization, etc. The curious fact remains, however, that the initial magmatic phase still contains, in its oldest manifestations, the ultramafic rocks which we have already met as the most characteristic feature of this phase in the youngest Alpine orogenies. We are thus confronted from the beginning of the geologic history of our earth by the contrast of the ultramafic and granite rocks.

The folding characteristics do not differ from those we know from younger chains; most of it is of the schistose type, but occasionally we meet purely concentric shapes. Our detailed structural knowledge is, however, very restricted—confined to a single mine or exploration field here and there. The larger belts appear only with the 1,000-m.y. Laurentian orogeny, like the Grenville belt, or the Kibara-Urundi belt. The older ones seem to be much less confined to specific belts; they appear more scattered on a large surface, often with a specific trend as in Canada, but this impression may be due only to insufficient knowledge. On the other hand, we find a certain provisional synchronization of orogenies around the ages of —1,100, —1,800, and older on the several Precambrian shields.

Chapter 33

Basin Structures

THE SEDIMENTARY AND STRUCTURAL PROPERTIES OF A BASIN

The structural history of a basin has been recorded by its sediments during its epeirogenic development and by its structural features during its orogenic periods. Nowhere else is the close relation between the two kinds of development more clearly demonstrated than in folded basins; and no structures are better known, for it is in these basins that oil occurs, stimulating an extensive research reaching to great depth.

The filling up of a basin, geosynclinal or cratonic, with sediments is in itself a complex and peculiar phenomenon. Two factors must contribute, otherwise the mechanism would stop, namely, the sinking of the basin and the rising of land at one or both sides. If the sinking stopped, the sediments would be carried farther away and deposited elsewhere, and if the rising of the land stopped, there would be no further source of material. The fact that so many basins have been continuously supplied with sufficient material to maintain a relatively unchanging depth of the sea within the basin proves that the two motions (downward within the basin and upward at its margins) are so closely related that the sinking and the filling are neatly balanced. This balance is thought to be controlled and maintained by isostatic sinking of the basin as a result of the increasing load of the accumulating sediments and by the isostatic rise of the land as a result of denudation. Isostasy can of course never be more than a controlling factor; the amount of sinking due to loading can never be more than a fraction of the thickness of the load.

The classification of areas with particularly thick sedimentary series into geosynclines and basins is arbitrary. Some basins are clearly subdivisions of geosynclines; others are independent units on a shield. In general, a sedimentary region which is of limited size and not severely

452

folded is referred to as a basin, as outlined in Chap. 1, whereas geosynclines are either themselves folded and uplifted in mountain chains or are closely connected with such mountain building. They are, moreover, of a larger size and much longer than they are broad. Some geologists ban the term basin from their terminology. I prefer to retain it for areas of relatively thick sedimentation without severe folding. Whether they are in close connection with mountain building or not is immaterial. Thus a basin may be a latent minor geosyncline if one supposes that in the future it will be folded into a real mountain chain, and a basin may also have a typical geosynclinal facies of the graywacke type, like the Ventura basin (Natland and Kuenen, 1951).

A basin, like a geosyncline, has a long sedimentary history and usually passes through various orogenic phases, none of them very severe. It might be wholly continental or wholly marine or anything between. In simple basins we can recognize one cycle of sedimentation, starting with a continental facies (transgressive series), followed by the gradual incursion of marine conditions, and ending in another continental facies (regressive series) as the basin becomes shallower again. Its development may be interrupted once or several times by the orogenic phases of a nearby mountain chain, and we are often in doubt as to whether its present state really is its final stage. Usually, its borders shift a little, widening when it deepens and narrowing when it becomes shallower, but in general, the shift of its borders is very restricted, indicating that the subsidence is not due to a rise of the sea level, but is really a sinking of its bottom in relation to surrounding stable or rising borders characterized by much thinner sedimentation.

Some basins are hardly folded at all. Some are folded toward the end of their history. Some are disturbed by folding during the early stages in their development.

In order to get a better insight into their characteristics we shall study some of them in greater detail.

THE SOUTHERN CALIFORNIAN BASINS

The following discussion is based on Reed and Hollister (1936), Reed (1933 and 1943), and the extensive descriptions contained in *California Division of Mines Bulletin* 170, 1954.

The San Joaquin Valley is the southern extremity of the Great Valley of California, situated west of the Sierra Nevada, and is the best known portion of the valley because of extensive exploration for oil (Fig. 296).

The Capistrano embayment with the Los Angeles basin originally made part of the same basin, but was separated from it by the mid-

Cretaceous folding of the transverse ranges, which also created the Santa Barbara embayment and the Ventura basin.

The Great Valley basin is the Tertiary and latest stage of a much longer geosynclinal history. It began as a separate unit in the coastal area of the Cordilleran system, after the Nevadan orogeny in the Late Jurassic. West of this great mountain chain of the Sierra Nevada, with its strong magmatic phases, a new geosynclinal trough developed, filled with uppermost Jurassic and Lower Cretaceous (Franciscan-Knoxville, Shasta, etc.) sediments; these were derived partly from the east, from the rising Nevadan chain, and partly from the west, from a hypothetical island arc which provided the volcanic content of these sediments. The Franciscan is characterized by numerous spilitic lavas and ultrabasic sills, which constitute the initial magmatic phase of the coastal geosynclines. This new coastal geosyncline was not a true marginal trough, because of the uplift and thrusting of the Nevadan mountain chain; as we shall presently perceive, it was a new geosyncline with its own initial magmatic phase and its own stress field. The Upper Cretaceous Chico Formation (Cenomanian and Senonian) derived its coarse sediments from the west and its finer sediments from the east. The axis of the Chico basin is shifted to the east, indicating that a gradual emergence of a western chain was under way (Fig. 296).

Although local unconformities exist between the Tertiary and the Chico Formation, the general picture is a continuation of the process

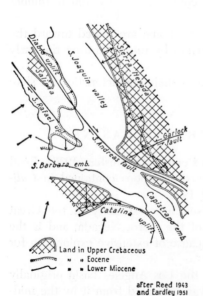

Land in Upper Cretaceous
  "   " Eocene
  "   " Lower Miocene

after Reed 1943
and Eardley 1951

Fig. 296   The development of the Upper Cretaceous–Tertiary basins of southern California.

which started in the Upper Jurassic, that is, a further emergence of the western arc, accompanied by a shift to the east of the axis of the basin.

The Tertiary history of the San Joaquin basin is merely a repetition of its earlier history. A further uplift of the coastal range, accompanied by slight folding at the end of the Miocene, shifted the axis of the Pliocene basin further east and narrowed the basin again. Further folding took place after the Pliocene, and was the strongest since the Nevadan orogeny which originally started the basin. The final stage was the filling up with Pleistocene continental detritus and alluvium, and the trough axis was again shifted farther to the east (Fig. 297).

There is strong evidence of volcanic activity on the Pacific side in the Upper Jurassic and in the Miocene. The supposed Pacific volcanic arc, which at the beginning of this long Mesozoic-Cenozoic history constituted the western margin of the marginal geosyncline of the Nevadan mountain chain, became more and more distant from the center of sedimentation because new territory emerged to the west of it, narrowing the basin and shifting it to the east. The later stages of this emerging coastal chain are preserved in the San Rafael uplift and San Diablo uplift, separated by the shallow basin of the Salinas Valley. The cumulative effect of the three stages of subsidence, separated by minor but clearly defined folding phases in the mid-Cretaceous and post-Miocene, is a fairly symmetric basin, so far as the shape of the basement is concerned. The eastern limit of the basin was the tilting block of the Sierra Nevada, rising in the east, where a large fault separated it from the Cordilleran geanticline, and subsiding in the west (Fig. 297).

The mid-Cretaceous orogeny split the Mesozoic geosyncline into separate basins. We have seen, in Chap. 11, that the San Andreas fault dates also from this orogeny. It seems very probable that the fragmentation of the original basin was due to the deflected direction of stress, now acting from the south instead of from the southwest, giving rise to the San Andreas fault and the transverse ranges, and thus causing the separation of the Great Valley from the Los Angeles

Fig. 297   The shift of the basin axis of the Great Valley, California, from Jurassic to Tertiary.

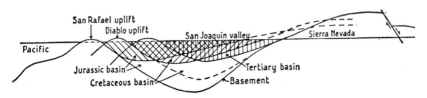

basin (Fig. 296). The Laramide orogeny and the post-Miocene orogeny had the same southerly stress direction.

The east side of the San Joaquin basin is not folded. The thin veneer of sediments on the tilted Nevadan block was protected against folding by their solid basement. The oil accumulations are all determined by unconformities and faults.

In the Los Angeles basin, we find both directions again. The Newport-Inglewood trend is located on a wrench fault parallel to the San Andreas fault (Chap. 19, Fig. 198); the structures of the Los Angeles area all trend roughly E-W; but the Capistrano embayment is parallel and the direct continuation of the San Joaquin basin.

The Santa Barbara embayment and the Ventura basin are purely E-W structures, dating from the mid-Cretaceous. Here the fold axes are parallel to the basin borders. No doubt the extremely thick Pliocene of the Ventura basin, witnessing the rapid subsidence of the basin, is due to this parallelism of the basin with the folding stress and further evidence of the identity of orogenic and epeirogenic stress.

BIGHORN AND WIND RIVER BASINS, WYOMING

Both adjoining basins belong to a row of Cretaceous basins in front of the big Laramide orogeny of the Rocky Mountains. They are a part of the stable inland and are at the same time an integral part of Laramide orogeny in the sense that they represent the direct influence of the orogeny on the shield. Both are surrounded by uplifted areas of the Precambrian—the Bighorn and the Laramie uplifts to the east, the Sweetwater uplift to the south, the Wind River and Beartooth uplifts to the west, and the Owl Creek uplift between the two basins (Fig. 298).

The stratigraphic sequence is built up by four cycles: an older Paleozoic cycle from Cambrian to Lower Ordovician, a younger Paleozoic-Mesozoic cycle from the Devonian up to the Jurassic, a Cretaceous-to-Paleocene cycle, and finally a postorogenic filling with Eocene and Oligocene rocks. The Paleozoic rocks are relatively thin and thicken toward the west; in other words, they represent the epicontinental border of the Paleozoic orthogeosyncline. In the center of both basins the Paleozoic section is some 3,000 ft thick and is followed by continental deposits of Triassic and Jurassic age of some 1,600 ft. The Cretaceous starts with nonmarine strata some 200 ft in thickness and continues with a marine series of 4,000 to 6,000 ft. The uppermost Cretaceous and Paleocene are again nonmarine. The major folding occurred between the Paleocene and the Eocene, and the postorogenic filling with the detritus of the uplifted surrounding blocks and volcanic deposits was wholly continental in both basins. Intensive erosion in the Wind River basin preceded the deposition of coarse river deposits of Oligocene age.

Both basins have an extremely simple structure, but the Wind River basin is strongly asymmetric. Its two main bordering Precambrian uplifts, the Owl Creek arch to the north and the Wind River uplift to the south, are blocks which have been upthrusted toward the south and southwest, with the result that the axis of the basin is just in front of the Owl Creek uplift.

Both basins are characterized by a series of mostly asymmetric anticlines, often oil-bearing, parallel to the uplifts and folded against the gently dipping flanks of the basin. The central area of the basin probably contains folds also, but much of it is covered by unconformable Eocene strata which hamper their detection. In the basin extremities, however, where this unconformable blanket is missing, many folds are present, still parallel but more symmetric. The two basins selected from among the large group of Rocky Mountains basins are typical of this province. They represent a type in which the structural

Fig. 298 Bighorn and Wind River basins. (*From tectonic map of the United States. Published by permission of the U.S. Geological Survey.*)

history is not quite so closely bound to the preceding sedimentary history as we have found elsewhere. Neither the Paleozoic sediments (as the border of the great Cordilleran geosyncline) nor the Cretaceous strata (as an epicontinental margin of the Cretaceous basin preceding the Laramide orogeny) foreshadow the future separation of this shelf region into separate basins. The basin structure is wholly posttectonic, and only the Eocene filling is truly a basin sedimentation. The differentiation into separate basins by the strong uplift of the boundary arches is due to a great variety of causes, among which the Precambrian structure of the basement is possibly an important factor.

MICHIGAN BASIN

The Michigan basin is remarkable for its practically undisturbed condition, its symmetric shape, and its great size; its diameter is about 450 miles. Its sediments range from Cambrian to Pennsylvanian. Its present structure is always referred to as a pile of saucers, each higher one being smaller than its predecessor. Until the Devonian, the Michigan basin was an extension of the Illinois basin to the south, the two together forming a depression east of the great transcontinental arch, the backbone of the continent (Fig. 288). This depression is limited to the east by the Cincinnati arch, another N-S swell in the Precambrian shield.

Beginning in the Devonian, a transverse arch with a NW-SE direction developed, the Kankakee arch, which separated the Michigan basin from the Illinois basin.

Oil exploration discovered several flat anticlines roughly parallel to the Kankakee arch. In some of them faults have been proved in the lower beds, indicating that they overlie faults in the basement, which are probably contemporaneous with the Kankakee arch. The total thickness of the Paleozoic, which is overlain by glacial drift only, is nowhere greater than 10,000 ft.

The Michigan basin can be considered as the most perfect example of the stable shield basins: a long, very slow undisturbed subsidence, with only 10,000 ft of accumulated sediments in the whole Paleozoic (Fig. 299). Its development is governed by two perpendicular directions, the older NE-SW transcontinental and Cincinnati arches and the younger NW-SE direction, which we find in the line from the Ozark dome to the Ellis arch, and the Amarillo-Wichita system farther south. Again we find that a basin formation is due to two fold directions, which in this case cause fold amplitudes 500 miles across, a width that is perhaps dictated by the thickness of the strata involved, in this case the whole solid crust of the earth.

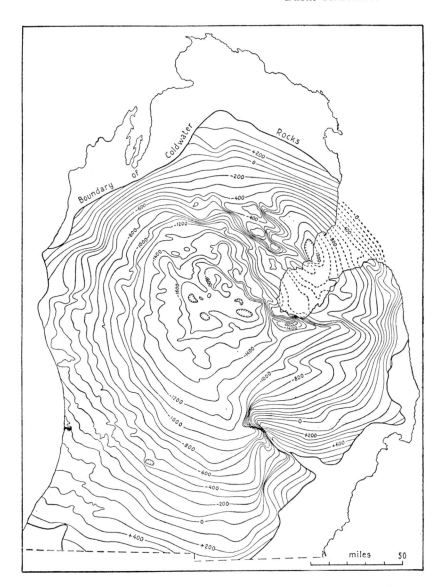

Fig. 299   Michigan basin, structure contours on the Coldwater Formation. (*After Brown–Monnet, 1948. Published by permission of the American Association of Petroleum Geologists.*)

THE PARIS BASIN

The Paris basin is one of the northwest European basins which
developed during the Mesozoic on the abraded Paleozoic surface.
Their emplacement is strongly influenced by the Hercynian structure
of this area, but in their present configuration on the map they have
certainly a discordant character. We can distinguish in the south the
Alpine geosyncline, the future site of the Alpine mountain chain; its
prolongation toward the west, the Languedoc basin; and the Aquitanian basin north of the Pyrenees, originally extending southward
toward the Hercynian Pyrenean mountain chain. The Languedoc and
Aquitanian basins are separated by the Hercynian Montagne Noire
orogeny, which was connected with the Pyrenees (Fig. 300).

To the north of these southern basins we find the great shield of
the French Plateau-Central Rhineland, a broad uplifted plateau, with
western extension in the Armorican mountain chain of Brittany. On
its eastern slope the Bavarian basin developed, originally the northern
epicontinental extension of the eastern Alpine basin. Still farther
north the Hercynian orogeny of south England and Belgium and the
Variscan chains of Germany form the southern boundary of the Baltic
shield of that epoch. The Paris basin developed between the Armorican orogeny in the south, the Hercynian orogeny in the north, and
the central platform in the southeast and east. The English North Sea
basin and the North German basin, separated by a buried ridge
running from SE to NW through Holland, together form the North
European basins, with an extremely complicated Mesozoic history,
largely buried beneath a Tertiary blanket.

Fig. 300 The northwest European Mesozoic-
Tertiary basins.

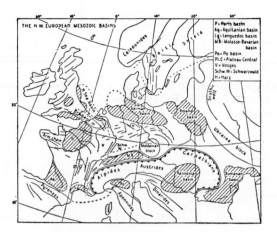

In outline these basins are therefore the Mesozoic reflections of Hercynian structures. This relation is demonstrated in particular in their earlier history; it is only in the later epeirogenic phases that the transgressions of the younger series, in particular Upper Cretaceous, give these basins a discordant character.

In the northern part of the Paris–Southern England basin proper are reflected the structure of the Brabant massif, which had probably originated during the Caledonian orogeny, and that of the Hercynian chain of the Ardennes (Fig. 301). South of the Brabant massif the Carboniferous geosynclines of the Ruhr-Liège-Charleroi-North French coal basin developed. This Upper Carboniferous basin was bounded in the south by the core of Ardennes mountains, the Precambrian Stavelot and Rocroi massifs. It is south of this older basin that the Paris and Wealden basins started to develop in the Jurassic as a longitudinal basin parallel to the old Brabant massif. Only later

Fig. 301   The Paris basin.

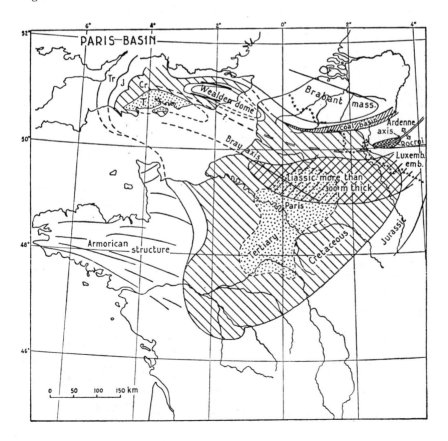

did it extend to the south and acquire its round shape. The post-Eocene doming of the Wealden-Boulonnais dome is also mainly restricted to this original Jurassic basin.

Structure of the Wealden Dome. The Wealden district basin began to develop in Early Mesozoic times. Thin Liassic strata wedge out in the north against the Paleozoic mass, which represents the westerly continuation of the Brabant mass. The same strong tendency to increasing thickness toward the south is exhibited by the Middle and Upper Jurassic and is accentuated by the Lower Cretaceous Wealden delta deposits, which are slightly transgressive. The transgression caused overlapping to the north and eventually passed over the northern ridge in Upper Cenomanian times. The Chalk still shows, however, a thickening toward the south. In the Eocene the whole basin was folded into one large dome striking E-W; most of the area emerged above sea level, and only in its southern flank continental Eocene deposits are preserved. They wedge out toward the north. Oligocene and Miocene are practically missing (Fig. 302).

The inception of the movement occurred in pre-Eocene post-Cretaceous time; the maximum was reached in the Miocene.

The Wealden dome is complicated by many parallel and asymmetric folds, also trending east to west, and with their steep-dipping flanks to the north.

The combined effect of the epeirogenic and orogenic movement is a gently dipping Paleozoic floor with southward-thickening Mesozoic sediments on top, arched in a large dome with secondary asymmetric folds, probably due to faults in the basement.

Structure of the Paris Basin. South of the Ardennes chain there developed in earliest Mesozoic times a relatively deep furrow parallel to the trend of the Ardennes, starting in the east and gradually extending westward, filling with Triassic in the east and Liassic in the center. Although its axis is north of the Seine River, the transgression reached much farther south in the Dogger, encroaching on the Central Plateau

Fig. 302 Structure of the Wealden dome. (*After Edmunds, 1948. Published by permission of Her Majesty's Stationery Office.*)

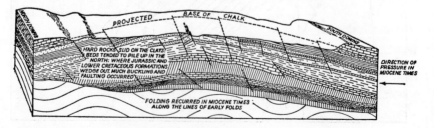

and the Armorican chain of Brittany and Normandy and the Hercynian chain of southern England. In the Lower Cretaceous the basin narrowed, to its central part around Paris and eastward; it became enlarged again, in the Upper Cretaceous, to its former extension. In the Eocene, the basin became much smaller—around its present center, which is Paris, and its southern England center, around Southampton.

The total thickness of the Mesozoic sediments is relatively small, some 5,000 ft in the center.

The folds of the Paris basin are in general very gentle, parallel to the general NE-SW trend of the northern border. Whether they reflect faults or fold movements in the basement or not is difficult to tell. Their general asymmetric shape, like that of the largest one, the Bray anticline, and their large wavelength indicate that the basement is concerned in the tectonics. The faults on its southern border, trending north to south, are certainly basement faults; they extend from the southern border into the basin and belong to the Limagne rift and a Plateau-Central system of Oligocene faults.

The Paris–southern England basin is thus a basin feature very much like the Michigan basin, developing on an older abrasion surface as a new feature. It is unlike the Michigan basin in being much more dependent on the structure of its basement, but this is readily understandable; the Hercynian structure of the North European region had much younger and more pronounced trends in its mountain chains and its basins of sedimentation than did the Precambrian of the Canadian shield in relation to the Paleozoic sedimentation of the Michigan basin.

From this brief review of these selected basins we can see that the style of relationship between basin formation and orogenies varies widely. On the one hand are the examples of the Californian and Rocky Mountain basins, which can both be compared with posttectonic marginal troughs. On the other hand, the Michigan and Paris basins are remote from such a direct relation. The Californian and Rocky Mountain basins differ again, since the history of the Californian basins is wholly postorogenic in relation to the Nevadan orogeny, but eventually developed into a dismembered geosyncline in its own right, whereas the history of the Rocky Mountain basins is essentially preorogenic in relation to the Laramide orogeny, and they received their basin structure only at the last moment during that phase.

The Michigan and Paris basins differ in that the first is formed by swells parallel to contemporaneous geosynclines which were forming elsewhere, and the second by subsidence parallel to preceding orogenies.

Chapter 34

Blocks

Our perusal of the Mediterranean region brought us into contact with relatively stable regions, between the mountain chains, which we designated as "blocks." We recognized in North Africa the Moroccan block and the High Plateau of Algeria; in Spain the Castillian block; and a probable submerged block in the western Mediterranean. Farther east we can recognize the Pannonian block, the east Mediterranean block, and the Anatolian block (cf. Chap. 28, Fig. 276).

In the Cordilleran system of North America we found the Colorado Plateau, surrounded by Laramide belts of folding, and in the Antillean system of island arcs, several submerged blocks may be anticipated.

The same arrangement of stable blocks surrounded by folded chains is represented by the pattern of the Indonesian island arcs. Apparently the stable block within extensive mountain systems is quite a common occurrence, and it certainly merits a somewhat closer examination.

The difficulty in this respect is that the historic development of many of these blocks is virtually unknown because they are either covered by the sea or by flat-lying young sediments.

THE COLORADO PLATEAU

One of the best-known blocks is the Colorado Plateau, well exposed by the deep section cut into it by the Colorado River and its tributaries.

Its Precambrian abrasion surface, which has distinct topographical features, is covered by a maximum of 5,000 ft of Paleozoic sediments and 9,000 ft of Mesozoic.

In the Precambrian we find a tilted Algonkian series on a highly metamorphic basement. The Paleozoic is very incomplete; the Cambrian is mostly present; the Ordovician, very reduced. The Devonian is either absent or thin; some Mississippian limestone may be present;

464

only the Pennsylvanian and Permian reach large thickness, often in a red-bed continental facies.

The Mesozoic shows a similar development of intermittent sedimentation; only the Cretaceous reaches great thicknesses and then only in small basins.

Disconformities are therefore numerous; folding is practically absent, and anticlinal belts and shallow basins exist, but are ascribed mostly to fault movements in the basement because their shape is very asymmetrical. The uplifts are often called monoclines, because the opposite flank is nothing but a flexure. The Cretaceous basins are certainly related to the Laramide folding of their surroundings, and thus represent the faint reflections of the stress field in a particular stable block. Some narrow structures are due to longitudinal salt diapirs with accompanying collapse due to solution. Elsewhere on the plateau, most perfectly developed laccoliths, fed from a central vent, have been described (Hunt, 1946). Their age is probably Pliocene; there was extensive contemporaneous volcanic activity which produced basalts, andesites, and rhyolites.

After the Late Cretaceous Laramide deformation, the origin of the elongated uplifts and faults, the basins were filled with Eocene and younger sediments. The plateau was uplifted as a whole in the Pliocene (Longwell, 1946), and the volcanic activity continued from then to the Recent.

From a general point of view we can conclude from this evidence that the Colorado block has acted as a stable block since the Archean. It was submerged only in those periods preceding a major orogenesis in the neighborhood, the Upper Paleozoic and the Cretaceous. Its volcanic activity is of the continental type.

THE MOROCCAN MESETA

Between the very mildly folded Tertiary chains of the Middle Atlas in the east, the High Atlas in the south, the Atlantic in the west, and the strongly folded Riff arc in the north, there extends the Moroccan Meseta, a stable region during the whole of the Mesozoic (Fig. 303).

Its Paleozoic history, however, is different. The Paleozoic in the western part of the meseta reaches great thicknesses; there is some 4,000 m of Cambrian and Ordovician of similar thickness; on its eastern border the Devonian and Mississippian also attain similar thicknesses. Caledonian and Hercynian periods of folding can be distinguished; the direction is mostly N-S or NE-SW.

Its Mesozoic history was extremely quiet, in strong contrast with this Paleozoic history. On its eastern border are some transgressive Jurassic limestones, in the center some Cretaceous and Eocene strata,

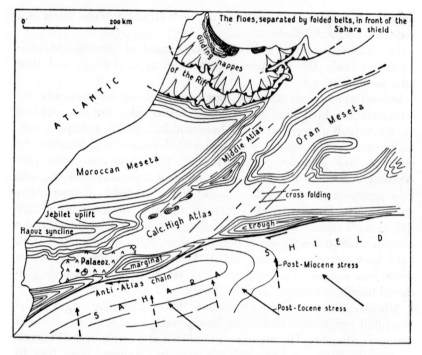

Fig. 303 Blocks in the Moroccan region between Sahara and Riff orogeny. (*After G. Choubert, Notes et Memoires du Service Géologique, no. 100, 1952, Rabat.*)

both on the original widespread Triassic cover of the Hercynian abrasion surface.

The Tertiary orogeny had but slight influence on the now stable block. In the south a geanticline with an E-W strike, the Jebilets, was warped up and flanked on both sides by shallow depressions. Its Atlantic margin was bent down toward the ocean, particularly in the south, and its eastern margin was warped up along faults striking NE-SW, parallel to the mildly folded Middle Atlas chain. Its northern border became depressed by the load of advancing gliding nappes of the Riff.

This block, which in the Paleozoic Period still belonged to the flexible part of the earth's crust, became stable after the Hercynian folding and acted as a block during the Tertiary diastrophism, weakly reflecting the stress fields around it.

OCEANIC BLOCKS

If we considered other blocks we should find the same characteristics. Some have been stable since the Precambrian, some only since the

Mesozoic. Some have been filled up with Tertiary sediments, often of continental facies like the Oligocene and Miocene cover of the Castillian block or the Hungarian plain, but others are far below sea level. Kuenen (1935) has made a special study of these blocks in the Indonesian Archipelago. His first group of ocean basins are characterized as "large, broad and deep (5,000 m) basins with steep sides and a flat, horizontal bottom" (p. 38). He thinks that a basin of this type is due to downfaulting of a stable area, because "its considerable size, the box-like section, the equi-dimensional shape, the absence of complication of the floor are so many features opposing a folded structure" (p. 41). The situation of these basins is shown in Chap. 27, Fig. 266, and we see how the folded belts curve around them. There can be little doubt that, structurally, they have the same function as the continental blocks we have already considered, their only distinguishing feature being their extremely low level. An explanation of the difference in level offers itself almost automatically: the continental blocks are sial blocks; the Indonesian blocks are oceanic without a sial blanket. This explanation has been proved correct by seismic refraction measurements made by Ewing (1952). Their depth of 5,000 to 6,000 m is exactly what one might expect from an isostatic point of view for a sial-free ocean bottom.

THE SAXONIC STRUCTURAL TYPE

The function of the blocks from a structural point of view is not altogether passive. They are active in the sense that a large block, like the Moroccan Meseta, can divert the stress from its original direction. As it is pushed in one direction it may be slightly rotated, with the result that one of its other sides exerts a stress in another direction on its margin and causes folding with another strike, different from that which the original stress would cause.

This phenomenon, with all its intricate results of tear faulting, tension faults, thrust faults, and localized folding, has been the subject of a very extensive research by Stille (1924a and b), Lotze (1938, 1953), and many of their pupils in Germany. Stille has coined the term "Saxonic folding" or "Germano-type orogeny" and still later "paratectonics" for this structural type, in contrast with the "orthotectonics" of mountain chains; and in a series of studies in *Geotektonische Forschungen*, this subject has been treated extensively.

The typical Saxonic field is situated between the Alpine mountain chains in the south and the Baltic shield in the north. This territory was severely folded after several extensive geosynclinal phases during the Paleozoic, causing an intricate pattern of mountain chains—Precambrian or Early Paleozoic blocks like the French Massif Central, the Brabant massif, and the Harz Mountains, with different trends

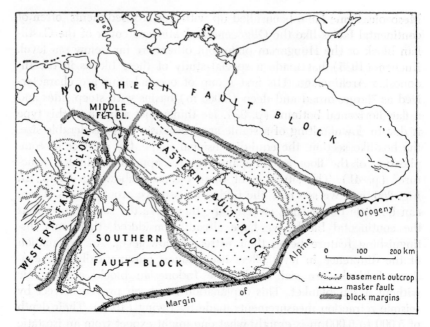

Fig. 304 Blocks north of the Alpine orogeny. (*After Lotze, 1953. Published by permission of E. Schweizerbart'sche Verlagsbuchhandlung. Stuttgart.*)

and different grades of mobility or rigidity. During the Mesozoic, basins were formed, some extensive and persistent, some only very limited in space and time, and the whole platform was broken up and pushed about by the great Alpine stress directed N-S. The heterogeneity of the substratum, an inheritance from its Paleozoic history, caused a great heterogeneity in structural trends in its Cenozoic history. These trends have mostly been named after the trends of old mountain chains, Hercynian for the NW trend of the Armorican chain,* for instance; but others have a younger date, e.g., the Upper Rhine Valley rift, which is an Alpine structure. Its N-S trend has been called the Rhine direction.

The fact that the NW Hercynian direction, the NE trend of the Variscan systems farther east, and other old trends are represented again and again in the younger fault and fold systems is in itself proof enough that the heterogeneous basement has had a great influence on the trends of its Alpine paratectonic structure, although it must be admitted that the principle has certainly been overworked.

In Fig. 304 is reproduced Lotze's conception (1953) of the way in

---

* This is the reason why "Hercynian" as a time indication is not used in German, but has been replaced by "Variscan."

which this foreland of the Alpine chain has been broken up into blocks. The blocks have to be considered as mobile units, moving together and relatively to each other, each gliding on the substratum, the asthenosphere. The block margins are characterized by greatly increased tectonic mobility in relation to the center of the blocks. There may be extensive normal faulting, as along the Upper Rhine rift, but elsewhere we may find very flat and peculiar overthrusts, as on the margin of the western block in the Osning zone (Fig. 305), or we may find tear faulting.

The intensity of movement need not be equal along one border zone; it is often masked by younger discordant formations, or it may grow consistently in one direction, or one kind of movement may be replaced by another; but all along their borders we find the same increase of intensity of tectonic features.

The blocks themselves are not free from structural deformation; parallel faults are frequent both in the eastern and in the central blocks, and which zone of disturbance one considers as a master fault is often a matter of preference.

In the northern block in particular, we find secondary complications due to a horizontal detachment within the block along incompetent salt horizons of the Permian, where smaller blocks drifting on this salt horizon create their own style of diapiric disturbance. The great Hercynian northern master fault of the eastern block can be followed in the northern block along a row of salt diapirs, for instance. Figure 162 of Chap. 17 gives a good example of the tectonics of this block movement on a salt layer. Along many of the master faults one can recognize contrasting movements in succeeding periods. Thus we find, both along the Osning zone and along the Roer Valley rift, that a particular block was raised in all the pre–Upper Cretaceous movements, sank in the Upper Cretaceous, and rose again in the Miocene phases. Such contrasting movements are comprehensible in a block

Fig. 305 Overthrusts in the Osning zone. (*After Stille, 1924b.*)

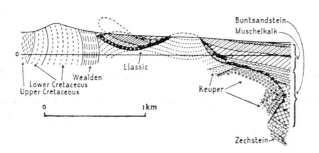

field where the individual blocks sometimes drift asunder and some-times press against each other. When we consider the pattern of the master faults of the German foreland of the Alpine mountain chains in Europe (Fig. 304), we are struck by the fact that the bisectrix of the sharp northern angle of the central block is exactly the stress direction of the Alpine orogeny. The conclusion seems warranted that the Rhine trend (NNE) and the Hercynian trend (NW) are in their origin a simple conjugate set of tear faults, caused by the N-S-directed Alpine stress.

But before forming a judgment on the great Rhine rift we shall have to consider large rifts in general.

TENSION, OR DILATATION, ZONES IN THE EARTH'S CRUST

Great tension (dilatation) regions, of which the principal ones are the African rift system, the Great Basin fault system, and mid-oceanic rifts, are not very numerous. On the other hand, dilatation is a con-stant companion of stress, as one of its secondary consequences in all minor structures.

The question now arises whether the great dilatation areas could be the secondary consequences of other large structures, mountain chains or orogenic belts. Some of their general characteristics can be formu-lated as follows: there is recurrence of movement during long periods; their total dilatation is small in comparison with total compression of mountain chains; they are typical of stable regions.

The thought that the dilatation in the stable shelves is the reflection of orogenic processes in their surrounding mobile belts is very sugges-tive and can be more or less proved for the best-known rift, the Rhine Valley rift (cf. Fig. 83). There the start of the subsidence of the rift is synchronous with one of the major phases of the Alps (post-Eocene), and its situation and that of its accompanying fault blocks (see Figs. 83, 276, and 300) make it almost imperative to link the two phenom-ena in one catastrophic event. The picture of the blunt bow of a ship crushing into an ice sheet and pushing the floes in front arises in one's mind. This image is not necessarily false, although it is too much of a simplification, and questions immediately arise: how the Rhone Valley rift, the Limagne faults, and the Lower Rhone faults, which are certainly expressions of the same dilatation but have a totally different orientation in relation to the Alpine arc, are to be accounted for.

The subsidence of the rifts may have been initiated by the orogenic push of the Alps; that is, their bordering faults were the direct re-sult of this push; but the subsidence itself was a slow process, with

all the characteristics of cyclic epeirogenic motion. Moreover, as Cloos
(1932, 1936) has demonstrated very convincingly, the actual rupture
of the faults is preceded by a long process of bulging, of arching of the
shield (cf. Chap. 10, Fig. 83). Therefore our image of the ship bump-
ing against an ice sheet is wrong in so far as the process is not one of
a sudden bump but a slow process which, at a moment of maximum
pressure, caused rupture. The pressure existed before and continued
after the rupture. This result is in perfect accordance with our general conception of epeirogenic and orogenic stress, in which the
orogeny is the moment of yield in a continuous stress field. Accordingly, the notion of a close relation between folding and rift formation is strengthened by a closer examination of the characteristics of
both processes, but the mechanism is perhaps less obvious.

We shall have to go back to another of our fundamental concepts of
earth distortion, the notion of the different tiers of the earth's crust
which react differently under stress. The lower tiers are characterized
by homogeneous deformation, the upper tier by discontinuous deformation. Obviously, the rift faults originate in and are typical of the
upper tier, but what happens in the lower tier? There we shall find
compression in the direction of the main stress, and dilatation, but no
tensional stress, in the two perpendicular directions; or, in the case of
the foreland of the Alps, compression in the N-S direction and dilatation in the vertical and E-W direction. The vertical dilatation caused
the bulging of the Rhine shield, and not only there, but also farther
west and east, in the whole stable shield north of the Alpine belt.
The horizontal E-W dilatation in the lower tier apparently caused,
here and there, a tensional stress in the upper tier, expressed by rift
valleys and their subsidence. The tensional stress in the upper reaches
of the crust is not necessarily bound to the bulges in the crust, but
would only have a preference for them. A rift was initiated as in the
region of the Upper Rhine shield, starting in the center of the bulge
and progressing to the north and south, and not just in front of the
Alpine arc as we should expect if our metaphor of the ship and the ice
floes were true. And because the deformation of the lower tier is not
limited by the surficial expression of stress, it is evident that the
faults can extend into the outer reaches of the Alpine arc, where they
have been traced, in the Jura Mountains and even in the Molasse
trough (Schuppli, 1952), and even across the entire chain, by seismic
evidence (Oulianof, 1947). Once the rift had been formed, one could
understand that it was widened by further thrust of the Alpine chain
in particular because a wedge at its southern extremity was driven
into the gap.

Nevertheless, the bulge of the Rhine shield was not the only effect
of the compression in N-S direction in the block facing the Alps. On

the contrary, the compression also manifested itself in great tear faults which divided the European continent in separate blocks, as could be expected on the principles laid down in Chap. 8. The Rhine Valley rift is a secondary feature due to the Rhine shield bulge and its accompanying tear faults with NW and NNE trends.

The African rift system is much less directly connected with any major mountain chain than the Rhine Valley rift is with the Alps. Nevertheless, we find here in the same way a direct connection between a N-S stress direction and an E-W tensional direction. Different authors have pointed out that the pattern of the system is built up by two directions, NNW- and NNE-striking faults. Such a consistent conjugate set of faults is compatible with a N-S stress direction, which would be in harmony with an E-W dilatation, but the faults are apparently not tear faults but normal faults. Again the conclusion is warranted that the fault direction has been dictated by the main stress, but the fault type by the actual movement, or in other words, the fault pattern is due to the stress condition in the lower tier, and the fault movement to the resulting dilatation in the upper tier.

Both the European rift systems, the Rhine and Limagne faults, and the African rift systems are characterized by extensive volcanism on the faults, proving that the faults cut deep into the substratum.

The fault system of the Great Basin in the North American Cordilleras has another character and another cause. It consists of innumerable relatively small faults, small in length and width and not necessarily small in slip; they have mostly the same strike and dip-slip movement, and form, instead of prominent rifts, a series of tilted blocks. Their strike is parallel to the general strike of the flanking orogenies, and not perpendicular to it as in the case of the Rhine Valley rift. We may suppose that this general character is a result of a superficial dilatation due to arching of the old Cordilleran geanticline in Mesozoic and Cenozoic time. They differ also in one important aspect from the great rift faults: they are not accompanied by any volcanic activity.

THE FUNCTION OF BLOCKS IN THE STRUCTURAL PATTERN OF THE EARTH

Our survey of the stable blocks has revealed that we can distinguish two different kinds of blocks, those which are remnants of the continental or oceanic shields engulfed between orogenic belts and those which are simply part of the continental shield.

The first kind has been called "Zwischengebirge" by Kober (1928) and nuclear basins by Umbgrove (1947), and we can distinguish among them continental blocks and oceanic blocks, proving once more that the earth's crust is not less rigid in the oceanic region, where it consists exclusively of basalt and its ultramafic substratum, than in the continents, where a sialic blanket is provided.

The second kind of blocks is much less universally recognized; it has been described in detail and fully analyzed only in the European foreland of the Alps. One might expect a similar structure, for instance, in the Indian Peninsula in front of the great Himalayan chain where long fault zones are known to exist and in Anatolia and Persia. The fault systems which divide the Arabian, Syrian, and Abyssinian shields into separate blocks certainly form a pattern similar to that which we found in Europe, but here the blocks are more rigid, still more of the cratonic type, and the intervening channels are not folded.

We found that the great rift systems of Africa and Europe are the most spectacular form of master faults in the crust, but are not fundamentally different from other block boundaries. In this respect it is of some interest to recall the great compression faults of Chap. 12, such as the North Pyrenean fault zone and the Anti-Atlas fault zone.

There is one other very long zone of disturbances which could be associated with the same group, in particular with the African rifts, that is, the Mid-Atlantic swell and rift valley, also characterized by a long row of volcanoes reaching from Iceland to Ascencion.

Looking back over all this evidence of large-scale cracking of the earth's crust, we must conclude that the stress field in the crust has apparently never subsided. It causes world-wide fault zones on continents and oceans, it loosens small blocks from the great shields, and it thus continuously changes the shape of the continents.

Chapter 35

Relation in Time and Space of Orogenies

DIFFERENCE IN MECHANISM
OF DIFFERENT OROGENIC PERIODS

We have already had occasion to observe that the concept of world-wide revolutions of short duration separated by world-wide long periods of quiet must be revised, in the sense that the earth's crust has never been absolutely quiet and that the paroxysms are only culminations in deformation which goes on continuously; that they are certainly not world-wide, although there are cycles of some 200 million years of relative quiescence, separated by shorter periods of greater activity; and finally, that folding phases in paratectonic regions are different from orogenic phases in orthotectonic belts.

It has also been suggested that the great orogenic periods, those of the Precambrian and of the Hercynian and the Alpine periods, are not true equivalents. This is certainly true when we consider the magmatic phases. No doubt the deeper erosion of the older orogenic belts exposes the infrastructure to a greater extent than in the younger belts, with the result that the intrusive and metamorphic rocks occupy larger surfaces and that the metamorphism is more intense in the older belts; but the scarcity of Tertiary granites in Tertiary belts (none in the Atlas, none in the Pyrenees, and very few in the Alps) as compared with their abundance in the Hercynian Period and the predominant role of granitization phenomena in the Precambrian belts cannot be explained exclusively by this difference in denudation level. No doubt the magmatic phases decrease in importance from old to young. In this sense the orogenic phases are not equivalent.

474

On the other hand, it has also been suggested by Fallot (1944) and Goguel (1952) that the surficial structural characteristics are also not equivalent in the different phases; that the Alpine Period is characterized by greater compression and more frequent overthrusts than the older periods. Nappes and large overthrusts were described early during the investigations of Paleozoic and Precambrian rocks. In fact, the first large nappe ever described was the Sparagmite nappe in central Scandinavia (Törnebohm, 1896). This nappe and the world-famous Moine thrust of Scotland both form part of the Caledonian ranges of northwest Europe. The imposing nappe of gneiss and older granite in the youngest Precambrian of Dalsland, southwest Sweden (Heybroek and Zwart, 1949), a perfectly horizontal sheet at least 15 km wide, is Precambrian (Chap. 32, Fig. 290). In the Montagne Noire the plunging frontal lobes of Hercynian age are of the same size as the Helvetian nappes (cf. Chap. 18, Figs. 187 and 188; Gèze et al., 1952). The Moine thrust of Caledonian age in Scotland is one of the most famous overthrusts in the world, and recently we mapped a whole set of superposed thrust sheets of Carboniferous age, typically Helvetian, in the Cantabrian Mountains which, as we pointed out before, are very much like the Appalachian thrusts of the Valley and Ridge province (de Sitter, 1962b).

Superficial folding with a basal detachment plane is therefore also quite frequent in Hercynian orogenies, but perhaps less easily discerned. Besides the difference of denudation and the fact that older systems have tended to be worked out in much less detail, there is another important influence on the expression of the original structure of the older orogenic belts. There is a striking difference in the physiographic expression of the structure in Alpine belts as compared with Hercynian (or Caledonian) and Precambrian belts, which is perhaps best appreciated by the photogeologist who tries to infer the structural details from aerial photographs. When working in favorable circumstances on Tertiary structures one is able to analyze their structure in great detail, but in the same circumstances a Hercynian structure is often not revealed at all. One important restriction must be made, however: there are some Hercynian structures of paratectonic character which show the same degree of physiographic expression as any Tertiary belt. I think, for instance, on the one hand, of the Hercynian structures of the axial zone of the Pyrenees, where the physiographic features are almost completely independent of the structure and very little can be learned from the aerial photographs, and on the other hand, of the wonderful clear physiographic expression of the Anti-Atlas folding. The same was found in comparing the central Hercynian High Atlas, having very little physiographic expression, with, for instance, the largely Hercynian Asturian-Cantabrian mountain chain, which shows beautiful physiographic structural detail.

As far as I can ascertain, this striking difference is due to the cleavage of the older Hercynian structures; this does not demolish the structures, but does reduce their physiographic expression by obliterating the differential resistance to erosion of the different lithological rock types. A limestone is then no longer more resistant than a schist. The effects of the deep weathering undergone by the rocks of the Hercynian mountain chain after the postorogenic uplift have often been preserved beneath a blanket of Mesozoic rocks. Post-Alpine erosion has frequently exhumed this ancient land surface in which the resistance of the rocks has been much reduced, so that such a decomposed granite may erode to a valley instead of forming a mountain peak as so often occurred in the Alps.

In order to ascertain to what degree the difference in structure of orogenies of different age is apparent, we have to make a more thorough comparison. For convenience, the characteristics are tabulated in Table 14.

From this table we learn that almost every characteristic of an orogeny may be present in any kind of mountain chain, but that some are much more frequent in the older ones than in the younger ones, and vice versa. There is apparently one group of phenomena, intensity and magmatic phases coupled with schistosity and similar folding, which is common in the older mountain chains and much rarer or absent in the younger chains. On the other hand, concentric fold-

Table 14

Characteristic	Archean	Paleozoic	Cenozoic	
			Circum-Pacific (Laramide)	Mediterranean
Initial magmatic phase	Ultrabasic and granites	Ultrabasic	Ultrabasic occasionally	Ultrabasic occasionally
Syntectonic magmatic phase	Granites, pegmatites, granitization	Granites, pegmatites, granitization	Absent	Occasional granites and migmatization
Late-tectonic magmatic phase	Frequent granites	Frequent granites	Frequent granites	Rare granites
Posttectonic magmatic phase	Undistinguishable	Frequent volcanism	Active volcanism	Rare volcanism
Metamorphism	Profound	Important	Rare	Rare
Concentric folding	Absent?	Frequent	Common	Almost exclusively
Low-angle overthrust	Absent?	Common	Rare	Common
Schistosity and similar folding	Almost exclusively	Common	Rare	Rare
Island arcs	Absent?	Rare?	Common	Occasionally?

ing and overthrusts are typical of the youngest chain and scarce in the oldest ones.

In this respect we have to remember that at the time of their folding the Paleozoic rocks were as fresh as the Mesozoic rocks now and that the difference in type of folding can therefore not be due to stronger lithification of the older rocks. Nor can it be true that the epimetamorphic state of the folded Paleozoic rocks can be due to any Alpine folding phase, for there are many Hercynian chains which have not been submitted to any noticeable Alpine stress, yet have the same general habit. On the other hand, unfolded Paleozoic sediments can be as little lithified as unfolded or folded Mesozoic rocks; one has only to remember the perfectly unconsolidated Paleozoic sedimentary rocks of the Russian and American shields.

The difference in metamorphic state must therefore be closely connected with the folding itself, and we are tempted to assume that the much greater frequency of the magmatic phases in the Paleozoic chains and a more intensive stress field are the deciding factors.

OROGENIC CHARACTERISTICS OF MOUNTAIN CHAINS

At this point of our investigation into the nature of the orogenic deformations of the earth's crust, it would be useful to look back and summarize our experience.

We started from the point of view that we might expect great differences in the nature of mountain chains and that any general rules should be formulated only after we had studied the characteristics of several mountain chains of different ages and in different positions in relation to continents and oceans.

After this review there can be little doubt that our original presumption was justified: that each mountain chain has its own character and that it will be difficult to find a common basis for any specific rule of development. Nevertheless, we can perceive, for instance, a striking analogy in shape in cross sections through the Appalachians and the Alps (cf. Lombard, 1948). The Ridge and Valley province can be compared with the Helvetian unit, the Blue Ridge province with the thrust zone of the central massifs (cf. Figs. 280 and 277), and the Piedmont province with the Pennine nappes. The Molasse basin of the Alps is a typical marginal trough of postorogenic origin; its equivalent is missing in the Appalachians.

When we consider the boundary between the central Nevadan orogenic zone and its foreland to the west, we see that the Sierra Nevada has acted as a tilted block and that there is no trace of any thrusting on its boundary with the great valley; instead we descend a gently inclined block whose sedimentary cover is hardly folded and is disturbed by only a few small faults.

In the structure of the Californian coastal basins we face a distinct element of nonparallelism between earlier and later compression directions, which also played an important role in the history of the Alpine area, although less easily identified. The strong axial plunges in the coastal-basin structure are certainly due to this element, and we may presume that the same reasoning holds good in the Alps, although former basement heterogeneities have no doubt also had their influence on the axial plunges of the external massives of the Helvetian zone. In the Pyrenees we found the same discrepancy in folding directions, both between Hercynian and Alpine periods and between phases of the same period. Hence the satellite massives of the Pyrenees are primarily due to a preexisting heterogeneity of the basement. In contrast with these examples of the strong dismemberment of a formerly large unified basin into smaller units, we find the whole of the Appalachians, and in particular the Valley and Ridge province, in a state of perfect unity, with hardly any axial plunges or individual domes.

When we turn our attention to the island arcs, we find a consistent pattern of surficial expression of earth-crust deformation.

We find minor internal geosynclines with mild or very mild folding around the continental basement, enclosed in turn by slightly elevated geanticlines with frequent volcanism. This geanticline is surrounded either by an external basin and geanticlinal structure or by an immediate deep-sea furrow. Evidence of strong lateral orthotectonic compression is rare, except as evidence of an older orogenic period, as in Japan or the Antilles, and the whole structural pattern looks as if most of its deformation is directly expressed by its morphological features. It is wholly unwarranted to assume anything like a central metamorphic zone of strong compression below the blanket of Cenozoic volcanics that covers the geanticlinal arc; on the contrary, when anything of the structure is revealed below this blanket, we find either mild folding and arching or tension rifts, both consistent with a large arching of a geanticline. Can we take this kind of structure as the prototype of an orogeny? Obviously not; it might perhaps eventually develop into an orogenic system comparable with the Cordilleran system or the Alpine system, but it certainly has not done so yet. The only general rule that can be derived from its structural features is that volcanism can be particularly frequent on the external side of an orogeny; this we also found in the Cordilleran system and, to some extent, but much more doubtfully, in the Appalachian system. On the other hand, the Mediterranean chains are completely free from this external volcanic arch, which is therefore more or less confined to the circum-Pacific zone.

It is therefore impossible to establish any kind of prototype of an orogenic system, but it is not a hopeless task to determine the influence of each factor separately, as we have shown in Chaps. 31 and 32.

THE STRESS FIELD OF THE EARTH

Stress and Resistance. In my description of the folding of various mountain chains and various basins we have learned that contraction in a cross section can vary from a very mild degree of only a few per cent to paroxysms in which more than 50% overall contraction is noted.

Although we started from the presumption that there is a clear division between a mountain chain and a folded basin, we have to conclude from our experience that the subdivision is quite arbitrary and is often more influenced by a postorogenic elevation of the folded belt than by the folding itself. We should hardly classify the High Atlas as a mountain chain, for instance, if it had not been elevated to its present altitude long after the folding took place.

Nevertheless, we can make a distinction between mild, or paratectonic, folding and strong, or orthotectonic, folding, even if we recognize that there is considerable transition between these categories.

The really strong folding of a mountain chain is characterized by a syntectonic magmatic phase; but even without that, in particular for the Alpine orogenies, strong folding shows low-angle thrusts of considerable width or closely packed folds. We concluded that the onset of the folding was due either to a growing stress, exceeding the yield point of the rock resistance, or to a decrease of resistance, bringing the yield point below the stress, or both actions having effect at the same time.

Another question that we need to consider is why the folding stopped at all, and why it stopped in one case after mild folding and in another case only after it had built up a real mountain chain. The question is probably answered adequately by pointing out that, when the stress field achieved its purpose, it ceased to exist, or in other words, when the disequilibrium that caused the stress had been wiped out, the stress obviously subsided. This answer includes, however, the notion that the stress field is not permanently at the same height, but that it grows and subsides. A folding phase should therefore be due to a rise of stress.

As a fall in rock resistance can presumably occur only when the temperature rises, and because the latter is always related to a particular rise of stress, we can assume that a major orthotectonic orogene is the result of a rise of stress accompanied by a rise of temperature and that in a paratectonic process the temperature rise is lacking. If the stress increase is quick, more energy is available for rock deformation, and instead of paratectonic concentric folding, a cleavage folding sets in, which, if it is accompanied by a rise of temperature, develops into regional metamorphism and its related magmatic phases.

While the arrest of the folding in the mountain chain is due to the subsidence of the stress, the arrest of the folding in a folded basin might be due to several factors, one of which might be a stiffening of the resistance, another, the relief of the stress field in another area. In large-scale mountain building all these factors play a role when we consider particular zones of the structure. In one zone the folding starts, but stops because the yield is taken over by another zone where the resistance has dropped lower in the meantime; in another, the start is relatively late in the period and is due to growing resistance elsewhere, and the arrest is just the end of the whole contraction. Moreover, the yield in one cross section will increase the stress to the left and right, and the folding will spread horizontally in the direction perpendicular to the stress. This principle of distribution of yield zones by variations in resistance can be applied to much larger areas than that of single mountain chains and would imply a certain interdependence of different zones of yield, over large distances. We naturally apply this principle when we consider the American Cordilleran system, which is at least ten times larger than the Alps; and I would not hesitate to view the whole "Mediterranean" belt from Gibraltar to Australia from this point of view. I think that a worldwide study of the interdependence of orogenies would yield remarkable results, because we know already (through the Stille principle of world-wide synchronization of orogenies, however defective its formulation may have been) that an interaction does exist.

Stress and Time. Before we enter into speculations about the mechanism which regulates this relation between stress and folding, we have to remember some of the salient facts about stress and time relations. The most obvious common denominator for structural disturbances is their timing. We have seen that we know of orogenic periods occurring roughly each 200 million years since the Archean, separated by periods of quiescence. Further, we have seen that each period consists of recurring folding phases which are perhaps irregularly distributed when regarded from a global point of view, but which are more or less regular, in periods of perhaps 10 million years, in one mountain belt.

We can break these intervening spaces of some 10 million years down further, into smaller units, not from folds or faults themselves, but by looking at the sedimentary history of sinking basins. Each faunal break, disconformity, or unconformity is in some way related to crustal disturbance, and we have found some forty of them in the Miocene of California. Each detailed section of each sedimentary basin reveals the same frequency of disturbances. Even relatively short intervals, minor unconformities of perhaps 500,000 years, may be further broken down into smaller units when we take into account the remarkable sedimentary cycles known from coal-bearing beds, for instance, or those very convincingly described by R. C. Moore (1950), Wanless (1950), and Lombard (1953). The megacycles of Moore are identical with what we have called minor unconformities.

The characteristic of earth disturbance in time, when considered in this way, is that the energy distribution is not smooth, but comes in shocks, small shocks with small consequences in a quick succession, big shocks with big consequences in a slow succession. The larger the shock, the larger the time interval:

	In Shocks of:
Sedimentary cycles	25,000 years
Sedimentary unconformities and megacycles	500,000 years
Orogenic phases	10 million years
Orogenic periods	200 million years

Stress and Strain.   In mountain building we can discern a space distribution of the same character. The largest unit is the orogenic belt, either circum-Pacific or equatorial, some 7,000 km in length and some 500 km in width. The next unit is the mountain chain, some 800 km long and some 50 km wide. Still smaller is the single fold, with perhaps an average of 10 km length and a width of 2 km. In a major fold we can discern even smaller units when we consider microtectonics, with sedimentary folds of the order of 50 m width, microfolds of 10 cm width, and finally the smallest possible unit, which depends perhaps on the average grain size, let us say, 0.1 mm. Not only do the strongly disturbed belts of the earth's crust show this sequence of diminishing sizes; blocks have the same habit. The largest blocks are the great blocks such as Gondwana, the Pacific, and the Northern Hemisphere block (Canada-Greenland-Fennosarmatia-Angara). The next unit is of blocks of the size of Fennosarmatia itself, the Sahara block and the Brazilian block. But even these blocks have been broken up into such smaller units as those of the North German blocks of Fig. 304. Still smaller blocks can be distinguished when we look to shattered areas. I think it would be futile to assign an average mass to any of these units; they vary too much. For the larger blocks and the smaller orogenic unit we can compare the cratogenic and orogenic elements:

Orogenic belts	Mountain chains	Single folds
Global blocks	Continental shields	Blocks

The Relation between Time and Space in Orogenic Processes. There is obviously a relation between spatial distribution and sequence in time; both come in definite quanta, which one could formulate by supposing that it takes an orogenic period of 200 million years to

accumulate enough energy to move an orogenic belt or a global block
and 10 million years of accumulation of energy to form a mountain
chain or move a continental shield, and so on.

The reason for this relation is perhaps rather simple. If we assume
that the energy is steadily and evenly growing, it is the mass that
regulates the release of potential energy into kinetic energy. If the
proposed time and spatial relation between the shocks of energy release is real, it would imply that there is only one single source of
energy in the earth's crust, a source which is, however, variable in its
outward symptoms. The question, what is the mechanism that regulates this energy release, can be answered when we recall the relation
which we established between folds and secondary folds. It was demonstrated in our discussion that the smaller fold is directly induced
by the larger one. The anticline which reached down to the bottom
of a particular sedimentary base caused the formation of secondary
folds, whose size was again determined by the thickness of a single
bed. The same relation exists between an orogenic belt and a mountain chain. When only the crust, of some 30 km depth, is concerned
in the folding of a single mountain chain of some 50 to 60 km width,
the orogenic belt of some 500 km width should reach down to at least
200 km depth and probably much deeper. Intermediate and deep-
focus earthquakes, all connected with major orogenic belts, prove
that such a depth is not in the least improbable. When we think of
the extreme thinness of the crust as compared with the earth's
diameter, a factor of 0.02, then it becomes quite plausible that the
origin of a major disturbance of some 600 km width, 20 times the
thickness of the crust, cannot be lodged in the crust itself. The mountain chain, on the other hand, could be an exclusively crustal feature.

If these considerations carry weight, we can suppose that the upper
two or three hundred kilometers of the earth's crust possesses some
property which allows the slow accumulation of potential energy,
during 200 million years, which is released in a much shorter period
of some 50 million years. On this release the resulting distribution of
kinetic energy is regulated by the distribution of mass in these upper
layers of the earth. Possibly the Conrad and Moho discontinuities,
and in particular the low-velocity layer, are the causes of the mass
distribution and therefore also of the time distribution involved in the
mountain chains. In the same way the limit between crystalline basement and sedimentary rocks determines the type and mass of the
individual folds.

When we have to look so far below the crust for the origin of orogenic force, it becomes impossible in our present state of knowledge
of the earth's interior to predict anything definite about its nature,
but we can be convinced that all typical properties of the upper crust,

such as the radioactivity of granite or contraction by cooling, ought to be disregarded.

From the available evidence we have concluded an omnipresence of the stress field, growing when resisted, subsiding when the resistance yields. Every heterogeneity in the crust will therefore orientate the stress, and since we presumed that in the Early Archean the major features of heterogeneity of the crust were fixed once and for all, the stress field directions also became fixed at that period. However, a uniform compression direction all over the earth's surface would not satisfy the stress field; e.g., a shortening in a N-S direction would not satisfy the E-W stress, or in other words, the yield in any direction around the earth would have to be roughly uniform. There are, of course, an infinite number of solutions to this problem. One could, for instance, imagine a multitude of contraction centers around which the compression took place, or a multitude of straight lines orientated at random, or only a few lines which would have to have sufficiently different orientations and sufficient length to allow a uniform contraction. Even one N-S line and one E-W line, each a great circle, would satisfy the requirements, provided some minor adjustments at the corners were allowed for. We can perceive every one of these solutions—which by no means exclude one another—in the earth's crust, with, however, a preponderance of the last and simplest case of only two perpendicular lines. Without doubt we can distinguish one hemisphere with a N-S contraction along an E-W line, which would necessarily have to be about equatorial, and one hemisphere with an E-W contraction along N-S lines, e.g., the Eastern Hemisphere with its Mediterranean folded belt and a Western Hemisphere with its circum-Pacific folded belt (Fig. 306). One sees no cogent reason why the major trends are orientated along the meridian and the parallel, but one can just feel that this orientation to the rotation axis of the earth is plausible.

As the stress will be equally distributed over the earth's surface after a period of quiescence, any local disturbance of the stress field by a yield will necessarily be followed by an increase of stress, and therefore by a yield somewhere else in compensation. When this disturbance is small in extension, it requires only a small compensating yield, of the same direction, but as soon as it has reached the extension of half the circumference of the earth, a compensating contraction in a direction perpendicular to the first will be called for, and this in its turn will not finish until it has also spanned half the circumference.

In this mechanism of a trigger-action character—with one disturbance leading to a world-wide revolution—one finds the reason for the contemporaneity of the world revolutions, the orogenic periods.

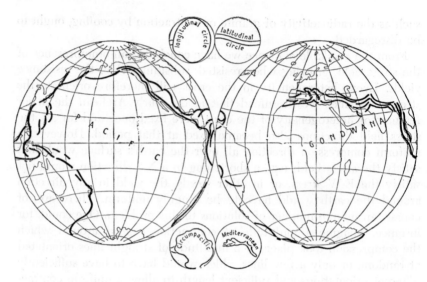

Fig. 306   The circum-Pacific and Mediterranean orogenic belts of the earth's crust.

A certain divergence of contemporaneity is also inherent in the mechanism, and the orogenic phases of one period illustrate the mutual interdependence of the yield points distributed over the earth's surface.

The cyclic nature of the orogenic periods also finds ready explanation in the conception of a world-wide stress field. Once the stress has worked out all over the world in a long succession of phases during one period, the necessary contraction has been achieved, and a long period of quiescence is needed to build up enough stress to start another world-wide revolution. This period of quiescence is not free from stress. On the contrary, from the very beginning the stress is already building up, and small readjustments may take place here and there continuously. An almost necessary result of this conception is that the elastic bending of the earth in the new geosynclines would proceed more slowly just after a major period, and considerably more quickly just before a new period. Reviewing the general sequence of the sedimentation in a geosyncline, it is certainly true that the quick sinking of the basin, indicated by steepening of its margins and deepwater facies, i.e., by the flysch facies, is typical of the late geosynclinal periods, although this rule is far from being universal. But the sinking of a basin is not only expressed by the depth of its axis; it is equally well stressed by the rising of its borders; the facies changes can therefore differ considerably from one geosyncline to another. There is, however, one general rule of almost universal truth: the last lap of the geosynclinal stage is characterized first by a world-wide transgression, followed immediately by a regression.

Chapter 36

Theories on the Cause of Orogeny

Theories about the origin of tectonic forces are numerous and diverse. Modern knowledge of facts about the earth, together with modern theories developed in the light of more advanced theoretical investigations, seems to justify considering only relatively new theories. Before we start on this excursion into the realm of conjecture I should like, however, to point out the extremely flimsy grounds on which such theories are built.

First of all, we have seen hardly anything of the earth's crust below a depth of 2 km; second, only one-third of the surface of the globe is open to geological investigation—the rest is ocean; third, a large portion of the continents is covered by shallow water or alluvial deposits, and of the remaining fraction, only a very small portion is really well known. Fortunately, geophysical research in oceans and continental regions is progressing rapidly, and much more will soon be known about the fundamental structure of the upper layers of the earth.

It is obviously premature to attempt an all-embracing theory of orogeny. Many of the fundamental data are lacking. The most weird conceptions are therefore often just as well founded as the more sober ones, and we have no adequate reasons for rejecting one or accepting the other.

Heretofore, in describing deformations of the earth's crust I have avoided mention of the origin of the forces that caused these deformations, because we are still completely in the dark in this respect. Many theories have been advanced, and many have been rejected, but from each of them something has stayed in our collective mind, with the result that the total picture is far from clear. When we try to classify the various theories we can distinguish two large groups: (1) those based on lateral-tangential forces and (2) those based on radial forces, but very often the two are combined in one theory.

In historical sequence we can distinguish as major theories the following:

1. The classical contraction theory, contraction due to cooling of the earth
2. Joly's theory of expansion due to radioactive heat
3. Wegener's theory of continental drift
4. Haarmann's, Bailey Willis's, and van Bemmelen's oscillation and undation theories
5. Convection-current theory
6. Expansion theory

In theories 1, 2, 3, and 5, lateral forces in the crust are the origin of all deformation, whereas in theories 4 and 6, the cause is sought in vertical forces. In theories 4, 5, and 6, the origin of the force is located in the interior of the earth; in theories 1, 2, and 3, the cause is located in the crust itself.

Evidently, the central problem of the origin of orogenic deformation has given rise to a twofold controversy: on one hand, as to whether the obvious lateral compression is a secondary manifestation of primary vertical movements or whether it is in itself the primary cause; on the other hand, as to what is, in both cases, the origin of the force and energy.

Without doubt the first question is more within the scope of our possibilities of observation than the second, and the answer depends to a large degree on our adjustment to the second question. In this book I have continuously reasoned from the central conception of a primary lateral compression and have advocated vertical movements as the origin of lateral movements in the case of gravitational gliding structures and the fanning out of upthrusts. This traditional point of view has been strongly attacked by van Bemmelen, and it behooves us to check it again in relation to our present knowledge of the great mountain chains.

A fundamental question which must be posed to test each theory is whether the supposed driving force is adequate or not and whether the physical phenomenon can or cannot exist. The classical contraction theory, based on the consideration that the earth is constantly losing energy by radiation and therefore cooling, had to be abandoned because, with the recognition of radioactive energy, probably concentrated in the crust, the cooling itself becomes very doubtful. The other extreme, that radioactive energy is heating an expanding earth, is equally improbable and also had to be abandoned. Nevertheless, both theories taught us viewpoints that have their advantages, which we are reluctant to throw overboard with the theories.

Wegener's theory of drifting continents started from the obvious resemblance in shape of the South American and African continents and found many other homologues on the two continents; these viewpoints too we should be sorry to give up altogether.

A similar observation can be made about the convection currents. The possibility of convection currents following on a chaotic state before any crust or core had been formed has rarely been challenged, but their formation in simple adjoining cells turning in opposite directions is theoretically unproved and looks improbable when one takes the rotation of the earth into consideration. Moreover, as soon as the application of the simple cells is carried forward in time and has to explain all kinds of peculiarities in the configuration of the pattern of the earth's crust and of its gravitation field, one again becomes suspicious, because the solid state of at least the upper half of the mantle has become very probable. Nevertheless, it would be a pity to have to give up the advantages of imagining the primeval state of the large convection current by rejecting the later stages.

For all these reasons I shall have to review briefly some of the more prominent hypotheses of the cause of the distribution of the earth's continents and oceans and of the orogenic forces that have been acting throughout its history.

THE CONTRACTION THEORY

The idea of the contraction of the earth through cooling was formulated in the middle of the nineteenth century in Europe by Elie de Beaumont (1852) and in America by James Dana (1847).

The conception at that time generally admitted that the earth at the dawn of its history was very much hotter and lost its heat gradually by radiation, and that at the same time its heavy core and light crust were formed, survived criticism for a long time. The consequence, that since the crust had been formed the loss of heat has proceeded at a much lower rate, to be sure, but has never stopped, leads naturally to the conception of a shrinking earth.

As only the crust was thought to be solid, enveloping the whole earth, a shrinking results in tensional stress in the interior and compressional stress in the crust. In between there must be a surface of no tension or stress, the asthenosphere, originally thought to be at something like 60 km depth, now more probably to coincide with the low-velocity layer at 60 to 200 km depth. The tangential stress in the crust would result in more or less uniform crumpling unless it possessed special zones of weakness between continental blocks of greater rigidity. Hence the rigid portions of the crust glide over the substratum along a surface in the asthenosphere, and the shortening is concentrated in the zones of weakness, the orogenic belts. The continental blocks are therefore surrounded by orogenic belts, which, when once folded and thickened by this folding, acquired the same rigidity as the original block, and thus the shield grew outward, each orogenic period adding another circumcontinental ring to the shield.

It was, in particular, Ed Suess (1909) who insisted on the accompanying phenomenon of collapse—of zones of the crust sinking in the intervals when no tangential pressure made itself felt; the collapse of geosynclines, the collapse of rift valleys, etc., and even, as the most prominent consequence of the shrinking earth, of the orogenes—as the advancing of the stable shields toward the sunken basins or oceans.

Even the bare outlines of the contraction theory as formulated here are sufficient to demonstrate its usefulness. It gives an excellent explanation of the fact that the crust possesses many zones where the total compression must be measured in at least tens of miles, perhaps as much as 100 miles, whereas zones of dilatation are relatively scarce and never show more than a few miles maximum dilatation. Furthermore, the obvious submergences are explained in a satisfactory way, and the zoning of orogenes around the continental blocks is comprehensible only when a general stress condition on the whole surface is postulated, as by the contraction theory.

As Hales (1953) pointed out, the contraction of the crust through cooling, using Jeffreys's temperature distribution, would amount to only about 3.5 km in 200 million years, the asthenosphere being at a depth of 60 km only. But a much greater value of stress increase could be obtained if the lower mantle and the core were compressed as a result of cooling between the surface and a depth of 700 km; and failure would occur at depths of 250 to 600 km depth, with a periodicity of 200 million years.

I presume that the effect would be the same if the contraction of the core and mantle were primary and the contraction of the shell secondary, instead of the case of compression of the core by a cooling outer shell 700 km thick.

The objections that have been raised are very serious, however. First of all, there is overwhelming evidence that the earth's *crust* has *not* cooled since the Cambrian; the recurrence of ice ages and many other considerations point unequivocally to that conclusion. Second, it is very doubtful whether cooling would ever result in such a contraction; and third, the cooling itself has become questionable, to say the least, since the radioactive energy of the crust acts in the opposite direction.

Summarizing, one may evaluate the contraction theory as one that is very attractive, as far as its consequences on the earth's crust are concerned, but very dubious in relation to its origin and to its motive force. No wonder that many well-known names of geotectonicians are among its adherents: Marcel Bertrand, Kober, T. C. Chamberlin, Stille, and many others; and if another adequate reason for a shrinking earth could be found, the reserve that many modern geologists feel about it for the reasons given above would vanish, and the contraction theory on a new basis might recapture the general acceptance it once held.

This has been done by Brian Mason (1953), with his theory of "polymorphism" as the cause of earth contraction. This concept is based on the assumption of Birch (1952 and 1954) that the seismic second-order discontinuities are due to conversion of olivine, pyroxene, feldspars, and quartz into denser minerals. If the mantle material were fluid, the denser minerals would sink down and the less dense would ascend, and a gradual expansion of the core boundary could be expected.

If contraction through polymorphism is true, we should have a contraction of core and of a considerable part of the mantle, to which the upper part of the mantle and the crust would have to yield.

This concept is a revival of the contraction theory, with its merits and without its most obvious drawbacks. The origin of the force is adequate and located somewhere deep in the mantle. In the crust we no longer have to worry about any gaps of the same width as the contraction of a mountain chain would leave to be filled.

It is immaterial to this concept whether the transport of the lithophile elements upward and of the siderophile elements downward is effected by slow diffusion or by convection currents, or whether the chemical reactions are considered from the point of view of classical chemistry or atomic chemistry.

It is impossible to determine the upper boundary of the siderophile supplying part of the mantle; there need not even be any boundary at all; perhaps the whole thickness of the mantle is supplying the core with siderophile elements and the crust with lithophile elements—the effect would be the same as long as the denser packing near the core is predominant over the looser packing near the crust.

The only consequence of importance in connection with the problem of the growth of the core is a general lateral stress in every part of the upper regions of the mantle and in the crust.

THE DRIFTING CONTINENTS

The theory of the wandering continents proposed by Wegener (1929) and defended fervently by du Toit (1937) originates in the remarkable similarity in the shapes of the west coast of Africa and the east coast of South America. If one could join them by shifting the two continents toward one another, very little space would be left void. When worked out accurately on a globe, and taking the 2,000-m isobath as boundary of the continents, as has been done by Carey (1958), the close fit is really remarkable. Once this principle of drifting rigid floes of sialic matter on a viscous substratum is accepted, it becomes a kind of game to join all the pieces together as in a jigsaw puzzle, and its result can be checked by comparing the age and facies of the geological formations and disturbances on the pieces that have been joined together (Fig. 307). A remarkable fact then arises: marine sediments of the Cretaceous on both sides of the Atlantic Ocean join almost perfectly, and the separation of the two continents is therefore believed to have happened after this period. The rift advanced northward so that the American continent became separated from Europe only in the Tertiary, and Greenland drifted westward only very recently. The westward drift is thought to have created the Pacific Cordilleras on the west coast of the American continents by friction of the continental shield on its sima bottom, causing a surge on its front.

The splitting up of the other continental areas mostly happened somewhat earlier, according to Wegener's theory, but as late as at the beginning of the Mesozoic all the continents still formed one continuous shield, called Pangaea, on which a meridional epicontinental sea, the Tethys, had been formed. The Tethys geosyncline was later compressed by a northward drift of India. It would take us too far to quote all the arguments in favor of the theory, but obviously many difficulties connected with the distribution and similarity of faunas

Fig. 307 The continents joined together before they drifted apart at the end of the Mesozoic. (*After Wegener, 1929.*)

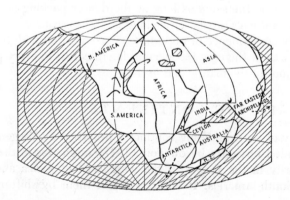

are solved at one stroke; nevertheless, many dissimilarities replace them as unsolved questions.

The game of the jigsaw puzzle has been played by many geologists, of which Taylor (1923), Argand (1922), and Staub (1928) were perhaps the best-known representatives. Each of them had his own preferred solution of the puzzle, but it must be admitted that the greatest objection to the theory—that it was concerned only with the latest phase of the earth's history and left all the earlier developments alone—could never be met (cf. van Waterschoot v. d. Gracht et al., symposium, 1928).

Many other ideas were added to the original concept. In order to explain the distribution of ice-age climates and the climatological zoning of the Carboniferous, the poles had to be shifted too. Furthermore, the shifting had to have a motive force, and this was found partly in the centrifugal force toward the equator exerted on the continents by the rotation of the earth (Köppen, 1922) and in the westward drift due to the retardation caused by the tidal action of sun and moon. It has been proved without any doubt and with a very large margin that both forces are completely inadequate (Jeffreys, 1959). Other objections, mainly by tectonicians, can be found in the above-cited symposium of 1928, which at that time more or less put an end to the theory.

The drifting-continents hypothesis taught us two important principles: first, that continents need not be regarded as fixed forever in their present position since the birth of the crust, and second, that pole wandering can be admitted. The concept has been revived very actively by the result of the paleomagnetic measurements and, combined with convection currents or an expanding earth as a motive force, has won acceptance in many circles.

A more recent symposium took place, in 1956, at the University of Tasmania, presided over by S. W. Carey. In a global analysis in which continents and islands drift around and are sheared loose from one another, Carey (1958) gives his conception of an expanding earth, expanding at an increasing rate with time.

THE UNDATION AND OSCILLATION THEORY

The oscillation theory advanced by Haarmann (1930) postulated vertical movements below the crust as a new principle for all structural deformations. It teaches that, through the influence of some undefined cosmic factor, a disequilibrium in the perfectly layered earth's crust could be established, and that this could be counteracted only by flow of subcrustal masses because the crust itself is rigid. Thus "geotumors" became established, separated by "geodepressions," by flow of vitreous sialic matter from the depressions to the tumors. The next stage in the development naturally became the erosion of tumors and sedimentation in the depressions. When the cosmic influence was moved in relation to the earth, the tumors had to move also, and it was thought that an oscillating action of emergence and submergence was thus originated.

The sediments in the depression were lifted up and consequently glided down the slopes of the new tumor; later the folded and structurally accumulated rocks were lifted up again and became mountain chains.

In Haarmann's conception all structural deformation takes place in a depression and below sea level; he therefore distinguishes a "tectogenesis," the uplift followed by a folding process due to gliding, and an "orogenesis," the subsequent uplift that formed the mountain chains. Moreover, he distinguishes a "primary tectogenesis," the first geotumors, and a "secondary tectogenesis," the uplift of the primary geodepression filled with sediments.

The theory never found many supporters, principally because the mysterious cosmic influence could satisfy hardly anybody, and second, because gliding tectonics as a universal cause of structural features were not found acceptable.

Nevertheless, the principle of geotumors and of subcrustal mass displacements is fascinating, and was soon adopted by van Bemmelen.

Before Haarmann proposed his theory, Bailey Willis (1929) had formulated another principle about the genesis of sialic crusts or continents. His starting point is the "planetesimal theory" of T. C. Chamberlin, in which the birth of the earth is seen as an accumulation of meteorites, or rather "planetesimals," which fused as a result of the gravitative pressure and then cooled again through loss of heat by radiation. Differentiation of the basaltic magma into a granite layer is the core of Bailey Willis's conception. According to him, the mantle of the earth consists of three shells, an inner highly elastic shell, the "stereosphere," 1,900 km thick, an intermediate nonelastic zone of 1,250 km thickness, the "asthenosphere," and an outer 60-km zone, the rigid crust. The asthenosphere receives more heat than it can transmit outward, its temperature is raised, and regions of molten magma are formed—the "asthenoliths," which are the cause of volcanic action, batholith intrusion, etc., or in other words, the regions from which the granitic layer originates. The asthenoliths first grow in height, and then laterally; between them we find the basins, filled with sediments.

The new element in Willis's conception is the fundamental role of magmatic differentiation in structural deformation.

Van Bemmelen (1935) then combined the elements of Willis's and Haarmann's theories by placing the magmatic differentiation that leads to granite in the center of his undation theory, forming asthenolithic mountain roots, undations, from which, by a mechanism principally of subcrustal gliding, the superficial mountain chains were formed (Fig. 308). The fact that the undation theory was conceived in Indonesia explains why the role of volcanic differentiation and interpretation of gravimetric data is prominent in its reasoning.

Table 15 summarizes the zoning of the outer shell of the earth according to van Bemmelen.

The salsima of the intermediate shell is regarded as the parental magma zone, and in it is concentrated the origin of all the "equilibria-turbale" forces, the forces that disturb the equilibrium. The mechanism of this force is the formation of asthenoliths by a process of "hypo-differentiation," a splitting up into an ultrabasic sima and an acid granitic asthenolithic magma rich in volatiles. The volatile content lowers the specific density of the asthenolith, which rises and flows laterally outward, causing salsima flow toward the center. The asthenolith is the root of a mountain or of the geanticline with geosynclines flanking it. During this stage of the hypodifferentiation the sialic crust above it was affected by a rising front of emanations, and a femic front was formed, giving rise to ophiolitic magma of the initial magmatic phase. Later, the asthenolith itself caused migmatization and batholithic intrusions.

The uplift of the geanticline, the lateral outward flow of the asthenolith, caused gliding tectonics in the epidermis, and these could reach very far out from the center because the masses involved were large.

We cannot fully pursue the complete theory of van Bemmelen with all its intricate mechanisms of subcrustal flow, rising and subsiding

Fig. 308   Section of the earth's crust in an orogeny according to the undation theory of van Bemmelen.

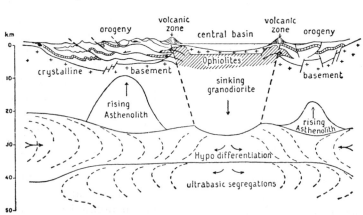

Table 15

	State and Composition	Mechanical Property	Thickness, km	Density	Velocity of Long Seismic Waves, km/sec
Epidermis	Sediments	Plastic	Max. 10	2.0–2.8	4.25
Sial outer shell	Crystalline granitic	Zone of fracture	10–25	2.7–2.8	5.5–6.0
Asthenolithic mountain root	Magmatic, intermediate acid	Flow No strength	Max. 30	2.3–2.7	?
Salsima, intermediate shell	Upper part crystalline basalt Lower part vitreous basalt	Flow	15–30	2.7–3.0	±6.5
	Mohorovicic Seismic Discontinuity Surface				
Sima basement shell	Partly crystalline ultrabasic	Flow	50	3.2–3.4	±8
Siferna substratum	Vitreous, ultrabasic	SiO_2 content diminishing with depth	Down to −1,200	3.4–4.4	7.9 increasing to 11.4

(Left margin labels: Silicate mantle — Tectonosphere; Bathysphere)

masses, etc.; suffice it to state that he finally arrives at a central mass, characterized by a high-gravity anomaly due to a fundamental basement which replaced the original asthenolith, the latter having flowed away to two flanking zones of negative gravity anomalies (Fig. 308).

Van Bemmelen's undation theory has won little support, partly because of its unsurveyable complexity, partly because of the consequence of the secondary character of all lateral stress in the structural phenomena, partly because of the uncontrollable postulates on hypodifferentiation.

Nevertheless, it represents an important point of view since it establishes a close relation between the magmatic and structural aspects of mountain building. It is true that we know nothing for certain about the diffusion that might lead to granite differentiation from a basaltic parental magma and that speculations about it are therefore premature, but neither can we be certain that it does *not* cause mass translations, which certainly might influence mountain building to a high degree.

From a structural point of view, the absence of any primary lateral stress is inadmissible. We know too many examples of lateral stress deformation totally unconnected with any "tumors" or "undations." Moreover, all gliding tectonics create, besides accumulation of crustal matter at one place, denudation at another place, and the latter are lacking in all simpler structures without an uplifted axial basement zone and are often metamorphosed *in situ* instead of having been displaced in larger orogenies. Further, there is no reason why the asthenoliths should have a linear character; on the contrary, they would tend to be circular, and therefore van Bemmelen prefers regions like the Banda arc or other Indonesian structures. But mountain chains are by nature linear structures, and arcs of 270° like the Banda or Antillean arcs are exceptions.

Finally, van Bemmelen's sections, which join, for instance, the Alps with the northern Apennines or the Betic Cordilleras of Spain with the Oran Meseta of North Africa in one dual orogeny, link up so many completely incompatible features that their usefulness is seriously impaired.

THE THEORY OF CONVECTION CURRENTS

The theory of convection currents is a theory which still doubtless finds many adherents. From the very beginning we must remember, however, that it is just another theory *ad hoc,* which nobody has ever succeeded in proving by independent measurements of any kind. The possibility of convection currents in a fluid or plastic mantle of the earth has perhaps been demonstrated; they furnish an origin of the deformative forces which have crumpled the crust, but whether they are adequate is difficult to judge because we know very little about the absolute value of the physical properties of the crust and even less of the mantle material.

Heat-convection currents are generated by temperature differences, the hotter part of a fluid usually having a lower density than the cooler parts, and they have the function of reestablishing the equilibrium in the temperature distribution. The current itself is a function of gravity, drawing the cooled and denser near-surface material of the mantle down and the hot material of deep levels up. In a good conductor of heat, convection currents are less likely because the relatively quick heat transfer prevents great differences of density from arising. High viscosity will clearly discourage, and may in fact prevent, such currents. Hence the existence of a steep temperature gradient and low viscosity may be taken to favor the possibility of convection currents, but unfortunately we know very little about the gradient in the mantle. The viscosity of a zone just below the crust has been calculated at -10^{22} poises, on the assumption of isostatic adjustment of Scandinavia to the melting of the Pleistocene icecap, but its validity is doubtful.

Vening Meinesz calculated that, in the beginning of the history of the earth, before there was any question of a crust or a core, the most probable convection-current system was a symmetrical double system

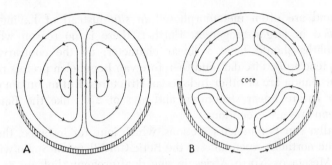

Fig. 309 The primeval convection current before, and the
second-order convection current after, the formation of the
core. (*After Vening Meinesz.*)

as shown in Fig. 309A. Such a system could accumulate the lighter
sialic components in a sialic continent in one hemisphere.

With the generation of continents a new factor in the heat distribution below the crust is introduced. Because of the protection offered
by a sialic crust and its generation of radioactive heat, a horizontal
temperature gradient will arise, between the substratum below the
continents and below the oceans. Very small gradients, for instance
1 to 3° per kilometer (Hales, 1936; Pekeris, 1935), would be sufficient
to set a horizontal current from continent to ocean in motion. The
most probable, effective, and strongest convection-current system
would then be one with a current in every octant of the mantle. How
the currents subsequently generated the metallic (?) core remains
unexplained, but a new second-order system originated when this core
became a fact; this could have the shape shown in Fig. 309B. Its
system would have torn apart the great primeval continent, and the
fragments would have drifted toward the equator. One might even
suggest that, because the north pole, lacking the crust blanket, cooled
more quickly, an opposite first-order current replaced the original
one, having the same effect as the second-order currents of Vening
Meinesz (1952) (Fig. 310).

These second convection currents broke up the blanket into large
floes and drove them northward, carried on the back of this mighty
surface current. Each of the floes naturally had a long broad front and
a tail end tapering away to the south. They were floated northward
until their edges collided, after having passed the equator. With some
shifting and squeezing they managed to travel quite a long way
toward the north, but finally they stuck, and the north pole remained
free from any sialic cover, but surrounded by a barrier of floes formed
by the broken sialic blanket that once covered the south pole. The
south pole itself was still covered by the last remnant of that once

extensive blanket, since a central rising current of this kind produces a dead spot without current where it starts turning to its lateral surface flow. Antarctica is the only portion of the blanket that never left its original position. The same is true for the north pole, where the surface current turns downward long before it reaches the pole and it is left uncovered.

Griggs (1939b) pointed out that, in order to sustain a permanent convection-current system, the cooling at the surface would have to be adequate; otherwise the downward stream would still be hot and the convection would be stopped. Because the substratum has without doubt a certain strength, the heat difference can build up a considerable stress before the current is well under way, with the result that, once it flows, it flows too quickly and is stopped. In this way the cyclic character of the crust movements, which Umbgrove called the "pulse of the earth," can be explained as a phenomenon of convection currents.

Griggs (1939b) constructed a simple mechanism with which he demonstrated the action on a plastic crust of convection currents in a viscous substratum. With two turning drums in the substratum, he actually succeeded in forming a sialic bulge downward in the "sima," representing the root of a mountain system, above the downward stream of the current.

The broad concept of a large convection current from continent to ocean is acceptable mainly for the simple and negative reason that no other adequate source of horizontal orogenic stress has been proposed. That this stress results in folding located on the wedge of sialic crust is probable, and that a thickening of the crust, either by overthrusting or by simple thickening or by buckling, then occurs there is logical, but all this reasoning depends on the reality of convection currents, which, at the very start, is not favored by the probable solid state of the mantle, the presence of the low-velocity layer,

Fig. 310 Successive stages of convection currents in the youthful stage of the earth's development.

and the increase in density downward. Moreover, as stated before, convection currents are counteracted by restriction in size and increase of viscosity, two factors which perhaps gained importance in the course of the earth's history. If they did, we might conclude that the original currents which followed on the chaotic stage were effectively stopped after a youthful stage of development.

Since the great development of the paleomagnetic studies which has given new life to the concept of drifting continents, convection currents have also become more popular again. Convection currents driving the American and Eurasian continents apart have also won support from the tensional features of the Mid-Atlantic rift on top of the ridge.

Apart from considerations of linking up structural features across the Atlantic, like the Scandinavian Caledonides with the Appalachians, we are confronted by the difficulty that such orogenes of typical continental character run out toward the ocean. The problem then arises whether a continental crust can be changed into an oceanic crust, or vice versa. This problem has also been regarded from the point of view of subcrustal currents. Convection currents in the mantle are supposed to erode the mountain roots of the circumcontinental orogenes, transporting the sialic material toward the ocean and creating in the border zone the transitional regions described before. This idea was first offered by Gilluly (1955) and later worked out by Gidon (1963). Such currents would have the opposite direction from those that are supposed to have caused the Mid-Atlantic rift and the drifting apart of the American and Eurasian continents.

THE EARTH-EXPANSION THEORY

Recently, the notion has been proposed that perhaps the earth is expanding instead of contracting. Undoubtedly, it was the results of paleomagnetic surveys and the discovery of the world-wide oceanic ridge rifts that gave rise to this new point of view. It has been ably expounded by Egyed (1957 and 1960). The geosynclinal phase is regarded as due to a tensional stress, either by causing rifts or thinning the crust. The orogenic phenomena are then the result of magma intrusion from far below, causing compression and gravitational gliding tectonics. As mentioned already, Carey (1958) took up this idea as a motive force for his drifting-continent concept. Egyed considers it possible that the original cosmic parent material is still present in the interior of the core, and is of very high density plasma of almost dissociated electrons and neutrons, and that the various layers (interior core, core, mantle) are degeneration phases of this material corresponding to the lower gravity within the earth compared with the primeval plasma of the solar system. This theory is complete in describing the cosmic evolution of the solar system and explains the positions, sizes, and densities of the planets in relation to the sun. It also has the advantage of explaining otherwise contradictory characteristics known of the core—high density, incompressibility, lack of shear strength, and magnetic susceptibility. The origin of the expansion is thus thought to be located in the core of the earth, the inner and outer cores being formed by silicates in unstable ultrahigh-pressure states, slowly evolving by expansion in the stable phase of the mantle.

Avoiding both contraction and expansion, Pavoni (1961) advocates horizontal shearing movements of continental blocks along funda- mental faults as the cause of mountain building, a proposition that has also arisen from the analysis of the direction of movement of circum-Pacific earthquakes. The same idea can be found in the work of Ashgirei (1962) and Benioff (1959), but is contradicted by Allen (1962).

CRITICAL REVIEW

Every attempt to formulate a general theory about the historical development of the earth's crust is necessarily highly conjectural, because we suspect that the origin of its long and complicated history of deformation is not located in the crust itself, but in regions below it, regions we have never seen, never touched with the hammer. As we have found, we have, nevertheless, some information about the distribution of stress, temperature, and density in mantle and core and their mechanical properties, but the effect of the combination of these physical properties, together with the almost totally unknown chemical properties of matter in these circumstances, can hardly be guessed. On the contrary, we are sure that unknown or unpredictable reactions can take place. Our ignorance ought to compel us, however, to observe the utmost modesty and simplicity in our assumptions, to avoid building a house-of-cards of assumptions; otherwise we may be sure that at the slightest provocation it will topple down and leave us again with the chaos out of which the earth was created.

I have tried to assemble the different theories discussed above in a comparative table (Table 16), which enables us to formulate some conclusions about their merits and deficiencies. The contraction theory, taking the cooling of the earth as its fundamental principle, can no longer be upheld, because we know now that, on the one hand, the radioactive energy of the crust makes cooling very doubtful, and on the other, cooling since the Precambrian is not reflected in any trend in the development of either the sediments or their organic content. Perhaps the new concept of contraction due to polymorphism

Table 16

	Contraction Theory	Expansion Theory
Origin of force	Cooling of the earth or polymorphism	Degeneration of original cosmic material
Comments on origin of force	Principle of cooling doubtful, polymorphism very probable	Possible but unproved
Stress field	Lateral stress, acting continuously	Lateral tensional stress acting continuously
Comments on stress field	Cyclic development unexplained	Adequate for rifts, inadequate for orogenies
Adequacy in relation to:		
Absence of tensional regions	Accounts adequately for lack of tensional regions	Inadequate
Folding	Adequate	Inadequate
Basin formation	Adequate	Adequate
Faulting	Adequate	Adequate
Magnetic cycles	Inadequate	Inadequate
Main advantages	Explains absence of tensional regions	Explains striking similarities of shape of continents
Secondary advantages	Very simple and universal	Very simple and universal
Main objections	Force inadequate; no connections magmatic orogenic cycles; not cyclic	Inadequate for orogenies

will revive it, because the contraction theory offers one great advantage over all other theories, that a compression of one zone is not coupled with a stretching of another zone. The very simple and very obvious fact that zones of compression are numerous, frequent, and intense whereas zones of tension are narrow and small, is one of the major characteristics of the earth's crust distortion, and has been overlooked by most theories, but not by the contraction theory.

Convection currents have the great advantage over their predecessors that they look for the origin of stress in the lower reaches of the crust and the mantle, and not in the crust itself. In this respect the convection theory, by reaching deeper into the mantle, is preferable to the other theories, because it can postulate currents of continent or oceanwide size; but as soon as it requires a current for every basin and mountain chain, it becomes self-contradictory.

The undation and oscillation and expansion theories, which put the radial before the lateral forces, undoubtedly have advantages over the others. In many cases emergence does precede lateral compres-

Undation and Oscillation Theory	*Drifting Continents and Convection Currents*
Chemical reactions in upper mantle	Thermal gradients horizontal and vertical
Possible but very conjectural	Possibility decreasing with size and dependent on temperature gradient, viscosity, etc., all $\pm$ unknown quantities
Vertical stress in cycles causing uplifts followed by gliding	Lateral stress in cycles
Gliding mechanism fully inadequate; cycles possible	Inadequate because each feature requires its own current; cycles inadequately explained
Inadequate for absence of tensional region of less intense structures	No explanation for absence of tensional regions
Inadequate	Adequate
Inadequate	Adequate
Inadequate	Adequate
Mainstay of theory	Somewhat forced
Correlation of magmatic cycles with orogenies	Large currents probable and attractive in effect
Large intricate orogenies explained	Large and small orogenies explained
Too complicated and construed; lateral stress inadequate; paratectonics unexplained	Too complicated for smaller structures; connection magmatic cycles—orogenies inadequate; larger currents contradicted by low velocity layer

sion, but in others the sequence is reversed. Where major mountain chains with crystalline cores are concerned, the universal lateral gliding motions toward the peripheries are not contradicted by the absence of tensional regions, but in less severely compressed chains, there is no central emergence and there is no trace of tectonic denudation.

The fact that earthquakes are generated in the upper 700 km of the mantle and that a layering in the upper 1,000 km has been proved by seismic evidence is not in direct contradiction to the mantle currents; the same material can react by shocks to sudden stresses and flow under the influence of long-acting low stresses. Nevertheless, this layering and, in particular, the low-velocity layer are not in favor of convection currents.

Although a close relation between drifting of continents and orogenies could be expected, no such connections, except in a very broad sense, have been postulated.

The structural problem of an orogene, with its metamorphic core due to a rising temperature front and its essential compressive and pronounced vertical phases of movement, is not cleared up in any way by any of these theories.

The principal objective of our future work as geotectonicians should be in the direction of providing the geophysicists with a better and a more diversified picture of the actual succession of deformation phases, which is essential to an understanding of the origin of the different kinds of orogenes and other structural units of the earth's crust.

References

Adams, F. D.: 1912. An experimental contribution to the question of the depth of the zone of flow in the earth's crust, *Jour. Geology*, vol. 20, pp. 97–118.

——— and J. T. Nicholson: 1901. An experimental investigation into the flow of marble, *Royal Soc. [London] Phil. Trans.*, ser. A, vol. 195, pp. 363–401.

Ahorner, L.: 1962. Untersuchungen zur quartären Bruchtektonik der Niederrheinischen Bucht, *Eiszeitalter und Gegenwart*, vol. 3, pp. 24–105.

Aki, K., and F. Press: 1961. Upper mantle structure under oceans and continents from Rayleigh waves, *Geophys. Jour. Royal Astron. Soc.*, vol. 5, pp. 292–305.

Allen, C. R.: 1962. Circum-Pacific faulting in the Philippines-Taiwan region, *Jour. Geophys. Research*, vol. 67, pp. 4795–4812.

Ancion, C.: 1948. Étude géologique du Bassin houiller de Liège: la concession de Marihaye, *Assoc. étude Paléologique et stratigrafique Houillères*, vol. 3.

Anderson, E. M.: 1951. "The Dynamics of Faulting," 2d ed., Oliver & Boyd Ltd., Edinburgh.

——— and H. Jeffreys: 1936. The dynamics of the formation of Cone-sheets, Ring-dykes, and Caldron-subsidence (A) with "Note on Fracture" (J), *Royal Soc. Edinburgh Proc.*, vol. 56, no. 2, pp. 128–163.

Andres, J.: 1959. Seismische Kartierung von Bruchzonen im mittleren und nördlichen Teil des Oberrheintalgrabens und deren Bedeutung für die Ölansammlung, *Erdöl und Kohle*, vol. 12, pp. 323–334.

Appalachian Geological Society: 1951. In possible future petroleum provinces of North America. Appalachian region. *Am. Assoc. Petroleum Geologists Bull.*, vol. 35, pp. 438–457.

Arbenz, P.: 1919. Probleme der Sedimentation und ihre Beziehungen zur Gebirgsbildung in den Alpen. *Heim-Festsch. Viertelj. Naturf. Gesell., Zürich*, vol. 64.

Argand, E.: 1916. Sur l'arc des Alpes occidentales, *Eclogae geol. Helv.*, vol. 14, pp. 146–204.

———: 1922. La tectonique de l'Asie, 13e Cong. géologique internatl. *Belgique, Comptes rendus*, no. 5, pp. 171–372.

Ashauer, H.: 1934. Die östliche Endigung der Pyrenäen, *Gesell. Wiss. Göttingen Abh., Math. phys. Kl.*, ser. 3, vol. 10, pp. 5–115.

Ashgirei, G. D.: 1962. Einige Wesenszüge der Tektonik und Entwicklungsgeschichte globaler Mobilzonen, I, Tiefenbrüche, *Geologie*, vol. 11, pp. 133–153.

Asklund, B.: 1938. Hauptzüge der Tektonik und Stratigraphie der mittleren Kaledoniden in Schweden, *Sveriges Geol. Undersökn., ser.* C, no. 417.

Aubert, D.: 1945. Le Jura et la tectonique d'écoulement, *Univ. de Lausanne, Lab. Géologie Bull.,* vol. 83.

Aubouin, J.: 1959. A propos d'un centenaire: les aventures de la notion de géosynclinal, *Rev. géog. phys. géol. dyn.,* vol. 2, pp. 135–188.

————: 1959. Contribution à l'étude géologique de la Grèce septentrionale: les confins de l'Épire et de la Thessalie, *Annales géol. Pays Helléniques,* vol. X, Athènes.

Augenheister, G.: 1957. Die gegenwärtige Stand der palaeomagnetischen Forschung, *Geol. Rundschau,* vol. 46, pp. 87–99.

Backlund, H. G.: 1936. Der "Magmaaufstieg" in Faltengebirgen, *Soc. géol. Finlande Comptes rendus,* vol. 9.

Bailey, E. B., and W. J. McCallien: 1960. Some aspects of the Steinmann trinity: mainly chemical, *Geol. Soc. London Quart. Jour.,* vol. 116, pp. 365–395.

Baker, B. H.: 1958. Geology of the Magadi Area, *Geol. Survey Kenya Rept.* 42.

Bartram, J. G.: 1929. Elk Basin oil and gas field, in "Typical American Oilfields," vol. II, American Association of Petroleum Geologists, Tulsa, Okla., pp. 577–588.

Bearth, P.: 1933. Ueber Gangmylonite der Silvretta, *Schweiz Mineralog. Petrol. Mitt.,* vol. 13, pp. 347–355.

————: 1956. Geologische Beobachtungen im Grenzgebiet der lepontinischen und penninischen Alpen, *Eclogae geol. Helv.,* vol. 49, no. 2, pp. 279–290.

Becker, G. F.: 1904. Experiments on schistosity and slaty cleavage, *U.S. Geol. Survey Bull.* 241.

Behr, H. J.: 1961. Beiträge zur petrographischen und tektonischen Analyse des sächsischen Granulitgebirges *Freiberger Forschungsh.,* C119, *Geologie,* pp. 5–118.

Behrmann, R. B.: 1949. Geologie und Lagerstätte des Oelfeldes Reitbrook bei Hamburg, *Erdöl und Tektonik in N. W. Deutschland,* pp. 190–221.

Beloussov, V. V.: 1959. Les divers types de plissements et leurs modes de formation, *Rev. géog. phys. géol. dyn.,* vol. 2, no. 2, pp. 97–112.

————: 1960. Tectonophysical investigations, *Geol. Soc. Am. Bull.,* vol. 71, pp. 1255–1270.

Beneo, E.: 1956. Il problema "Argile scagliose": "Flysch" in Italia e sua probabile risoluzione, Nuova nomenclatura, *Soc. geol. italiana Boll.,* vol. 75, pp. 3–18.

Benioff, H.: 1959. Circum-Pacific tectonics, *Dominion Observatory Ottawa Pub.* 20, pp. 395–402.

Bersier, A.: 1958. Examples de sédimentation cyclothématique dans l'Aquitanien de Lausanne, *Eclogae geol. Helv.,* vol. 51, pp. 842–853.

————: 1958. Séquences détritiques et divagations fluviales, *Eclogae geol. Helv.,* vol. 51, pp. 854–893.

Bertrand, Marcel: 1897. Structure des Alpes françaises et récurrence de certains facies sédimentaires. *Cong. géol. internat. Comptes rendus*, pp. 161–177.

Bhattacharji, S.: 1958. Theoretical and experimental investigations of cross folding, *Jour. Geology*, vol. 66, pp. 625–667.

Billings, M. P.: 1943. Ring dikes and their origin. *N.Y. Acad. Sci. Trans.*, ser. 2, vol. 5, no. 6, pp. 131–144. With literature references.

Biot, M. A.: 1961. Theory of folding of stratified viscoelastic media and its implications in tectonics and orogenesis, *Geol. Soc. Am. Bull.*, vol. 72, pp. 1595–1620.

———, H. Ode, and W. L. Roever: 1961. Experimental verification of the theory of folding of stratified viscoelastic media, *Geol. Soc. Am. Bull.*, vol. 72, pp. 1621–1631.

Birch, F.: 1952. Elasticity and constitution of the earth's interior. *Jour. Geophys. Research*, vol. 57, no. 227–286.

———: 1954. Elasticity and constitution of the earth. *Am. Geophys. Union Trans.*, vol. 35, pp. 79–85.

———: 1955. Physics of the crust, *Geol. Soc. Am. Spec. Papers*, no. 62, pp. 101–118.

———: 1960. The velocity of compressional waves in rocks to 10 kilobars, I, *Jour. Geophys. Research*, vol. 65, pp. 1083–1102.

———: 1961. Composition of the earth's mantle, in A. H. Cook and T. F. Gaskell, "The Earth Today," Royal Astronomical Society, London, pp. 295–311.

——— and P. LeComte: 1960. Temperature-pressure plane for albite composition, *Am. Jour. Sci.*, vol. 258, pp. 209–217.

Blanchet, P. H.: 1957. Development of fracture analysis as exploration method, *Am. Assoc. Petroleum Geologists Bull.*, vol. 41, pp. 1748–1759.

Böker, R.: 1915. Die Mechanik der bleibenden Formänderungen in kristallinisch aufgebauten Körper, *Forsch. Gebiete Ingenieurw.*, pp. 175–176.

Borchert, H.: 1957. Der initialen Magmatismus und die zugehörigen Lagerstätten, *Neues Jahrb. Mineralogie*, vol. 91, pp. 54–572.

———: 1958. Die Chrom- und Kupfererzlagerstätten des initialen ophiolitischen Magmatismus in der Türkei, *Inst. Lagerstätten Türkei Verh.*, vol. 102, pp. 1–173.

Boschma, D.: 1963. Successive Hercynian structures in some areas of the Central Pyrenees, *Leidse Geol. Med.*, vol. 28, pp. 104–176.

Bowen, N. L.: 1928. "The evolution of igneous rocks." Princeton University Press, Princeton, N.J.

Brace, W. F.: 1955. Quartzite pebble deformation in central Vermont, *Am. Jour. Sci.*, vol. 253, pp. 129–145.

———: 1958. Interaction of basement and mantle during folding near Rutland, Vermont, *Am. Jour. Sci.*, vol. 256, pp. 241–256.

Breddin, H.: 1956. Die tektonische Deformation der Fossilien im Rheinischen Schiefergebirge, *Deutsche geol. Gesell. Zeitschr.*, vol. 106, no. 2, pp. 227–305.

Brown, R. W.: 1928. Experiments relating to the results of horizontal shearing, *Am. Assoc. Petroleum Geologists Bull.*, vol. 12, p. 715.

Brown Monnet, V.: 1948. Mississippian Marshall Formation of Michigan, *Am. Assoc. Petroleum Geologists Bull.*, vol. 32, pp. 629–688.

Bucher, W. H.: 1920, 1921. Mechanical interpretation of joints, *Jour. Geology*, vol. 28, p. 707; vol. 29, p. 1.

————: 1933. Cryptovolcanic structures in the U.S., *16th Internat. Geol. Cong.*, vol. 2, pp. 1055–1084.

————: 1952. Geologic structures and orogenic history of Venezuela, *Geol. Soc. Am. Mem. 49*.

Buddington, A. F.: 1959. Granite emplacement with special reference to North America, *Geol. Soc. Am. Bull.*, vol. 70, pp. 671–747.

Bullard, E. C.: 1936. Gravity measurements in East Africa, *Royal Soc. [London] Phil. Trans.*, ser. A, vol. 235, no. 757, pp. 445–531.

———— and A. Day: 1961. The flow of heat through the floor of the Atlantic Ocean, in A. H. Cook and T. F. Gaskell, "The Earth Today," Royal Astronomical Society, London, pp. 282–294.

————, A. E. Maxwell, and R. Revelle: 1956. Heat flow through the deep sea floor, *Advances in Geophysics*, vol. 3, pp. 153–182.

Bullen, K. E.: 1958. Solidity in the inner core, *Contr. in Geophysics*, in honor of B. Gutenberg, London.

Burgers, W. G., and J. M.: 1935. First report on viscosity and plasticity, *Koninkl. Nederlandse Akad. Wetensch., Verh.*, ser. 1, vol. 15, no. 3, pp. 1–256.

Burri, C., and P. Niggli: 1945. "Die jungen Eruptivgesteine des mediterranen Orogens, die Ophiolite," Vulkan Institut, Immanuel Friedländer No 3, Zürich.

Buxtorf, A.: 1910. Geologische Beschreibung des Weissenstein-tunnels und seiner Umgebung, *Mater. crt. géol. Suisse*, 21.

————: 1916. Prognosen und Befunde beim Hauenstein-basis und Grenchenberg tunnel, und die Bedeutung der letzteren für die Geologie des Juragebirges, *Naturf. Gesell. Basel, Verh.*, vol. 27.

Byerly, P.: 1956. Subcontinental structure in the light of seismological evidence, *Advances in Geophysics*, pp. 105–152.

Cadisch, J.: 1953. "Geologie der Schweizer Alpen," 2d ed., Wepf, Basel.

Carey, S. W.: 1958. The tectonic approach to continental drift, Symposium paper, University of Tasmania, Department of Geology.

————: 1962. Folding, *Alb. Soc. Petroloum Geolists. Jour.*, vol. 10, pp. 95–144.

Caribbean Petroleum Company: 1948. Oilfields of Royal Dutch Shell group in western Venezuela, *Am. Assoc. Petroleum Geologists Bull.*, vol. 31, pp. 517–628.

Carr, D. C., and J. L. Kulp: 1953. Age of Mid-Atlantic Ridge basalt boulder, *Geol. Soc. Am. Bull.*, vol. 64, pp. 253–254.

Caster, D. F.: 1948. Coniaurum Mine, in "Structural Geology of Canadian Ore Deposits," *Canadian Institute of Mining and Metallurgy*, Montreal.

Choubert, G.: 1952. Géologie du Maroc, I., Aperçu structural, *Mon. 19e Cong. géologie internat. Mon. régionales*, ser. 3, vol. 6, Histoire du domaine de l'Anti-Atlas, Rabat.

Clark, C. P., E. C. Robertson, and F. Birch: 1957. Experimental determination of kyanite-sillimanite equilibrium relations at high temperature and pressures, *Am. Jour. Sci.*, vol. 255, pp. 628–640.

Clifford, P.: 1960. The geological structure of the Loch Luichart area, Ross-shire, *Geol. Soc. London Quart. Jour.*, vol. 115, pp. 365–388.

———, et al.: 1957. The development of lineation in complex fold systems, *Geol. Mag.*, vol. 94, pp. 1–24.

Cloos, E.: Lineation. 1946. *Geol. Soc. Am. Mem.* 18.

———: 1947a. Boudinage, *Am. Geophys. Union Trans.*, vol. 28, pp. 626–632.

———: 1947b. Oolite deformation in the South Mountain fold, Maryland, *Geol. Soc. Am. Bull.*, vol. 58, pp. 843–918.

——— and A. Hietanen: 1941. Geology of the Marctic overthrust and the Glenarm Series in Pennsylvania and Maryland, *Geol. Soc. Am. Spec. Pub.* 35.

Cloos, H.: 1929. Tektonische Experimente und die Entstehung von Bruchlinien, *15e Cong. géol. Internat. South Africa Comptes rendus*, vol. 2.

———: 1929, 1930. Künstliche Gebirge, I and II, *Natur u. Museum*, vols. 5 and 6.

———: 1930, 1931. Zur Experimentellen Tektonik, I and II, *Naturwissenschaften*, vol. 18, no. 34, pp. 741–747; vol. 19, no. 11.

———: 1932. Zur Mechanik grosser Brüche und Gräben, *Central bl. Min., etc.* ser. 8, pp. 273–286.

———: 1936. "Einführung in die Geologie," pp. 258–272, Gebrüder Borntraeger, Berlin.

Collinson, D. W., and S. K. Runcorn: 1960. Polar wandering and continental drift: evidence from paleomagnetic observations in the U.S., *Geol. Soc. Am. Bull.*, vol. 71, pp. 915–958.

Cornelius, H. P., and M. Furlani-Cornelius: 1930. Die Insubrische Linie vom Tessin bis zum Tonale pass, *Denkschr. Akad. Wiss. Math.-Naturw. Kl.*, 102.

Cox, A., and R. R. Doell: 1960. Review of paleomagnetism, *Geol. Soc. Am. Bull.*, vol. 71, pp. 645–768.

Crowell, J. C.: 1954. Probable large lateral displacement on San Gabriel fault, S. California, *Am. Assoc. Petroleum Geologists Bull.*, vol. 36, pp. 2026–2035.

Currie, J. B.: 1956. Role of concurrent deposition and deformation of sediments in development of salt-dome graben structures, *Am. Assoc. Petroleum Geologists Bull.*, vol. 40, pp. 1–16.

———, H. W. Patnode, and R. P. Trump: 1962. Development of folds in sedimentary strata, *Geol. Soc. Am. Bull.*, vol. 73, pp. 655–674.

Dana, J. D.: 1847. Geological results of the earth's contraction in consequence of cooling, *Am. Jour. Sci.*, ser. 2, vol. 3, pp. 176–188.

———: 1873. On some results of the earth's contraction on cooling, *Am. Jour. Sci.*, vol. 5, pp. 423–443; vol. 6, pp. 6–14, 104–115, 161–172.

Darton, N. H.: 1940. Some structural features of the Northern Coal Basin, Pennsylvania, *U.S. Geol. Surv. Prof. Paper* 193D.

Daubrée, A.: 1878. Expériences tendant à uniter des formes diverses de pletements, contournements et ruptures que présente l'écorce terrestre, *Acad. Sci. Comptes rendus*, vol. 86, pp. 733, 864, 928.

David, T. W. E.: 1950. The Geology of the Commonwealth of Australia, Edward Arnold (Publishers) Ltd., London.

de Beaumont, Elie: 1852. "Notice sur les systèmes de montagnes," P. Bertrand, Paris, 3 vols.

de Bruyn, J. W.: 1951. Isogam maps of Caribbean Sea and surroundings and of South-East Asia, *3d World Petrol. Cong. Proc.*, The Hague.

Deenen, J. M.: 1942. Breuken in kool en gesteente, *Geol. Stichting Heerlen Med.*, C 1–2, no. 1.

de Raaf, J. F. M.: 1953. Rumania, in "Science of Petroleum," vol. 6, "The World's Oilfields," pt. I, The Eastern Hemisphere, pp. 9–17.

de Sitter, L. U.: 1939a. Origin of oil in the Lower Oligocene of the Upper Rhine Valley, Pechelbronn field, *Geologie en Mijnbouw*, vol. 1, pp. 221–230.

————: 1939b. The principle of concentric folding and the dependence of tectonic structure on original sedimentary structure, *Koninkl. Nederlandse Akad. Wetensch. Verh.*, vol. 42, no. 5, pp. 412–430.

————: 1939c. Les porphyres luganois et leurs enveloppes, l'histoire géologique des Alpes tessinoises entre Lugano et Varese, *Leidse Geol. Med.*, vol. 11, pp. 1–61.

————: 1942. The Alpine geological history of the northern borders of the South Limburg coal district, Holland, *Jaarversl, Geol. Bur., Heerlen Med.*, pp. 5–25.

————: 1944–1945. De Keulsche Bocht en de horsten van de Peel en van Geldern-Crefeld, *Verh. Geol. Mijnb. Gen.*, vol. 14.

————: 1947a. Antithesis Alps-Dinarides, *Geol. en Mijnbouw*, vol. 9 (1), pp. 1–13.

————: 1947b. Geophysical survey of the south-east Netherlands, *Geol. Stichting, Heerlen Med.*, C 1–3, no. 1.

————: 1949. Le style Nord-Pyrénéen dans les Alpes Bergamasques, *Soc. géol. France Bull.*, ser. 5, vol. 19, pp. 617–621.

————: 1950. La tectonique d'écoulement dans les Alpes Bergamasques, *Geologie en Mijnbouw*, pp. 361–365.

————: 1952. Plissement croisé dans le Haut Atlas, *Geologie en Mijnbouw*, vol. 14, pp. 277–282.

————: 1953. Essai de géologie structurale comparative de trois chaînes tertiaires, Alpes, Pyrénées et Haut-Atlas, *Soc. Belge de Géologie Bull.*, vol. 62, no. 1.

————: 1954. La faille Nord-Pyrénéenne dans l'Ariège et la Haute Garonne, *Leidse Geol. Med.*, vol. 18, pp. 287–291.

————: 1959. The Rio Esla nappe in the zone of León of the Asturian-Cantabric mountain chain, *Inst. geol. minero. España, Notas y commun.*, no. 56, pp. 3–24.

————: 1962a. Structural development of the Arabian shield in Palestine, *Geologie en Mijnbouw*, vol. 41, pp. 116–124.

————: 1962b. The structure of the southern slope of the Cantabrian Mts., *Leidse Geol. Med.*, vol. 26, pp. 255–264.

———— and C. M. de Sitter-Koomans: 1949. Geology of the Bergamasc Alps, *Leidse Geol. Med.*, ser. B, vol. 14, pp. 1–257.

————— and H. J. Zwart: 1960. Tectonic development in supra- and infra-structures of a mountain chain, 21*st Internat. Geol. Cong. Norden,* Part 18, pp. 248–256.

Destombes, J. P.: 1948. La couverture post-hercynienne du massif de l'Arize au pays de Serou (Ariège), *Soc. géol. France Bull,* ser. 3, vol. 18, pp. 327–340.

Dietz, R. S., and H. W. Menard: 1953. Hawaiian swell, deep, and arch and subsidence of the Hawaiian Islands, *Jour. Geol.,* vol. 61, pp. 99–113.

Dikkers, A. J., and R. J. H. Patijn: 1944. De Heerlerheide storing in het veld der Oranje Nassau mijnen, *Geologie en Mijnbouw,* N.S., vol. 6.

Dixey, F.: 1946. Erosion and tectonics in the East African rift system, *Geol. Soc. London Quart. Jour.,* vol. 102, pp. 339–378.

Dohr, G.: 1959. Uber die Beobachtungen von Reflexionen aus dem tieferen Untergrunde im Rahmen routinemäsziger reflexionsseismischen Messungen, *Zeitschr. Geophys.,* vol. 25, no. 6, pp. 280–300.

Donath, F. A.: 1962. Analysis of Basin-Range Structure, South-Central Oregon, *Geol. Soc. Am. Bull.,* vol. 73, pp. 1–16.

Dorman, J., M. Ewing, and J. Oliver: 1960. Study of shear-velocity distribution in the upper mantle by mantle Rayleigh waves, *Seismol. Soc. Am. Bull.,* vol. 50, pp. 87–115.

Dozy, J. J.: 1935. Die Geologie der Catena Orobica zwischen Corno Stella und Pizo del Diavolo, *Leidse Geol. Med.,* vol. 4, pp. 133–230.

Drake, C. L., M. Ewing, and G. H. Sutton: 1959. Continental margins and geosynclines: the east coast of N. America, north of Cape Hatteras, *Phys. Chem. Earth,* vol. 3, pp. 110–198.

Dubar, G.: 1949. Note explicative de la carte géologique provisoire du Haut Atlas de Midelt. 1:200.000. *Notes et Mém. Serv. Géol. Maroc,* no. 59bis.

Dubertret, L.: 1953. Géologie des roches vertes du nord-ouest de la Syrie et du Hatay, *Moyen-Orient Notes et mém.,* vol. 6, pp. 5–175.

Du Toit, A. L.: 1937. "Our Wandering Continents," Oliver & Boyd Ltd., Edinburgh.

Eardley, A. J.: 1933. Structure and Physiography of the southern Wasatch Mountains, *Mich. Acad. Sci. Papers,* vol. 19.

—————: 1962. "Structural Geology of North America" 2d ed., Harper & Row, Publishers, Incorporated, New York.

Eaton, J. P., and K. J. Murata: 1960. How volcanics grow, *Science,* vol. 132, pp. 925–938.

Edmunds, F. H.: 1948. British regional geology: the Wealden district, *Geol. Survey (London).*

Egyed, L.: 1957. A new dynamic conception of the internal constitution of the earth, *Geol. Rundschau,* vol. 46, pp. 101–121.

—————: 1960. On the mechanism of mountain building and folding, *Geol. Rundschau,* vol. 50, pp. 225–234.

Emery, W. B.: 1935. Gas fields of Big Horn basin structural province, Wyoming and Montana, in "Geology of Natural Gas," pp. 277–296, American Association of Petroleum Geologists, Tulsa.

Engels, B.: 1959. Die kleintektonische Arbeitsweise unter besondere

Berücksichtigung ihrer Anwendung im deutschen Paläozoikum, *Geotekt. Forsch.*, vol. 13, pp. 1–129.

Escher, B. G., and P. H. Kuenen: 1929. Experiments in connection with saltdomes. *Leidse Geol. Med.*, vol. 3, pp. 152–182.

Eskola, P.: 1948. Ueber die Geologie Ostkareliens, *Geol. Rundschau*, vol. 35, no. 2, pp. 154–165.

Ewing, J., J. Antoine, and M. Ewing: 1960. Geophysical measurements in the western Caribbean Sea and in the Gulf of Mexico, *J. Geophys. Research*, vol. 65, pp. 4087–4126.

Ewing, M.: 1952. Seismic investigation in great ocean depths, *Assoc. Oceanogr. Phys.*, vol. 5, pp. 135–136.

———, D. B. Ericson, and B. C. Heezen: 1955. Geophysical and geological investigations in the Gulf of Mexico, I, *Geophysics*, vol. 20, pp. 1–18.

———, ———, and ———: 1958. Sediments and topography of the Gulf of Mexico, in "Habitat of Oil," pp. 995–1053, American Association of Petroleum Geologists, Tulsa, Okla.

——— and B. C. Heezen: 1955. Puerto Rico Trench topographic and geophysical data, *Geol. Soc. Am. Spec. Papers*, No. 62, pp. 255–268.

——— and ———: 1960. Continuity of Mid-Oceanic Ridge and rift valley in the southwestern Indian Ocean confirmed, *Science*, vol. 131, pp. 1677–1679.

——— and F. Press: 1955. Geophysical contrasts between continents and ocean basins, *Geol. Soc. Am. Spec. Papers*, No. 62, pp. 1–6.

——— and J. L. Worzel: 1954–1957. Gravity anomalies and structure of the West Indies, I–III, *Geol. Soc. Am. Bull.*, vol. 65, pp. 165–174, 195–200; vol. 68, pp. 263–266.

Fairbairn, H. W.: 1942. "Structural Petrology of Deformed Rocks," Addison-Wesley Publishing Company, Inc., Reading, Mass.

Fairbridge, R. W.: 1947. Possible causes of intraformational disturbances in the carboniferous varve rocks of Australia (with extensive bibliography), *Royal Soc. New South Wales Jour. and Proc.*, vol. 81, pp. 99–121.

Fallot, P.: 1944. Tectonique hercynienne et tectonique Alpine, *Soc. géol. France Bull.*, ser. 5, vol. 14.

———: 1949. Les chevauchements intercutanés de Roya, *Annales Hébert et Haug*, vol. 7, pp. 161–169.

Fath, A. E.: 1920. The origin of the faults, anticlines and buried "granite ridge" of the northern part of the Mid-Continent oil and gas field, *U.S. Geol. Survey Prof. Paper* 128-A, pp. 75–84.

Fisher, R. L.: 1961. Middle America trench, topography and structure, *Geol. Soc. Am. Bull.*, vol. 72, pp. 703–720.

Fleuty, M. J.: 1961. The three fold-systems in the metamorphic rocks of Upper Glen Orrin, Ross-shire and Inverness-shire, *Geol. Soc. London Quart. Jour.*, vol. 117, pp. 447–449.

Flinn, D.: 1956. On the deformation of the Funzie Conglomerate, Fetlar, Shetland, *Jour. Geol.*, vol. 64, pp. 480–505.

———: 1961. Continuation of the Great Glenn fault beyond the Moray Firth, *Nature*, vol. 191, pp. 589–591.

Foose, R. M., D. U. Wise, and G. S. Garbarini: 1961. Structural geology of the Beartooth Mountains, Montana and Wyoming, *Geol. Soc. Am. Bull.*, vol. 72, pp. 1143–1172.

Fourmarier, P.: 1951. Schistosité, foliation et microplissement, *Archives Sci., Geneva*, vol. 156, pp. 5–23.

———: 1953a. Schistosité et phénomènes connexes dans les séries plissés, 19e *Cong. géol. internat.*, vol. 3, no. 3, pp. 117–131.

———: 1953b. Schistosité et grande tectonique, *Annales Soc. Géol. Belgique*, vol. 76, pp. 275–301.

Fox, F. G.: 1959. Structure and accumulation of hydrocarbons in southern Foothills, Alberta, Canada, *Am. Assoc. Petroleum Geologists Bull.*, vol. 43, pp. 992–1025.

Gansser, A.: 1959. Ausseralpine Ophiolithprobleme, *Eclogae geol. Helv.*, vol. 52, no. 2, pp. 659–680.

———: 1960. Ueber Schlammvulkane und Salzdome, *Geol. Inst. Eidgenossiche Technische Hochschule Zürich Mitt.*, ser. B, vol. 15, pp. 1–46.

Gastil, G.: 1960. Continents and mobile belts in the light of mineral dating, *Internat. Geol. Cong. Norden*, vol. IX, pp. 162–169.

Gèze, B.: 1949. Etude géologique de la Montagne Noire et des Cévennes méridionales, *Soc. géol. France Mém.* 62.

———, L. U. de Sitter, and R. Trümpy: 1952. Sur le sens du déversement des nappes de la Montagne Noire, *Soc. Géol. France Bull.*, ser. 6, vol. 2, pp. 491–533.

Gidon, P.: 1963. "Courants magmatiques et évolution des continents," Masson et Cie, Paris.

Gignoux, M.: 1948. La tectonique d'écoulement par gravité et la structure des Alpes, *Soc. Géol. France Bull.*, vol. 18, pp. 739–761.

Gill, W. D., and P. H. Kuenen: 1958. Sand volcanoes on slumps in the Carboniferous of County Clare, Ireland, *Geol. Soc. London Quart. Jour.*, vol. 113, pp. 441–460.

Gilluly, J.: 1932. Geology and ore deposits of the Stockton and Fairfield quadrangles, Utah, *U.S. Geol. Surv. Prof. Papers*, no. 173.

———: 1949. Distribution of mountain building in geologic time, *Geol. Soc. Am. Bull.*, vol. 69, pp. 561–591.

———: 1955. Geologic contrasts between continents and ocean basins, *Geol. Soc. Am. Spec. Papers*, no. 62, pp. 7–18.

Girdler, R. W.: 1958. The relationship of the Red Sea to the East African rift system, *Quart. Jour. Geol.*, vol. 114, pp. 79–105.

Glaessner, M. F., and C. Teichert: 1947. Geosynclines: a fundamental concept in geology, *Am. Jour. Sci.*, vol. 245, pp. 463–482, 571–591.

Glangeaud, L.: 1944. Le rôle des failles dans la structure du Jura externe, *Soc. Hist. Nat. du Doubs*, vol. 51, pp. 17–38.

———: 1949. Les caractères structuraux du Jura, *Soc. Géol. Bull.*, vol. 5, no. 19, p. 669.

Goguel, J.: 1943. Introduction a l'étude mécanique des déformations de l'écorce terrestre, *Carte géol. France Mém.*

———: 1945. Sur l'origine mécanique de la schistosité, *Soc. Géol. France Bull.*, ser. 5, vol. 15, pp. 519–522.

512   *References*

———: 1950. L'influence de l'échelle dans les phénomènes d'écoulement, *Geol. en Mijnb.*, vol. 12, pp. 346–351.

———: 1952. "Traité de tectonique," Masson et Cie, Paris.

———: 1957. Gravimétrie et fosse rhénan, *Koninkl. Geol. Mijnb. Gen. Verh.*, vol. 18, pp. 125–147.

———: 1958. L'influence des failles et des autres irrégularités de l'écorce sur la compensation isostasique dans l'hypothèse de la régionalité, *Am. Geophys.*, vol. 14, pp. 1–30.

Goldschmidt, V. M.: 1924–1926. Geochemische Verteilungsgesetze der Elemente, *Videnskaps Skr. Kristiania, Math. Nat. Kl.*

Grabau, A. W.: 1940. "The Rhythm of the Ages," Henri Vetch, Peking.

Gräf, I. E.: 1958. Tektonische deformierte Goniatiten aus dem Westfal der Bohrung Rosenthal (Schacht Sophia-Jacoba v) im Erkelenzer Steinkohlenrevier, *Neues Jahrb. Geologie und Paläontologie Abh.*, pp. 68–95.

———: 1960. Die Berechnung der Normalform tektonisch deformierter Fossilien, *Neues Jahrb. Geologie und Paläontologie Abh.*, pp. 5–27.

Graham, J. W., A. F. Buddington, and J. R. Balsley: 1957. Stress-induced magnetizations of some rocks with analyzed magnetic minerals, *Jour. Geophys. Research*, vol. 62, pp. 465–474.

Griffith, A. A.: 1925. The theory of rupture, *1st Internat. Cong. Appl. Mech. Proc.*, Delft, pp. 55–63.

Griggs, D.: 1936. Deformation of rocks under high confining pressures, *Jour. Geology*, vol. 44, pp. 541–577.

———: 1939a. Creep of rocks, *Jour. Geol.*, vol. 47, p. 225.

———: 1939b. A theory of mountain building, *Am. Jour. Sci.*, vol. 237, pp. 611–650.

———: 1940. Experimental flow of rocks under conditions favouring recrystallization, *Geol. Soc. Am. Bull.*, vol. 51, pp. 1001–1022.

——— and J. Handin: 1960. Rock deformation, *Geol. Soc. Am. Mem.* 79.

——— and G. C. Kennedy: 1956. A simple apparatus for high pressure and temperatures, *Am. Jour. Sci.*, vol. 254, pp. 722–735.

——— et al.: 1951–1956. Deformation of Yule Marble, pts. I–VII, *Geol. Soc. Am. Bull.*, vol. 62, pp. 853–906, 1385–1406; vol. 64, pp. 1327–1353; vol. 67, pp. 1259–1294.

Guitard, G.: 1955. Sur l'évolution des gneiss des Pyrénées, *Soc. Géol. France Bull.*, ser. 6, vol. 5, pp. 441–469.

———: 1958. Aperçus et réflexions sur les schistes cristallins et les granites de la zone axiale pyrénéenne entre l'Ariège et la Méditerranée, *Soc. Géol. France Bull.*, 6e sér., vol. 8, pp. 825–852.

Gutenberg, B.: 1951. "Internal Constitution of the Earth," 2d ed., Dover Publications Inc., New York.

———: 1958. Wave velocities in the earth's core, *Seismol. Soc. Am. Bull.*, vol. 48, pp. 301–314.

———: 1959. The asthenosphere low-velocity layer, *Annali Geofisica*, vol. 12, pp. 439–460.

——— and C. F. Richter: 1941 and 1945. Seismicity of the earth, *Geol. Soc. Am. Spec. Papers*, no. 34, and *Bull.*, vol. 56, pp. 603–667.

———— and ————: 1949. "Seismicity of the Earth and associated phenomena," Princeton University Press, Princeton, N.J.

Haarmann, E.: 1930. "Die Oscillationstheorie," Ferdinand Enke Verlag, Stuttgart.

————: 1935. "Um das geologische Weltbild," Ferdinand Enke Verlag, Stuttgart.

Haas, J. O., and C. R. Hoffmann: 1928. Le gisement de calcaire asphaltique de Lobsann, *Service géol. Alsace-Lorraine Bull.*, Strassbourg, vol. 1, pp. 277–301.

Hales, A. L.: 1936. Convection currents in the earth, *Royal Astron. Soc. Monthly Not. Geoph. Suppl.*, vol. 3, pp. 372–379.

————: 1953. The thermal contraction theory of mountain building, *Royal Astron. Soc. Monthly Not. Geoph. Suppl.*, vol. 6, no. 728.

Hall, A. L., and G. A. F. Molengraaff: 1925. The Vredefort Mountainland in the Southern Transvaal and the Northern Orange Free State, *Koninkl. Nederlandse Akad. Verh.*, vol. 24, no. 3.

Hall, J.: 1813. On the vertical position and convolution of certain strata, *Royal Soc. Edinburgh Trans.*, vol. 7.

————: 1859. "Natural History of New York," vol. 3, Paleontology, D. Appleton & Company, Inc., New York.

Haller, J.: 1955. Der zentrale metamorphe Komplex von NE-Grönland, *Medd. om Grönland*, vol. 73, no. 3, pp. 1–174.

————: 1956. Probleme der Tiefentektonik: Bauformen im Migmatit-Stockwerk der Ostgrönländischen Kaledoniden, *Geol. Rundschau*, vol. 45, pp. 159–167.

Hamilton, E. L.: 1956. Sunken islands of the Mid-Pacific Mountains, *Geol. Soc. Am. Mem.* 64, pp. 1–97.

————: 1957. Marine geology of the southern Hawaiian Ridge, *Geol. Soc. Am. Bull.*, vol. 68, pp. 1011–1026.

Handin, J., and H. W. Fairbairn: 1955. Experimental deformation of Hasmark Dolomite, *Geol. Soc. Am. Bull.*, vol. 66, pp. 1257–1274.

———— and R. V. Hager: 1957, 1958. Experimental deformation of sedimentary rocks under confining pressure, *Am. Assoc. Petroleum Geologists Bull.*, vol. 41, nos. 1–5, 42, pp. 2892–2934.

Harland, W. B., and M. B. Bayly: 1958. Tectonic regimes, *Geol. Mag.*, vol. 95, pp. 89–104.

Harris, J. F., G. L. Taylor, and J. L. Walper: 1960. Relation of deformational fractures in sedimentary rocks to regional and local structure, *Am. Assoc. Petroleum Geologists Bull.*, vol. 44, pp. 1853–1873.

Harrison, J. V., and N. L. Falcon: 1934. Collapse structures, *Geol. Mag.*, vol. 71, pp. 529–539.

———— and ————: 1936. Gravity collapse structures and mountain ranges as exemplified in south-western Iran, *Geol. Soc. London Quart. Jour.*, vol. 92, pp. 91–102.

Haug, E.: 1900. Les géosynclinaux et les aires continentales, *Soc. Géol. France Bull.*, ser. 3, vol. 28, pp. 617–711.

Haughton, S.: 1856. On slaty cleavage and the distortion of fossils, *Phil. Mag.*, vol. 12, pp. 409–421.

Heezen, B. C.: 1960. The rift in the ocean floor, *Sci. Am.*, Oct., 1960.
——— and M. Ewing: 1961. Extension of the Mid-Oceanic Ridge through the Arctic basin, *Geology of the Arctic*, Toronto, vol. 1, pp. 622–642.
———, M. Tharp, and M. Ewing: 1959. The floors of the oceans, I, the North Atlantic, *Geol. Soc. Am. Spec. Papers*, no. 65, pp. 1–122.
Heim, A.: 1919–1922. Geologie der Schweiz, I, pp. 613–623 (Jura wrench faults); II, vol. 1, pp. 367–369 (Sax-Schwendi fault), Tauchnitz, Leipzig.
Heiskanen, W.: 1945. The gravity anomalies on the Japanese islands and in the waters east of them, *Inst. Internat. Assoc. Geodesy Pub. Isost.*, vol. 13.
Herman, H.: 1923. Structure of Bendigo Goldfield, *Bull. Geol. Survey, Victoria*, vol. 47.
Hernes, I.: 1956a. Surnadalssynklinalen, *Norsk geol. tidsskr.*, vol. 36, pp. 25–39.
———: 1956b. Kaledonisk tektonik i Midt Norge, *Norsk geol. tidsskr.*, vol. 36, pp. 157–166.
Hersey, J. B., E. T. Bance, R. F. Wyrick, and F. T. Dietz: 1959. Geophysical investigation of the continental margin between Cape Henry, Virginia, and Jacksonville, Florida, *Geol. Soc. Am. Bull.*, vol. 70, pp. 437–466.
Hess, H. H.: 1938. Gravity anomalies and island arc structure, with particular reference to the West Indies, *Am. Phil. Soc. Proc.*, vol. 79, pp. 71–96.
———: 1939. Island arcs, gravity anomalies, and serpentinite intrusions, *17th Internat. Geol. Cong., Moscow*, vol. 2, pp. 263–283.
———: 1948. Major structural features of the western North Pacific: an interpretation of H. O. 5485, bathymetric chart, Korea to New Guinea, *Geol. Soc. Am. Bull.*, vol. 59, no. 5, pp. 417–546.
———: 1955. Serpentines, orogeny and epeirogeny, *Geol. Soc. Am. Spec. Papers*, no. 62, pp. 391–407.
Heybroek, P., and J. Zwart: 1949. The overthrust between Teåkersjön and Marsjön, Dalsland, *Geol. Fören. Stockholm Förh.*, vol. 71, pp. 425–434.
Hiessleitner, G.: 1951. Serpentin und Chromerz Geologie der Balkanhalbinsel, *Jahrb. Geol. Bundesanstalt.*
Higgins, C. G.: 1961. San Andreas fault north of San Francisco, California, *Geol. Soc. Am. Bull.*, vol. 72, pp. 51–68.
Higgs, D. V., and J. Handin: 1959. Experimental deformation of dolomite single crystals, *Geol. Soc. Am. Bull.*, vol. 70, pp. 245–278.
Hill, Mason L.: 1954. Tectonics of faulting in southern California, *California Div. Mines Bull.* 170, chap. 4.
———: 1959. Dual classification of faults, *Am. Assoc. Petroleum Geologists Bull.*, vol. 43.
——— and T. W. Dibblee, Jr.: 1953. San Andreas, Garlock, and Big Pine faults, California, *Geol. Soc. Am. Bull.*, vol. 64, pp. 443–458.
Hill, M. N.: 1960. A median valley of the Mid-Atlantic Ridge, *Deep-Sea Research*, vol. 6, pp. 193–205.
Hodgson, R. A.: 1961. Classification of structures on joint surfaces, *Am. Jour. Sci.*, vol. 259, pp. 493–502.

————: 1961. Regional study of jointing in Comb Ridge, Navajo Mountain area, Arizona and Utah, *Am. Assoc. Petroleum Geologists Bull.*, vol. 45, pp. 2–38.

Hoeppener, R.: 1955. Tektonik im Schiefergebirge, *Geol. Rundschau*, vol. 44, pp. 26–58.

————: 1956. Zum Problem der Bruchbildung, Schieferung und Faltung, *Geol. Rundschau*, vol. 45, pp. 247–283.

————: 1957. Zur Tektonik des SW Abschnittes der Moselmulde, *Geol. Rundschau*, vol. 46, pp. 318–348.

Hollingworth, S. E., M. K. Wells, and R. Bradshow: 1960. Geology and structure of the Glanfjord region, N. Norway, *21st Internat. Geol. Cong.*, vol. 21, pp. 33–42.

Holmes, A.: 1949. The sequence of the Pre-Cambrian orogenic belts in South and Central Africa, *18e Geol. Cong., London, Internat. Comptes rendus*, 1948.

———— and L. Cahen: 1955. African geochronology, *Colonial Geol. Min. Resources*, vol. 5, pp. 3–38.

Holmquist, P. J.: 1931. On the relations of the boudinage structure, *Geol. Fören. Stockholm*, vol. 53, pp. 193–208.

Holser, W. T., and C. J. Scheer: 1957. Polymorphism in the earth's mantle, *Am. Geophys. Union Trans.*, vol. 38, pp. 569–577.

Hospers, J.: 1953, 1954. Reversals of the main geomagnetic field, *Koninkl. Nederlandse Akad. Wetensch. Verh.*, ser. B, vol. 56, no. 5; vol. 57.

Hubbert, M. K.: 1937. Scale models and geologic structures, *Geol. Soc. Am. Bull.*, vol. 48, p. 1459.

———— and W. W. Rubey: 1959. Role of fluid pressure in mechanics of overthrust faulting, *Geol. Soc. Am. Bull.*, vol. 70, pp. 115–206, with discussion by F. Birch, vol. 72, pp. 1441–1452, and W. L. Moore, vol. 72, pp. 1581–1594.

Humblet, E.: 1941. Le bassin houiller de Liège, *Rev. Universelle Mines*, ser. 8, vol. 17, no. 12.

Hundt, R.: 1950. "Erdfalltektonik," Wilhelm Knapp Verlag, Düsseldorf.

Hunt, C. B.: 1946. Guidebook to the geology and geography of the Henry Mountain region, Utah, *Utah Geol. Soc. Guidebook Geol. Utah*, no 1.

Ide, J. M.: 1936. The elastic properties of rocks: a correlation of theory and praxis, [*U.S.*] *Natl. Acad. Sci. Proc.*, vol. 32, pp. 482–486.

Irving, E.: 1956. Palaeomagnetic and palaeoclimatological aspects of polar wandering, *Geofis. pura appl.*, vol. 33, pp. 23–41.

Jacobs, J. A.: 1956. The interior of the earth, *Advances in Geophysics*, vol. 3, pp. 183–239.

Jaeger, J. C.: 1960. Shear failure of anisotropic rocks, *Geol. Mag.*, vol. 97, pp. 65–72.

James, T. C.: 1956. The nature of rift faulting in Tanganyika, *1st Meeting, E. Central Regional Comm. Geology*, Dar-es-Salaam, pp. 81–94.

Jeffreys, H.: 1959. "The Earth," 4th ed., Cambridge University Press, Cambridge, England.

Joly, J.: 1909. "Radioactivity and Geology," Constable & Co., Ltd., London.

516 References

————: 1925. "The Surface History of the Earth," Clarendon Press, Oxford.

Jones, O. T.: 1937. On the sliding and slumping of submarine sediments in Denbighshire, North Wales, *Geol. Soc. London Quart. Jour.*, vol. 93, pp. 272–273.

————: 1938. The development of a geosyncline, *Geol. Soc. London Quart. Jour.*, vol. 94, pp. ix–cx.

Judson, S. A., P. C. Murphy, and R. A. Stanley: 1932. Overhanging cap rock and salt at Barbers Hill, Chambers Cty., Texas, *Am. Assoc. Petroleum Geologists Bull.*, vol. 16, pp. 469–482.

Kaisin, Jr., F.: 1947. Le bassin houiller de Charleroi, *Louvain Univ. Inst. géol. Mém.*, vol. 15.

Kay, G. M.: 1947. Geosynclinal nomenclature and the craton: geological note, *Am. Assoc. Petroleum Geologists Bull.*, vol. 31, pp. 1289–1293.

————: 1951. North American geosynclines, *Geol. Soc. Am. Mem.* 48.

Kennedy, G. C.: 1959. Phase relations in the system Al_2O_3-H_2O at high temperatures and pressures, *Am. Jour. Sci.*, vol. 257, pp. 563–573.

Kennedy, W. Q.: 1938. Crustal layers and the origin of magmas: petrological aspects of the problem, *Bull. volcanol.*, vol. 2, no. 3.

————: 1946. The Great Glen fault, *Geol. Soc. London Quart. Jour.*, vol. 102, pp. 41–76.

Keverling Buisman, A. S.: 1940. "Grondmechanica," Waltman, Delft.

Kieken, M.: 1962. "Les traits essentiels de la géologie algérienne," vol. I, pp. 545–614, Livre en mémoire de P. Fallot, Société Géologique de France.

King, P. B.: 1950. Tectonic framework of south-western United States, *Am. Assoc. Petroleum Geologists Bull.*, vol. 34, pp. 635–671.

————: 1959. "The Evolution of North America," Princeton University Press, Princeton, N.J.

Kingma, J. T.: 1959. The tectonic history of New Zealand, *New Zealand Jour. Geology and Geophysics*, vol. 2, pp. 1–55.

Knopf, E. B., and E. Ingerson: 1938. Structural petrology, *Geol. Soc. Am. Mem.* 6.

Koark, H. J.: 1961. Zur Deformation des Venna-Konglomerates im Trondheim Gebiet, Norwegen, *Geol. Inst. Univ. Uppsala Bull.*, vol. 40, pp. 139–161.

Kober, L.: 1928. "Der Bau der Erde," 2d ed., Gebrüder Borntraeger, Berlin.

Köppen, W.: 1922. Über die Kräfte, welche die Kontinentverschiebungen und Polarwanderungen bewirken, *Geol. Rundschau*, vol. 12, pp. 314–320.

Korn, H., and H. Martin: 1959. Gravity tectonics in the Naukluft Mountains of S.W. Africa, *Geol. Soc. Am. Bull.*, vol. 70, pp. 1047–1078.

Köster, R.: 1957, 1958. Experimente zur glazialen Schuppung, *Neues Jahrb. Geol.*, 1957, *Monh.* 11, pp. 510–517; 1958, *Monh.* 10, pp. 460–468; Experimente zur glazialen Faltung, *ibid.*, 1958, *Monh.* 1, pp. 33–40.

Kranck, E. H.: 1957. On folding movements in the zone of basement, *Geol. Rundschau,* vol. 46, pp. 261–282.

Kraus, E.: 1951. "Die Baugeschichte der Alpen," vols. 1 and 2, Akademie-Verlag GmbH, Berlin.

Kuenen, P. H.: 1935. The Snellius expedition, *Geol. Results,* vol. 5, Part 1, Geological interpretation of the bathymetrical results, *Kemink en Zoon,* Utrecht.

———: 1938. Observations and experiments in ptygmatic folding. *Soc. Géol. Finlande Comptes rendus,* vol. 12, pp. 11–28.

———: 1949. Slumping in the carboniferous rocks of Pembrokeshire, *Geol. Soc. London Quart. Jour.,* vol. 104, pp. 365–385.

——— and L. U. de Sitter: 1938. Experimental investigation into the mechanism of folding, *Leidse Geol.,* vol. 10, pp. 271–240.

——— and C. I. Migliorini: 1950. Turbidity currents as a cause of graded bedding, *Jour. Geol.,* vol. 58, pp. 91–127.

Kugler, H. G.: 1933. Contribution to the knowledge of sedimentary volcanism in Trinidad, *Jour. Petroleum Technology,* vol. 19, pp. 743–760.

Kukuk, P.: 1938. "Geologie der Niederrheinisch-Westfälischen Steinkohlengebiete," Springer-Verlag, Berlin.

Kulling, O.: 1955. Den Kaledoniska flällkedjans berggrund inom Västerbottens Län, *Sveriges Geol. Undersakn.,* ser. Ca, no. 37.

Kulp, J. L.: 1961. Some potassium-argon ages on rocks from the Norwegian basement, *Annals N.Y. Acad. Sci.,* vol. 91, pp. 469–475.

Kündig, E.: 1956. The position in time and space of the ophiolites with relation to orogenic metamorphism, *Geologic en Mijnbouw,* vol. 18, pp. 106–114.

———: 1959. Eugeosynclines as potential oil habitats, *5th World Petrology Cong.*

Kurtman, F.: 1960. Fossildeformation und Tektonik im nördlichen Rheinischen Schiefergebirge, *Geol. Rundschau,* vol. 49, 2, pp. 439–459.

Lahee, F. H.: 1929. Oil and gas fields of the Mexia and Tehuancana fault zones, Texas, in "Typical American Oilfields," vol. 1, p. 304, American Association of Petroleum Geologists, Tulsa, Okla.

Laubscher, H. P.: 1961. Die Mobilisierung klastischer Massen, *Eclogae geol. Helv.,* vol. 54, pp. 283–334.

Lawson, H. C.: 1932. Insular arcs, foredeeps and geosynclinal seas of the Asiatic coast, *Geol. Soc. Am. Bull.,* vol. 43.

Lees, G. M.: 1953. "Persia: Science of Petroleum," vol. 6, pp. 73–82, Oxford University Press, London.

Lehmann, I.: 1961. S and the structure of the upper mantle, *Royal Astron. Soc. Geophys. Jour.,* vol. 4, pp. 124–138.

Lemke, L.: 1937. Der tektonische Bau des Gebietes zwischen Vogelsberg und Rhön, *Geotekt. Forsch.,* vol. 1.

Leuchs, K.: 1933. Ueber Breccien, *Geol. Rundschau,* vol. 24, pp. 273–281.

Lindström, M.: 1961. Tectonic fabric of a sequence of areas in the Scandinavian Caledonides, *Inst. Min. Paleontology Pub., Quart. Geol. Lund,* vol. 98, pp. 15–64.

Link, T. A.: 1949. Interpretations of Foothills structures, Alberta, *Am. Assoc. Petroleum Geologists Bull.*, vol. 33, pp. 1175–1501.

Lohest, M.: 1909. De l'origine des veines et des géodes des terrains primaires de Belgique, *Annales Soc. Géol. Belgique*, ser. B., vol. 36, pp. 275–282.

————: 1913. Expériences de tectonique, *Annales Soc. Géol. Belgique*, vol. 39, Mém.

Lombard, A. E.: 1948. Appalachian and Alpine structures: a comparative study, *Am. Assoc. Petroleum Geologists Bull.*, vol. 32, pp. 709–744.

————: 1953. Les rythmes sédimentaires et la sédimentation générale, *Inst. Français Pétrole Rev.*, vol. 8, pp. 9–45.

Long, L. E., J. L. Kulp, and F. D. Eckelmann: 1959. Chronology of major metamorphic events in the southeastern United States, *Am. Jour. Sci.*, vol. 257, pp. 585–603.

Longwell, C. R.: 1946. How old is the Colorado River? *Am. Jour. Sci.*, vol. 244, pp. 817–835.

Lotze, F.: 1933. Zur Erklärung der tektonische Klüfte, *Central bl. Min.*, etc., ser. B, vol. 193.

————: 1938. Das Problem der "saxonischen Faltung," *Geotekt. Forsch.*, vol. 3, pp. 73–84.

————: 1953. Einige Probleme der Osningtektonik, *Geotekt. Forsch.*, vol. 9, no. 10, pp. 7–17.

Lovering, J. F.: 1958. The nature of the Mohorovicic discontinuity, *Am. Geophys. Union Trans.*, vol. 39, pp. 947–955; discussion by H. Kuno, *Jour. Geophys. Research*, vol. 64, pp. 1071–1073, 1959.

Lovering, T. S.: 1928. The fracturing of incompetent beds, *Jour. Geol.*, vol. 36, p. 709.

Lugeon, M., and E. Gagnebin: 1941. Observations et vues nouvelles sur la géologie des Préalpes romandes, *Univ. Lausanne Lab. géol. Bull. 72.*

MacDonald, G. J. F.: 1956. Quartz-coesite stability relations at high temperatures and pressures, *Am. Jour. Sci.*, vol. 254, pp. 713–721.

Macgregor, A. M.: 1951. Some milestones in the Pre-Cambrian of Southern Rhodesia, *Geol. Soc. S. Africa Trans. and Proc.*, vol. 54, p. xxvii.

Macgregor, M., and A. G.: 1948. The Midland Valley of Scotland, *Geol. Survey and Mus., London, British Regional Geol.*, vol. 73.

Magnusson, N.: 1937. Die Granitisationstheorie und deren Anwendung für Svionische Granite und Gneise Mittleschwedens, *Geol. Fören Stockholm Förh.*, vol. 59, pp. 525–547.

————: 1960. Age determinations of Swedish Precambrian rocks, *Geol. Fören. Stockholm Förh.*, vol. 82, pp. 407–432.

————: 1960. The Swedish Precambrian outside the Caledonian mountain chain, *Sveriges Geol. Undersökn.*, ser. Ba, no. 16, pp. 5–66.

———— and P. Geyer: 1944. De mellansvenska järnmalmernas Geologi, *Sveriges Geol. Undersökn.*, ser. Ca, no. 35.

————, P. Thorslund, F. Brotzen, B. Asklund, and O. Kulling: 1960. Description to accompany the map of the pre-Quaternary rocks of Sweden, *Sveriges Geol. Undersökn.*, ser. Ba, no. 16.

Malaroda, R.: 1946. Revisione e aggiornamento della sistematica delle tettoniti a deformazione post-cristallina, *Soc. Mineralog. italiana Rend.*, vol. III, no. 3, pp. 1–24, with exhaustive literature on mylonites.

Martini, H. J.: 1937. Groszschollen und Graben zwischen Habichtswald und Rheinischen Schiefergebirge, *Geotekt. Forsch.*, vol. 1.

Mason, B.: 1953. Polymorphism and orogeny, *Am. Geophys. Union Trans.*, vol. 34, pp. 921–923.

Mason, R. G.: 1958. A magnetic survey of the west coast of the United States between lat. 32° and 30°N, long. 121° and 128°W, *Royal Astron. Soc. Geophys. Jour.*, vol. 1, pp. 320–329.

Mead, W. J.: 1920. Notes on the mechanics of geologic structures, *Jour. Geol.*, vol. 28, pp. 505–523.

Mehnert, K. R.: 1959. Der gegenwärtige Stand des Granitproblems, *Fortschr. Mineralogie*, vol. 37, pp. 117–206.

Melton, F. A., 1929. A reconnaissance of the joint systems in the Ouachita Mountains and central plains of Oklahoma, *Jour. Geol.*, vol. 37, no. 8, pp. 729–746.

Menard, H. W.: 1955. Deep-sea channels, topography and sedimentation, *Am. Assoc. Petroleum Geologists Bull.*, vol. 39, pp. 236–255.

———: 1955. Deformation of the northeastern Pacific basin and the west coast of North America, *Geol. Soc. Am. Bull.*, vol. 66, pp. 1149–1198.

———: 1959. Geology of the Pacific sea floor, *Experientia*, vol. 15, no. 6, pp. 205–213.

———: 1960. The East Pacific Rise, *Science*, vol. 132, pp. 1737–1746.

——— and R. S. Dietz: 1952. Mendocino submarine escarpment, *Jour. Geol.*, vol. 60, pp. 266–278.

——— and R. L. Fisher: 1958. Clipperton fracture zone in the northeastern equatorial Pacific, *Jour. Geol.*, vol. 66, pp. 239–253.

Mengaud, L.: 1920. Recherches géologiques dans la région Cantabrique, thèse, Paris, p. 370.

———: 1932. Sur la structure de la chaîne Cantabrique, *Acad. Sci. Paris Comptes rendus*, vol. 195, p. 1092.

———: 1939. Etudes géologiques dans la région de Gavarnie et du Mont Perdu, *Service Carte géol. France Bull.* 199, pp. 197–223.

Merla, G.: 1952. Geologia dell'Appennino settentrionale, *Soc. geol. italiana Boll.*, vol. 70, pp. 95–382.

Michot, P.: 1956. La géologie des zones profondes de l'écorce terrestre, *Soc. Géol. Belgique Annales*, vol. 80, pp. 19–60.

———: 1957. Phénomènes géologiques dans la Catazone profonde, *Geol. Rundschau*, vol. 46, pp. 147–173.

Migliorini, C. I.: 1933. Considerazioni su di particolare effetto dell'orogenesi, *Soc. geol. italiana Boll.*, vol. 52, pp. 293–304.

———: 1936. "Alcune questioni geologiche casentinesi," M. Ricci, Florence.

———: 1948. I cunei composti nell'orogenesi, *Soc. geol. italiana Boll.*, vol. 67, pp. 31–142.

Milch, L.: 1900. Ueber dynamometamorphen Erscheinungen an einem nordischen Granitgneiss, *Neues Jahrb.* 1, *Mineralogie*, vol. 2, pp. 39–51.

Miller, R. L., and J. O. Fuller: 1955. Geology and oil resources of the Rose Hill district: the fenster area of the Cumberland overthrust, Lee County, Virginia, *Virginia Geol. Survey Bull.* 71.

Misch, P.: 1934. Der Bau der mittleren Südpyrenäen, *Akad. Wiss. Göttingen Abh., Math. phys. Kl.*, ser. 3, vol. 12.

————: 1949. Metasomatic granitization of batholitic dimensions, I–III, *Am. Jour. Sci.*, vol. 247, pp. 209–245, 372–406, 673–705.

Mohr, O.: 1914. Abhandlungen aus dem Gebiete der technischen Mechanik, 2d ed., Wilhelm Ernst & Sohn KG, Berlin.

Mohr, P. A.: 1962. The Ethiopian Rift system, *Bull. Geophysical Obs. Addis Ababa*, vol. 3, pp. 33–62.

Monod, T.: 1954. Sur quelques accidents circulaires du Sahara occidental, 19*th Internat. Geol. Cong.*, vol. 20, pp. 85–93.

Moore, R. C.: 1950. Late Paleozoic cyclic sedimentation in central United States, 18*th Internat. Geol. Cong.*, no. 4, pp. 5–16.

Morris, T. O., and W. G. Fearnsides: 1962. The stratigraphy and structure of the Cambrian slate-belt of Nantle (Carnarvonshire), *Geol. Soc. London Quart. Jour.*, vol. 82, pp. 250–303.

Muehlberger, W. R.: 1959. Internal structure of the Grand Saline salt dome, *Univ. Texas Bur. Econ. Geol. Rept. Inv.* 38, 22 pp.

Muller, J. E.: 1945. De post-carbonische tektoniek van het Z. Limburgse Mijngebied, with English summary (4 pp.), *Geol. Stichting Med.*, C I-1, no. 2, pp. 1–32.

Murawski, H.: 1957. Zur Altersfrage von Tektonik und Metamorphose im mittleren Vorspessart, *Abh. Hess. Landesamtes Bodenforsch.*, no. 18, pp. 135–148.

————: 1960. Das Zeitproblem bei der Tektogenese eines Groszgrabensystem, *Notizbl. Hess. Landesamtes Bodenforsch.*, no. 88, pp. 294–342.

Nabholz, W. K.: 1953. Das mechanische Verhalten der granitschen Kernkörper der tiefen penninischen Decken bei der Alpinen Orogenese, *Cong. Internat. géol. Comptes rendus, Alger*, ser. 3, vol. 3, pp. 9–23.

————: 1956. Untersuchungen über Faltung und Klüftung im nordschweizerischen Jura, *Eclogae geol. Helv.*, vol. 49, pp. 373–406.

Nairn, A. E. M.: 1960a. Paleomagnetic results from Europe, *Jour. Geol.*, vol. 68, pp. 285–306.

————: 1960b. A paleomagnetic survey of the Karroo System, *Overseas Geol. Mineral. Research*, vol. 7, pp. 398–410.

Natland, M. L., and P. H. Kuenen: 1951. Sedimentary history of the Ventura basin, California, *Soc. Econ. Paleontologists Mineralogists. Spec. Pub.* 2, pp. 76–107.

Neale, E. R. W., J. Beland, R. R. Potter, and W. H. Poole: 1961. A preliminary tectonic map of the Canadian Appalachian region based on age of folding, *Canada Mining Metall. Bull.* 593, pp. 687–694.

Nederlof, M. H.: 1960. Structure and sedimentology of the Upper Carboniferous of the Upper Pisuerga valleys, Cantabrian Mountains, Spain, *Leidse Geol. Med.*, vol. 24, no. 2, pp. 603–703.

Nettleton, L. L.: 1943. Recent experimental and geophysical evidence of mechanics of salt dome formation, *Am. Assoc. Petroleum Geologists Bull.*, vol. 27, pp. 51–63.

Niggli, E.: 1953. Zur Stereometrie und Entstehung der Aplit- Granit- und Pegmatitgänge im Gebiete von Sept-Laux (Belledonne massiv S.L.), *Leidse Geol. Med.*, vol. 17, pp. 215–236.

Noble, L. F.: 1926. The San Andreas rift and some other active faults in the desert region of south-eastern California, *Carnegie Inst. Wash. Yearbook* 25, pp. 415–428.

————: 1954. The San Andreas fault zone from Soledad Pass to Cajon Pass, California, *California Div. Mines Bull.* 170, chap. 4.

Nolan, T. B.: 1943. The Basin and Range province in Utah, Nevada and California, *U.S. Geol. Surv. Prof. Paper* 197 D, pp. 141–196.

Northrop, J., R. A. Frosch, and R. Frassetto: 1962. Bermuda–New England Seamount arc, *Geol. Soc. Am. Bull.*, vol. 73, pp. 587–594.

Norton, W. M.: 1917. A classification of breccias, *Jour. Geol.*, vol. 25, p. 160.

O'Brien, C. A. E.: 1957. Salt diapyrism in southern Persia, *Geologie en Mijnbouw*, N.S., vol. 19, pp. 357–376.

Ode, H.: 1960. Faulting as a velocity discontinuity in plastic deformation, *Geol. Soc. Am. Mem.* 79, pp. 293–321.

Officer, C. B., J. J. Ewing, R. S. Edwards, and H. R. Johnson: 1957. Geophysical investigations in the eastern Caribbean, *Geol. Soc. Am. Bull.*, vol. 68, pp. 359–378, 897–912.

————, ————, J. F. Hennion, D. G. Harkrider, and D. E. Miller: 1959. Geophysical investigations in the eastern Caribbean, summary of 1955–1956 cruises, *Physics and Chemistry of the Earth*, vol. 3, pp. 17–109.

————, ————, and P. C. Woenschel: 1952. Seismic refraction measurements in the Atlantic, IV, Bermuda Rise and Nares basin, *Geol. Soc. Am. Bull.*, vol. 63, pp. 777–808.

Oftedahl, C.: 1948. Deformation of quartz conglomerates in central Norway, *Jour. Geol.*, vol. 56, pp. 476–487.

————: 1952. Cauldron subsidence of the Oslo region, *18th Internat. Geol. Congr. London*, pt. XIII.

————: 1953. Studies in the igneous rock complex of the Oslo region: the Cauldrons, *Skrifter Norske Videnskaps-Akad. Oslo, I, Mat. Naturv. Kl.*, no. 3.

Osterwald, F. W.: 1961. Critical review of some tectonic problems in Cordilleran foreland, *Am. Assoc. Petroleum Geologists Bull.*, vol. 45, pp. 219–237.

Otuka, Y.: 1933. The geomorphology and geology of northern Idu peninsula, the earthquake figure of Nov. 26, 1930 and the pre- and post-seismic crust deformations, *Tokyo Univ. Earthquake Research Inst. Bull.*, vol. 11, p. 530.

Oulianoff, N.: 1947. Infrastructure des Alpes et tremblement de terre du 25 janvier 1946, *Soc. Géol. France Bull.*, ser. 5, vol. 17.

Overeem, A. J. A.: 1948. A section through the Dalformation, thesis, *Geol. Inst.*, Leiden.

Parker, J. M.: 1942. Regional jointing systematic in slightly deformed sedimentary rocks, *Geol. Soc. Am. Bull.*, vol. 53, p. 381.

Paschall, R. H., and T. Off: 1961. Dip-slip versus strike-slip movement on San Gabriel fault, S. California, *Am. Assoc. Petroleum Geologists Bull.*, vol. 45, pp. 1941–1956.

Paterson, M. S.: 1958. Experimental deformation and faulting in Wombeyan Marble, *Geol. Soc. Am. Bull.*, vol. 69, pp. 466–476.

Pavoni, N.: 1961. Faltung durch Horizontalverschiebung, *Eclogae geol. Helv.*, vol. 54, pp. 515–534.

Pekeris, C. L.: Thermal convection in the interior of the earth, *Royal Astron. Soc. Monthly Not. Geoph. Suppl.*, vol. 3, pp. 343–367.

Pilger, A., and W. Schmidt: 1957. Die Mullion-Strukturen in der Nord-Eifel, *Abh. Hess. Landesamtes Bodenforsch.*, no. 20, pp. 1–53.

Pitcher, W. S.: 1953. The Ross granitic ring-complex, Ct. Donegal Eire, *Geol. Assoc. Proc.*, vol. 64, pp. 158–182.

Polkanov, A. A., and E. K. Gerling: 1960. The Pre-Cambrian geochronology of the Baltic shield, *Internat. Geol. Cong. Norden*, pt. IX, pp. 183–191.

Pruvost, P.: 1934. Bassin houiller de la Sarre et de la Lorraine, III, Description géologique, *Service Carte géol. Alsace-Lorraine, Strassbourg.*

Quennel, A. M.: 1958. The structural and geomorphic evolution of the Dead Sea rift, *Geol. Soc. London Quart. Jour.*, vol. 114, pp. 1–24.

————: 1959. Tectonics of the Dead Sea rift, *20e Cong. Géol. Internat. Mexico, 1956, Assoc. Service Géol. Afrique*, pp. 385–405.

Raff, A. D.: 1961. The magnetism of the ocean floor, *Science*, October, 1961, pp. 146–156.

Raguin, E.: 1946. Géologie du granite, Masson et cie., Paris.

Raitt, R. W.: 1956. Seismic refraction studies of the Pacific Ocean basin, *Geol. Soc. Am. Bull.*, vol. 67, pp. 1623–1640.

Ramberg, H.: 1955. Natural and experimental boudinage and pinch-and-swell structures, *Jour. Geol.*, vol. 63, pp. 512–526.

————: 1959. Evolution of ptygmatic folding, *Norsk geol. tidsskr.*, vol. 39, no. 2/3, pp. 99–151.

————: 1960. Relationships between length of arc and thickness of ptygmatically folded veins, *Jour. Sci.*, vol. 258, pp. 36–46.

————: 1961. Relationship between concentric longitudinal strain and concentric shearing strain during folding of homogeneous sheets of rocks, *Am. Jour. Sci.*, vol. 259, pp. 382–390.

Ramsay, J. G.: 1958. Superimposed folding at Loch Monar, Inverness-shire and Ross-shire, *Geol. Soc. London Quart. Jour.*, vol. 113, pp. 271–308.

————: 1960. The deformation of early linear structures in areas of repeated folding, *Jour. Geol.*, vol. 68, pp. 75–93.

————: 1961. The effects of folding upon the orientation of sedimentation structures, *Jour. Geol.*, vol. 69, pp. 89–100.

————: 1962. The geometry and mechanics of formation of similar type folds, *Jour. Geol.*, vol. 70, pp. 309–327.

Rankama, K., and Th. G. Sahama: 1949. "Geochemistry," Univ. of Chicago Press," Chicago.

Rast, N., and J. I. Platt: 1957. Cross-folds, *Geol. Mag.*, vol. 94, pp. 159–167.

Read, H. H.: 1928. A note on ptygmatic folding in the Sutherland Granite Complex, *Summ. Prog. Geol. Survey for* 1927, pt. II, vol. 72.

————: 1957. The granite controversy, Thomas Murby, London.

Reed, R. D.: 1933. "Geology of California," American Association of Petroleum Geologists, Tulsa, Okla.

————: 1943. California's record in geologic history of the world, *California Dept. Natl. Resources Bull.* 118, pp. 99–118.

———— and J. S. Hollister: 1936. Structural evolution of southern California, *Am. Assoc. Petroleum Geologists Bull.*, vol. 20, no. 12, pp. 1529–1721.

Reeves, F.: 1946. Origin and mechanics of thrust faults adjacent to the Bearpaw Mountains, Montana, *Geol. Soc. Am. Bull.*, vol. 57, pp. 1033–1047.

Reid, H. F.: 1911. The elastic rebound theory of earthquakes, *Univ. California Geol. Dept. Pub. Bull.* 6, pp. 13–444.

Reid, J. A.: The California earthquake of April 18, 1906. *State of California, Rept. State Earthquake Inv. Comm.*, vol. 2, The mechanics of earthquakes.

Reynolds, S. H.: 1928. Breccias, *Geol. Mag.*, vol. 65, pp. 97–108.

Rich, J. L.: 1950. Flow markings, groovings and intrastratal crumpling as criteria for recognition of slope deposits, with illustrations from Silurian rocks of Wales, *Am. Assoc. Petroleum Geologists Bull.*, vol. 34, pp. 717–741.

Richards, T. C., and D. J. Walker: 1959. Measurement of the thickness of the earth's crust in the Albertan plain of western Canada, *Geophysics*, vol. 24, pp. 262–284.

Richey, J. E.: 1939. The dykes of Scotland, *Geol. Soc. Edinburgh Trans.*, vol. 13, no. 4, p. 393.

Richter-Bernburg, G.: 1955. Ueber salinare Sedimentation, *Deutsche geol. Gesell. Zeitschr.*, vol. 105, pp. 593–645.

————: 1959. Die nordwestdeutschen Salzstöcke und ihre Bedeutung für die Bildung von Erdöl-Lagerstätten, *Erdöl und Kohle*, vol. 12, pp. 294–303. (English transl. in *5th World Petroleum Cong.*, 1959, pp. 81–94.)

Riedel, W.: 1929. Zur Mechanik Geologischer Brucherscheinungen, *Central bl. Min., etc.*, ser. B, pp. 354–368.

Ringwood, A. E.: 1958–1959. The constitution of the mantle, *Geochimics et Cosmochimica Acta*, vol. 13, pp. 303–321; vol. 15, pp. 18–29, 195–212; vol. 16, pp. 192–193.

Roberts, J. C.: 1961. Feather-fracture and the mechanics of rock-jointing, *Am. Jour. Sci.*, vol. 259, pp. 481–492.

Robertson, E. C.: 1955. Experimental study of the strength of rocks, *Geol. Soc. Am. Bull.*, vol. 66, pp. 1275–1314.

————, F. Birch, and G. J. F. MacDonald: 1957. Experimental determination of jadeite stability relations to 2,500 bars, *Am. Jour. Sci.*, vol. 255, pp. 115–137.

Rodgers, J.: 1950. Mechanics of Appalachian folding as illustrated by Sesquatchie anticline, Tennessee and Alabama, *Am. Assoc. Petroleum Geologists Bull.*, vol. 34, pp. 672–682.

————: 1953a. Geologic map of East Tennessee with explanatory text, *State of Tennessee, Div. Geol. Bull.* 58.

————: 1953b. The folds and faults of the Appalachian Valley and Ridge province, *Kentucky Geol. Survey Spec. Pub.* 1, pp. 150–156.

Roll, A.: 1949. Die strukturelle Entwicklung und die Geschichte der Salzstockbildung im Hanoverischen Becken, *Erdöl und Tektonik in N.W. Deutschland*, pp. 69–90.

Rost, F.: 1961. Zur Stellung der Granatultrabasite des sächsischen Grundgebirges, *Freiberger Forschungsh*, C119, *Geologie*, pp. 119–134.

Runcorn, S. K.: 1956. Rock magnetism: geophysical aspects, *Philos. Mag. Supp.* 4, pp. 244–291.

————: 1959. Rock magnetism, *Science*, vol. 129, pp. 1002–1012.

Rutland, R. W. R.: 1959. Structural geology of the Sokumvatn area, N. Norway, *Norsk geol. tidsskr.*, vol. 39, pp. 287–337.

Rutsch, F. R.: 1948. Die Bedeutung der Fossil-deformation, *Assoc. Suisse géol. petrologie Bull.*, vol. 15, no. 49. With extensive literature.

Rutten, L. M. R.: 1949. Frequency and periodicity of orogenic movements, *Geol. Soc. Am. Bull.*, vol. 60, pp. 1755–1770.

Rutten, M. G.: 1943. Enkele gegevens over de helling van de Feldbiss, *Geol. en Mijnbouw* N.S., vol. 5, pp. 91–92.

Salomon, W.: 1911. Die Bedeutung der Messung und Kartierung von gemeinen Klüften und Harnischen, mit besonderer Berücksichtigung des Rheintal-Grabens, *Deutsche Geol. Gesell. Zeitschr.*, vol. 63, pp. 496–521.

————: 1925. Beobachtungen über Harnische, *Sitz. ber. Heidelberg Akad. Wiss. Math-Naturw. Kl.*, ser. A, vol. 4, p. 21.

————: 1927. Neue Kluft- und Harnischmessungen im südl, Odenwald, *Ber. Naturf. Gesell. Freiburg und Breisgau*, vol. 27, pp. 173–180.

Sampelayo, P. H.: 1928. Discusión de algunos puntos de la Hoja geológica de Llanes (Asturias), *Inst. geol. y Min. Esp. Notas y commun.*, vol. 1, no. 1.

Sander, B.; 1930. Gefügekunde der Gesteine, Springer-Verlag OHG, Vienna.

————: 1950. Einführung in die Gefügekunde der geologischen Körper, vols. I and II, Springer-Verlag OHG, Vienna.

Sanford, A. R.: 1959. Analytical and experimental study of simple geologic structures, *Geol. Soc. Am. Bull.*, vol. 70, pp. 19–52.

Savage, J. F.: 1961. The Geology of the country round Portilla de la Reina, León, N. W. Spain. Unpublished MSc. thesis, University of London.

Sax, H. G.: 1946. De tektoniek van het Carboon in het Zuid Limburgsch Mijngebied (with abridged English translation: The tectonics of the South Limburg Coalfield), *Geol. Stichting Med.*, ser. C I-1, no. 3.

Schatski, N. S., and A. A. Bogdanow: 1958. "Grundzüge des tektonischen Baues der Sowjetunion," Akademie-Verlag GmbH, Berlin.

Scheidegger, A. E.: 1963. "Principles of Geodynamics," 2d ed., Springer-Verlag, Berlin.

Schlüter, H.: 1949. Das Ölfeld Steimbke-Rodewald und die Struktur Anderten-Lichtenhorst, *Erdöl und Tektonik in N.W. Deutschland*, pp. 230–241.

Schnaebele, R.: 1937. Carte structurale de la partie Nord du champ petrolifère de Pechelbronn, *2e Cong. Mondial Pétrologie, Paris*, vol. 1, pp. 439–441.

Schneegans, D.: 1938. La géologie des nappes de l'Ubaye-Embrunais entre la Durance et l'Ubaye, *carte géol. France Mém.*

Schuchert, C.: 1925. Sites and nature of North American geosynclines, *Geol. Soc. Am. Bull.*, vol. 34, pp. 151–230.

Schuppli, H. M.: 1952. Erdölgeologische Untersuchungen in der Schweiz, 4, *Beiträge Geologie Schweiz*, ser. 26, vol. 4.

Scotford, D. M.: 1956. Metamorphism and axial-plane folding in the Pound Ridge area, New York, *Geol. Soc. America Bull.*, vol. 67, pp. 1155–1198.

Sederholm, J. J.: 1913. Ueber ptygmatische Faltungen, *Neues Jahrb. Min.*, etc., vol. 36, pp. 491–512.

————: 1932. On the geology of Fennoscandia, *Comm. géol. Finlande Bull.*, vol. 98, pp. 5–30.

Shackleton, R. M.: 1954. The tectonic significance of alkaline igneous activity, in "The Tectonic Control of Igneous Activity," University of Leeds Department of Geology.

Shand, J.: The pseudotachylyte of Parijs (Orange Free State), *Geol. Soc. Quart. Jour.*, vol. 72, pp. 198–221.

Sharp, R. P.: 1939. Basin-range structure of the Ruby East Humboldt Range, north-eastern Nevada, *Geol. Soc. Am. Bull.*, vol. 50, no. 6, pp. 881–915.

Sharpe, D.: 1847 and 1849. On slaty cleavage, *Geol. Soc. Quart. Jour.*, vol. 3, pp. 74–105; vol. 5, pp. 111–129.

Shelby, T. H., Jr.: 1951. Talco Field, in Occurrence of oil and gas in N.E. Texas, *Univ. of Texas pub.* 5116, pp. 372–378.

Sherrill, R. E.: 1929. Origin of the en échelon faults in north central Oklahoma, *Am. Assoc. Petroleum Geologists*, vol. 13, pp. 31–37.

Shor, G., and R. L. Fischer: 1961. Middle America Trench, *Geol. Soc. Am. Bull.*, vol. 72, pp. 703–730.

Shumway, G.: 1954. Carnegie Ridge and Cocos Ridge in the east equatorial Pacific, *Jour. Geol.*, vol. 62, pp. 573–586.

Slater, G.: 1927. On studies in drift deposits of south-west Suffolk. *Geol. Assoc. Proc.*, vol. 38, pp. 157–216.

Smith, K. G.: 1952. Structure plan of clastic dikes, *Am. Geophys. Union Trans.*, vol. 33, no. 6.

Smith, W. K.: 1951. Quitman Field, in Occurrence of oil and gas in N.E. Texas, *Univ. Texas Pub.* 5116, pp. 315–319.

Smoluchowski, M.: 1909. Ueber ein gewisses Stabilitätsproblem der Elastizitätslehre, *Anzeiger Akad. Wiss. Krakau Math.-phys. Kl.*

Sokolowski, S., and J. Znosko: 1960. Eléments principaux de la tectonique de Pologne, *Inst. Geol Warszawa*, vol. 30, pp. 441–464.

Sollas, W. J.: 1903. The figure of the earth, *Geol. Soc. London Quart. Jour.*, vol. 59, pp. 180–188.

Sorby, H. C.: 1856. On the theory of slaty cleavage, *Philos. Mag.*, vol. 12, pp. 127–129.

————: 1908. On the application of quantitative methods to the study of the structure and history of rocks, *Geol. Soc. London Quart. Jour.*, vol. 64, pp. 171–233.

Spencer, E. W.: 1959. Geologic evolution of the Beartooth Mountains, 2, Fracture patterns, *Geol. Soc. Am. Bull.*, vol. 70, pp. 467–508.

Staub, R.: 1928. "Der Bewegungsmechanismus der Erde," Gebrüder Borntraeger, Berlin.

Steinbrugge, K. V., and E. G. Zacher: 1960. Creep on the San Andreas fault: Fault creep and property damage, *Seismol. Soc. Am. Bull.*, vol. 50, pp. 389–395.

Steinmann, G.: 1926. Die ophiolitischen Zonen in den mediterranen Kettengebirge, *14e Cong. Internat. Géol. Comptes rendus, Madrid*, pp. 637–666.

Stille, H.: 1924a. "Grundfragen der vergleichenden Tektonik," Gebrüder Borntraeger, Berlin.

————: 1924b. Die Osning-Ueberschiebung, *Abh. Pr. geol. L-Ansalt, N.S.*, vol. 95, pp. 32–56.

Stockwell, C. H., and J. M. Harrison: 1948. Structural control of ore deposits in Northern Manitoba, in "Structural Geology of Canadian Ore Deposits," Canadian Institute of Mining and Metallurgy, Montreal, pp. 284–291.

Stolz, H. P.: 1943. Long Beach Oilfield, *California Div. Mines, Dept. Nat. Resources, Bull.* 118, pp. 320–324.

Strand, T.: 1944. Structural petrology of the Bygdin Conglomerate, Norsk geol. tidsskr., vol. 24, pp. 14–31.

Suess, Ed.: 1909. "Das Antlitz der Erde," Tempsky, Vienna.

Sutton, G. H., and E. Berg: 1958. Seismological studies of the western rift valley of Africa, *Am. Geophys. Union Trans.*, vol. 39, pp. 474–481.

Sutton, J.: 1960. Some structural problems in the Scottish Highlands, *Internat. Geol. Cong. Norden*, pt. 18, pp. 317–383.

Sutton, J., and J. Watson: 1959. Structures in the Caledonides between Loch Duich and Glenelg, N.W. Highlands, *Geol. Soc. London Quart. Jour.*, vol. 114, pp. 231–257.

Taber, S.: 1927. Fault troughs, *Jour. Geol.*, vol. 35, pp. 557–606.

Taliaferro, N. L.: 1943. Geological history and structure of the central Coast Ranges of California, *California Div. Mines, Dept. Nat. Resources, Bull.* 118, pp. 119–162.

Talwani, M., G. H. Sutton, and J. L. Worzel: 1959. A crustal section across the Puerto Rico Trench, *Jour. Geophys. Research*, vol. 64, pp. 1545–1555.

Tatel, H. E., and M. A. Tuve: 1955. Seismic exploration of a continental crust, *Geol. Soc. Am. Spec. Papers*, no. 62, pp. 35–50.

Taylor, F. B.: 1923. The lateral migration of land masses, *Wash. Acad. Sci. Proc.*, vol. 13, no. 29, pp. 445–447.

ten Haaf, F.: 1956. Significance of convolute lamination, *Geologie en Mijnbouw*, vol. 18, pp. 188–194.

Tercier, J.: Le Flysch dans la sédimentation alpine, *Eclogae geol. Helv.*, vol. 40, pp. 164–198.

Tolstoy, I.: 1951. Submarine topography in the North Atlantic, *Geol. Soc. Am. Bull.*, vol. 62, pp. 441–450.

Törnebohm, A. E.: 1896. Grunddragen av det centrala skandinaviens byggnad, *Kungl. Svensk Ventensk. Akad. Handl., Mem.*, vol. 28, no. 5.

Trevisan, L.: 1939. II Gruppo di Brenta, *Ist. Geol. R. Univ. Padova Mem.*, vol. 13, pp. 1–128.

————: 1950. L'Elba orientale e la sua tettonica di scivolamento per gravita, *Ist. Geol. R. Univ. Padova Mem.*, vol. 16, pp. 1–40.

Trümpy, R.: 1955. Wechselbeziehungen zwischen Palaeogeographie und Deckenbau, *Viertel Jahrschr. Naturf. Gesell. Zürich*, pp. 217–231.

Trusheim, F.: 1957. Uber Halokinese und ihre Bedeutung für die strukturelle Entwicklung Norddeutschlands, *Deutsche geol. Gesell. Zeitschr.*, vol. 109, pp. 111–158.

————: 1960. Mechanism of salt migration in northern Germany, *Am. Assoc. Petroleum Geologists Bull.*, vol. 44, pp. 1519–1540.

Turner, F. J.: 1948. Mineralogical and structural evolution of the metamorphic rocks, *Geol. Soc. Am. Mem.* 30.

————: 1957. Lineation, symmetry and internal movement in monoclinic tectonic fabrics, *Geol. Soc. Am. Bull.*, vol. 68, pp. 1–18.

————, D. T. Griggs, and H. Heard: 1954. Experimental deformation of calcite crystals, *Geol. Soc. Am. Bull.*, vol. 65, pp. 883–934.

————, and J. Verhoogen: 1960. "Igneous and metamorphic Petrology," 2d ed., McGraw-Hill Book Company, New York.

Umbgrove, J. H. F.: 1938. Geological history of the East Indies, *Am. Assoc. Petroleum Geologists Bull.*, vol. 22, pp. 1–70.

————: 1947. "The Pulse of the Earth," 2d ed., Nijhoff, The Hague.

————: 1949. Structural History of the East Indies, Cambridge University Press, Cambridge, England.

van Bemmelen, R. W.: 1934. Ein Beispiel für Sekundärtektogenese auf Java, *Geol. Rundschau*, no. 25, pp. 175–194.

————: 1935. The undation theory on the development of the earth's crust, *16th Internat. Geol. Cong. Proc., Washington*, vol. 2, pp. 965–982.

————: 1937. Examples of gravitational tectogenesis from central Java, *Ingr. in Indonesie*, vol. 4, pp. 55–65.

————: 1949. The Geology of Indonesia, vol. IA, Government Printing Office, The Hague.

van Hilten, D.: 1962. Presentation of Paleomagnetic data, polar wandering, and continental drift. *Am. Jour. Sci.*, vol. 260, pp. 401–426.

van Waterschoot van der Gracht, W.A.J.M.: 1928. The problem of continental drift, in A.A.P.G. Symposium "Theory of Continental Drift," *Am. Assoc. Petroleum Geologists Bull.*, vol. 12.

528   References

Väyrynen, H.: 1933. Ueber die Stratigraphie der Karelischen Formationen, *Bull. Commun. Geol. Finlande,* vol. 101.

Vening Meinesz, F. A.: 1934. "Gravity expeditions at sea 1923–1932," vol. II, Netherlands Geodetic Commission.

————: 1947. Shear patterns of the Earth's crust, *Am. Geophys. Union Trans.,* vol. 28, pp. 1–61.

————: 1950. Les "graben" africains, résultat de compression ou de tension dans la croûte terrestre, *Koninkl. Belg. Kol. Inst. Bull.,* vol. 21, pp. 539–552.

————: 1952. Convection-currents in the earth and the origin of the continents, 1, *Koninkl. Nederlandse Akad. Wetensch. Proc.,* ser. B, vol. 55, pp. 528–553.

Viete, G.: 1960. Zur Entstehung der glazigene Lagerungsstörungen unter besonderer Berücksichtigung der Flözdeformationen im mitteldeutschen Raum, *Freiberger Forschungsh.,* C78, pp. 1–257.

Voll, G.: 1960. New work in petrofabrics, Liverpool and Manchester, *Geol. Jour.,* vol. 2, no. 3, pp. 503–567.

von Bubnoff, S.: 1952. "Fennosarmatia," Akademie-Verlag GmbH, Berlin.

von Kármán, T.: 1911. Festigkeitsversuche unter allseitigem Druck, *Verh. deutsch. Ing. Zeitschr.,* vol. 55, pp. 1749–1757.

Wager, L. R.: 1931. Jointing in the Great Scar Limestone of Craven and its relation to the tectonics of the area, *Geol. Soc. London Quart. Jour.,* vol. 87, pp. 392–420.

————: 1947. The stratigraphy and tectonics of Knud Rasmussens Land and the Kangerdlugssuag region, *Medd. om Grønland,* vol. 134, no. 5, pp. 1–62.

———— and W. A. Deer: 1938. A dyke swarm and crustal flexure in East Greenland, *Geol. Mag.,* vol. 75, pp. 39–46.

————: 1958. Beneath the earth's crust, *Advances in Science,* vol. 58, pp. 1–15.

Wallace, R. E.: 1949. Structure of a portion of the San Andreas rift in southern California, *Geol. Soc. Am. Bull.,* vol. 60, pp. 781–806.

Wanless, H. R.: 1950. Late Paleozoic cycles of sedimentation in the United States, *18th Internat. Geol. Cong.,* pt. 4, pp. 17–28.

Wegener, A.: 1929. "Die Entstehung der Kontinente und Ozeane," 4th ed., Friedr. Vieweg & Sohn, Brunswick, Germany.

Wegmann, C. E.: 1928. Über die Tektonik der jüngeren Faltung in Ostfinland, *Fennia,* vol. 50, no. 16, p. 22.

————: 1931. Zur Deutung der Migmatite, *Geol. Rundschau,* vol. 26, pp. 305–350.

———— and E. H. Kranck: 1931. Beiträge zur Kenntniss der Svecofenniden in Finnland, pts. I and II, *Comm. Géol. Finlande Bull.,* vol. 89, pp. 1–107.

Weiss, L. E.: 1959. Geometry of superposed folding, *Geol. Soc. Am. Bull.,* vol. 70, pp. 91–106.

Wellman, H. W.: 1956. Structural outline of New Zealand, *New Zealand Dept. Sci. Indus. Research Bull.,* vol. 121, pp. 1–36.

Wenk, E.: 1953. Principelles zur geologisch-tektonischen Gliederung des Penninikums im zentralen Tessin, *Eclogae geol. Helv.*, vol. 46, pp. 9–22.

————: 1955. Eine Strukturkarte der Tessiner Alpen, *Schweiz. Mineralog. Petrog. Mitt.*, vol. 35, pp. 311–319.

————: 1956. Alpines und ostgrönländisch-kaledonisches Kristallin, ein tektonisch-petrogenetischer Vergleich, *Verh. Naturf. Gesell. Basel*, vol. 67, no. 2, pp. 75–102.

Wentlandt, E. A.: 1951. Hawkinsfield, in Occurrence of oil and gas in north-east Texas, *Univ. Texas Pub.* 5116, pp. 153–158.

Weyl, R.: 1961. "Die Geologie Mittel-Amerikas," Gebrüder Borntraeger, Berlin.

Whitten, E. H. T.: 1959. A study of two directions of folding: the structural geology of the Monadhliath and Mid-Strathspey, *Jour. Geol.*, vol. 67, pp. 14–47.

Williams, A.: 1958. Oblique-slip faults and rotated stress systems, *Geol. Mag.*, vol. 95, pp. 207–218.

Williams, E.: 1960. Intra-stratal flow and convolute folding, *Geol. Mag.*, vol. 97, pp. 208–218.

Williams, H.: 1941. Calderas and their origin, *Univ. Calif., Dept. Geol. Sci., Pub.*, vol. 25, no. 6.

Willis, B.: 1893. The mechanics of Appalachian structures, *13th Annual Rept. U.S. Geol. Survey*, vol. 2, pp. 211–283.

————: 1929. Continental genesis, *Geol. Soc. Am. Bull.*, vol. 40, pp. 281–336.

————: 1936. East African plateaus and rift valleys, *Carnegie Inst. Wash. Pub.* 470.

————: 1938. San Andreas rift in California, *Jour. Geol.*, vol. 46, pp. 793–827, 1017–1051.

Wilson, C. W., and R. G. Stearns: 1958. Structure of the Cumberland Plateau, Tennessee, *Geol. Soc. Am. Bull.*, vol. 69, pp. 1283–1296.

Wilson, G.: 1946. The relationship of slaty cleavage and kindred structures to tectonics, *Geol. Assoc. Proc.*, vol. 62, pp. 263–302.

————: 1952. Ptygmatic structures and their formation, *Geol. Mag.*, vol. 89, pp. 1–21.

————: 1953. Mullion and rodding structures in the Moine Series of Scotland, *Geol. Assoc. Proc.*, vol. 64, no. 2, pp. 118–151.

Winkler, H. G. F.: 1957–1961. Experimentelle Gesteinsmetamorphose, I–V, *Geochimica and Cosmochimica Acta*, vol. 13, pp. 42–69; vol. 15, pp. 91–112; vol. 18, pp. 294–316; vol. 24, pp. 48–69; vol. 24, pp. 250–259.

Winterthurn, R.: 1943. Wilmington Oilfield, Bul. 118, *California Dept. Nat. Resources Div. Mines*, pp. 301–305.

Wolf, J. R.: 1959. The geology of Hormuz Island at the entrance of the Persian Gulf, *Geologie en Mijnbouw*, N.S., vol. 21, pp. 390–395.

Wölk, E.: 1937. Zur Klüfttektonik des Niederrheinischen Haupt-Braunkohlenflözes, *Deutsche Geol. Gesell. Zeitschr.*, vol. 91, no. 2, p. 109.

Woodring, W. P., and R. Stewart: 1934. Geologic map of Kettleman Hills, California, U.S. Geological Survey.

Woollard, G. P.: 1959. Crustal structure from gravity and seismic measurements, *Jour. Geophys. Research,* vol. 64, pp. 1521–1544.

Worzel, L., and G. L. Shurbet: 1955. Gravity anomalies at continental margins, [U.S.] *Natl. Acad. Sci.,* vol. 41, pp. 458–469.

Wyart, J., and G. Sabatier: 1959. Transformation des sédiments pélitiques à 800°C sous une pression d'eau de 1800 bars et granitisation, *Soc. Française Mineralogie Cristallographie,* vol. 82, pp. 201–210.

Zandvliet, J.: 1960. The Geology of the Upper Salat and Pallaresa Valleys, Central Pyrenees, *Leidse Geol. Med.,* vol. 25, pp. 1–127.

Zijlstra, G.: 1941. De Permschubben van de Salmurano Culminatie, *Geologie en Mijnbouw,* vol. 3, pp. 93–102.

Zwart, H. J.: 1954a. La geologie du Massif du St. Barthélemy, *Leidse Geol. Med.,* vol. 18, pp. 1–228.

———: 1954b. Sur les lherzolites et ophites des Pyrénées, *Leidse Geol. Med.,* vol. 18, pp. 281–286.

———: 1959. Metamorphic history of the Pyrenees, 1, Arize, Trois Seigneurs and St. Barthélemy massifs, *Leidse Geol. Med.,* vol. 22, pp. 417–490.

———: 1960a. The chronological succession of folding and metamorphism in the central Pyrenees, *Geol. Rundschau,* vol. 50, pp. 203–218.

———: 1960b. Relations between folding and metamorphism in the central Pyrenees, and their chronological succession, *Geologie en Mijnbouw,* vol. 22, pp. 163–180.

———: 1962. On the determination of polymetamorphic mineral associations and its application to the Bosot area (Central Pyrenees), *Geol. Rundschau,* vol. 52, pp. 38–65.

———: 1963. Some examples of the relations between deformation and metamorphism from the Central Pyrenees, *Geologie en Mijnbouw,* vol. 42, pp. 143–154.

Index